D1231735

PRINCIPLES OF
TRANSISTOR
CIRCUITS

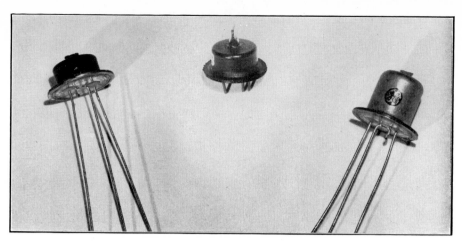

Hermetically sealed junction transistors
(1½ times actual size)

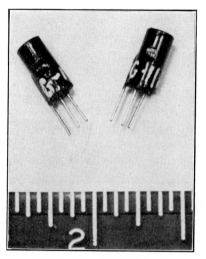

Point-contact transistors
(Two times actual size)

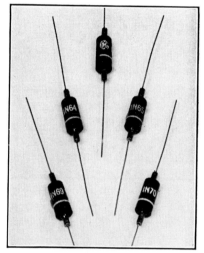

Point-contact diodes
(Actual size)

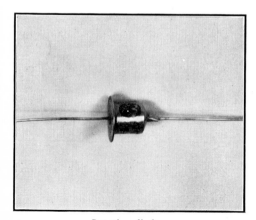

Junction diode
(1¼ times actual size)

Medium-power diode
(1¼ times actual size)

Principles of

TRANSISTOR CIRCUITS

Edited by
RICHARD F. SHEA

Co-Authors

WOO FOUNG CHOW

SORAB K. GHANDHI

EDWARD KEONJIAN

VERNON P. MATHIS

CHARLES A. ROSEN

JOHN S. SABY

JOHANNES S. SCHAFFNER

RICHARD F. SHEA

JEROME J. SURAN

Electronics Laboratory
General Electric Company
Electronics Park
Syracuse, New York

JOHN WILEY & SONS, INC., NEW YORK
LONDON

EIGHTH PRINTING, MAY, 1960

Library of Congress Catalog Card Number: 53–10944

Printed in the United States of America

Preface

An elementary type of transistor was announced by the Bell Telephone Laboratories in an article entitled "The Transistor, A Semiconductor Triode," by J. Bardeen and W. H. Brattain in the July 15, 1948, issue of the *Physical Review*. With this announcement the door was opened to widespread application of semiconductor devices in fields where vacuum tubes had reigned supreme since they had displaced the original semiconductor device, the crystal detector. From the intensive effort that has gone into the development of the transistor in many laboratories since 1948 many forms and shapes of devices have resulted. Thus, several types of point-contact transistors have been available for some time, and now a new type, the junction transistor, is appearing in a number of forms. Active research is still going on, which will continue to produce new forms of transistors, possibly utilizing new materials, such as silicon.

As a result of the development of the many types and forms of transistors a wide variety of electronic circuits have become practicable and the field of application is continually being broadened. Contemplation of the great potential field of transistor applications cannot but engender a spirit of enthusiasm, well evidenced by the remarkable contributions made by the workers in the field in its relatively short existence.

A brief résumé of the principal features of the transistor is in order. The transistor is small, yet extremely rugged, and is capable of withstanding shocks many thousands of times greater than the force of gravity. It consumes no filament power; in fact, the junction transistor is capable of operation at power consumption of the order of a microwatt. Power outputs of the order of watts have been obtained from the earlier forms of transistors. The upper limit of power dissipation, however, is primarily a function of mechanical design, and power outputs of hundreds of watts are not beyond the realm of possibility. Noise, a severe limitation in early transistor design, has been reduced considerably. In junction transistors, noise figures under 20 db are attainable; and in point-contact transistors a 20-db improvement has been made, current units having noise figures of the order of 50 db. Future development is expected to improve these figures further.

In addition to their low power consumption, transistors operate with low-voltage supplies, especially the junction transistor, whose operation at a fraction of a volt is practicable. This feature makes the application of transistors to the field of portable electronic devices exceedingly profitable. Finally, and possibly most important of all, transistors have a long lifetime, of the order of 100,000 hours or more, and even at the end of this period there is no abrupt cessation of operation. Transistors are therefore extremely important both in industrial and in military applications where failure may be very costly, or even fatal. In the computer field, where one complicated machine may require thousands of electron devices, the long-lived transistor can easily be a vital factor in maintaining continuous operation.

It goes without saying that no device is perfect, even the transistor. Improvement is needed in respect to frequency range, noise, temperature effects, and uniformity of manufacture, to mention a few items. Constant effort is being directed toward improving these features, and doubtless this improvement will continue for many years. It is reasonable to assume that the transistor will ultimately reach a stage of uniformity comparable to that of the vacuum tube, in addition to possessing the advantages listed above. Although transistors are currently high priced, anticipated large-scale production should make them attractive from the economic standpoint.

Concurrent with the development of different types of transistors has been the detailed study of their characteristics and of the circuits for which they are best suited. This study has entailed the construction of intricate equipment for the measurement of characteristics, the making of detailed measurements on large numbers and varieties of transistors, the calculation of operating impedances and gains under many circuit configurations, and applications of these calculations to a great variety of fields. It is the purpose of the present book to gather under one cover a large portion of the volume of material that has been accumulated on the subject of transistor circuits. No claim is made that the material is entirely original; in fact, we have borrowed freely from the works of contemporary authors, as noted in the bibliography and references. Even though we realize that no all-encompassing textbook is possible at such an early stage of the art, still we hope that this book will provide the necessary fundamental theory of a general nature, plus elaboration of various techniques applicable in the field. Thus, as the art progresses and new forms of transistors appear, these fundamentals and techniques will permit adequate utilization of the devices.

Since the field is so comparatively new it was decided to aim the book at graduate students and practicing engineers alike. This decision has posed several problems, owing to the wide variety of mathematical tools with which the engineer must be familiar if he is to fully utilize network theory. We have elaborated in considerable degree on the fundamental equivalent circuits for various configurations and for different frequency ranges, and have expanded considerably on this portion of the text for the benefit of the older engineer who does not have all the above mathematical tools at his command. For the same reason a chapter on duality has been included, and the resemblances to vacuum-tube circuits has been pointed out in several chapters. Eventually, engineers will become familiar with transistor circuits on their own, but the present book enables engineers well schooled in the vacuum-tube field to draw upon their experience.

For the graduate student and for engineers who have been comparatively well grounded in network theory we have included a chapter on matrix methods of analysis and one on feedback, utilizing the current network theory, modified to fit transistor circuits. This material is presented in considerable detail so that the reader may apply the techniques directly to transistor circuits without the necessity of making a complete study of network theory and of then translating it to transistor circuits.

If the desire to achieve maximum utility as a reference book has led to some repetition, the object has been to make each chapter as self-explanatory as possible and to reduce to a practical minimum the amount of cross referencing.

Transistors assume many different physical forms, including point-contact types and the many varieties of the junction devices, new permutations of which are being evolved continually. In order to make the material applicable to as many of these devices as possible the treatment has been general in nature, rather than specific, and is built up around generalized equivalent circuits which can be used to conveniently represent the great majority of these devices. Thus the distinction between p-n-p and n-p-n units is avoided, and the analysis may be used for either type. In practice, specific applications will favor one type over the other, depending on the state of the art. The method of analysis employed here is intended to permit proper evaluation of the various forms of transistors for these applications. Thus, as the newer forms of transistors are developed their utility may be adequately determined.

One necessary decision was whether to emphasize circuits more adaptable to point-contact or to junction transistors. For example, point-contact transistors can utilize series-resonant tuned circuits for high-frequency applications, whereas parallel tuned circuits are more suitable for junction devices. It was decided to emphasize the device considered most suitable at the time or in the foreseeable future in a specific application, and where there is a comparatively free choice, to present information applicable to both types. Thus the low-frequency applications are directed entirely toward the use of junction transistors. Point-contact and junction transistors are treated alike at higher frequencies, and in computer circuits most of the emphasis is on point-contact devices.

After a brief introduction intended to give the reader a reasonable familiarity with semiconductor physics and with the various types of transistors the book is divided mainly into three parts, covering essentially low-frequency, high-frequency, and large-signal, non-linear applications. In each section the same general organization is followed: presentation and analysis of equivalent circuits; analysis of the mathematical relationships; and development of applicable circuits. Currently there is considerable debate over the relative merits of specifying the equivalent circuits in terms of open-circuit impedances, short-circuit admittances, or other parameters, such as the h factors which involve impedance, admittance, and current and voltage ratios. It was decided to utilize the equivalent T circuit, as having achieved greatest acceptance in the literature to date, but to include sufficient material to enable the user to suit himself and to choose whichever method is most convenient. Thus in the chapter on matrix analysis, a more generalized analysis is presented which permits the use of parameters as directly measured, rather than as computed. For example, the above h parameters can be measured and the complete circuit behavior analyzed without the necessity of conversion to the equivalent T and determination of its component impedances.

Similarly the material in the chapter on measurements is general in nature, and, though a considerable portion is concerned with the measurement of the parameters of the equivalent T circuit, the methods whereby the other, equivalent parameters may be determined are also described. Thus, the above-mentioned h factors may be measured directly by methods described here.

The first part of the book deals with operation at low frequencies, for both small- and large-signal amplitudes. In this section will be found material relative to direct-current, audio and ultrasonic amplifiers in their various forms and combinations. As this is one of the most promising fields of transistor application, the material is presented in considerable detail.

The second part treats small-signal operation at higher frequencies, of the order of 100 kilocycles to 10 megacycles, as amplifiers and oscillators. Here the mesh impedances and current amplification become complex, and a variety of effects, negligible at lower frequencies, assume great importance. Included in this section are circuits for the utilization of transistors in oscillators, intermediate-frequency amplifiers, and radio-frequency amplifiers.

The last major part discusses large-signal and non-linear operation, as utilized in such applications as flipflops, multivibrators, and pulse amplifiers. One chapter treats the theory of transient operation of transistors in considerable detail. This material is of particular importance in the computer and radar fields.

The text is liberally interspersed with illustrative examples and problems intended to provide the reader with a test of his grasp of the subject matter. A comprehensive bibliography is included.

My co-authors and I wish to express our sincere appreciation of the assistance given us by members of the Semiconductor Applications Unit, Semiconductor Components Unit, and Engineering Analysis Unit of the Electronics Laboratory, by members of the Commercial and Government Equipment Department, and by members of the Research Laboratory, particularly Dr. R. L. Pritchard and Dr. R. N. Hall. Our sincere thanks go also to Mr. I. J. Kaar, Dr. L. T. DeVore, Mr. W. Hausz, Mr. B. R. Lester, and Mr. J. P. Jordan for their inspiration and guidance in this work.

This work has been supported by the U.S.A.F. Air Research and Development Command, U.S.A.F. Air Matériel Command, Army Signal Corps, and Navy Bureau of Ships, under Contract AF 33 (600)-17793.

RICHARD F. SHEA

Contents

CONTENTS

Symbols

The following general rules govern the symbols used in this text:

1. In general, capital letters are used to designate invariant or d-c quantities; lower-case letters, to designate varying or incremental quantities. Where the quantity of interest contains direct current plus a variable a special symbol such as $I(t)$ is used, indicating a current which is a function of time.

2. This rule is also applied to the resistances employed in the various circuits, as there are frequently large differences between the d-c values of certain resistors and their resistance at alternating current. Thus a reflected load resistance may be r_l, while the d-c resistance of the transformer winding might be R_l; admittances, reactances, susceptances, and impedances may use either type of designation, although generally lower-case letters are used.

3. Successive stages are generally indicated by the use of subscripts. Thus r_{i1} and r_{i2} designate the input resistances of the first and second stages, respectively.

English Letter Symbols

Symbol	Description	First used on page
A	Amplification	51
$\mathbf{A}^0$	Vector current ratio	342
A_i	Current amplification	51
$\mathbf{A}_i$	Vector current ratio	187
A_{in}	Current amplification of nth stage	81
A_{io}	Short-circuit current amplification	77
$\mathbf{A}^0{}_{sc}$	Short-circuit current ratio without feedback	344
$\mathbf{A}_v$	Vector voltage ratio	212
A_v	Voltage amplification	51
A_{v0}	Voltage amplification at low frequency	213

Symbol	Description	*First used on page*
a	Current amplification factor	35
a_{ij}	General term in the a matrix	304
a_0	Low-frequency current amplification factor	198
a-c	Alternating-current (adjective)	40
B	Base	24
B	Frequency band	440
b	Grounded-emitter current amplification factor	37
b	Mobility ratio $(=\mu_e/\mu_h)$	9
b	Susceptance	199
b_i	Input susceptance	246
b_{ij}	General term in the b matrix	304
b_o	Output susceptance	246
C	Capacitance	81
C	Collector	24
C_c	Collector capacitance	187
c	Capacitance	191
D	Delay	425
D	Diffusion constant	9
D	Diode	179
D_n	Diffusion constant	370
D_o	Clamping diode	425
d-c	Direct-current (adjective)	90
db	Decibel	65
div	Divergence of	369
E	D-c supply voltage	25
E	Electric field	5
E, e	Emitter	24
E_b	D-c base supply voltage	119
E_c	D-c collector supply voltage	25
E_{c1}	Collector voltage operating point	145
E_e	D-c emitter supply voltage	25
E_{e1}	Emitter voltage operating point	145
E_o	Output voltage	469
E_m	Maximum junction field	22
e	Electronic charge	5
e	Naperian base $(2.71828\cdots)$	14

Symbol	Description	*First used on page*
G_0	Low-frequency power gain	211
G_t	Transducer gain	76
g	Conductance	192
g	A-c space function of carrier concentration	371
g_c	Collector conductance	147
g_i	Input conductance	239
g_i'	Transformed input conductance	241
g_{ij}	Element of the g matrix	304
g_l	Tuned circuit conductance	239
g_m	Mutual conductance	329
g_o	Output conductance	239
g_o'	Transformed output conductance	241
g_p	Plate conductance	329
grad	Gradient of	369
$g(x)$	A-c space function of carrier concentration	371
h_{ij}	Element of the h matrix	304
$h(t)$	Impulse response	391
h_{11}	Input impedance, output short-circuited	304
h_{12}	Reverse voltage ratio, input open-circuited	304
h_{21}	Current transfer ratio, output short-circuited	304
h_{22}	Output admittance, input open-circuited	304
I	D-c current	8
I_b	D-c base current	98
I_b'	Peak class B base current	152
I_c	D-c collector current	13
I_{c0}	D-c collector current for zero emitter current	17
$(I_c)_0$	Quiescent operating d-c collector current	399
$(I_c')_0$	Zero-signal class B collector current	144
I_c'	Peak class B collector current	144
$I_c(t)$	Instantaneous collector current	145
I_d	D-c diode current	179
$I_{\text{d-c}}$	D-c component of collector current	401
I_e	D-c emitter current	13
I_e'	Peak class B emitter current	144
$(I_e)_0$	Quiescent operating d-c emitter current	399
I_{es}	D-c emitter current corresponding to saturation	402
$I_e(t)$	Instantaneous emitter current	145
I_i	Input current	468

Symbol	Description	*First used on page*
$V_c(t)$	Instantaneous collector voltage as a function of time	145
V_{c0}	Average d-c collector voltage	502
$(V_c)_0$	Quiescent operating d-c collector voltage	399
V_c'	Peak class B collector voltage	153
$(V_c')_0$	Peak class B collector voltage	144
V_e	D-c emitter voltage	27
$V_e(t)$	Instantaneous emitter voltage as a function of time	145
V_e'	Peak class B emitter voltage	152
V_i	Input voltage	468
$V(t)$	Instantaneous voltage as a function of time	145
V_1	Network input voltage	33
V_2	Network output voltage	33
v	A-c voltage	34
v_c	A-c collector voltage	38
$\mathbf{v}_c$	Vector collector voltage	186
$v_c(t)$	Instantaneous signal on collector side	145
v_e	A-c emitter voltage	38
$\mathbf{v}_e$	Vector emitter voltage	186
$v_e(t)$	Instantaneous signal on emitter side	145
v_g	A-c source voltage	51
v_i	A-c input voltage	52
$\hat{v}_i$	Peak a-c input voltage	138
v_o	A-c output voltage	51
v_o'	Open-circuit output voltage	76
v_0	A-c measurement voltage	489
v_1	Network a-c input voltage	34
v_2	Network a-c output voltage	34
W	A generalized network parameter	352
W	Width	20
W_B	Width of base region	14
W_E	Width of emitter region	14
x	Distance	367
x	Number of carriers drawn from collector to base for each carrier collected	16
x	Number of holes ejected	476
x	Reactance	187

		First used
Symbol	*Description*	*on page*
z_{12}	Output-input mesh transimpedance, input open-circuited	186
z_{21}	Input-output mesh transimpedance, output open-circuited	186
z_{22}	Output mesh impedance, input open-circuited	186

Greek Letter Symbols

α (alpha)	Short-circuit current amplification factor	13
α^*	Intrinsic carrier multiplication at collector	13
α_D	Dynamic current amplification factor	401
α_0	Short-circuit current amplification at low frequencies	190
β (beta)	Fraction of injected carriers which cross base region	13
β	Feedback ratio	342
β	Current amplification of feedback network	279
γ (gamma)	A normalized variable	377
γ	Fraction of emitter current increment injected into base region	13
γ_h	γ for case where holes are injected	14
γ_e	γ for case where electrons are injected	14
γ	Per cent output current fed back to the network	342
Δ (delta)	Determinant	40
Δ	Increment of	125
δ	Dirac impulse function	384
Δf	Bandwidth	233
Δ^i	Determinant of the ith matrix	305
Δ^0	Determinant with transistor inoperative	353
ϵ (epsilon)	Dielectric constant (permittivity), relative	11
ϵ_0	Permittivity of free space	11
η (eta)	Efficiency	145
μ (mu)	Amplification factor of a vacuum tube	296
μ	A step function	375
μ	Mobility	5
μ_e	Electron mobility	5
μ_h	Hole mobility	5
$\mu\mu f$	Micro-microfarad	202
μf	Microfarad	119
ξ (xi)	Angle of clipping	141

Symbol	Description	*First used on page*
π (pi)	Ratio of circumference to diameter of circle (3.14159)	141
π	Number of radians equivalent to 180°	185
ρ (rho)	Charge density	11
ρ	Fluid density	369
ρ	A factor ($=e_{ne}/e_{nc}$)	444
ρ_i	Intrinsic resistivity	21
Σ (sigma)	Summation	375
σ (sigma)	Electrical conductivity	5
σ_B	Conductivity of base region	13
σ_E	Conductivity of emitter region	13
σ_n	Conductivity of an n-type region	8
σ_p	Conductivity of a p-type region	8
τ (tau)	Time, time constant	347
τ	Carrier lifetime	9
τ_n	Carrier lifetime	370
τ_α	Time constant corresponding to $f_{\alpha 0}$	347
τ_c	Time constant of collector resistance and capacitance	382
ϕ (phi)	Phase angle	205
ϕ_m	Maximum phase angle	205
ω (omega)	Angular frequency	90
$\omega_{\alpha 0}$	$2\pi f_{\alpha 0}$	185
$\omega_{b 0}$	$2\pi f_{b 0}$	196
$\omega_{g 0}$	$2\pi f_{g 0}$	212
ω_0	Resonant angular frequency	228

Mathematical Symbols

∇	Del operator
$\cong$	Approximately equal to
$\neq$	Not equal to
$\gg$	Very large compared with
$\ll$	Very small compared with
Σ	Sum of
$\lvert A \rvert$	Magnitude of A
Δ	Determinant
Δ	Increment of
$\cdot$	Dot product
$\times$	Cross product

Symbol	*Description*
grad	Gradient of
log	Common logarithm
ln	Natural logarithm
∞	Infinity
div	Divergence of
erf	Error function
erfc	Complementary error function
exp	*e* to the power of

GRAPHICAL SYMBOLS			
	p–n–p Transistor		Microphone
	n–p–n Transistor		Receiver
	Amplifier		Reproducer (pick–up)
	Battery		Resistor
	Capacitor		Speaker
	Capacitor, variable		Transformer
	Diode		
	A-c generator		Transformer (with core)
	Inductor		

Chapter 1

Semiconductor Principles

1.1   Introduction to Semiconductor Devices

In the development of new circuits employing the unique characteristics now available in semiconductor devices, it is highly desirable that
the circuit engineer have a general knowledge of the physical processes
involved.   This permits him to make efficient use of existing devices
and accelerates the application of new devices as they become available.

It is the purpose of this chapter to describe in simple terms some of
the properties of semiconductors which are of importance in transistor
electronics.

Metals are characterized by the presence of many so-called "free"
electrons, whereas good insulators have virtually none—all their outer
electrons are tied up in interatomic bonds.   Semiconductors are solid
materials which are neither good conductors nor good insulators.   Electrical conduction occurs in so-called insulators at high temperatures,
however, when a few electrons are thermally torn loose from their bonds
and can move about in the solid and conduct electricity.   The insulator
has now become what we call an intrinsic semiconductor.   Thus, there
is no sharp distinction between insulators and intrinsic semiconductors.
If the bonds are easily broken, then a noticeable amount of conduction
occurs even at room temperature, and the material is classed as a semiconductor.

Germanium is a good example of a semiconductor, whose properties
will be used as a basis for discussion [1,2,3,4] in most of this chapter.   Germanium's diamond cubic lattice requires four "shared-pair" electron
bonds per atom, thus involving all the available electrons, and pure
germanium would be an insulator were it not that these bonds are
relatively easily broken thermally, producing intrinsic conduction.
The conduction due to impurities is of great importance in germanium.
When atoms with five valence electrons (P, As, Sb) enter the lattice in
place of germanium atoms, four of their electrons are required by the

1

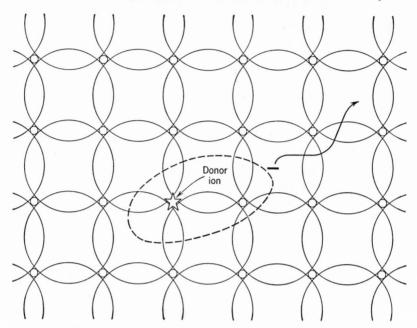

Fig. 1.1   Donor center in n-type germanium.

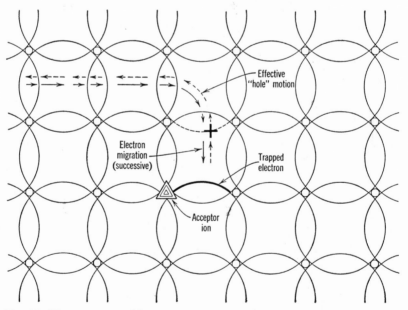

Fig. 1.2   Electrons trapped by acceptor centers give rise to mobile holes in p-type germanium.

lattice bonds, the fifth being very loosely bound and free at room temperature to conduct as shown in Fig. 1.1. Such impurities are called donors, and the electron conduction is called n-type.

When atoms with three valence electrons (B, Al, Ga, In) enter the lattice substitutionally, the lattice bonds are unsatisfied, and an electron from a neighboring region in the lattice may jump into the incomplete bond, leaving a vacancy behind. Thus, as electrons migrate to successively fill the hole under the influence of an electric field, as shown by the solid arrows in Fig. 1.2, the hole may be considered to have moved in the opposite direction, as shown by the dotted arrows. Impurities which trap electrons are called acceptors, and this type of conduction is called p-type, since the holes move like positive charges. Zinc and copper also can act as acceptors, but the mechanism is not as simple for these elements.

When the conduction is principally by holes, the semiconductor is called p-type; when it is by electrons, n-type. When n-type and p-type regions occur in the same crystal, the boundary between them is called a p-n junction.

The injection and rectification properties of p-n junctions can be inferred in a general way from Fig. 1.3. When the p-type region is

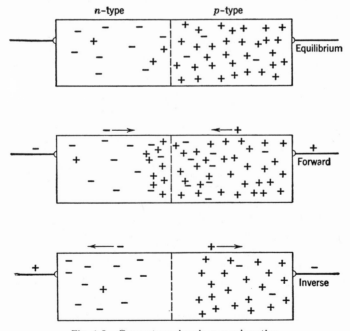

Fig. 1.3   Current carriers in a p-n junction.

made positive with respect to the n-type region, holes and electrons are driven toward each other. If the p-type carriers are more numerous, most of the current crossing the junction is carried by holes. Very high currents may flow, and the voltage need only be enough to keep the

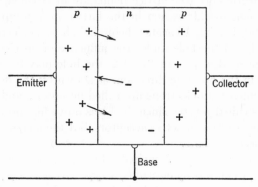

Fig. 1.4 p-n-p transistor.

holes and electrons moving toward each other. This is called the forward direction.

On the other hand, if the p-type region is made negative with respect to the n-type region, the holes and electrons are moved away from each

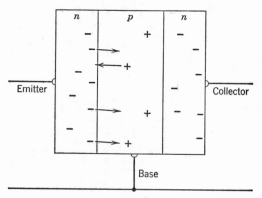

Fig. 1.5 n-p-n transistor.

other leaving the junction region devoid of charge carriers. This is called the inverse direction. Very little current flows, unless charge carriers are somehow introduced into this insulating "barrier" region.

The junction transistor is a combination of two p-n junctions back-to-back in a "sandwich" arrangement, as sketched in Fig. 1.4, which shows a p-n-p transistor. If the collector is biased negatively with respect to the base, little current will flow unless the emitter is biased positively. Some of the holes then injected by the emitter will diffuse through the base and be attracted to the collector, increasing the collector current. The current in the high-power collector circuit can thus be controlled by the low-power emitter circuit, providing a power gain. The n-p-n transistor of Fig. 1.5 is similar except that the polarities are reversed so that a negatively biased emitter injects electrons which are collected by a positively biased collector.

The processes of injection, diffusion, and collection of minority carriers are basic to all transistor action, and the relation of these processes to high-power, high-frequency, and high-temperature operation holds the key to future transistor applications. In order to consider these processes more closely, we shall first re-examine semiconductors and p-n junctions in more detail.

1.2   Conduction Processes in Semiconductors

The electrons and holes have finite mobilities in semiconductors, which may be defined as the speed per unit field; i.e.,

$$\mu_e = u_e/E \qquad \mu_h = u_h/E \qquad\qquad [1.1]$$

where μ_e and μ_h are electron and hole mobilities; u_e and u_h electron and hole statistical average terminal velocities corresponding to the electric field E in the semiconductor.

The actual motion of the charges is composed of this average drift velocity superimposed upon their wildly erratic, random thermal motion. One effect of the thermal motion is to cause diffusion of each type of carrier toward regions of smaller concentration, sometimes resulting in a flow of electrical current by diffusion. In many cases either the drift or the diffusion mechanism may predominate, but the complete expression for the motion of charges will often include the simultaneous effects of both mechanisms.

For germanium, $\mu_e = 3600 \ \mathrm{cm}^2/\mathrm{volt \ sec}$ and $\mu_h = 1700 \ \mathrm{cm}^2/\mathrm{volt \ sec}$, in good single crystals, being somewhat lower in inhomogeneous imperfect crystals.

When both holes and electrons are present, the total current is the sum of the currents carried by each.[5] It follows that the conductivity σ (the current density per unit field) is given by

$$\sigma = e(n_e \, \mu_e + n_h \, \mu_h) \qquad\qquad [1.2]$$

where n_e and n_h are electron and hole populations per cubic centimeter and e is the electronic charge.

As the temperature rises, there is an increase in the statistically probable number n_i of electrons per unit volume torn loose thermally from the interatomic bonds. This is analogous to the thermal increase in the number of electrons which have sufficient energy to escape from a heated metal by thermionic emission. The density n_i of thermally generated hole-electron pairs [1] increases exponentially with temperature, and for germanium this relation may be written

$$n_i = 4.5 \times 10^{19} \exp(-4390/T) \qquad [1.3]$$

where T is the absolute temperature. For $T = 300°$ K, $n_i = 1.7 \times 10^{13}$. Thus, above a certain temperature, the intrinsic carriers become so numerous that the conduction due to impurities can be ignored. This is called the intrinsic temperature and is higher for low-resistivity (more highly contaminated) germanium.

In intrinsic material, each thermally liberated electron leaves behind one hole, so that $n_e = n_h = n_i$. Since the electrons are more mobile than holes, their conductivity predominates, and intrinsic germanium is actually n-type, as indicated by thermoelectric or Hall effect measurements. The number n_i is a statistical average since electrons and holes are continually being separated and recombining.

Consider a semiconductor containing intrinsic holes and electrons plus the electrons from a few donor atoms. The electron density has increased. But this increases the chances for filling up each hole, and the hole population therefore decreases. Quantitatively, it turns out that to a good approximation [6] over a very wide range of resistivities of practical importance

$$n_e n_h = n_i^{2} \qquad [1.4]$$

so that, if, for example, the number of donor atoms is an order of magnitude greater than n_i, the effect of holes is negligible.

Thus, at donor or acceptor concentrations more than an order of magnitude greater than n_i, the resistivity is inversely proportional to concentration, and the minority carriers can be ignored. The resistivity as a function of donor and acceptor density is shown in Fig. 1.6.

If a mixture of donor and acceptor atoms is present, a cancellation occurs. The more numerous carriers almost completely suppress the less numerous type, following eq. 1.4, so that the only effect, for example, of adding 10 per cent † acceptors to a highly n-type semiconductor is to cancel 10 per cent of the donors (whose electrons have filled the

† That is, a number of acceptor atoms equal to 10 per cent of the number of donor atoms already present.

acceptors' holes). Paradoxically, the effect of adding an impurity in this case is to increase the resistivity of the material, although the same impurity addition would have decreased the resistivity of either pure or *p*-type material.

The number of acceptor centers in germanium can be increased by heating above 500° C and quenching. The original resistivity can be restored by slowly annealing below 500° C. This thermally induced

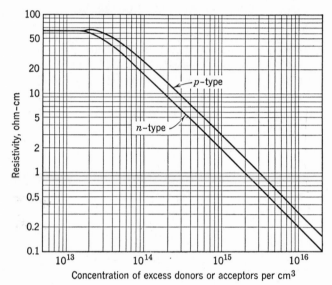

Fig. 1.6   Resistivity vs. donor and acceptor concentration for germanium.

conductivity plays an important role in the formation of point-contact junctions. The migration of lattice defects (which can trap electrons and act as acceptors) as well as the behaviors of certain impurities, notably copper, have been invoked to explain these phenomena, but the mechanisms are not yet completely clear.

1.3   The *p-n* Junction

1.3.1   Physical Forms

p-n Junctions sometimes occur spontaneously as the result of crystallization of inhomogeneous material. They can also be produced at will, both in the growing crystal and after crystallization. Grown single crystal junction bars, such as those prepared by doping the melt during crystal growth [7] or by changing the growth rate,[8] are finally cut into the size and shape desired, usually as rectangular bars.

Junctions can also be created in homogeneous single crystal germanium by local radiation damage by particle bombardment,[9] by selective thermal conversion, or by alloy contact and solid diffusion of impurities [10] into the desired region. In such cases, the germanium is first cut to the desired form, and the junctions are created where they are needed, e.g., under the "whisker" of a germanium point-contact diode.

1.3.2 Current-Voltage Relationships for a p-n Junction

If we return to Fig. 1.3, we note that, in thermal equilibrium, some holes from the p-type region have wandered into the n-region. Conversely, electrons have wandered into the p-region by thermal diffusion. This charge motion results in a slight contact potential difference just sufficient to counteract further diffusion. The effect of a voltage applied across a p-n junction is to disturb the equilibrium, increasing or suppressing diffusion.

The current-voltage relationship [11] can be written

$$I = I_0(\exp eV/kT - 1) = (I_{0e} + I_{0h})(\exp eV/kT - 1) \quad [1.5]$$

where k is the Boltzmann constant, e the electronic charge, and T the absolute temperature of the junction. The last equality evaluated for germanium at room temperature becomes $I = I_0(\exp 39V - 1)$. The quantities I_{0e} and I_{0h} represent the current densities carried by electrons and holes respectively (moving in opposite directions, of course). The shape of the theoretical curve, valid for all V (+ forward, − inverse), is determined entirely by the exponential term, the properties of the particular germanium appearing only in the multiplying term, as specified below in eq. 1.6.

The exponential term in eq. 1.5 becomes negligible at moderate inverse voltages (a few tenths of a volt for germanium), and the current asymptotically approaches a value equal to the first bracket of this equation which is independent of voltage for isothermal characteristics below the breakdown voltage as shown in Fig. 1.7. This constant inverse current is called the saturation current $I_0 = I_{0e} + I_{0h}$. For an inversely biased junction, I_{0e} arises from the thermal generation of electrons as minority carriers in the p-type region and their diffusion toward the junction where they cross into the positively biased n-region. Conversely, I_{0h} depends upon the rates of generation and diffusion of holes in the n-region. Their dependence upon the properties of the germanium is given by

$$I_{0e} = K\sigma_i{}^2/\sigma_p L_e \qquad I_{0h} = K\sigma_i{}^2/\sigma_n L_h \quad [1.6]$$

where σ_i is the intrinsic conductivity, K is a proportionality factor $b/(b+1)^2$ (where $b = \mu_e/\mu_h$), σ_p and σ_n are conductivities of the p-type and n-type regions, and L_e and L_h are diffusion distances † for electrons in the p-type region and holes in the n-type region, respectively. It will be noted that larger σ_p and σ_n (low-resistivity materials) result in smaller inverse saturation currents. This would be expected since, from eq. 1.4, minority carrier generation is suppressed at high donor or acceptor concentrations.

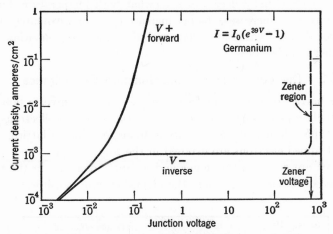

Fig. 1.7   Theoretical current-voltage curves for p-n junction.

In the forward direction, the hole and electron currents are also given by eq. 1.5, observing that V is now positive. The forward current is, therefore, increased or decreased in the same proportion as the inverse current, by changing the germanium constants in eq. 1.6, but the changes are of less practical significance for forward currents, since a change of only 0.02 volt is sufficient to change the forward current by a factor of 2. On the other hand, the properties of the germanium are extremely important in determining the relative proportions of the forward current carried by holes and by electrons, as required, for example, in the design of a junction for use as an efficient emitter as described below in Sec. 1.4.1.

It is to be noted from eq. 1.5 that the current in the forward $(V+)$ direction increases exponentially with the voltage, as the (-1) term

† The diffusion distance is given by $L = (D\tau)^{1/2}$, where D is the diffusion constant and τ the average lifetime of the injected carriers. Smaller values of τ cause shorter values of L, which increase the concentration gradients and lead to greater diffusion rates.

becomes negligible. Consequently the incremental forward junction resistance dV/dI is inversely proportional to I. One result of practical importance in transistor circuits is that the emitter resistance decreases as the emitter current is increased.

The current in a p-n junction at any voltage increases rapidly with temperature because, by eq. 1.6, both I_{0e} and I_{0h} are proportional to the square of the intrinsic conductivity σ_i, which is proportional to n_i and, by eq. 1.3, increases exponentially with temperature. The exponential term actually decreases somewhat with temperature, but not as rapidly as I_0 increases, the net increase being approximately 10 per cent per degree Centigrade. The mobilities also are somewhat lower at higher temperatures.

1.3.3   The Barrier Layer and Junction Capacitance

The barrier region, swept free of carriers by the inverse potential, is actually a space charge region,[12] since the exodus of electrons from the n-type side has exposed positive donor ions in the lattice. Similarly trapped electrons are exposed in the p-type side. These charge densities are equal to the donor and acceptor densities in the neighborhood of the junction. Since the inverse current densities are small,

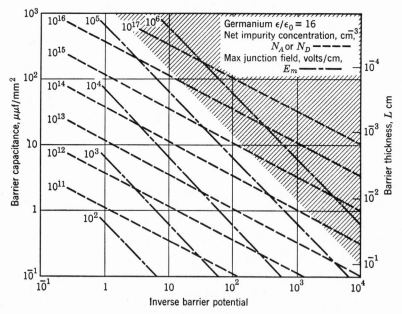

Fig. 1.8   Capacitance-voltage relations for alloy-diffusion junctions.

the potential distribution can be determined from Poisson's law of electrostatics for a medium of relative dielectric constant ϵ/ϵ_0:

$$\nabla^2 V = \rho/\epsilon \qquad\qquad [1.7]$$

In general, V and its gradient E depend upon the distribution of impurities near the junction. For one important case of the alloy-

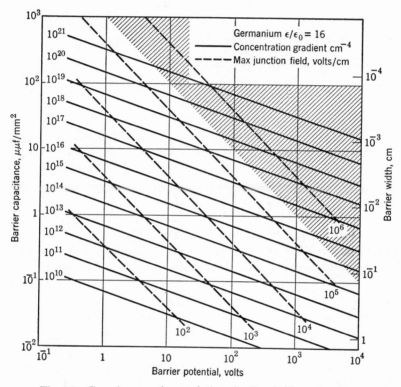

Fig. 1.9   Capacitance-voltage relations for "graded" p-n junctions.

diffusion junction, there is a very rapid transition from the constant undisturbed region to the highly doped contact. Here, nearly all the voltage is across the undisturbed region of constant charge density ρ. The voltage (obtained by integrating eq. 1.7 twice, recalling that ρ/ϵ is a constant throughout the region of interest) is, therefore, proportional to the square of the barrier thickness.

If the germanium changes from n to p in a relatively gradual manner, as is common with grown junctions, the charge density is proportional to the distance away from the junction. Two integrations of eq. 1.7, with ρ proportional to distance, yield V proportional to the cube of the barrier thickness.

The barrier charge increases with voltage, and, therefore, the barrier has a capacitance. The rapid transition junction has an effective a-c capacitance which is inversely proportional to the square root of V. The graded junction capacitance is inversely proportional to the cube root of V.

These relations are summarized for germanium in Figs. 1.8 and 1.9. There is also an additional frequency-dependent capacitive reactance due to charge flow if the current density is not negligible.

1.3.4   The p-n Junction Rectifier

The p-n junction itself is an extremely efficient rectifier. The characteristics of germanium junction rectifiers may be inferred from the voltage-current density graph of Fig. 1.7. The actual currents involved in a specific rectifier depend upon the effective junction area. For example, if the junction area is 1 mm^2, the inverse current may be of the order of 1 to 100 microamperes. Characteristics of actual devices are discussed in greater detail in Chapter 21.

Extremely high electric fields exist at an inversely biased junction. Electric fields of the order of 10^5 volts/cm are not uncommon in operating devices. When the field approaches 2×10^5 volts/cm, conduction electrons are spontaneously excited, and the current density increases extremely rapidly. This is known as the Zener breakdown field. It sets an upper voltage limit for junctions, depending upon the impurity distributions. For this reason, the shaded areas of Figs. 1.8 and 1.9 are to be regarded as inaccessible for germanium. The Zener current in junctions has possible voltage-control applications since the sharp current rise is equivalent to an extremely low incremental impedance, and operation is analogous to the familiar voltage regulator tubes.

1.3.5   Current Control in p-n Junctions

The barrier region of an inversely biased junction is a near-insulator only because of the scarcity of carriers in it. The inverse current consists principally of thermally generated minority carriers, and these increase rapidly with temperature as described in Sec. 1.3.2. The inverse current can be controlled by temperature and can therefore be used to indicate the junction temperature.

Similarly, the inverse currents in a p-n junction can be increased by illuminating it,[13] each photon absorbed producing a hole-electron pair.

Field effects near the surface can also be used to modify junction currents, as in the fieldistor.[14]

Transistor action is based on the control of current in an inversely biased (collector) junction by the injection of carriers into the barrier region from another nearby junction.

1.4 The Junction Transistor

There are some differences in the detailed behavior of n-p-n and p-n-p transistors, owing to the fact that the mobility of holes is somewhat smaller than that of electrons. However, the mechanisms of injection, diffusion, and collection control the operation of both in the same manner.[15, 16] The collector current control is defined by the quantity

$$\alpha = \left| \partial I_c / \partial I_e \right|_{V_c}$$

If all the emitter current were injected as minority carriers into the base, and if all these diffused through the base without recombination and were collected, α would be unity; i.e., the collector current changes would equal the emitter current changes, and base current would remain constant.

α can be described by the relation

$$\alpha = \gamma \beta \alpha^* \qquad\qquad [1.8]$$

where γ is the fraction of the emitter current injected into the base region as minority carriers, β is the fraction of these which survive the diffusion process in the base region, arriving at the collector junction, and α^* is the intrinsic carrier multiplication at the collector. (See Sec 1.4.3.)

1.4.1 Carrier Injection at the Emitter

Consider the injection of holes from a p-type emitter into the n-type base region of a p-n-p transistor. Returning to Fig. 1.4, we note that part of the forward current is carried by holes injected into the base region. If the p-type emitter material has a much higher carrier density (i.e., a much lower resistivity) than the n-type base material, then (as in the figure) most of the current would be carried by the injected holes. Since the electric field is negligible in the base region, the carriers move primarily by diffusion.

If the holes and electrons moved with equal rapidity, the ratio of current carried by electrons to that carried by holes would be the ratio of their densities, σ_B/σ_E, where σ_E and σ_B are conductivities of the emitter and base region, respectively. However, the diffusion rates depend upon the diffusion length † in the region the carriers enter, and the actual ratio of electron current to hole current is $(\sigma_B/\sigma_E)(L_{hB}/L_{eE})$. This ratio may be verified to be the ratio of the electron and hole currents in eqs. 1.5 and 1.6 for the junction current. The fraction γ_h of the total current injected as holes is then

$$\gamma_h = 1/[1 + (\sigma_B/\sigma_E)(L_{hB}/L_{eE})] \cong 1 - (\sigma_B/\sigma_E)(L_{hB}/L_{eE}) \qquad [1.9]$$

The approximate form of eq. 1.9 is valid for cases where the last term is much smaller than unity.

For a good emitter, γ should be very nearly unity. This requires that the last term in eq. 1.9 be negligible. This is usually accomplished by having very low-resistivity germanium in the emitter region. The base thickness W_B is usually much smaller than the nominal diffusion distance L_{hB} of holes in it. The concentration gradient at the emitter junction, therefore, is determined largely by the boundary condition that the injected carrier density is zero at the collector junction (located a distance W_B from the emitter) instead of the previous condition of gradual recombination over an average distance L_{hB}. Equation 1.9 for such transistors thus becomes

$$\gamma_h = 1 - (\sigma_B/\sigma_E)(W_B/L_{eE}) \qquad [1.10]$$

Similarly for electron injection in n-p-n transistors:

$$\gamma_e = 1 - (\sigma_B/\sigma_E)(W_B/L_{hE}) \qquad [1.11]$$

Should the emitter region be thinner than L_{eE} or L_{hE}, its thickness W_E would replace L_{eE} or L_{hE}.

The above relations have implicitly assumed low-level operation, i.e., that the injected minority carrier densities are small compared to the equilibrium density of majority carriers in the base region. At high current densities the effective lifetime of injected carriers is smaller, and the total hole and electron densities tend to become more nearly equal. Both effects tend to result in a decrease of α at high emitter currents.

1.4.2 Recombination and Diffusion of Minority Carriers

When *minority carriers* are injected into the base region (such as holes injected into the n-type base of a p-n-p transistor), no extended

† The diffusion length for holes injected into the base region L_{hB} is the distance over which the concentration is reduced by a factor of approximately e (2.72). The shorter L_{hB}, the greater the concentration gradient, and the greater the diffusion of holes into the base. Conversely, for smaller L_{eE}, the greater the diffusion of electrons from the base region into the emitter region.

space-charge region is set up, in distinction to the situation around the hot cathode in a vacuum tube, since there are majority carriers available to occupy the same average volume and neutralize the space charge. In further distinction to the electrons in a vacuum tube, the injected carriers move by diffusion in all available directions, since no appreciable electric field is maintained in the semiconductor base region. Thus, they are not actually attracted toward the collector. The collector junction, however, collects all the carriers which reach it, and this sets up a concentration gradient resulting in diffusion toward the collector.

A quantitative solution of the diffusion equation has been carried out in Chapter 17, where it is applied to the calculation of transistor parameters.

Furthermore, the surplus holes and electrons are continually recombining, the concentration exponentially decaying toward the equilibrium density corresponding to the temperature of the base germanium. It is desirable to have as many of the injected carriers as possible reach the barrier region of the inversely biased collector junction before recombining. This requires fairly close spacing between emitter and collector; i.e., the separation must be small, compared to the diffusion length for the base region germanium, since the diffusion length is the distance over which the injected carrier concentration has decreased by a factor of $1/e$.

For one-dimensional diffusion across a base region of width W_B, the maximum fraction β of injected carriers which can reach the collector is

$$\beta = \text{sech } (W_B/L_B) \cong 1 - (W_B{}^2/2L_B{}^2) \qquad [1.12]$$

neglecting edge and surface effects, which may increase recombination and thus lower β still further. Carriers which recombine in the base region appear as current in the base circuit.

In germanium, L may range from a few mils to more than 100 mils, corresponding to values of the characteristic "lifetime" of less than 1 microsecond to several thousand microseconds. The diffusion time, which must be much less than the lifetime for high α, results in a transit time phase lag between emitter and collector.

1.4.3   Collection of Carriers at a p-n Junction

As mentioned in Sec. 1.3.4, extremely high electric fields occur in the vicinity of an inversely biased p-n junction. Injected carriers which arrive at the junction are irresistibly swept into the collector region.

However, the nature of the collector junction may be such as to cause multiplication of collected carriers. For example, if injected holes are being collected after passing through the n-type base layer of a p-n-p transistor, they momentarily alter the charge density of the collector junction as they pass through the barrier into the p-type collector region. If the p-type germanium in the collector contains an appreciable concentration of electrons, some of these may be attracted back through the barrier region into the base. If x electrons thus cross

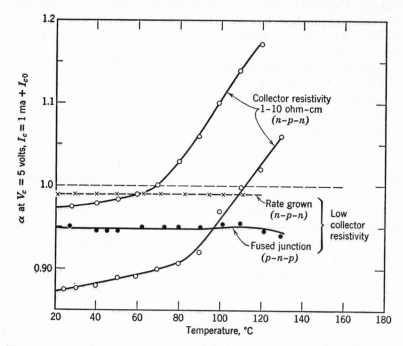

Fig. 1.10   Alpha vs. temperature for junction transistors of different collector resistivity.

the junction for each hole collected, then the collector multiplication factor α^* may be expressed

$$\alpha^* = 1 + x \qquad [1.13]$$

The quantity x, normally very much smaller than unity for single junctions, increases with the density of minority carriers in the collector region and hence increases with temperature, but can be minimized at all temperatures by having low-resistivity germanium on the collector side of the junction, so that the minority carriers are suppressed by the great abundance of majority carriers. α-temperature curves [17] for transistors of different collector resistivity are shown in Fig. 1.10.

1.5   High-Temperature Effects in Transistors

There are three changes in transistor parameters at high temperatures which are of principal concern to the circuit design engineer. In many transistors, α increases and may exceed unity. In all transistors, the collector saturation current, I_{c0}, increases exponentially with temperature as shown in Fig. 1.11, and the collector resistance decreases with temperature.

The α increase described in Sec. 1.4.3 can be disastrous, particularly in grounded-emitter circuits which require α less than unity for stable

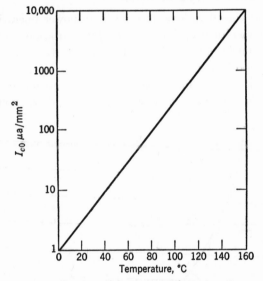

Fig. 1.11   Thermal increase of I_{c0} for typical p-n junction transistors.

operation as described later. Fortunately, this difficulty can be eliminated by proper control of impurities in the collector. Since I_{c0} is the minimum value of collector current, its increase reduces the available current variation for large-signal operation and decreases the available output power and efficiency. Also, its change may change the operating point radically unless stabilization is provided. Finally, the benefits of very low level operation may disappear at temperatures where I_{c0} may approach 1 milliampere or more. At sufficiently high temperatures, the dissipation due to I_{c0} may even cause thermal runaway.

The value of I_{c0} depends to some extent upon the germanium electrical properties, since I_{c0} is equal to the first bracket of the junction current equation (1.5). Also, I_{c0} can be reduced by using devices of smaller junction area, but the general range of values is fixed by unalterable properties of the pure germanium itself, as is the exponential increase with temperature.

The collector resistance decreases fairly rapidly with temperature, but it is possible to build transistors which maintain collector resistance greater than 0.5 megohm above 100° C.

Properly designed germanium transistors permit stable operation at temperatures above 130° C.

1.6   High-Power Effects in Transistors

The general considerations affecting high-power operation of transistors include voltage limitations, current limitations, ambient temperature, and package limitations. The interrelation among these factors is illustrated in Fig. 1.12.

The collector voltage limitation is set by the inverse characteristics of the collector junction, particularly the breakdown voltage. Such

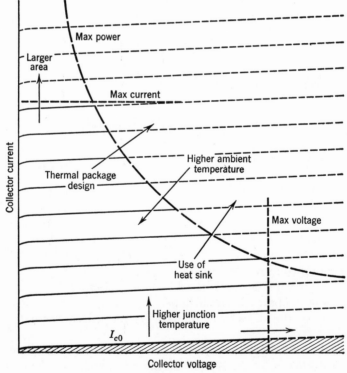

Fig. 1.12   Factors that limit high-power operation of junction transistors.

voltage limits may be of the order of 100 volts or more in properly designed transistors.

There is no sharply defined maximum collector current for a transistor. However, it will be found that the required emitter voltage increases at high currents, the amount of recombination also increases, lowering α, and the collector resistance decreases. Since all these effects lower the gain or cause distortion, a practical current limitation will thus be imposed in each case by the requirements of the circuit. For high currents, transistors with large junction areas are desirable.

Finally, the collector junction of a power transistor is operated at a temperature which depends upon the ambient temperature, the "thermal resistance" of the encapsulation, and the dissipation. The highest junction temperature for thermal stability will depend upon the circuitry to some extent but may be as high as 150° C. Considerations of gain, etc., may indicate a lower junction operating temperature; but, whatever the criterion for satisfactory operation, the temperature limitation will define a hyperbola of maximum collector dissipation for a given device in a specified medium of given ambient temperature, as shown in the figure. This factor can be controlled by proper thermal design of a package which conducts the heat from the junctions to the exterior cooling surfaces with a minimum temperature drop. In containers properly designed for efficient cooling, transistors having junction areas of the order of 1 mm^2 can be operated safely at dissipations in excess of 1 watt.[17]

1.7   High-Frequency Effects in Transistors

The high-frequency gain of a transistor is determined by the combined effects of collector barrier capacitance, phase shift, and the carrier diffusion mechanism itself.

The collector capacitance is principally the junction capacitance described in Sec. 1.3.3. Its value is determined principally by the voltage across the junction, and the current through it, the area of the junction, and the nature of the junction. Capacitances in the range of 5 $\mu\mu f$ to 50 $\mu\mu f$ are commonly encountered. The effect on gain depends, of course, upon the external circuit.

As described in Sec. 1.4.2, the diffusion of carriers results in a time lag between the emitter and collector currents. Since the alternating base current (proportional to $1 - \alpha$) is the instantaneous difference between emitter and collector currents, the complex "vector" difference must be employed to determine the actual base current. A time lag of the order of 1 microsecond can cause a noticeable change in $(1 - \alpha)$ at a few kilocycles, if α is close to unity. This imposes a serious frequency limitation upon grounded-emitter circuits whose gain depends directly upon $1 - \alpha$.

Finally, the magnitude of α itself decreases with frequency. As the emitter and collector currents get farther out of phase at higher frequencies, the straggling and thermal dispersion in the arrival time of the carriers becomes a larger fraction of the time per cycle. More of the carriers injected toward the peak current of the cycle tend to arrive closer to those injected at the low current part of the cycle. If all the diffusion paths are not the same length, this can cause partial cancellation at higher frequencies. As a result, the absolute value of α decreases with frequency, and the α cut-off frequency (3 db) decreases with the square of the base thickness W. α cut-off frequencies above 1 megacycle can be obtained in ordinary triode junction transistors with reasonable care. The extension of the usable frequency range of junction transistors through the 10–100 megacycle range and above is a challenging subject for further development.

1.8   Comparison of Point-Contact and Junction Transistors

Point-contact transistors have many fundamental features in common with junction transistors. In both types, minority carriers are injected into a base region by a forward-biased emitter electrode, and are collected by an inversely biased collector electrode after diffusion through the base region. The p-n-p junction transistor corresponds roughly to the n-type base point-contact transistor; the n-p-n junction transistor corresponds to the p-type base point-contact transistor. The analogy is further reinforced by experimental evidence that p-n junctions are formed under point contacts such as those used in transistors. A fundamental distinction between junction and point-contact transistors is geometrical: the point-formed junctions are extremely small, and the geometry is hemispherical in the region of the junctions. This results in spreading effects, a greater dependence upon surface phenomena, and a smaller collector capacitance. Point-contact transistors have been operated at much higher frequencies than the present triode junction transistors.

On the other hand, the junction barriers are formed in the point-contact units by a current pulsing process which is not subject to the precision of control achieved in the processes used for junction transistors. Consequently, the pulse-formed junctions have inferior voltage-current characteristics, resulting in noise and in low collector resistance in spite of the small collector area.

In point-contact transistors, α is commonly greater than unity owing to a physical multiplication at the collector, probably due to a combination of trapping effects,[18] and the "*p-n* hook" multiplication mechanism [19] (see Chapter 21). This prevents stable operation in certain circuits but makes possible extremely simple oscillator and "flipflop" circuits.

1.9 Application of Other Semiconductors to Junction Devices

Much of the content of this chapter applies to semiconductor devices in general, although germanium has consistently been used as an example. The properties which make germanium highly suitable in junction devices include chemical stability, high carrier mobility, long injected carrier lifetime, large diffusion constant (i.e., diffusion lengths comparable to controllable device dimensions), reasonably high resistivity, and availability in extremely pure single crystals. The last item at first glance would not appear to be a fundamental property, but reliable information on the attainable characteristics of a semiconductor is never available until satisfactory purification and crystallization methods have been laboriously developed.

The first applications of other semiconductors will undoubtedly be made in the areas where germanium is weakest. Silicon, for example, has its electrons more tightly bound, and, therefore, silicon junctions should operate to much higher temperatures than germanium before thermally generated carriers render devices inefficient or unreliable. The mobility and lifetime data indicate that transistor action for silicon should also be feasible at higher temperatures than for germanium.

The compound semiconductors include many metallic oxides, sulfides, selenides, tellurides, etc. In these, the stoicheiometric ratios must be controlled with great precision before they can be widely used. As fundamental information gradually becomes available, applications will suggest themselves for unusual properties.

1.10 Problems

1. Calculate the resistivity of silicon as a function of donor and acceptor concentration (find n_i, using eqs. 1.2 and 1.4), as shown in Fig. 1.6 for germanium. Use the values $\mu_e = 1250 \text{ cm}^2/\text{volt sec}$, $\mu_h = 250 \text{ cm}^2/\text{volt sec}$, and $\rho_i = 5 \times 10^5$ ohm-cm at 300° K. Assume that impurities in silicon are all activated at 300° K. What errors are introduced by this simplifying assumption?

2. The rectification ratio R for *p-n* junctions is sometimes defined as the ratio of forward current at a given (+) voltage to the inverse current at the same (−) voltage. Calculate this ratio as a function of $|V|$, and plot on log log paper. Also plot R as a function of forward current. Compare two numerical cases: $I_0 = 10^{-6}$ amp and $I_0 = 10^{-3}$ amp.

3. Solve Poisson's equation for an alloy-diffusion p-n junction as outlined in Sec. 1.3.3, and verify the following relations, using mks units:

$$V = eN_D L^2/2\epsilon \qquad C = (\epsilon e N_D/2V)^{1/2} \qquad E_m = 2VL^{-1}$$

where N_D is donor density, L barrier thickness, E_m maximum junction field, and V junction potential difference. (Note that the conductivity of the germanium in the alloy region is larger by at least 10^3 than that corresponding to N_D. Hence the potential drop in the alloy region may be neglected.)

4. Using the results of problem 3, verify that the Zener voltage of alloy-diffusion junctions is proportional to the resistivity of the germanium used as the base material. Evaluate the proportionality constants for n-type and for p-type germanium in volts per ohm-centimeter.

5. Assuming that the transition from n- to p-type germanium takes place in a "graded" junction via a constant impurity concentration gradient G, evaluate expressions for junction potential, capacitance, maximum field, and Zener voltage, in solutions analogous to those of problems 3 and 4.

1.11   Bibliography

1. W. Shockley, *Electrons and Holes in Semiconductors*, Van Nostrand, New York, 1950.

2. D. A. Wright, *Semi-Conductors*, Wiley, New York, 1950.

3. Torrey and Witmer, *Crystal Rectifiers*, McGraw-Hill, New York, 1950.

4. F. Seitz, *Modern Theory of Solids*, McGraw-Hill, New York, 1940.

5. Ref. 1, p. 16ff, also Chapter 8.

6. Ref. 1, Sec. 10.3, Sec. 12.4, Sec. 12.8.

7. G. K. Teal et al., "Growth of Germanium Single Crystals Containing p-n Junctions," *Phys. Rev.*, *81*, 637 (1951).

8. R. N. Hall, "p-n Junctions Produced by Growth Rate Variation," *Phys. Rev.*, *88* (1952).

9. K. Lark-Horowitz et al., "Deuteron Bombarded Semiconductors," *Phys. Rev.*, *73*, 1256 (1948).

10. R. N. Hall and W. C. Dunlap, "p-n Junctions by Impurity Diffusion," *Phys. Rev.*, *80*, 467 (1950).

11. Ref. 1, Sec. 4.2a; also Sec. 12.5.

12. W. Shockley, "Theory of p-n Junctions in Semiconductors and in p-n Junction Transistors," *Bell Sys. Tech. J.*, *29*, 560 (1950), Sec. 2.

13. See disclosures of R. S. Ohl, U. S. patent 2,402,662.

14. O. M. Stuetzer, "Junction Fieldistors," *Proc. IRE*, *40*, 1377 (1952).

15. Ref. 12, entire article.

16. E. L. Steele, "Theory of α for p-n-p Diffused-Junction Transistors," *Proc. IRE*, *40*, 1424 (1952).

17. J. S. Saby, "Fused Impurity p-n Junction Transistors," *Proc. IRE*, *40*, 1358 (1952).

18. W. R. Sittner, "Current Multiplication in the Type A Transistor," *Proc. IRE*, *40*, 448 (1952).

19. L. B. Valdes, "Transistor Forming Effects in n-Type Germanium," *Proc. IRE*, *40*, 445 (1952).

Chapter 2

Forms, Types, and
Characteristics
of Transistors

2.1 Point-Contact Transistors

Point-contact transistors, the first type developed, were introduced in the type A form by the Bell Telephone Laboratories in 1948.
Shortly thereafter similar units were constructed in the Research
Laboratory of the General Electric Company, and within the following
year point-contact transistors were also produced by RCA, Raytheon,
and Sylvania. All these transistors were similar in form, although
different in various mechanical details. Performance of these early
designs was variable, and in many respects submarginal; however, they
laid the groundwork upon which the newer and better forms of transistors were to rise. Current point-contact transistors bear only a super-
ficial resemblance to these original forms and are capable of much more
predictable, more stable, and more uniform performance.

2.1.1 Construction

In basic construction, a point-contact transistor consists of a germanium pellet mounted in some form of container, with two contacts
pressed against the surface of the pellet. Figure 2.1 shows the construction of the General Electric type G-11 transistor, which is typical.
In this unit the pellet is 0.065 in. square, 0.015 in. thick, of high-purity
single-crystal germanium, and is soldered with pure tin to a brass plug.
The outer case is of brass, $11\frac{1}{32}$ in. long and $5\frac{1}{32}$ in. in diameter, with
three 0.016-in.-diameter gold-plated phosphor bronze leads projecting
from one end. The whisker assembly consists of a 0.005-in.-diameter
phosphor bronze collector and a 0.005-in.-diameter platinum ruthenium
emitter spaced approximately 0.002 in. apart at the point of contact.

The pellet assembly is forced into the case and advanced until contact is made with the whiskers. The whole assembly is then vacuum-impregnated to provide moisture seal. As an additional stability feature the emitter is welded to the germanium.

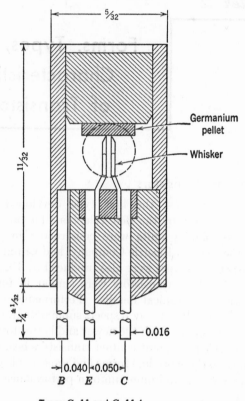

Types G-11 and G-11A

Fig. 2.1 Construction of General Electric type G-11 and G-11A transistors.

The above construction provides a compact unit, capable of high dissipation for its small size, suitable for either plug-in or wired-in installation.

Point-contact transistors made by other companies follow a somewhat similar construction, differing mainly in physical size, construction and spacing of contacts, and arrangements of connecting terminals. Though the general physical characteristics are similar, different electrical characteristics are obtained by these variations and also by variations in the electrical characteristics of the germanium.

2.1.2 Connections

Figure 2.2 shows the electrical connections to a point-contact transistor. Two bias batteries are required: one to supply a positive potential to the emitter, the other to supply negative potential to the collector. Current flows into the emitter, out of the collector. In transistor operation it is generally desirable to supply essentially constant current to the emitter, as will be explained in later chapters, while the collector is usually supplied from a constant potential source. A resistor, R_l, is usually inserted in the collector lead, across which the

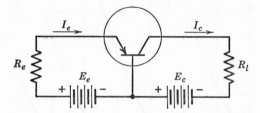

Fig. 2.2   Bias connections for point-contact transistor.

output signal is taken. In some connections the emitter resistor R_e is used as a load resistor, with the input applied to the base.

In vacuum-tube practice it is customary to specify operating point in terms of grid bias and plate potential. In transistors, however, there are four interrelated parameters: emitter current, emitter-base voltage, collector current, collector-base voltage. Specification of any two will determine the other two. The usual practice is to specify collector potential and either emitter current or collector current. Typical operation in the circuit of Fig. 2.2 might be a collector voltage of -25 volts, emitter current of 0.5 milliampere. Under these conditions the emitter voltage would be about 0.1 volt and the collector current 2–3 milliamperes.

2.1.3 Static Characteristics

In any device, such as the transistor, wherein the various currents and voltages are interdependent, a considerable choice exists as to the best forms in which to plot characteristics. Thus collector current may be plotted against collector voltage, for different values of constant emitter current; similarly, emitter current may be plotted against emitter voltage for constant collector voltage; or emitter voltage may be plotted against collector current, etc. Two families of curves have achieved general acceptance in transistor application work. The first, called the "collector family," is illustrated in Fig. 2.3. This is a plot of collector current against collector voltage (where the term "collector voltage" or "emitter voltage" is used to designate the voltage measured between the indicated electrode and base, unless otherwise indicated), with a series of constant values of emitter current. The similarity to vacuum-tube characteristics is marked, provided the current and voltage axes are interchanged. The lowest curve, that for $I_e = 0$, is

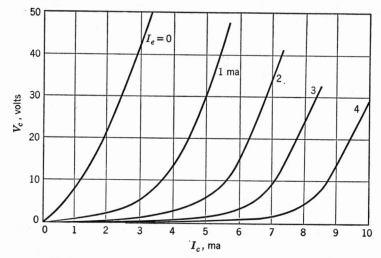

Fig. 2.3 V_c-I_c characteristics for point-contact transistor.

called the I_{c0} characteristic, and corresponds to the diode characteristic of the collector.

The other principal characteristic curve is called the "emitter family" and shows emitter voltage plotted against emitter current, for a series of constant values of collector current. Figure 2.4 illustrates such a family. These curves have no similar counterpart in customary tube practice.

From these two principal characteristics all the operating data may be deduced. Given the emitter current and collector voltage, the collector current may be found from the collector family; and using this collector current and the above emitter current, the emitter voltage may be obtained from the emitter family.

A word of caution is in order here, concerning polarities of voltages and directions of currents. The characteristic curves of Figs. 2.3 and 2.4 indicate magnitudes of voltages and currents of polarity and direction as indicated on Fig. 2.2 for the usual n-type base point-contact transistors.   Similarly, subsequent characteristics in this and other chapters may not designate polarity or direction, in order that the same general characteristics may apply alike to p-n-p (or point-contact) or n-p-n units.   The reader must *always* remember that the emitter potential is normally *positive* for p-n-p and point-contact transistors, the collector *negative*, with current flowing *into* the emitter, *out* of the collector.   The reverse will apply for n-p-n units.

These static characteristics may be used to determine the small or large signal low-frequency dynamic characteristics.   For example, the

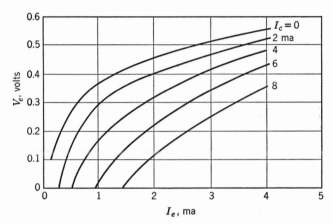

Fig. 2.4 V_e-I_e characteristics for point-contact transistor.

slope of the I_c-V_c curve is a measure of the output resistance of the transistor.   Similarly, input resistance, feedback resistance, etc., may be obtained.   This is covered in considerable detail in Chapter 3, where the equivalent mesh is developed, and the values of the component resistances are derived from the static characteristics.

2.1.4   Typical Units

The Frontispiece includes a photograph of the General Electric type G-11 point-contact transistor, together with a scale to illustrate the small size.

2.2   Junction Transistors

The junction, or broad-area, transistor is a relative newcomer in the transistor field, having been introduced in 1951, yet it bids fair to become the predominating form, primarily because of great improvement in such characteristics as noise, power efficiency, operating voltage, power-handling ability, and similar items, over the point-contact transistor. A large variety of forms of junction transistors have already been introduced, and a great deal of research is still under way; it is anticipated that ultimately some type of junction transistor will be available for practically any form of application. This does not mean that the point-contact transistor will automatically become obsolete, as there will undoubtedly remain such applications as computer or high-frequency applications where it has certain advantages.

2.2.1   Construction

The basic construction of a junction transistor is illustrated in Fig. 2.5, which shows, in block form, the essential details. The reader is also

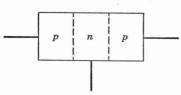

Fig. 2.5   Basic construction of p-n-p junction transistor.

referred to the discussion of semiconductor properties in Chapter 1. In general, a junction transistor consists of a germanium body in which three (or more, in special cases) areas of different conductivity exist. A p-type area is one in which excess carriers of the so-called "hole" or electron-deficiency type exist; in n-type material, conduction is by excess electrons. Thus in a p-n-p junction transistor two of the areas of the germanium are p-type, with n material in between, and conversely an n-p-n transistor has two n areas sandwiching a p area. The similar areas may have approximately equal or widely different resistivities. The middle layer is usually very thin, of the order of 0.001 in.

Many processes are used to produce these junction transistors. Generally the germanium is a single crystal, produced by seeding and pulling a crystal from a melt. The various p-n junctions may be produced during the growing process or may be produced by diffusion in the cut crystal. The p-n-p or n-p-n

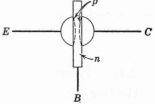

Fig. 2.6   Construction of diffused-junction transistor.

transistors may be produced by either method. It should be mentioned in passing that the point-contact transistor is actually a p-n-p transistor, a p-n junction being created during the forming process.

Figure 2.6 illustrates a typical diffused-junction transistor developed by General Electric. In this construction the single-crystal pellet is processed by cutting from the pulled crystal; then two indium dots are attached to the opposite surfaces, and the internal p-n junctions are produced by diffusing the indium into the germanium by heat. Connections are made to the two dots, forming the emitter and collector, and to the germanium forming the base. The germanium may be mounted to a Fernico strip to provide additional heat conduction for moderate-power units, and similar techniques may be utilized for higher-power units.

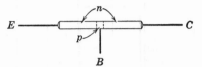

Fig. 2.7 Basic construction of n-p-n grown-junction transistor.

Figure 2.7 illustrates an n-p-n rate-grown transistor, also developed by General Electric. In this unit the p-n junctions are produced while the crystal is being grown, and then are cut from the whole crystal and leads are attached.

2.2.2 p-n-p Transistor Connections

Since the point-contact transistor is essentially a p-n-p transistor, though not a junction transistor, the connections shown previously in Fig. 2.2 also apply to the p-n-p junction transistor. Generally the currents and voltages will be lower, taking advantage of the ability of this form of transistor to operate at extremely low power consumption. Thus a typical operation might be with collector voltage of -1 volt and collector current of 0.5 milliampere. Emitter current in junction transistors is generally very nearly equal to the collector current; emitter voltage, of the order of 0.1 volt. Operation of junction transistors has been achieved at much less than 1 volt on the collector with currents of a few microamperes. In power-amplifier operation higher voltages are used, limited generally by permissible peak inverse ratings, and the currents may approach an ampere.

2.2.3 n-p-n Transistor Connections

In n-p-n transistors the connections are identical, except that all potentials and directions of current flows are reversed, as previously stated. Thus the collector is at positive polarity, relative to the base; the emitter, negative. Orders of magnitude of currents and voltages are the same as for p-n-p transistors.

2.2.4 Static Characteristics

As with the point-contact transistor, the two most commonly used sets of characteristics are the collector family and the emitter family.

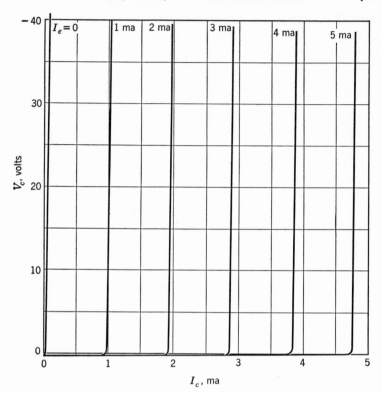

Fig. 2.8 V_c-I_c characteristics for junction transistors.

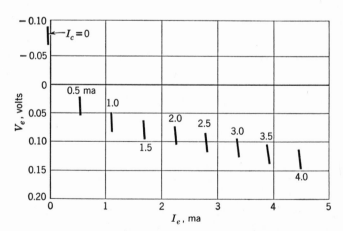

Fig. 2.9 V_e-I_e characteristics for junction transistors.

Figure 2.8 shows a typical family of collector characteristics for a *p-n-p*
junction transistor.   Figure 2.9 shows the corresponding emitter family.
Figure 2.10 is an enlarged version of the low-power portion of the
collector family; Fig. 2-11 is the corresponding emitter family.

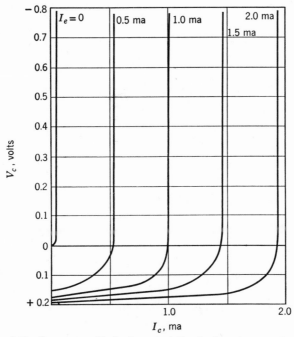

Fig. 2.10   Low-power V_c-I_c characteristics for junction transistors.

Several interesting details are apparent from these characteristics as
compared to the corresponding point-contact transistor characteristics.
First, the collector characteristics are essentially straight and parallel,
and nearly vertical to the current axis.   Next, the initial curve, the I_{c0}

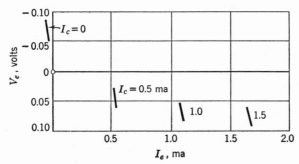

Fig. 2.11   Low-power V_e-I_e characteristics for junction transistors.

curve, corresponding to zero emitter current, is very close to the voltage axis, and the point at which the curves depart markedly from linearity is close to the current axis. The curves are evenly spaced. These indicate that the output resistance is very high, the diode back resistance of the collector also very high, the linearity excellent, and the class A power efficiency potentially very nearly the ideal 50 per cent.

The emitter curves are only segments, indicating little variation in emitter voltage with change of collector potential. The emitter voltage is not a linear function of emitter current, indicating non-linear input resistance, and this imposes one of the basic requirements for power operation, that the input current be sinusoidal, rather than the voltage, as in vacuum tubes.

From the low-power characteristics it can be observed that good performance may be expected at voltages of the order of a few tenths of a volt, currents in the 10-microampere range. Operation at such low levels, however, is subject to much greater variation due to non-uniformity of I_{c0}, for example, and to variation between units.

2.2.5 Effect of Temperature

In all transistors temperature has a marked effect upon many of the operating characteristics. The zero-emitter collector current, I_{c0}, increases exponentially with temperature and may rise several thousand per cent from room temperature to temperatures of the order of 100° C. The short-circuit current amplification, α, may rise, stay relatively constant, or drop slightly, depending on the physical construction of the transistor. The collector resistance will drop, frequently one order of magnitude over the above temperature range.

Referring to the static characteristics shown in Fig. 2.8, these changes will evidence themselves as follows: The lowest curve, I_{c0}, will rise, and its slope will be decreased. The other curves which are essentially parallel to the I_{c0} curve will also rise by about the same amount. If α remains constant the spacing between curves will remain unchanged; otherwise, they will contract or expand, depending upon whether α decreases or increases. The slope will also be reduced.

The temperature effects will be described in greater detail in Chapter 3, together with representative data showing variation of all operating characteristics.

2.2.6 Typical Units

The Frontispiece shows a typical diffused-junction transistor, developed by General Electric, and also a rate-grown unit.

Transistors as Low-Frequency Circuit Elements

3.1 The Transistor Considered as a "Black Box"

A complete understanding of the functioning of transistors involves the detailed study of the physics of semiconductors and entails laborious computations for the solution of relatively simple circuit problems. With transistors, as with vacuum tubes, the problem is considerably simplified by describing the operation of the transistor in terms of equivalent circuits which yield useful, if approximate, results. Such simple equivalent circuits will describe the small-signal properties of the transistor, with the assumption that operation is over a range in

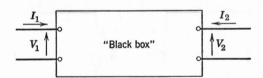

Fig. 3.1 Four-terminal active network.

which the resistive parameters are linear and constant in value. If, as they do, the parameters vary with operating conditions, such as biases or temperature, the formulas developed on the basis of the above assumptions may be modified and interpreted in the light of the postulated or measured variations.†

A picture of the transistor considered as a four-terminal active network is shown in Fig. 3.1.

Of the four variables V_1, V_2, I_1, I_2, it is convenient to assume I_1 and I_2 to be the independent variables, where the relations between the voltages V_1, V_2 and the currents I_1, I_2 on which they depend can be

† In any case, for a particular operating point, frequency range, and temperature, the equivalent circuit using fixed parameters will represent the true state of affairs.

thought of as representing static characteristics. Formally, these relations can be represented by

$$V_1 = f_1(I_1, I_2) \qquad V_2 = f_2(I_1, I_2) \qquad [3.1]$$

The small-signal variations in V_1, V_2, namely v_1, v_2, in terms of the variations in I_1, I_2, namely i_1, i_2, are expressed by

$$v_1 = \frac{\partial f_1}{\partial I_1} i_1 + \frac{\partial f_1}{\partial I_2} i_2 \qquad v_2 = \frac{\partial f_2}{\partial I_1} i_1 + \frac{\partial f_2}{\partial I_2} i_2 \qquad [3.2]$$

If we let

$$r_{11} = \frac{\partial f_1}{\partial I_1} \qquad r_{12} = \frac{\partial f_1}{\partial I_2} \qquad r_{21} = \frac{\partial f_2}{\partial I_1} \qquad r_{22} = \frac{\partial f_2}{\partial I_2} \qquad [3.3]$$

we have, by substitution,

$$v_1 = r_{11}i_1 + r_{12}i_2 \qquad v_2 = r_{21}i_1 + r_{22}i_2 \qquad [3.4]$$

3.2   The Inverted-Pi Equivalent Circuit

By interpreting the circuit equations 3.4 one is led to the simplest of several equivalent circuits, as shown in Fig. 3.2.

It is seen that the quantities r_{11}, r_{22}, r_{12}, r_{21} are open-circuit resistances; for example, r_{11} is equal to the ratio v_1/i_1 with the right-hand

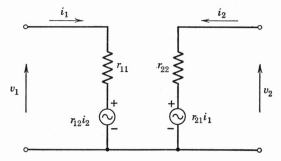

Fig. 3.2   Inverted-pi equivalent circuit.

mesh open-circuited, r_{21} is equal to the ratio v_2/i_1 with the right-hand mesh open-circuited, etc.

3.3   The T Network Voltage-Generator Equivalent Circuit

A more useful equivalent circuit, which to some extent resembles the physical picture of the transistor, is shown in Fig. 3.3. Writing the mesh equations for the circuit of Fig. 3.3:

$$v_1 = (r_e + r_b)i_e + r_b i_c \qquad v_2 = (r_b + r_m)i_e + (r_b + r_c)i_c \qquad [3.5]$$

and comparing with equations 3.4 one sees that

$$\left.\begin{array}{ll} r_{11} = r_e + r_b & r_{12} = r_b \\ r_{21} = r_b + r_m & r_{22} = r_b + r_c \end{array}\right\} \qquad [3.6]$$

It is seen that a fictitious voltage generator is the device that transforms a passive T network into one that represents the active transistor equivalent network. The configuration shown has some physical significance, inasmuch as each resistance is associated with one of the

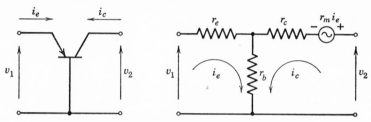

Fig. 3.3   T network equivalent circuit.

actual transistor leads, the voltage-amplifying action being represented in the collector lead by the fictitious generator.

3.4   The T Network Current-Generator Equivalent Circuit

Let us replace the fictitious voltage generator with a constant-current source as shown in Fig. 3.4.

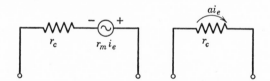

Fig. 3.4   Voltage and current-generator equivalents.

Equating the open-circuit voltages of the two equivalent meshes, one obtains:

$$r_m i_e = a r_c i_e \qquad [3.7]$$

Therefore

$$a = r_m / r_c$$

If short-circuit currents are equated,

$$i = r_m i_e / r_c = a i_e \qquad \text{or} \qquad a = r_m / r_c$$

which checks.

We thus arrive at the equivalent circuit shown in Fig. 3.5.

For simplicity, the equivalent circuits shown in Figs. 3.3 and 3.5 have been developed for one possible configuration of the transistor, namely, the grounded-base. If the emitter lead is grounded in lieu of the base lead, the collector circuit remaining unaltered, the grounded-emitter configuration is obtained, in which the voltage v_1 is now applied between ground and base, and the input current is now the base current. Since the relations between the emitter and collector voltages

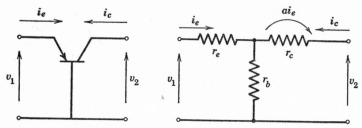

Fig. 3.5   Current-generator equivalent circuit.

and currents are determined only by the static characteristics, the equivalent circuit is merely rearranged by the arbitrary choice of which electrode is to be grounded. The input current and voltage, however, do not represent emitter current and voltage. Similar considerations hold for the grounded-collector configuration, where the collector lead is grounded, the base lead becomes the input, and the emitter lead the output. It has been found convenient to set up other equivalent circuits to describe these configurations using the same or derived parameters. The constant-current generator acting in the collector circuit is closest to the physical picture of transistor action.

3.5   Grounded-Emitter Voltage-Generator Equivalent Circuit

Figure 3.6 shows a convenient equivalent circuit for the grounded-emitter configuration. It is seen that the voltage generator is now determined by the value of i_b, the base current, rather than i_e, the emitter current, as with the grounded-base equivalent circuit. The

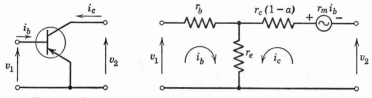

Fig. 3.6   Grounded-emitter voltage-generator equivalent circuit.

internal collector resistance is now $r_c(1 - a)$, which is defined in terms of the previous parameters as

$$r_c(1 - a) = r_c - r_m \qquad [3.8]$$

The circuit equations now can be written

$$v_1 = (r_b + r_e)i_b + r_e i_c \qquad v_2 = (r_e - r_m)i_b + [r_c(1 - a) + r_e]i_c \quad [3.9]$$

3.6   Grounded-Emitter Current-Generator Equivalent Circuit

By replacing the voltage generator in Fig. 3.6 with the equivalent current generator, the very useful equivalent circuit shown in Fig. 3.7

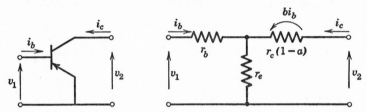

Fig. 3.7   Grounded-emitter current-generator equivalent circuit.

results.   If, as previously shown, either the open-circuit voltages or the short-circuit currents are equated for the two equivalent circuits,

$$b = \frac{r_m}{r_c(1 - a)} = \frac{r_m}{r_c - r_m} \qquad [3.10]$$

and, since

$$a = r_m/r_c \qquad [3.11]$$

$$b = a/(1 - a)$$

In most cases of practical interest this equivalent circuit indicates clearly the relationship between input and output currents, namely, that a current generator of b times the magnitude of input current is operating in the output circuit.

3.7   Grounded-Collector Equivalent Circuits

It is convenient to derive both voltage-generator and current-generator equivalent circuits for the grounded-collector configuration from those used for the grounded-emitter case.   Thus Figs. 3.8 and 3.9 show these circuits using the same parameters.

The circuit equations for the voltage-generator case in Fig. 3.8 can be shown to be

$$v_1 = (r_b + r_c)i_b + (r_c - r_m)i_e \qquad v_2 = r_c i_b + (r_e + r_c - r_m)i_e \quad [3.12]$$

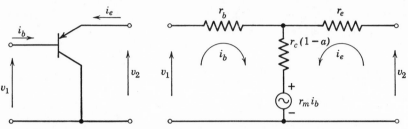

Fig. 3.8   Grounded-collector voltage-generator equivalent circuit.

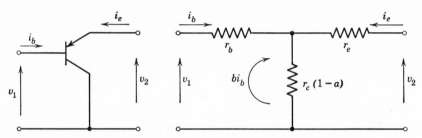

Fig. 3.9   Grounded-collector current-generator equivalent circuit.

3.8   Derivation of Parameters from Characteristic Curves

In Sec. 3.1 we arbitrarily chose the currents as independent variables, and the voltages as dependent variables, in deriving the open-circuit resistances r_{11}, r_{12}, r_{21}, r_{22}. Shown in Fig. 3.10 is a set of four families of curves representing the static characteristics V_c vs. I_c, V_c vs. I_e, V_e vs. I_c, V_e vs. I_e of a typical p-n-p junction transistor.

Rewriting eqs. 3.2,

$$v_e = \left(\frac{\partial V_e}{\partial I_e}\right) i_e + \left(\frac{\partial V_e}{\partial I_c}\right) i_c \qquad v_c = \left(\frac{\partial V_c}{\partial I_e}\right) i_e + \left(\frac{\partial V_c}{\partial I_c}\right) i_c \quad [3.13]$$

and

$$r_{11} = \left(\frac{\partial V_e}{\partial I_e}\right) = \text{slope of } V_e, I_e \text{ curve for } I_c \text{ constant}$$

$$r_{12} = \left(\frac{\partial V_e}{\partial I_c}\right) = \text{slope of } V_e, I_c \text{ curve for } I_e \text{ constant}$$

$$[3.14]$$

$$r_{21} = \left(\frac{\partial V_c}{\partial I_e}\right) = \text{slope of } V_c, I_e \text{ curve for } I_c \text{ constant}$$

$$r_{22} = \left(\frac{\partial V_c}{\partial I_c}\right) = \text{slope of } V_c, I_c \text{ curve for } I_e \text{ constant}$$

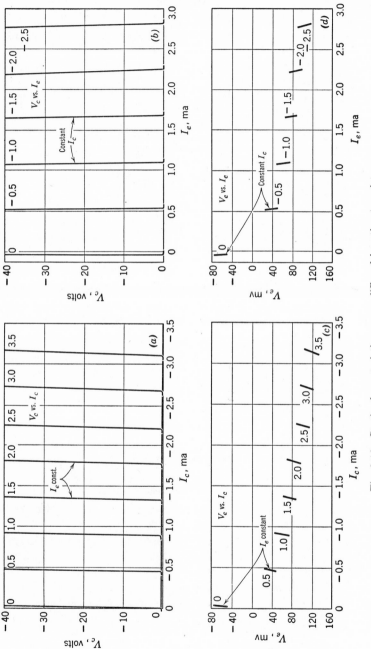

Fig. 3.10 Static characteristics, *p-n-p* diffused-junction transistor.

Referring to eq. 3.6, the quantities r_{11}, r_{12}, r_{21}, r_{22} have been interpreted in terms of the equivalent circuit parameters r_e, r_b, r_c, and r_m, and thus these latter quantities can be determined by measurements of the slopes of the static characteristic curves.

If we set $v_c = 0$ in eqs. 3.13 it is the equivalent of stating that V_c is constant.

These equations then become

$$v_e = r_{11}i_e + r_{12}i_c \qquad 0 = r_{21}i_e + r_{22}i_c \qquad [3.15]$$

Then

$$i_e = \frac{\begin{vmatrix} v_e & r_{12} \\ 0 & r_{22} \end{vmatrix}}{\Delta} \quad \text{and} \quad i_c = \frac{\begin{vmatrix} r_{11} & v_e \\ r_{21} & 0 \end{vmatrix}}{\Delta}$$

where Δ is the determinant $\begin{vmatrix} r_{11} & r_{12} \\ r_{21} & r_{22} \end{vmatrix}$. The ratio

$$\left| \frac{i_c}{i_e} \right| = \frac{r_{21}}{r_{22}} = \frac{r_m + r_b}{r_c + r_b}$$

The short-circuit current amplification α is thus defined:

$$\alpha = \frac{r_m + r_b}{r_c + r_b} \qquad [3.16]$$

This quantity can be found from the V_c, I_c static curves by measuring the change in I_c for a given change in I_e at a constant value of V_c.

It should be noted that with junction transistors, since $r_m \gg r_b$ and $r_c \gg r_b$,

$$\alpha \cong r_m/r_c = a \qquad [3.17]$$

3.9   Variation of Parameters with Operating Point

The values for r_e, r_b, r_c, r_m can be obtained at any given operating point from the static characteristics shown in Fig. 3.10. It is a tedious process, however, to measure and plot these characteristics to the accuracy required to obtain the desired values. With junction transistors the problem is accentuated as values of r_c and r_m of the order of magnitude of 1 megohm are frequently encountered. The graphical measurement of slopes involving these magnitudes would be prohibitively difficult. Accordingly, these parameters are usually measured by a-c methods, at small-signal levels, and at arbitrarily chosen d-c operating biases. Methods are described in detail in Chapter 22.

Measurements of the various parameters which have been made on a typical diffusion-type p-n-p junction transistor yield the curves shown in Figs. 3.11, 3.12, 3.13, 3.14, 3.15, and 3.16.

It should be noted that, for the constant I_e curves, V_c ranges from a few tenths of a volt minimum to 30 volts maximum at an arbitrary

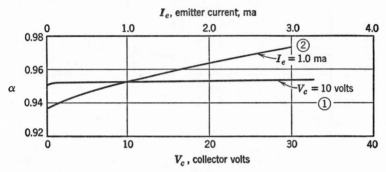

Fig. 3.11   Variation of α with emitter current and collector voltage.

value of I_e equal to 1 milliampere. The minimum is set by extreme variations of parameters at very low collector voltages; the maximum, by thermal effects due to heat generated at the junctions. The constant V_c curves are taken for an arbitrary value of $V_c = 10$ volts.

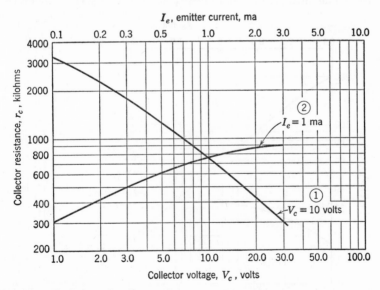

Fig. 3.12   Variation of collector resistance with emitter current and collector voltage.

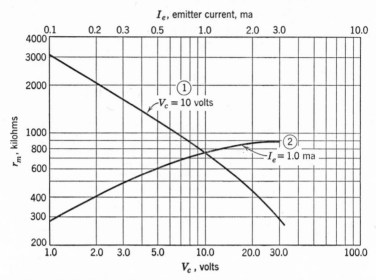

Fig. 3.13   Variation of r_m with emitter current and collector voltage.

The variations in the parameters which affect circuit design to the greatest degree are those exhibited by r_e, r_c, and r_m. The indications are that variations of α in the range considered are small enough to be negligible, although α would be expected to decrease as the emitter

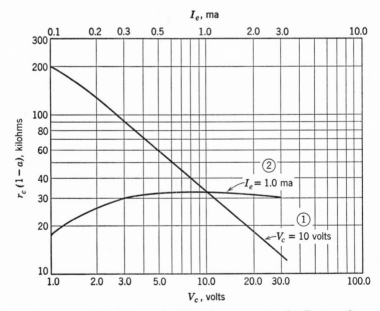

Fig. 3.14   Variation of $r_c(1 - \alpha)$ with emitter current and collector voltage.

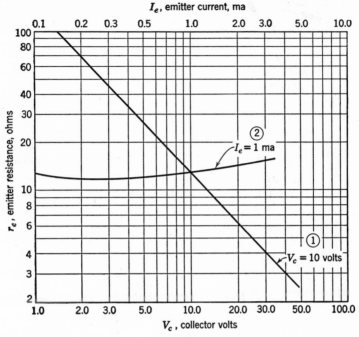

Fig. 3.15 Variation of emitter resistance with emitter current and collector voltage.

current is greatly increased as mentioned in Chapter 1. As was also shown in that chapter the emitter resistance would be expected to vary

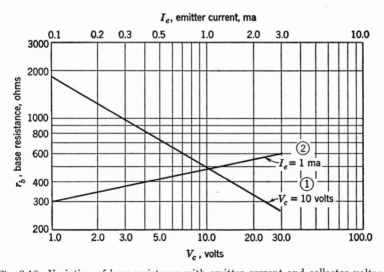

Fig. 3.16 Variation of base resistance with emitter current and collector voltage.

approximately inversely proportional to emitter current as can be expressed by the relation

$$r_e \cong r_{e1}/I_e \qquad [3.18]$$

where r_{e1} is the emitter resistance measured at 1 milliampere emitter current, r_e = emitter resistance in ohms, and I_e = emitter current in milliamperes.

It also appears that over the range measured r_c, r_m, $r_c(1 - a)$, and r_b vary approximately inversely with emitter current I_e.

It should be noted that these curves apply to one developmental type of p-n-p diffused-junction transistor. Considerably different behavior may be expected with n-p-n grown junction or point-contact types; in fact, any major change in the geometry or method of forming the junction may provide quite different sets of variations of parameters. Therefore design of circuits for a wide range of operating points will require a knowledge of the exact variations in characteristics for the specific type of transistor used.

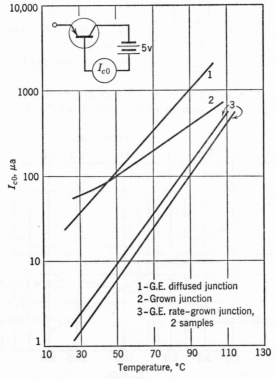

Fig. 3.17 Variation of I_{c0} with temperature.

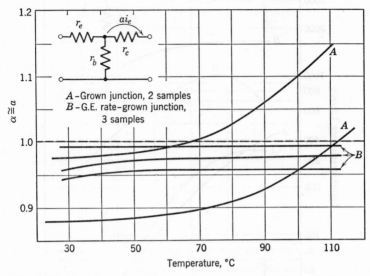

Fig. 3.18 Variation of α with temperature, grown-junction transistors.

3.10 Variation of Parameters with Temperature

Operation of transistors in equipment, especially where designed to the rigorous specifications required by the Armed Services, will usually involve the consideration of effects produced by changes in ambient temperature. Of course it is the temperature at the junctions that is

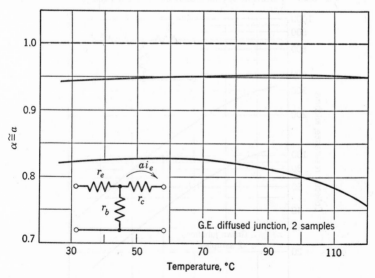

Fig. 3.19 Variation of α with temperature, diffused-junction transistors.

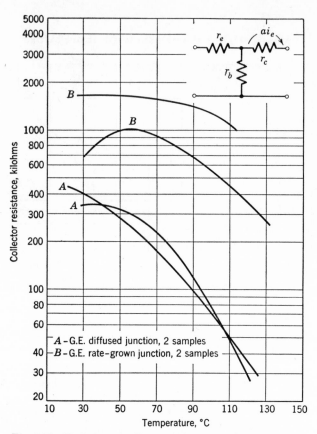

Fig. 3.20   Variation of collector resistance with temperature.

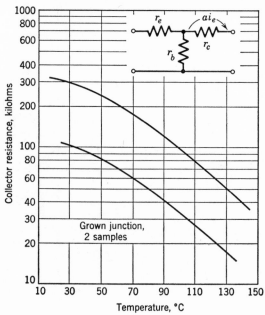

Fig. 3.21   Variation of collector resistance with temperature.

important rather than the ambient temperature; however, in most circuits other than power stages we are concerned with power dissipations so low that junction temperatures are very close to ambient. With power stages the rise in junction temperature due to dissipation must be considered.

Small-signal measurements have been made with several transistors maintained in a temperature-controlled oil bath. The curves shown in Figs. 3.17 to 3.24 are representative of parameter variation with temperature for three basically different types of junction transistor.

Of special interest and importance are the variations of α with temperature. It is quite important in many circuits that the value of α

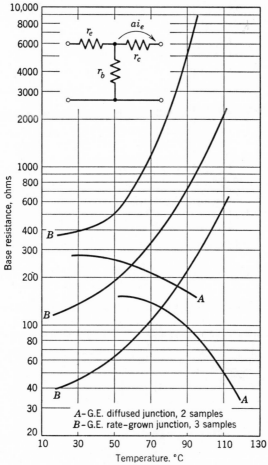

Fig. 3.22   Variation of base resistance with temperature.

never exceed unity, or instability may be present. Furthermore, with high-α transistors the rapid increase in b as α approaches unity may change the power gain and the input and output impedances drasti-

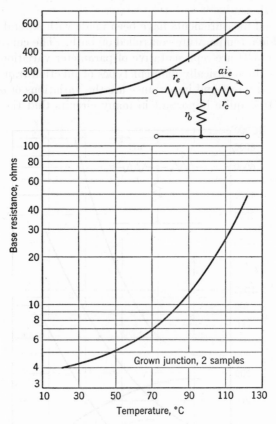

Fig. 3.23   Variation of base resistance with temperature.

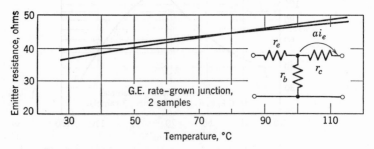

Fig. 3.24   Variation of emitter resistance with temperature.

cally. From this it would appear that the diffused junction and rate-grown junctions have better temperature characteristics. It is interesting to note that operation of transistors at temperatures around 100° C is certainly feasible with these types, although some degradation of performance is evident due to decrease in r_c and increase in I_{c0}. The effect of variations of r_e, r_b, r_c, I_{c0} on the operating resistances and power gain is discussed in Chapter 4. The physical basis for some of these variations is discussed in Chapter 1.

3.11 Problems

1. Using the equivalent circuit of Fig. 3.5 and the parameters given, show equivalent circuits for grounded-emitter and grounded-collector configurations.

2. For the circuit shown in Fig. 3.7 write the Kirchhoff equations.

3. Define the short-circuit current amplification factor α in terms of I_c, I_e, and V_c.

4. Devise a practical method of measurement of the parameters α, b, and r_c.

3.12 Bibliography

R. M. Ryder and R. J. Kircher, "Some Circuit Aspects of the Transistor," *Bell Sys. Tech. J.*, *28*, 367–400 (July, 1949).

L. P. Hunter, "Graphical Analysis of Transistor Characteristics," *Proc. IRE*, *38*, 1387–1391 (December, 1951).

R. L. Wallace, Jr., W. J. Pietenpol, "Some Circuit Properties and Applications of *n-p-n* Transistors," *Bell Sys. Tech. J.*, *30*, 530–563 (July, 1951).

M. J. E. Golay, "Equivalent Circuit of the Transistor," *Proc. IRE*, *40*, 360 (March, 1952).

Chapter 4

Basic Principles of
the Amplifier Stage

4.1 Introduction

In Chapter 3 equivalent circuits were developed to simplify the analysis of transistor circuits. These circuits were restricted to linear small-signal properties at low frequencies. The present chapter and several which follow will make use of these circuits in the analysis of audio-frequency and direct-coupled amplifiers. While such amplifiers are important in their own right, the methods of analysis derived in this chapter will serve to familiarize the reader with the basic equivalent circuits and their dependence upon the operating parameters.

4.2 Transistor Configurations

The three common configurations are known as (1) grounded-base, (2) grounded-emitter, and (3) grounded-collector. Comparing these configurations with vacuum tubes, they correspond roughly with (1) grounded-grid, (2) grounded-cathode, and (3) grounded-plate (or cathode follower). These are illustrated in Fig. 4.1. As will be shown in Chapter 15, by adding a feedback path in the vacuum-tube circuits it is possible to obtain very close tube analogues to the transistor configurations.

4.3 Single-Stage Amplifier Characteristics

It is common practice when dealing with tube amplifiers (except in power work) to work in terms of the voltage amplification since it is assumed (at low frequencies) that the grid circuit takes little or no power and the input impedance is set essentially by the value of the grid resistance used for establishing the bias potential. In transistor circuits, input impedances are relatively low and input power requirements must always be considered. Thus performance of transistor amplifiers can best be stated in terms of power gain; this requires that we know both the input and output impedances in each stage to be able to compute

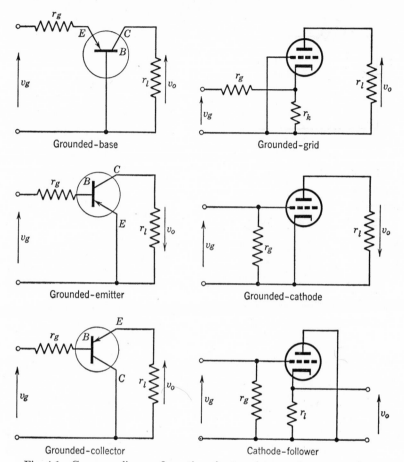

Fig. 4.1   Corresponding configurations for transistors and vacuum tubes.

overall performance in a multistage amplifier with or without interstage impedance matching for optimum power gain. As will be shown in Chapter 5, the current amplification per stage can be used in designing multistage amplifiers by a method which considerably simplifies calculation of the approximate performance. Thus the quantities of interest are: (a) input and output resistances, r_i and r_o; (b) voltage and current amplification, A_v and A_i; (c) power gain, G.

4.4   Grounded-Base Configuration: Exact Formulas

The equivalent circuit which is simplest to analyze for this configuration is shown in Fig. 4.2, which is identical with that shown in Fig. 3.3 with the addition of a generator e_g of internal resistance r_g, and a

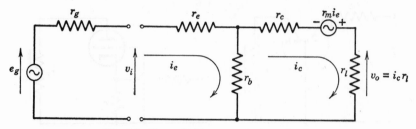

Fig. 4.2   Grounded-base, equivalent circuit.

load resistance r_l. The circuit analyses which follow apply to both junction and point-contact transistors for small-signal, low-frequency operation.

The Kirchhoff equations are

$$v_i = (r_e + r_b)i_e - r_b i_c$$
$$0 = -(r_m + r_b)i_e + (r_b + r_c + r_l)i_c \qquad [4.1]$$

The circuit determinant Δ is

$$\Delta = \begin{vmatrix} r_e + r_b & -r_b \\ -(r_m + r_b) & r_b + r_c + r_l \end{vmatrix}$$
$$= r_b(r_c - r_m + r_l + r_e) + r_e(r_c + r_l) \qquad [4.2]$$

$$\Delta \cdot i_e = \begin{vmatrix} v_i & -r_b \\ 0 & r_b + r_c + r_l \end{vmatrix}$$
$$i_e = \frac{v_i(r_b + r_c + r_l)}{\Delta} \qquad [4.3]$$

$$\Delta \cdot i_c = \begin{vmatrix} r_e + r_b & v_i \\ -(r_m + r_b) & 0 \end{vmatrix}$$
$$i_c = \frac{v_i(r_m + r_b)}{\Delta} \qquad [4.4]$$

The voltage amplification A_v is

$$A_v = \frac{i_c r_l}{v_i} = \frac{v_i(r_m + r_b)r_l}{v_i \cdot \Delta}$$

$$= \frac{(r_m + r_b)r_l}{r_b(r_c - r_m + r_l + r_e) + r_e(r_c + r_l)} \qquad [4.5]$$

The current amplification A_i is

$$A_i = \frac{i_c}{i_e} = \frac{v_i(r_m + r_b) \cdot \Delta}{v_i(r_b + r_c + r_l) \cdot \Delta} = \frac{r_m + r_b}{r_b + r_c + r_l} \qquad [4.6]$$

The input resistance r_i is

$$r_i = \frac{v_i}{i_e} = \frac{v_i \cdot \Delta}{v_i(r_b + r_c + r_l)} = \frac{r_b(r_c - r_m + r_l + r_e) + r_e(r_c + r_l)}{r_b + r_c + r_l} \qquad [4.7]$$

Rearranging terms,

$$r_i = r_e + r_b \cdot \frac{(r_c - r_m + r_l)}{r_b + r_c + r_l} \qquad [4.8]$$

The power gain G is

$$G = \frac{i_c^2 r_l}{i_e^2 r_i} = A_i^2 \frac{r_l}{r_i}$$

$$= \left(\frac{r_m + r_b}{r_b + r_c + r_l}\right)^2 \cdot \frac{r_l(r_b + r_c + r_l)}{r_b(r_c - r_m + r_l + r_e) + r_e(r_c + r_l)}$$

$$G = \frac{(r_m + r_b)^2 r_l}{(r_b + r_c + r_l)[r_b(r_c - r_m + r_l + r_e) + r_e(r_c + r_l)]} \qquad [4.9]$$

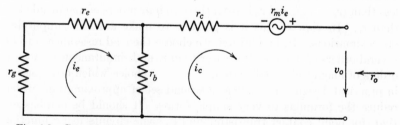

Fig. 4.3   Grounded-base, equivalent circuit for evaluating output resistance.

To solve for output resistance as a function of generator resistance r_g, we attach the generator to the circuit, set $e_g = 0$, and apply a voltage v_o to the output terminals, as shown in Fig. 4.3.

The Kirchhoff equations are

$$0 = (r_g + r_e + r_b)i_e - r_b i_c$$

$$v_o = -(r_m + r_b)i_e + (r_b + r_c)i_c$$

[4.10]

$$\Delta = \begin{vmatrix} r_g + r_e + r_b & -r_b \\ -(r_m + r_b) & r_b + r_c \end{vmatrix}$$

$$= r_c(r_e + r_b + r_g) + r_b(r_g + r_e - r_m)$$

[4.11]

$$i_c = \frac{\begin{vmatrix} r_g + r_e + r_b & 0 \\ -(r_m + r_b) & v_o \end{vmatrix}}{\Delta}$$

$$= \frac{v_o(r_g + r_e + r_b)}{r_c(r_e + r_b + r_g) + r_b(r_g + r_e - r_m)}$$

[4.12]

$$r_o = \frac{v_o}{i_c} = \frac{r_c(r_e + r_b + r_g) + r_b(r_g + r_e - r_m)}{r_g + r_e + r_b}$$

$$r_o = r_c - r_b \cdot \frac{r_m - r_g - r_e}{r_g + r_e + r_b}$$

[4.13]

4.5 Grounded-Base Configuration: Approximate Formulas: Junction Transistors

The exact expressions developed in the previous section may often prove unnecessarily cumbersome in making rapid calculations, although sometimes they must be used. However, for most junction transistors now available the value of r_e is approximately four orders of magnitude less than $(r_c - r_m)$, and r_b is from three to four orders of magnitude less than r_c. In view of this it is possible to make a set of simplifying approximations. If, in addition, we choose the load resistance r_l to be several orders of magnitude greater than r_e and simultaneously several orders of magnitude smaller than $r_c - r_m$, a choice which often occurs in practical design, we arrive at a second set of approximations which reduce the formulas to very simple forms. It should be emphasized that, for point-contact transistors and in some circuits using junction transistors, the exact formulas must be used for accurate results. If

$$r_e \ll r_c - r_m \quad\text{and}\quad r_b \ll r_c$$

recalling from eq. 3.18

$$\alpha \cong r_m/r_c = a$$

and applying to eqs. 4.5, 4.6, 4.8, 4.9, and 4.13,

$$A_v = \frac{r_m r_l}{r_b(r_c - r_m + r_l) + r_e(r_c + r_l)}$$

$$= \frac{a r_c r_l}{r_c[r_e + r_b(1 - a)] + r_l(r_e + r_b)} \qquad [4.14]$$

$$A_i = \frac{r_m}{r_c + r_l} = \frac{a}{1 + (r_l/r_c)} \qquad [4.15]$$

$$r_i = r_e + r_b \cdot \frac{r_c - r_m + r_l}{r_c + r_l} = r_e + r_b \cdot \frac{r_c(1 - a) + r_l}{r_c + r_l} \qquad [4.16]$$

$$G = \frac{r_m^2 r_l}{(r_c + r_l)[r_b(r_c - r_m + r_l) + r_e(r_c + r_l)]}$$

$$= \frac{a^2 r_c^2 r_l}{(r_c + r_l)\{r_c[r_e + r_b(1 - a)] + r_l(r_e + r_b)\}} \qquad [4.17]$$

$$r_o = r_c - r_b \cdot \frac{r_m - r_g}{r_g + r_e + r_b} = r_c - r_b \cdot \frac{a r_c - r_g}{r_g + r_e + r_b}$$

$$= r_c \cdot \frac{r_e + r_b(1 - a) + r_g}{r_e + r_b + r_g} \qquad [4.18]$$

If

$$r_e \ll r_c - r_m$$

$$r_b \ll r_c$$

$$r_e \ll r_l \ll r_c - r_m \qquad \text{or} \qquad r_e \ll r_l \ll r_c(1 - a)$$

Equations 4.14, 4.15, 4.16, 4.17, and 4.18 become

$$A_v = \frac{a r_c r_l}{r_c[r_e + r_b(1 - a)]} = \frac{a r_l}{r_e + r_b(1 - a)} \qquad [4.19]$$

$$A_i = a \qquad [4.20]$$

$$r_i = r_e + r_b \cdot \frac{r_c(1 - a)}{r_c} = r_e + r_b(1 - a) \qquad [4.21]$$

$$G = \frac{a^2 r_c^2 r_l}{r_c^2[r_e + r_b(1 - a)]} = \frac{a^2 r_l}{r_e + r_b(1 - a)} \qquad [4.22]$$

$$r_o = r_c \cdot \frac{r_e + r_b(1 - a) + r_g}{r_e + r_b + r_g} \qquad [4.23]$$

4.6　Grounded-Emitter Configuration: Exact Formulas

The equivalent circuit used for the grounded-emitter calculations of single-stage operation is that shown in Fig. 4.4, which has been described in Sec. 3.5.

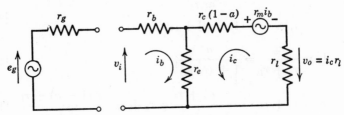

Fig. 4.4　Grounded-emitter, equivalent circuit.

The Kirchhoff equations are

$$v_i = (r_b + r_e)i_b + r_e i_c$$

$$0 = (r_e - r_m)i_b + (r_e + r_c - r_m + r_l)i_c$$

The circuit determinant Δ is

$$\Delta = (r_b + r_e)(r_e + r_c - r_m + r_l) - r_e(r_e - r_m)$$

$$= r_b(r_c - r_m + r_e + r_l) + r_e(r_c + r_l) \qquad [4.24]$$

which is identical with eq. 4.2.

$$\Delta \cdot i_b = \begin{vmatrix} v_i & r_e \\ 0 & r_e + r_c - r_m + r_l \end{vmatrix}$$

$$i_b = [v_i(r_e + r_c - r_m + r_l)]/\Delta \qquad [4.25]$$

$$\Delta \cdot i_c = \begin{vmatrix} r_b + r_e & v_i \\ r_e - r_m & 0 \end{vmatrix}$$

$$i_c = \frac{v_i(r_m - r_e)}{\Delta} \qquad [4.26]$$

$$A_v = \frac{-i_c r_l}{v_i} = \frac{-r_l(r_m - r_e)v_i}{\Delta \cdot v_i}$$

$$= \frac{-r_l(r_m - r_e)}{r_b(r_c - r_m + r_l + r_e) + r_e(r_l + r_c)} \qquad [4.27]$$

$$A_i = \frac{i_c}{i_b} = \frac{v_i(r_m - r_e)}{\Delta} \cdot \frac{\Delta}{v_i(r_e + r_c - r_m + r_l)}$$

$$A_i = \frac{r_m - r_e}{r_c - r_m + r_e + r_l} \tag{4.28}$$

$$r_i = \frac{v_i}{i_b} = \frac{v_i \cdot \Delta}{v_i(r_e + r_c - r_m + r_l)}$$

$$= \frac{r_b(r_c - r_m + r_e + r_l) + r_e(r_c + r_l)}{r_c - r_m + r_e + r_l}$$

$$= r_b + r_e \cdot \frac{r_c + r_l}{r_c - r_m + r_e + r_l} \tag{4.29]}$$

$$G = A_i^2 \cdot \frac{r_l}{r_i}$$

$$= \left(\frac{r_m - r_e}{r_c - r_m + r_e + r_l}\right)^2 \cdot \frac{r_l(r_c - r_m + r_e + r_l)}{r_b(r_c - r_m + r_e + r_l) + r_e(r_c + r_l)}$$

$$= \frac{r_l(r_m - r_e)^2}{(r_c - r_m + r_e + r_l)[r_b(r_c - r_m + r_e + r_l) + r_e(r_c + r_l)]} \tag{4.30}$$

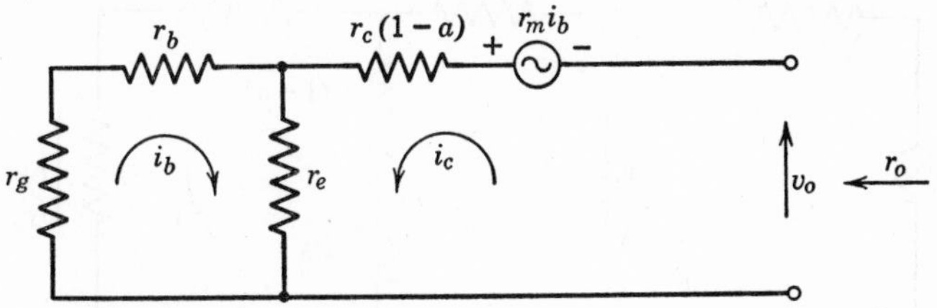

Fig. 4.5   Grounded-emitter, equivalent circuit for evaluating output resistance.

To solve for the output resistance we use the same method as for the grounded-base configuration. Referring to Fig. 4.5,

$$0 = (r_g + r_b + r_e)i_b + r_e i_c$$

$$v_o = (r_e - r_m)i_b + (r_c - r_m + r_e)i_c \tag{4.31}$$

$$\Delta = \begin{vmatrix} r_g + r_b + r_e & r_e \\ r_e - r_m & r_c - r_m + r_e \end{vmatrix}$$

$$= (r_c - r_m)(r_g + r_b + r_e) + r_e(r_g + r_b + r_m) \tag{4.32}$$

$$\Delta \cdot i_c = \begin{vmatrix} r_g + r_b + r_e & 0 \\ r_e - r_m & v_o \end{vmatrix} = v_o(r_g + r_b + r_e)$$

$$r_o = \frac{v_o}{i_c}$$

$$= \frac{v_o}{v_o(r_g + r_b + r_e)} \cdot (r_c - r_m)(r_g + r_b + r_e) + r_e(r_g + r_b + r_m)$$

$$= r_c - r_m + r_e \cdot \frac{r_g + r_b + r_m}{r_g + r_b + r_e} \qquad [4.33]$$

Approximate formulas may be determined in a similar manner to that shown for the grounded-base configuration, and are shown in Table 4.2 (p. 62).

4.7   Grounded-Collector Configuration: Exact Formulas

The equivalent circuit well suited for single-stage calculations is shown in Fig. 4.6 and is the one described in Sec. 3.7.

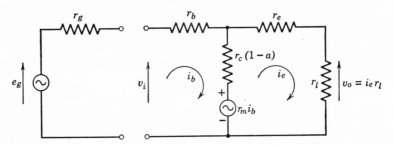

Fig. 4.6   Grounded-collector, equivalent circuit.

The Kirchhoff equations are

$$v_i = (r_b + r_c - r_m + r_m)i_b - (r_c - r_m)i_e$$

$$= (r_b + r_c)i_b - (r_c - r_m)i_e \qquad [4.34]$$

$$0 = -(r_c - r_m + r_m)i_b + (r_c - r_m + r_e + r_l)i_e$$

$$= -r_c i_b + (r_c - r_m + r_e + r_l)i_e \qquad [4.35]$$

$$\Delta = \begin{vmatrix} r_b + r_c & -(r_c - r_m) \\ -r_c & r_c - r_m + r_e + r_l \end{vmatrix}$$

$$= r_b(r_c - r_m + r_l + r_e) + r_c(r_e + r_l) \qquad [4.36]$$

$$i_b = \frac{\begin{vmatrix} v_i & -(r_c - r_m) \\ 0 & r_c - r_m + r_e + r_l \end{vmatrix}}{\Delta} = \frac{v_i(r_c - r_m + r_e + r_l)}{\Delta}$$

$$i_e = \frac{\begin{vmatrix} r_b + r_c & v_i \\ -r_c & 0 \end{vmatrix}}{\Delta} = \frac{v_i r_c}{\Delta}$$

Voltage amplification A_v

$$A_v = \frac{i_e r_l}{v_i} = \frac{v_i r_c r_l}{v_i \cdot \Delta} = \frac{r_c r_l}{r_b(r_c - r_m + r_e + r_l) + r_c(r_e + r_l)} \qquad [4.37]$$

Current amplification A_i

$$A_i = \frac{i_e}{i_b} = \frac{v_i r_c}{\Delta} \cdot \frac{\Delta}{v_i(r_c - r_m + r_e + r_l)} = \frac{r_c}{r_c - r_m + r_e + r_l} \qquad [4.38]$$

Input resistance r_i

$$r_i = \frac{v_i}{i_b} = \frac{v_i \cdot \Delta}{v_i(r_c - r_m + r_e + r_l)}$$

$$= \frac{r_b(r_c - r_m + r_e + r_l) + r_c(r_e + r_l)}{r_c - r_m + r_e + r_l}$$

$$= r_b + r_c \cdot \frac{r_e + r_l}{r_c - r_m + r_e + r_l} \qquad 4.39]$$

Power gain G is

$$G = \frac{A_i^2 r_l}{r_i}$$

$$= \frac{r_c^2}{(r_c - r_m + r_e + r_l)^2} \cdot \frac{r_l(r_c - r_m + r_e + r_l)}{r_b(r_c - r_m + r_e + r_l) + r_c(r_e + r_l)}$$

$$= \frac{r_c^2 r_l}{(r_c - r_m + r_e + r_l)[r_b(r_c - r_m + r_e + r_l) + r_c(r_e + r_l)]} \qquad [4.39a]$$

The output resistance is obtained using the circuit shown in Fig. 4.7.

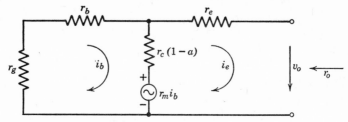

Fig. 4.7 Grounded-collector, equivalent circuit for evaluating output resistance.

The Kirchhoff equations are

$$0 = (r_g + r_b + r_c - r_m + r_m)i_b - (r_c - r_m)i_e \qquad [4.40]$$

$$v_o = -(r_c - r_m + r_m)i_b + (r_c - r_m + r_e)i_e$$

$$\Delta = \begin{vmatrix} r_g + r_b + r_c & -(r_c - r_m) \\ -r_c & r_c - r_m + r_e \end{vmatrix}$$

$$= (r_c - r_m)(r_g + r_b) + r_e(r_g + r_b + r_c) \qquad [4.41]$$

$$i_e = \frac{\begin{vmatrix} r_g + r_b + r_c & 0 \\ -r_c & v_o \end{vmatrix}}{\Delta} = \frac{v_o(r_g + r_b + r_c)}{\Delta}$$

$$r_o = \frac{v_o}{i_e} = \frac{(r_c - r_m)(r_g + r_b) + r_e(r_g + r_b + r_c)}{r_g + r_b + r_c}$$

$$= r_e + (r_c - r_m) \cdot \frac{r_g + r_b}{r_g + r_b + r_c} \qquad [4.42]$$

Approximate formulas are shown in Table 4.3.

Table 4.1 Grounded-Base Formulas

	Exact Formulas	Approximate Formulas $r_e \ll r_c - r_m;\ r_b \ll r_c;\ r_m/r_c = a$	Approximate Formulas $r_e \ll r_c - r_m;\ r_b \ll r_c;$ $r_e \ll r_l \ll r_c - r_m$
Input resistance, r_i	$r_e + r_b \cdot \dfrac{r_c - r_m + r_l}{r_b + r_c + r_l}$	$r_e + r_b \cdot \dfrac{r_c(1 - a) + r_l}{r_c + r_l}$	$r_e + r_b(1 - a)$
Output resistance, r_o	$r_c - r_b \cdot \dfrac{r_m - r_g - r_e}{r_g + r_e + r_b}$	$r_c \cdot \dfrac{r_e + r_b(1 - a) + r_g}{r_e + r_b + r_g}$	$r_c \cdot \dfrac{r_e + r_b(1 - a) + r_g}{r_e + r_b + r_g}$
Voltage amplification, A_v	$\dfrac{(r_m + r_b) r_l}{r_b(r_c - r_m + r_e + r_l) + r_e(r_c + r_l)}$	$\dfrac{a r_c r_l}{r_c[r_e + r_b(1 - a)] + r_l(r_e + r_b)}$	$\dfrac{a r_l}{r_e + r_b(1 - a)}$
Current amplification, A_i	$\dfrac{r_m + r_b}{r_b + r_c + r_l}$	$\dfrac{a}{1 + r_l/r_c}$	a
Power gain, G	$\dfrac{(r_m + r_b)^2 r_l}{\{(r_b + r_c + r_l)[r_b(r_c - r_m + r_e + r_l) + r_e(r_c + r_l)]\}}$	$\dfrac{a^2 r_c^2 r_l}{\{(r_c + r_l)\{r_c[r_e + r_b(1 - a)] + r_l(r_e + r_b)\}\}}$	$\dfrac{a^2 r_l}{r_e + r_b(1 - a)}$

Table 4.2 Grounded-Emitter Formulas

	Exact Formulas	Approximate Formulas $r_e \ll r_c - r_m;\ r_b \ll r_c;\ r_m/r_c = a$	Approximate Formulas $r_e \ll r_c - r_m;\ r_b \ll r_c;$ $r_e \ll r_l \ll r_c - r_m$
Input resistance, r_i	$r_b + r_e \cdot \dfrac{r_c + r_l}{r_c - r_m + r_e + r_l}$	$r_b + r_e \cdot \dfrac{r_c + r_l}{r_c(1-a) + r_l}$	$r_b + \dfrac{r_e}{1-a}$
Output resistance, r_o	$r_c - r_m + r_e \cdot \dfrac{r_g + r_b + r_m}{r_g + r_b + r_e}$	$r_c(1-a) + r_e \cdot \dfrac{r_m + r_g}{r_e + r_b + r_g}$	$r_c(1-a) + r_e \cdot \dfrac{r_m + r_g}{r_e + r_b + r_g}$
Voltage amplification, A_v	$-\dfrac{r_l(r_m - r_e)}{r_b(r_c - r_m + r_e + r_l) + r_e(r_c + r_l)}$	$\dfrac{-ar_c r_l}{r_c[r_e + r_b(1-a)] + r_l(r_e + r_b)}$	$\dfrac{-ar_l}{r_e + r_b(1-a)}$
Current amplification, A_i	$\dfrac{r_m - r_e}{r_c - r_m + r_e + r_l}$	$\dfrac{a}{1 - a + (r_l/r_c)}$	$\dfrac{a}{1-a} = b$
Power gain, G	$\dfrac{r_l(r_m - r_e)^2}{\left\{(r_c - r_m + r_e + r_l)[r_b(r_c - r_m + r_e + r_l) + r_e(r_c + r_l)]\right\}}$	$\dfrac{a^2 r_c^2 r_l}{\left\{[r_c(1-a) + r_l]\{r_c[r_e + r_b(1-a)] + r_l(r_e + r_b)\}\right\}}$	$\dfrac{a^2 r_l}{(1-a)[r_e + r_b(1-a)]}$

Table 4.3 Grounded-Collector Formulas

	Exact Formulas	Approximate Formulas $r_e \ll r_c - r_m$; $r_b \ll r_c$; $r_m/r_c = a$	Approximate Formulas $r_e \ll r_c - r_m$; $r_b \ll r_c$; $r_e \ll r_l \ll r_c - r_m$; $r_g \ll r_c$
Input resistance, r_i	$r_b + r_c \cdot \dfrac{r_e + r_l}{r_c - r_m + r_e + r_l}$	$r_b + r_c \cdot \dfrac{r_e + r_l}{r_c(1 - a) + r_l}$	$\dfrac{r_l}{1 - a} = (b + 1)r_l$
Output resistance, r_o	$r_e + (r_c - r_m) \cdot \dfrac{r_g + r_b}{r_g + r_b + r_c}$	$r_e + r_c(1 - a)\,\dfrac{r_g + r_b}{r_g + r_c}$	$r_e + (r_b + r_g)(1 - a)$
Voltage amplification, A_v	$\dfrac{r_c r_l}{r_b(r_c - r_m + r_e + r_l) + r_c(r_e + r_l)}$	$\dfrac{r_l}{r_e + r_b(1 - a) + r_l}$	1
Current amplification, A_i	$\dfrac{r_c}{r_c - r_m + r_e + r_l}$	$\dfrac{1}{(1 - a) + (r_l/r_c)}$	$\dfrac{1}{1 - a} = b + 1$
Power gain, G	$\dfrac{r_c^2 r_l}{\{(r_c - r_m + r_e + r_l)[r_b(r_c - r_m + r_e + r_l) + r_c(r_e + r_l)]\}}$	$\dfrac{r_l r_c}{[r_c(1 - a) + r_l][r_e + r_b(1 - a) + r_l]}$	$\dfrac{1}{1 - a} = b + 1$

4.8   Representative Curves: Junction Transistors

To illustrate the functional relationships that have been developed in the previous sections, curves shown in Figs. 4.8 to 4.19 inclusive have

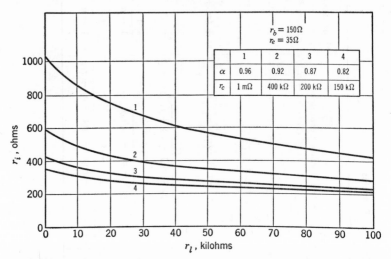

Fig. 4.8   Grounded-emitter, variation of input resistance with load resistance.

been plotted using the exact formulas applied to several junction transistors. The parameters chosen are those representative of experimental junction transistors, the classifications 1, 2, 3, 4 being purely

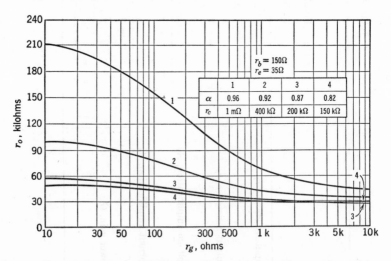

Fig. 4.9   Grounded-emitter, variation of output resistance with generator resistance.

arbitrary. Some general conclusions can be drawn from these calculations and curves.

1. The grounded-emitter configuration provides phase inversion; the grounded-base and grounded-collector do not.

2. The input resistance for one transistor operating at a given fixed load will be lowest for the grounded-base, intermediate for the

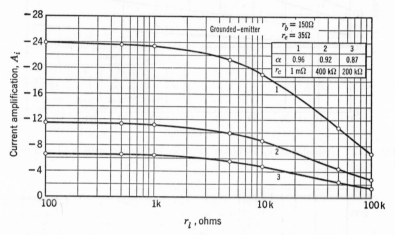

Fig. 4.10 Grounded-emitter, variation of current amplification with load resistance.

grounded-emitter, and largest for the grounded-collector configuration. For example, for a class 1 transistor operating with a load $r_l = 10,000$ ohms, the input resistances are 70, 850, and 200,000 ohms for grounded-base, grounded-emitter, and grounded-collector configurations, respectively.

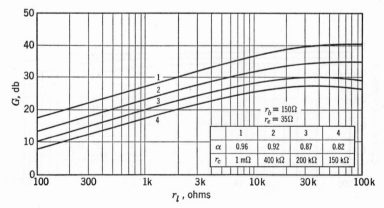

Fig. 4.11 Grounded-emitter, variation of power gain with load resistance.

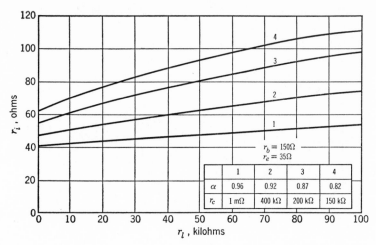

Fig. 4.12   Grounded-base, variation of input resistance with load resistance.

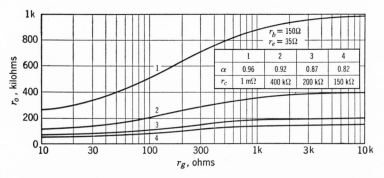

Fig. 4.13   Grounded-base, variation of output resistance with generator resistance.

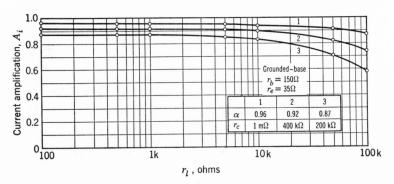

Fig. 4.14   Grounded-base, variation of current amplification with load resistance.

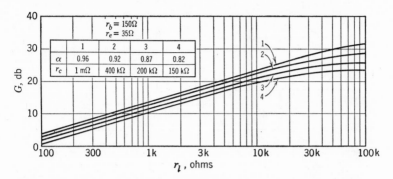

Fig. 4.15   Grounded-base, variation of power gain with load resistance.

3. The output resistance for one transistor operating from a generator resistance r_g, the same for all configurations, will be highest, intermediate, and lowest for grounded-base, grounded-emitter, and grounded-collector configurations respectively.   For example, a class 1

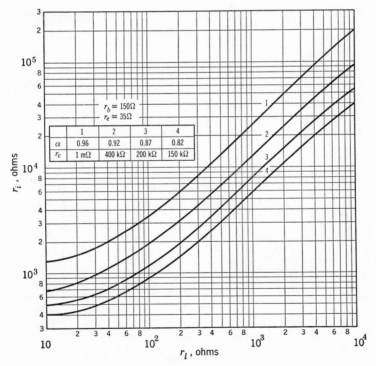

Fig. 4.16   Grounded-collector, variation of input resistance with load resistance.

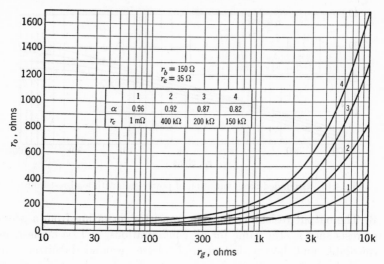

Fig. 4.17   Grounded-collector, variation of output resistance with generator resistance.

transistor with an r_g of 1000 ohms will have an output resistance of 880,000 ohms, 67,500 ohms, and 240 ohms for the grounded-base, grounded-emitter, and grounded-collector configurations respectively.

4. The voltage amplification for a given load resistance will be almost identical for grounded-base and grounded-emitter, and will be somewhat less than unity for the grounded-collector.

5. The current amplification approximates a for the grounded-base, approximates b for the grounded-emitter (for $a = 0.96$, $b = 24$),

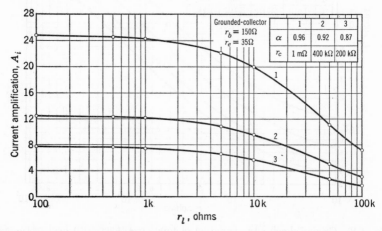

Fig. 4.18   Grounded-collector, variation of current amplification with load resistance.

and approximates $b + 1$ for the grounded-collector (for $a = 0.96$, $b + 1 = 25$).

6. In almost all cases of interest the power gain of the grounded-emitter is highest, the relative power gain of the other configurations depending on the size of the load resistance r_l.

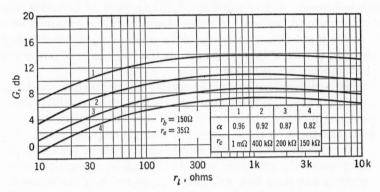

Fig. 4.19   Grounded-collector, variation of power gain with load resistance.

The above comments will illustrate the single-stage performance; multistage performance will be taken up in detail in Chapter 5, showing how single stages may be coupled together in the most efficient manner to form complete amplifiers. As an example of how the above curves may be used to give the qualitative performance of several stages in cascade, assume that we have a two-stage amplifier, as shown in Fig.

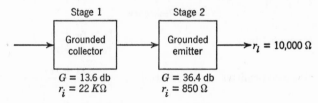

Fig. 4.20   Two-stage transistor amplifier.

4.20, where a grounded-collector stage is directly coupled to a grounded-emitter stage which has a load impedance of $r_l = 10,000$ ohms.

Assume that we are using class 1 transistors, and that there is no power loss in the coupling network between stages 1 and 2.

From the curves, stage 2 has a power gain of 36.4 db and an input resistance of 850 ohms for $r_l = 10,000$ ohms. The load resistance of stage 1 is now established at 850 ohms, and for this value the power gain of stage 1 is 13.6 db and input resistance is 22,000 ohms. Thus the total power gain is 50 db, and the input resistance is 22,000 ohms.

4.9 Stability Considerations

Examination of the equivalent circuit for the grounded-base configuration might indicate that, since r_b is a common resistance for both input and output currents, and since there appears to be positive feedback into the input circuit, it would be possible to have negative input resistance. Under suitable conditions such an amplifier stage could be made to oscillate. All that would be necessary would be to add to the input circuit some reactance (such as transformer leakage reactance), of such a value as to permit the stage to have power gain at the frequency of oscillation.

Similar considerations hold for a negative output resistance, although it is not quite as simple to see qualitatively how such a condition arises.

We have discussed above the possible effect of negative input and output resistances on the operation of a single amplifier stage. It is also important to realize that in multistage amplifiers, even with R-C coupling where the reactance may be negligible, a negative output resistance of one stage may so modify the operation of the succeeding stage as to make it subject to oscillation due to reactive elements in its output. Thus, for completely stable operation, the sufficient conditions are that input and output resistances must never become negative for any values of load or driving impedance, which, if reactive, have positive real parts.

Let us examine the expressions for input and output resistances and see under what conditions they may become negative, for both junction and point-contact transistors.

Input Resistance

Grounded-base
$$r_i = r_e + r_b \cdot \frac{r_c - r_m + r_l}{r_b + r_c + r_l} \qquad [4.8]$$

Grounded-emitter
$$r_i = r_b + r_e \cdot \frac{r_c + r_l}{r_c - r_m + r_e + r_l} \qquad [4.29]$$

Grounded-collector
$$r_i = r_b + r_c \cdot \frac{r_e + r_l}{r_c - r_m + r_e + r_l} \qquad [4.39]$$

Output Resistance

Grounded-base
$$r_o = r_c - r_b \cdot \frac{r_m - r_g - r_e}{r_g + r_e + r_b} \qquad [4.13]$$

Grounded-emitter
$$r_o = r_c - r_m + r_e \cdot \frac{r_g + r_b + r_m}{r_g + r_b + r_e} \qquad [4.33]$$

Grounded-collector
$$r_o = r_e + (r_c - r_m) \cdot \frac{r_g + r_b}{r_g + r_b + r_c} \qquad [4.42]$$

4.9.1   Junction Transistors

For junction transistors under normal operation the value of a is always less than unity. Thus $r_c - r_m = r_c (1 - a)$ is always positive. A cursory examination of eqs. 4.8, 4.29, 4.39, 4.33, 4.42 indicates that r_i and r_o for those cases are positive for all positive values of r_l and r_g. To see that this is also true for eq. 4.13 let us rearrange the terms slightly, using the equivalent:

$$r_m = ar_c$$

$$r_o = r_c - r_b \cdot \frac{ar_c - r_g - r_e}{r_g + r_e + r_b}$$

$$= \frac{r_c[r_g + r_e + r_b(1 - a)] + r_b(r_g + r_e)}{r_g + r_e + r_b}$$

Since $1 - a$ is positive for this case, r_o is positive for all values of r_g (positive real value, if complex).

If the driving or load impedances contain reactive elements having positive real parts, the output and input impedances of the transistor amplifier will have positive real parts also. Thus, under the stated conditions, at low frequencies, the junction transistor is unconditionally stable. As will be shown in Chapter 9, at high frequencies the equivalent circuit will contain complex parameters which may lead to negative input and output resistances in certain operating regions.

4.9.2   Point-Contact Transistors

The point-contact transistor has decidedly different circuit parameters, the most important of which, for this discussion, being the value of a. In general, a exceeds unity; hence, $r_c - r_m$ is always negative. In each of the formulas for input and output resistances there is therefore a region of instability. Let us examine these regions in more detail.

Grounded-base. For positive input resistance,

$$r_e + r_b \cdot \frac{r_c - r_m + r_l}{r_b + r_c + r_l} > 0$$

Since $r_b + r_c + r_l > 0$,

$$r_e r_b + r_e(r_c + r_l) + r_b(r_c + r_l) - r_b r_m > 0$$

Divide by $r_b(r_c + r_l)$,

$$\frac{r_e}{r_c + r_l} + \frac{r_e}{r_b} + 1 - \frac{r_m}{r_c + r_l} > 0$$

or

$$\frac{r_m - r_e}{r_c + r_l} < 1 + \frac{r_e}{r_b} \qquad [4.43]$$

Equation 4.43 gives the condition for input stability, indicating that r_b should be as small as possible. It can also be seen that increasing r_l sufficiently or adding external resistance to r_e will fulfill this condition.

For positive output resistance:

$$r_c - r_b \cdot \frac{r_m - r_g - r_e}{r_g + r_e + r_b} > 0$$

$$r_c(r_g + r_e) + r_c r_b - r_b r_m + r_b(r_g + r_e) > 0$$

Dividing by $r_c r_b$,

$$\frac{r_g + r_e}{r_b} + 1 - \frac{r_m}{r_c} + \frac{r_g + r_e}{r_c} > 0$$

or

$$\frac{r_m}{r_c} < 1 + (r_g + r_e)\left(\frac{1}{r_b} + \frac{1}{r_c}\right) \qquad [4.44]$$

Here, too, r_b should be small, and total resistance in emitter circuit $(r_g + r_e)$ should be large to insure positive output resistance.

Grounded-emitter. For positive input resistance,

$$r_b + r_e \cdot \frac{r_c + r_l}{r_c - r_m + r_e + r_l} > 0$$

$$r_b > -\left(r_e \cdot \frac{r_c + r_l}{r_c + r_l + r_e - r_m}\right)$$

or

$$r_b > -\left(\frac{r_e}{1 - (r_m - r_e)/(r_c + r_l)}\right) \qquad [4.45]$$

From the above equation it is evident that additional external base resistance may be necessary if the denominator of the right-hand side becomes negative.

For positive output resistance,

$$r_c - r_m + r_e \cdot \frac{r_g + r_b + r_m}{r_g + r_b + r_e} > 0$$

$$r_c(r_g + r_b) + r_c r_e - r_m(r_g + r_b) + r_e(r_g + r_b) > 0$$

Dividing by $r_c(r_g + r_b)$,

$$1 + \frac{r_e}{r_g + r_b} - \frac{r_m}{r_c} + \frac{r_e}{r_c} > 0$$

or

$$\frac{r_m}{r_c} < 1 + \frac{r_e}{r_g + r_b} + \frac{r_e}{r_c} \qquad [4.46]$$

This indicates that $r_g + r_b$ should be held to a low value, or r_e should be made large. Thus cascading grounded-emitter stages might be undesirable as r_g for the second stage would be the output resistance of the first stage, usually high enough to cause trouble.

Grounded-collector. For positive input resistance,

$$r_b + r_c \cdot \frac{r_e + r_l}{r_c - r_m + r_e + r_l} > 0$$

or

$$r_b > -\left(r_c \cdot \frac{r_e + r_l}{r_c - r_m + r_e + r_l}\right) \qquad [4.47]$$

As before, adding sufficient resistance in the base lead will insure stability. For positive output resistance,

$$r_e + (r_c - r_m) \cdot \frac{r_g + r_b}{r_c + r_g + r_b} > 0$$

$$r_e r_c + r_e(r_g + r_b) + r_c(r_g + r_b) - r_m(r_g + r_b) > 0$$

Dividing by $r_c(r_g + r_b)$,

$$\frac{r_e}{r_g + r_b} + \frac{r_e}{r_c} + 1 - \frac{r_m}{r_c} > 0$$

$$\frac{r_m}{r_c} < 1 + \frac{r_e}{r_g + r_b} + \frac{r_e}{r_c} \qquad [4.48]$$

This equation is identical with eq. 4.46, and the same remarks hold; i.e., stability may be poor in cascaded stages.

4.9.3   Comparison of Configurations

The differences in stability for the three configurations can be best seen by taking a commercial point-contact transistor, such as the General Electric type G-11, and computing critical values of r_b, r_l, and r_g. The manufacturer's specifications for the G-11 are: $r_c = 22,000$ ohms; $r_e = 275$ ohms; $r_b = 200$ ohms; $a = 2.2$. Therefore $r_m = 48,400$ ohms.

Using eq. 4.43 for the grounded-base configuration, it is possible to compute the maximum permissible total base resistance, i.e., r_b plus

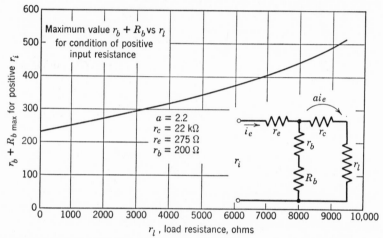

Fig. 4.21   Variation of maximum total base resistance $r_b + R_b$ with load resistance for positive input resistance.

external resistance R_b, for positive input resistance, plotted against load resistance r_l. This is plotted in Fig. 4.21 and illustrates that, for this type of transistor, one cannot exceed, at most, several hundreds of ohms in the base circuit before causing instability.

Using eqs. 4.45 and 4.47 for the grounded-emitter and grounded-collector configurations, for values of r_l below 26,125 ohms, this transistor has negative input resistance thus illustrating the relative instability for these configurations.

The output resistance for the grounded-base configuration is positive, for the condition shown by eq. 4.44. Plotted in Fig. 4.22 is the maximum total base resistance (r_b plus external base resistance R_b) against value of generator resistance r_g for positive output resistances. It is seen that for high values of r_g the permissible base resistance climbs rapidly.

A similar computation for grounded-emitter and grounded-collector configurations, using eqs. 4.46 and 4.48, indicates that the maximum permissible value of generator resistance (which is in the base lead) is 32 ohms for output resistance to be positive. Here again it is seen that those configurations have considerable disadvantages compared with the grounded-base.

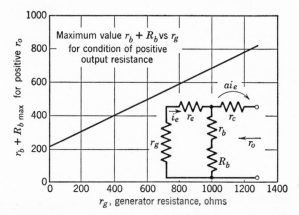

Fig. 4.22   Variation of maximum total base resistance $r_b + R_b$ with generator resistance for positive output resistance.

4.10   Transducer Gain and Available Power Gain

In Secs. 4.5 to 4.7 inclusive, formulas were developed for power gain G as a function of transistor parameters and load resistance. With a specified generator resistance, however, it is often useful to know how well we are making use of the maximum power that can be obtained from the generator. Circuit theory indicates that a generator with internal impedance z_g will deliver maximum power to a load impedance which is the complex conjugate of z_g, which we will call z_g*. If e_g is the open-circuit voltage of the generator, the maximum power delivered to the load is

$$P_a = \left(\frac{e_g}{z_g + z_g*}\right)^2 \cdot r_g = \left(\frac{e_g}{2r_g}\right)^2 \cdot r_g$$

$$= \frac{e_g^2}{4r_g} \qquad\qquad [4.49]$$

where r_g is the resistive component of impedance z_g. Equation 4.49 defines the available power, P_a, from a generator, which is the maximum power that a generator with given internal impedance and driving voltage can deliver.

In comparing two amplifiers that are to be driven from identical generators, the ratio of output to input power will not give any information as to how much of the generator available power is being amplified, for with different input impedances the output power will in general be different for the two amplifiers. We therefore can make a better comparison by defining the gain of an amplifier as the ratio of output power to the available power from the generator. This is known as transducer gain, G_t.

$$G_t = \frac{P_o}{e_g^2/4r_g} = \frac{4r_g P_o}{e_g^2} \qquad [4.50]$$

where P_o is power output of the amplifier.

Since $P_o = i_o^2 r_l$, where i_o is output current, and $e_g = (r_g + r_i)i_i$, where i_i is input current, r_i is input resistance,

$$G_t = \frac{4r_g r_l i_o^2}{(r_g + r_i)^2 i_i^2} = \frac{4r_g r_l}{(r_g + r_i)^2} \cdot A_i^2 \qquad [4.51]$$

Other terms for gain which are sometimes used are available power gain and maximum available power gain. The available power gain is defined as the ratio of the available power output from the amplifier to the available power output from the driving generator.

$$G_a = P_{ao}/P_a$$

where P_{ao} is available power output from amplifier, P_a is available power output from generator.

$$G_a = \frac{(v_o')^2/4r_o}{(e_g)^2/4r_g} = \left(\frac{v_o'}{e_g}\right)^2 \cdot \frac{r_g}{r_o} \qquad [4.52]$$

where v_o' is open-circuit output voltage of amplifier.

If both input and output resistances are matched, we obtain maximum transfer of energy from generator to amplifier, and maximum transfer of energy from amplifier to load. These are the conditions for which the maximum available power gain is defined.

Thus, for $r_i = r_g$ and $r_o = r_l$, eq. 4.52 becomes

$$(G_a)_{max} = A_i^2 r_o/r_i = A_i^2 r_l/r_g \qquad [4.53]$$

if A_i is current amplification under above conditions, since

$$v_o' = i_o(r_l + r_o) = 2i_o r_o$$

$$e_g = i_i(r_i + r_g) = 2i_i r_g$$

and

$$\left(\frac{v_o{}'}{e_g}\right)^2 \cdot \frac{r_g}{r_o} = \left(\frac{i_o}{i_i}\right)^2 \cdot \frac{r_o{}^2}{r_g{}^2} \cdot \frac{r_g}{r_o} = A_i{}^2 \cdot \frac{r_o}{r_g} = A_i{}^2 \cdot \frac{r_l}{r_g}$$

It is customary to express gain in decibels.

4.11   Available Gain for the Three Transistor Configurations

It is useful to know the available gain explicitly in terms of the transistor parameters for the various configurations. Equation 4.52 can be developed as follows:

$$G_a = \left(\frac{v_o{}'}{e_g}\right)^2 \frac{r_g}{r_o}$$

For any load r_l and generator resistance r_g,

$$v_o{}' = i_o(r_o + r_l)$$

$$e_g = i_i(r_g + r_i)$$

Therefore,

$$G_a = \left(\frac{i_o}{i_i}\right)^2 \left(\frac{r_o + r_l}{r_g + r_i}\right)^2 \frac{r_g}{r_o} = \left(\frac{r_o + r_l}{r_g + r_i}\right)^2 \frac{r_g}{r_o} A_i{}^2 \qquad [4.54]$$

Unfortunately, in the above expression, r_i and A_i depend on the value of r_l, but it should be noted from eq. 4.52 that G_a is the same for all values of r_l including $r_l = 0$. Setting $r_l = 0$, eq. 4.54 reduces to

$$G_a = \frac{A_{io}{}^2 r_g r_o}{(r_g + r_{io})^2} \qquad [4.55]$$

where A_{io} is the current amplification with the amplifier output short-circuited, r_{io} is the input resistance with the amplifier output short-circuited.

Referring to eqs. 4.6, 4.28, and 4.38, and setting $r_l = 0$ and $r_m = ar_c$, the expressions for short-circuit amplification A_{io} become

Grounded-base

$$A_{io} = \frac{ar_c + r_b}{r_c + r_b} \qquad [4.56]$$

Grounded-emitter

$$A_{io} = \frac{ar_c - r_e}{r_c(1 - a) + r_e} \qquad [4.57]$$

Grounded-collector

$$A_{io} = \frac{r_c}{r_c(1 - a) + r_e} \qquad [4.58]$$

Referring to eqs. 4.8, 4.29, and 4.39, and setting $r_l = 0$, and $r_m = ar_c$, the expressions for $r_g + r_{io}$ become

Grounded-base

$$r_g + r_{io} = \frac{(r_e + r_g)(r_c + r_b) + r_b r_c (1 - a)}{r_c + r_b} \qquad [4.59]$$

Grounded-emitter

$$r_g + r_{io} = \frac{(r_b + r_g)[r_c(1 - a) + r_e] + r_e r_c}{r_c(1 - a) + r_e} \qquad [4.60]$$

Grounded-collector

$$r_g + r_{io} = \frac{(r_b + r_g)[r_c(1 - a) + r_e] + r_e r_c}{r_c(1 - a) + r_e} \qquad [4.61]$$

Using expressions 4.55, 4.56, and 4.59, for the grounded-base,

$$G_a = \frac{A_{io}{}^2 r_g r_o}{(r_g + r_{io})^2}$$

$$= r_g \cdot \left(\frac{ar_c + r_b}{r_c + r_b}\right)^2 \cdot \left\{ \frac{(r_c + r_b)^2}{[(r_e + r_g)(r_c + r_b) + r_b r_c(1 - a)]^2} \right\} r_o \quad [4.62]$$

From eq. 4.13,

$$r_o = r_c - r_b \frac{r_m - r_g - r_e}{r_g + r_e + r_b}$$

$$= \frac{r_c(r_g + r_e + r_b) - ar_b r_c + r_b r_g + r_b r_e}{r_g + r_e + r_b}$$

$$= \frac{(r_e + r_g)(r_c + r_b) + r_b r_c(1 - a)}{r_g + r_e + r_b} \qquad 4.63]$$

Inserting 4.63 in 4.62,

$$G_a = \frac{r_g(ar_c + r_b)^2}{(r_e + r_b + r_g)[(r_e + r_g)(r_c + r_b) + r_b r_c(1 - a)]} \qquad [4.64]$$

Similar calculations can be made for the grounded-emitter and grounded-collector configurations yielding:

Grounded-emitter

$$G_a = \frac{r_g(ar_c - r_e)^2}{(r_e + r_b + r_g)\{(r_b + r_g)[r_c(1 - a) + r_e] + r_e r_c\}} \qquad [4.65]$$

Grounded-collector

$$G_a = \frac{r_g r_c{}^2}{(r_b + r_c + r_g)\{(r_b + r_g)[r_c(1 - a) + r_e] + r_e r_c\}} \qquad [4.66]$$

4.12   Problems

1. Derive the exact expressions for current amplification, input resistance, and power gain for the grounded-emitter configuration using the constant-current equivalent circuit shown in Fig. 3.7.

2. Show that the condition for positive input resistance for any configuration is that the circuit determinant must be greater than zero. Using this result, show the relation between the transistor equivalent circuit parameters for the condition of positive input resistance for the grounded-base configuration.

3. Compute, using exact formulas, the input resistance, output resistance, current amplification, and power gain for a grounded-emitter transistor with the parameters $r_e = 25$ ohms, $r_b = 500$ ohms, $r_c = 500,000$ ohms, $a = 0.95$: (a) with load resistance $r_l = 500$ ohms, generator resistance $r_g = 25,000$ ohms; (b) with load resistance $r_l = 25,000$ ohms, generator resistance $r_g = 100$ ohms; (c) compute the same quantities as in (a) and (b) using the approximate formulas, and compare.

4. Using the curves in Figs. 4.8 to 4.19 for class 1 transistors, find the power gain and input resistance for a three-stage amplifier working into a load of 5000 ohms, using: (a) grounded-emitter stages; (b) a grounded-emitter, grounded-collector, and grounded-emitter stage in the stated sequence; (c) grounded-base stages.

5. (a) In problem 4, if the generator resistance is given as 500 ohms, which set of configurations will deliver the most power to the load? (b) Repeat 5(a) for $r_g = 5000$ ohms.

6. (a) With a driving generator resistance $r_g = 1000$ ohms, load resistance $r_l = 5000$ ohms, compute the transducer gain for grounded-emitter, grounded-base, and grounded-collector single-stage amplifiers, using the same transistor parameters as in problem 3. (b) Compute available gain for the three configurations as in (a) using generator resistance of 1000 ohms, with the same transistor parameters as in (a).

7. (a) Derive an expression for the maximum available gain for the grounded-emitter stage. (b) What values of r_g and r_l are to be used to give maximum available gain to a grounded-emitter amplifier with transistor parameters as in Problem 3, and what is the value in decibels of this gain?

4.13   Bibliography

1. R. L. Wallace, Jr., and W. J. Pietenpol, "Some Circuit Properties and Applications of n-p-n Transistors," *Proc. IRE, 39*, 753–767 (July, 1951).

2. R. M. Ryder and R. J. Kircher, "Some Circuit Aspects of the Transistor," *Bell Sys. Tech. J., 28*, 367–401 (July, 1949).

Chapter 5

Junction Transistor
Multistage Amplifiers

5.1 Introduction

In general, a junction transistor amplifier will consist of several stages coupled by passive networks. The coupling networks must be designed so that they will not materially reduce the gain of the amplifier in the desired frequency range.

It is customary to characterize the individual stages of an amplifier by their current and voltage amplification or by their power gain. Such a characterization is useful only if the amplification or gain is

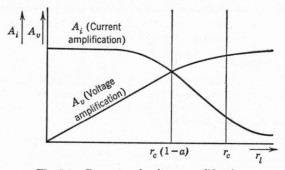

Fig. 5.1   Current and voltage amplification.

practically independent of the next stage. Figure 5.1 shows quali-tatively the current amplification A_i and the voltage amplification A_v of a grounded-emitter single-stage transistor amplifier as a function of the load resistance r_l. Since in an RC or direct-coupled amplifier the input resistance of the next stage will usually be considerably less than

$r_c(1 - a)$, we will characterize individual stages in an RC or direct-coupled amplifier by their current amplification. The total gain of an amplifier with n stages is, then,

$$G = (r_l/r_i)(A_{i1}A_{i2} \cdots A_{in})^2 \qquad [5.1]$$

where A_{i1} is the current amplification of the first stage, A_{i2} that of the second stage, etc.; r_i, the input resistance of the amplifier; and r_l the load resistance.

In amplifiers with coupling by matching transformers, the load resistance of each stage is equal to its output resistance and is therefore independent of the next stage. Individual stages in such a transformer-coupled amplifier may therefore be characterized by their voltage or current amplification or by their power gain.

In the following sections, RC-coupled and transformer-coupled amplifiers will be discussed in detail. The considerations made for the RC-coupled amplifiers apply to a large extent also to the direct-coupled amplifiers.

5.2 RC-Coupled Amplifiers

Figure 5.2 shows a single stage of an RC-coupled transistor amplifier. Resistors R_1, R_2, and R_3 provide bias to collector and base. Resistor R_4 is incorporated to reduce the variation of the collector current with

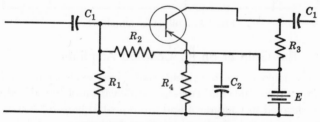

Fig. 5.2   Single-stage amplifier.

temperature (see Chapter 6). Capacitor C_1 couples succeeding stages, and capacitor C_2 bypasses resistor R_4 at audio frequencies. Without this bypass capacitor, the resistor R_4 would reduce the amplification of this stage considerably.

If the stage is properly designed, R_1 and R_2 are large compared to the input resistance of the stage and capacitors C_1 and C_2 will have effectively zero impedance, at least over the frequency range of interest. We may, therefore, as far as audio frequencies are concerned, replace the circuit of Fig. 5.2, as a first approximation, by that of Fig. 5.3.

Similar considerations may be made for single stages using grounded-base or grounded-collector stages.   Figure 5.4 shows a multistage amplifier with different types of stages.

In the following section, a number of problems will be discussed, using this simplified circuit.   In particular, approximate expressions

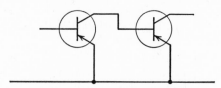

Fig. 5.3   Approximate circuit.

for the gains of entire amplifiers will be found and the problem of whether to use the grounded-emitter, grounded-base, or grounded-collector configuration in a given stage will be discussed.   In the second part, methods for calculating the resistances and capacitances of Fig. 5.2 will be given.

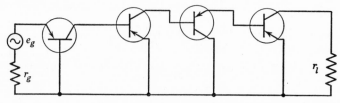

Fig. 5.4   Multistage amplifier.

5.2.1   The Gain of an RC Coupled Amplifier

For the calculation of multistage amplifiers, expressions are needed for the input resistance and current amplification of individual stages. They are derived in Chapter 4 and are repeated here for convenience: The conditions for which these equations hold are:

$$r_b \ll r_c \quad\text{and}\quad r_e \ll r_c(1 - a)$$

(a) *Input resistance*
Grounded-emitter

$$r_i = r_b + r_e \cdot \frac{r_c + r_l}{r_c(1 - a) + r_l} \qquad [5.2]$$

Grounded-base

$$r_i = r_e + r_b \cdot \frac{r_c(1 - a) + r_l}{r_c + r_l} \qquad [5.3]$$

Grounded-collector

$$r_i = r_b + r_c \cdot \frac{r_e + r_l}{r_c(1 - a) + r_l} \qquad [5.4]$$

(b) *Current amplification*

Grounded-emitter

$$A_i = \frac{ar_c}{r_c(1 - a) + r_l} \qquad [5.5]$$

Grounded-base

$$A_i = \frac{ar_c}{r_c + r_l} \qquad [5.6]$$

Grounded-collector

$$A_i = \frac{r_c}{r_c(1 - a) + r_l} \qquad [5.7]$$

The variation of r_i and A_i with r_l is shown qualitatively in Figs. 5.5 and 5.6. Figure 5.5 shows that for a small load resistance the input resistance of the grounded-base stage is small and practically independent of the load. The input resistance of the grounded-emitter

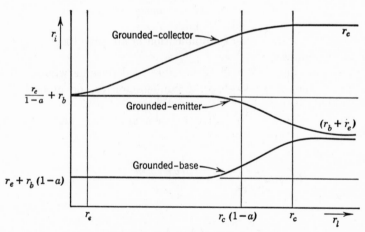

Fig. 5.5   The input resistance.

stage is larger but still independent of the load. As the load resistance becomes large, both resistances approach $(r_e + r_b)$. The input resistance of the grounded-collector stage is $r_b + r_e/(1 - a)$ for zero load resistance but increases rapidly as the load increases. Its value is approximately $r_l/(1 - a)$. As the load resistance becomes very large the input resistance approaches r_c. Figure 5.6 shows that for small load resistances the current amplification of the grounded-collector stage is approximately $1/(1 - a)$; for the grounded-emitter stage, $a/(1 - a)$; and for the grounded-base stage, a. As the load resistance increases above $r_c(1 - a)$ the current amplification of the grounded-collector and the grounded-emitter stages decreases while that of the grounded-base stage remains constant. As the load resistance in-

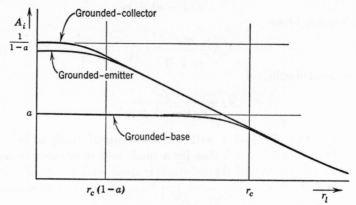

Fig. 5.6 The current amplification A_i.

creases above r_c, the current amplification of all three stages decreases and approximates r_c/r_l.

Using these figures it will be possible to determine which type of amplifier stage, grounded-base, grounded-emitter, or grounded-collector, should be used for a given application.

Figure 5.7 shows a block diagram of a multistage amplifier. The transducer gain † of this amplifier is

$$G_t = \frac{i_n^2 r_l}{e_g^2/4r_g} = 4\,\frac{r_l r_g}{(r_g + r_i)^2}\,\frac{i_n^2}{i_0^2}$$

$$= 4\,\frac{r_l r_g}{(r_g + r_i)^2}\,(A_{i1} \cdot A_{i2} \cdots A_{in})^2$$

$$= 4\,\frac{r_g A_{i1}^2}{(r_g + r_i)^2}\,(A_{i2} \cdots A_{in-1})^2(r_l A_{in}^2) \qquad [5.8]$$

† The "transducer gain" is defined as the ratio of the power delivered to the load to the power available at the input.

where A_{i1}, A_{i2}, and A_{in} are the current amplifications of the first, second, and nth stages. r_i is the input resistance of the amplifier.

For a multistage amplifier, working from a given source, the transducer gain is particularly significant as it dictates the overall requirements. For example, if the power available from a microphone is 10^{-9}

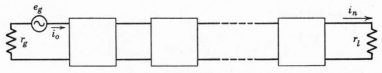

Fig. 5.7 Multistage amplifier.

watt and if the amplifier works into a loudspeaker requiring 3 watts, then the tranducer gain must be 3×10^9. The actual amplifier gain will depend on the matching at the input of the amplifier.

In order to obtain a maximum transducer gain, the right-hand side of eq. 5.8 must be a maximum, and therefore the following expressions must, individually, be as large as possible.

(a) *First stage*: $\dfrac{r_g}{(r_g + r_i)^2} A_i^2 = Y$ (Y has the form of a conductance)

(b) *Intermediate stages*: A_i

(c) *Last stage*: $r_l A_i^2 = R$ (an effective resistance)   [5.9]

These three expressions will be discussed separately. They will help to determine which type of amplifier, grounded-base, grounded-emitter, or grounded-collector, should be used.

First Stage. The conductance

$$Y = \frac{r_g}{(r_g + r_i)^2} A_i^2$$

should be as large as possible. This conductance will depend on the input resistance of the second stage due to its effect on A_i as shown in Fig. 5.6. It will decrease if this resistance becomes too large. By using either the grounded-emitter or grounded-base configuration in the second stage the input resistance can be kept small. Under these conditions, we have the following approximations, for $r_l \ll r_c(1 - a)$:

Grounded-emitter

$$Y \cong \frac{r_g}{[r_g + r_b + r_e/(1 - a)]^2} \left(\frac{a}{1 - a}\right)^2$$

$$\cong \frac{r_g a^2}{[r_e + (1 - a)(r_g + r_b)]^2} \qquad [5.10]$$

Grounded-base

$$Y \cong \frac{a^2 r_g}{[r_g + r_e + r_b(1 - a)]^2} \qquad [5.11]$$

Grounded-collector

$$Y \cong \frac{r_g}{[r_g + r_b + (r_e + r_l)/(1 - a)]^2} \left(\frac{1}{1 - a}\right)^2$$

$$\cong \frac{r_g}{[r_e + r_l + (r_g + r_b)(1 - a)]^2} \qquad [5.12]$$

Figure 5.8 shows qualitatively the values of Y. The maximum of Y occurs for the following values of r_g.

Grounded-emitter

$$r_g = r_b + r_e/(1 - a)$$

Grounded-base

$$r_g = r_b(1 - a) + r_e$$

Grounded-collector

$$r_g = r_b + (r_e + r_l)/(1 - a)$$

The optimum value that Y may have is (grounded-emitter)

$$Y_{\max} = \frac{a^2}{4(1 - a)[r_e + r_b(1 - a)]}$$

Figure 5.8 shows that, for an optimum design, the following configurations should be used:

r_g very small: grounded-base, grounded-emitter
r_g intermediate: grounded-emitter
r_g very large: grounded-emitter, grounded-collector

Intermediate Stages. For intermediate stages, the current amplification should be as large as possible. Figure 5.6 shows that this requires grounded-emitter or grounded-collector stages and load resistances of less than $r_c(1 - a)$. For large $a/(1 - a)$ this last requirement may exclude grounded-collector stages.

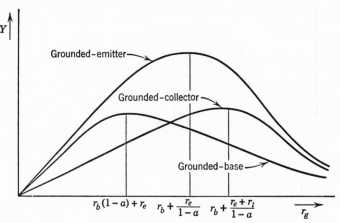

Fig. 5.8   The first stage.

Last Stages (excluding power stages, covered in Chapter 7).   For the last stage, for maximum power gain, the product $R = r_l A_i{}^2$ should be a maximum.

We have, from eqs. 5.5, 5.6, and 5.7,

Grounded-emitter

$$R = \frac{a^2 r_c{}^2 r_l}{[r_c(1 - a) + r_l]^2} \tag{5.13}$$

Grounded-base

$$R = \frac{a^2 r_c{}^2 r_l}{(r_c + r_l)^2} \tag{5.14}$$

Grounded-collector

$$R = \frac{r_c{}^2 r_l}{[r_c(1 - a) + r_l]^2} \tag{5.15}$$

These expressions are shown qualitatively in Fig. 5.9.

In many cases the last stage must be designed for maximum power output. The values of load resistance are then considerably smaller than those for which eqs. 5.13–5.14 have their maximum values.

Figure 5.9 should be considered with care since it seems to indicate that the grounded-collector stage may be used for all r_l.   The grounded-collector stage will present to the preceding stage a load of approximately $r_l/(1 - a)$.   Figure 5.6 shows that, for an r_l larger than a few

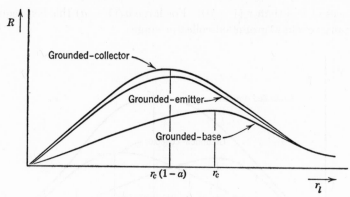

Fig. 5.9   The last stage.

hundred ohms, this may limit the current amplification of the preceding stage. We have, therefore,

r_l very small: grounded-emitter, grounded-collector
r_l intermediate: grounded-emitter
r_l very large: grounded-emitter, grounded-base

The expression $r_l A_i{}^2$ has a maximum for the grounded-emitter stage for $r_l = r_c(1 - a)$. The value of this maximum is

$$R_{\max} = \frac{a^2 r_c}{4(1 - a)}$$

The following table summarizes the results of the above discussion.

(a) *First stage*: r_g small: grounded-base or grounded-emitter
                          r_g intermediate: grounded-emitter
                          r_g large: grounded-emitter or grounded-collector

(b) *Intermediate stages*:   grounded-emitter or grounded-collector

(c) *Last stage*: r_l small: grounded-collector or grounded-emitter
                          r_l intermediate: grounded-emitter
                          r_l large: grounded-emitter or grounded-base

This table shows that, from a-c considerations, the grounded-emitter stage is always better than or equal to other stages. The following considerations will, therefore, be limited to grounded-emitter stages.

Figure 5.10 shows an amplifier containing grounded-emitter stages only. All coupling networks, etc., have been omitted.

The transducer gain of this amplifier is, with good approximation,

$$G_t = 4\,\frac{r_l r_g}{(r_g + r_{i1})^2}\,(A_{i1}\cdot A_{i2}\cdots A_{in})^2 \tag{5.8}$$

$$\cong \frac{4 r_l r_g}{(r_g + r_{i1})^2}\left[\frac{a_1}{1 - a_1}\cdot\frac{a_2}{1 - a_2}\cdot\frac{a_3 r_{c3}}{r_{c3}(1 - a_3) + r_l}\right]^2 \tag{5.16}$$

if both source and load are matched to the amplifier we have

$$r_g = r_{b1} + \frac{r_{e1}}{1 - a_1} \qquad r_l = r_{c3}(1 - a_3)$$

whence

$$G_t = \frac{a_1{}^2 a_3{}^2 r_{c3}}{4(1 - a_1)[r_{e1} + r_{b1}(1 - a_1)](1 - a_3)}\left(\frac{a_2}{1 - a_2}\right)^2 \tag{5.17}$$

This is the maximum available power gain that may be obtained with a three-stage transistor amplifier with capacitive or direct coupling.

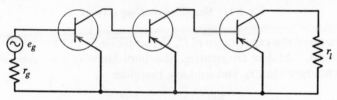

Fig. 5.10   Three-stage amplifier.

5.2.2   The Calculation of Coupling Networks

In Sec. 5.2 a circuit was shown containing a number of coupling elements (Fig. 5.2): four resistors for providing d-c bias to base and collector, one capacitor bypassing one of these resistors, and a capacitor for coupling succeeding stages. All these elements may reduce the gain of the amplifier. It is desirable to keep this loss to the minimum.

Figure 5.11 shows a simplified coupling network containing only two resistors, R_1 and R_2, and the capacitor C. It is first assumed that at the frequency of interest the impedance of the capacitor can be neglected. We have then for the current flowing into the second transistor:

$$i_1 \cong i_0\,\frac{a}{1 - a}\cdot\frac{R}{R + r_i} \tag{5.18}$$

where $R = R_1 R_2/(R_1 + R_2)$ is the resistance presented by R_1 and R_2 in parallel and r_i is the input resistance of the second stage. The reduction in current amplification due to R is

$$K = R/(R + r_i) \qquad [5.19]$$

for a loss of 1 db, R must be $8r_i$. For example, with an input resistance of 500 ohms, and $R_1 = R_2$, this gives $R_1 = R_2 = 8$ kilohms.

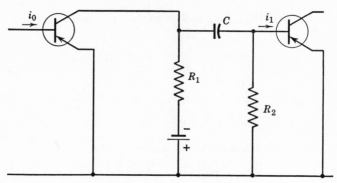

Fig. 5.11   Simplified coupling network.

Because of the capacitance of C, the amplification at low frequencies is reduced. At low frequencies, the impedance of this capacitance is much larger than r_i, and we have therefore

$$A_i \cong \frac{i_1}{i_0} \cdot \frac{ar_c}{r_c(1 - a) + r_l} \cdot \frac{R_1}{R_1 + (1/j\omega C)}$$

$$\cong \frac{ar_c}{r_c(1 - a) + [R_1/(1 + j\omega C R_1)]} \cdot \frac{R_1}{R_1 + (1/j\omega C)}$$

$$\cong \frac{ar_c R_1}{r_c(1 - a)R_1 + [R_1 + r_c(1 - a)]/j\omega C} \qquad 5.20$$

This equation shows that A_i is reduced by 3 db if

$$\frac{1}{\omega C} = \frac{r_c(1 - a)R_1}{R_1 + r_c(1 - a)} \qquad [5.21]$$

For example, if $R_1 = r_c(1 - a) = 10$ kilohms, the amplification is reduced by 3 db at a frequency of 50 cycles for $C = 0.7$ microfarad.

5.3   Transformer-Coupled Stages

Figure 5.12 shows a transformer-coupled amplifier stage. D-c bias is provided by the emitter resistors and emitter and collector batteries.

For alternating current they are bypassed by capacitors. For optimum power gain the transformers should be designed to match the output resistance of one stage to the input resistance of the next.

A simplified circuit may again be obtained when the elements that provide d-c bias are eliminated (Fig. 5.13).

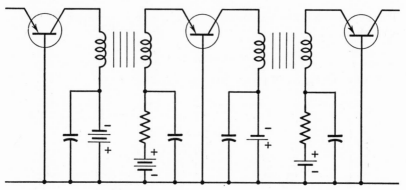

Fig. 5.12   Transformer-coupled amplifier.

Figure 5.14 shows a single stage of such an amplifier. The stages ahead of this stage are represented by a source with internal resistance r_g and open-circuit voltage e_g. The stages following this stage are represented by a resistor r_l. As seen from the amplifier stage, source and load resistances are changed by the transformers. The source resistance is

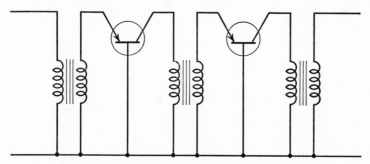

Fig. 5.13   Simplified transformer-coupled amplifier.

a resistance r_g', in series with a voltage e_g', and the load resistance is a resistance r_l', where $r_l' \cong r_l n^2$ and $r_g' \cong r_g/n^2$ (n being the turns ratio of the transformer) (Fig. 5.15). The gain of such an amplifier has been calculated in eqs. 4.9, 4.30, and 4.39a. It is a function of the load resistance r_l'.

For the grounded-emitter stage, we have, for the ratio of output to input power (4.30),

$$G = \frac{r_l'(ar_c - r_e)^2}{[r_c(1-a) + r_e + r_l']\{r_b[r_c(1-a) + r_e + r_l'] + r_e(r_c + r_l')\}}$$

[5.22]

This expression is a function of r_l'. It will have a maximum for a value of r_l' that satisfies the equation

$$dG/dr_l' = 0$$

[5.23]

The symbol r_l' $_{max}$ will be used in the following for this value.

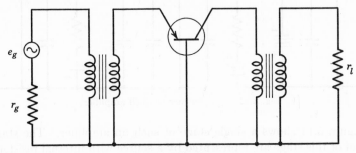

Fig. 5.14   Single stage.

Introducing this in eq. 5.22 will give us the maximum value of G. This is the maximum power gain that we can obtain from a single-stage amplifier. The input resistance of a stage terminated by $(r_l')_{max}$ can be obtained from eqs. 4.8, 4.29, and 4.39. These calculations will be carried out in the following.

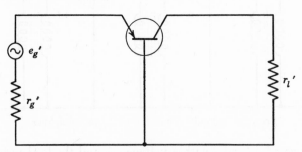

Fig. 5.15   Simplified single stage.

The equations for the gain G and the input resistances derived in Chapter 4 may be given the following simple forms as can be verified by inspection:

$$G = \frac{r_l' r_{21}^2}{(r_l' r_{11} + r_{11} r_{22} - r_{12} r_{21})(r_l' + r_{22})} \qquad [5.24]$$

$$r_i = \frac{r_l' r_{11} + r_{11} r_{22} - r_{12} r_{21}}{r_{22} + r_l'} \qquad [5.25]$$

where the symbols r_{11}, r_{12}, r_{21}, and r_{22} are

Grounded-emitter

$$r_{11} = r_e + r_b \qquad\qquad r_{21} = r_e - ar_c$$

$$r_{12} = r_e \qquad\qquad r_{22} = r_e + r_c(1 - a)$$

Grounded-base

$$r_{11} = r_e + r_b \qquad\qquad r_{21} = ar_c + r_b$$

$$r_{12} = r_b \qquad\qquad r_{22} = r_c + r_b$$

Grounded-collector

$$r_{11} = r_b + r_c \qquad\qquad r_{21} = r_c$$

$$r_{12} = r_c(1 - a) \qquad\qquad r_{22} = r_e + r_c(1 - a)$$

The gain G has a maximum for the condition of eq. 5.23; therefore,

$$0 = \frac{\left\{\begin{array}{l} r_{21}^2[(r_l'{}_{max} r_{11} + r_{11} r_{22} - r_{12} r_{21})(r_l'{}_{max} + r_{22}) \\ \quad - r_l'{}_{max}(2 r_{11} r_{22} - r_{12} r_{21} + 2 r_l'{}_{max} r_{11})] \end{array}\right\}}{(r_l'{}_{max} r_{11} + r_{11} r_{22} - r_{12} r_{21})^2 (r_l'{}_{max} + r_{22})^2}$$

$$0 = \frac{r_{21}^2[r_{22}(r_{11} r_{22} - r_{12} r_{21}) - r_{11} r_l'{}_{max}^2]}{(r_l'{}_{max} r_{11} + r_{11} r_{22} - r_{12} r_{21})^2 (r_l'{}_{max} + r_{22})^2}$$

This equation is satisfied for

$$r_l'{}_{max} = \sqrt{[r_{22}(r_{11} r_{22} - r_{12} r_{21})]/r_{11}}$$

$$= r_{22}\sqrt{1 - (r_{12} r_{21})/(r_{11} r_{22})} \qquad [5.26]$$

The maximum value for G is

$$
\begin{aligned}
G_{max} &= \frac{r_{21}{}^2 r_l'{}_{max}}{r_{22}(r_{11}r_{22} - r_{12}r_{21}) + (r_l'{}_{max})(2r_{11}r_{22} - r_{12}r_{21}) + (r_l'{}_{max})^2 r_{11}} \\[2mm]
&= \frac{r_{21}{}^2}{r_{22}(r_{11}r_{22} - r_{12}r_{21})(r_l'{}_{max})^{-1} + 2r_{11}r_{22} - r_{12}r_{21} + r_{11}r_l'{}_{max}} \\[2mm]
&= \frac{r_{21}{}^2}{2r_{11}r_{22} - r_{12}r_{21} + 2\sqrt{r_{11}r_{22}(r_{11}r_{22} - r_{12}r_{21})}} \\[2mm]
&= \frac{r_{21}{}^2}{(\sqrt{r_{11}r_{22} - r_{12}r_{21}} + \sqrt{r_{11}r_{22}})^2} \qquad\qquad [5.27]
\end{aligned}
$$

Combining eqs. 5.25 and 5.26 we obtain, after some simplifications, for the input resistance corresponding to $r_l'{}_{max}$:

$$
r_i' = \frac{r_{11}(r_l'{}_{max})^2 + r_{11}r_{22}r_l'{}_{max}}{r_{22}(r_{22} + r_l'{}_{max})} = \frac{r_{11}}{r_{22}} r_l'{}_{max} \qquad [5.28]
$$

If we introduce the values of r_{11}, r_{12}, r_{21} and r_{22} given above, we obtain for the three configurations

Grounded-emitter

$$
G_{max} = \frac{(ar_c - r_e)^2}{\{\sqrt{r_b[r_c(1 - a) + r_e] + r_e r_c} + \sqrt{(r_e + r_b)[r_c(1 - a) + r_e]}\}^2}
$$

$$
r_l'{}_{max} = [r_c(1 - a) + r_e]\sqrt{1 + \frac{r_e(ar_c - r_e)}{(r_e + r_b)[r_e + r_c(1 - a)]}}
$$

$$
r_i = (r_e + r_b)\sqrt{1 + \frac{r_e(ar_c - r_e)}{(r_e + r_b)[r_e + r_c(1 - a)]}} \qquad [5.29]
$$

Grounded-base

$$
G_{max} = \frac{(ar_c + r_b)^2}{[\sqrt{r_e(r_c + r_b) + r_b r_c(1 - a)} + \sqrt{(r_e + r_b)(r_c + r_b)}\,]^2}
$$

$$
r_l'{}_{max} = (ar_c + r_b)\sqrt{1 - \frac{r_b(ar_c + r_b)}{(r_e + r_b)(r_c + r_b)}}
$$

$$
r_i = (r_e + r_b)\sqrt{1 - \frac{r_b(ar_c + r_b)}{(r_e + r_b)(r_c + r_b)}} \qquad [5.30]
$$

Grounded-collector

$$G_{\max} = \frac{r_c{}^2}{\{\sqrt{r_b[r_c(1-a)+r_e]+r_e r_c}+\sqrt{(r_b+r_c)[r_e+r_c(1-a)]}\}^2}$$

$$r_l{}'{}_{\max} = [r_e+r_c(1-a)]\sqrt{1-\frac{r_c{}^2(1-a)}{(r_b+r_c)[r_e+r_c(1-a)]}}$$

$$r_i = (r_c+r_b)\sqrt{1-\frac{r_c{}^2(1-a)}{(r_b+r_c)[r_e+r_c(1-a)]}} \qquad 5.31]$$

For $r_b \ll r_c$, $r_e \ll r_c(1-a)$ these equations can be simplified considerably:

Grounded-emitter

$$G_{\max} = \frac{a^2 r_c}{[\sqrt{r_e+r_b(1-a)}+\sqrt{(r_e+r_b)(1-a)}\,]^2}$$

$$r_l{}'{}_{\max} = r_c(1-a)\sqrt{\frac{r_b(1-a)+r_e}{(r_e+r_b)(1-a)}}$$

$$r_i = \sqrt{(r_e+r_b)[r_b+r_e/(1-a)]} \qquad 5.32]$$

Grounded-base

$$G_{\max} = \frac{a^2 r_c}{[\sqrt{r_e+r_b(1-a)}+\sqrt{r_e+r_b}\,]^2}$$

$$r_l{}'{}_{\max} = r_c\sqrt{\frac{r_b(1-a)+r_e}{(r_e+r_b)}}$$

$$r_i = \sqrt{(r_e+r_b)[r_b(1-a)+r_e]} \qquad 5.33]$$

Grounded-collector

$$G_{\max} = \frac{r_c}{[\sqrt{r_e+r_b(1-a)}+\sqrt{r_c(1-a)}\,]^2} \cong \frac{1}{1-a}$$

$$r_l{}'{}_{\max} = (1-a)\sqrt{r_c[r_b+r_e/(1-a)]}$$

$$r_i = \sqrt{r_c[r_b+r_e/(1-a)]} \qquad [5.34]$$

Conclusions. From the point of view of power gain the grounded-emitter configuration is, in practically all applications, superior to the grounded-base and grounded-collector configurations. Impedance matching by means of transformers will produce the maximum possible gain; however, the difference in gain afforded by transformer coupling over RC coupling will decrease materially as transistors with high values of a are used, since the input and output resistances approach each other as a increases.

5.4   Problems

1. Give the upper limit for the transducer gain of an RC-coupled three-stage amplifier with a source resistance of 600 ohms, assuming the following parameters for all three transistors: $r_e = 30\ \Omega$, $r_b = 1000\ \Omega$, $r_c = 1$ megohm, $a = 0.98$.

2. Find the maximum single-stage power gain for all three configurations for a transistor having the following parameters: $r_e = 30\ \Omega$, $r_b = 1000\ \Omega$, $r_c = 1$ megohm, $a = 0.98$.

3. Calculate the variation of the maximum single-stage power gain as a function of a for the grounded-emitter and grounded-base configurations, for a transistor having $r_e = 30\ \Omega$, $r_b = 200\ \Omega$, $r_c = 1$ megohm.

Chapter 6

Bias Stabilization

6.1 Bias Requirements of Transistors

As shown in earlier chapters it is customary to operate transistors with constant emitter current and constant collector potential, as contrasted to constant grid and plate potentials for vacuum tubes. This is true of both point-contact and junction transistors. In junction transistors in particular it is possible to obtain high amplification at extremely low values of emitter current and collector potential.

Another factor entering into the problem of adequately supplying transistor bias is the variation of the various parameters with temperature, with operating point, and between units. This is especially true of the zero-emitter collector current I_{c0}, which varies exponentially with temperature (see Fig. 3.17). Unless the bias arrangement is correctly designed these variations will produce a marked departure from the desired operation, and equipment so designed will show undesirable sensitivity to temperature change or to change of transistors.

In this chapter the relationship will be developed between the direct currents and voltages supplied to the three transistor electrodes. A stability factor, S, will be developed, which relates the variation in output current to the variation of I_{c0}. It will be demonstrated that there is a practical range for S, below which excessive power is required from the power supply and above which the output current will vary excessively with temperature and between units. Under extreme conditions the variation in output current may produce a runaway, with the increasing current causing an increase in temperature, which further increases current. If this condition becomes cumulative the transistor

97

may either destroy itself or drift to a relatively inoperative condition, as, for example, when the net collector-base voltage drops to zero.

6.2 Conventional Bias Supply

In Fig. 6.1 is shown a transistor supplied with emitter bias from one battery of potential E_1 through resistor R_1 and with battery E_2 supplying potential to the collector through load resistor R_l. Resistor R_2 is inserted in the base lead. The polarities of these supplies and directions of currents are correct for p-n-p transistors, and are reversed for n-p-n units.

If R_1 is large compared to the internal emitter resistance, and the total resistance in the base circuit is not excessive, the emitter current

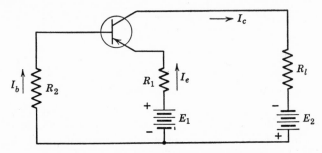

Fig. 6.1   Two-battery bias connections.

will be relatively constant. Since the collector current is essentially independent of collector potential in junction transistors the collector will be at essentially constant potential. Thus the original bias requirements are adequately met. In order to achieve this arrangement a considerable amount of power is dissipated in the stabilizing resistors, and in addition either two batteries or a tapped battery are required.

In the following analysis of stabilization the following assumptions are made:

1. V_c, the collector-base voltage, is held within the region where it has a minor effect on collector current.

2. $\alpha = \left(\dfrac{\partial I_c}{\partial I_e}\right)_{V_c}$ is constant over the operating range.

3. V_e, the emitter-base voltage, is zero. In most actual cases it will be less than 0.1 volt.

Under these conditions we have the following basic relationships: †

---

† Throughout this chapter positive values of voltages and currents indicate that the polarities and directions are in accordance with the associated figure, a negative sign indicating a reversal.

$$I_c = I_b + I_e \qquad [6.1]$$

$$E_1 = R_1 I_e - R_2 I_b \qquad [6.2]$$

$$E_2 = R_l I_c + R_2 I_b + V_c \qquad [6.3]$$

From inspection of typical junction transistor static characteristics it is evident that the collector current is made up of the zero-emitter collector current, I_{c0}, plus an amount which is the emitter current multiplied by the current amplification. Thus:

$$I_c = I_{c0} + \alpha I_e \qquad [6.4]$$

I_e and I_b may be expressed in terms of I_c, α, and I_{c0}:

$$I_e = (I_c - I_{c0})/\alpha \qquad [6.5]$$

$$I_b = [I_{c0} - I_c(1 - \alpha)]/\alpha \qquad [6.6]$$

Substituting these values of I_e and I_b in eq. 6.2, and solving, we obtain

$$I_c = I_{c0}\left[\frac{R_1 + R_2}{R_1 + R_2(1 - \alpha)}\right] + \frac{\alpha E_1}{R_1 + R_2(1 - \alpha)} \qquad [6.7]$$

If we differentiate I_c with respect to I_{c0} we derive a stability factor which we will designate as S:

$$S = \frac{\partial I_c}{\partial I_{c0}} = \frac{R_1 + R_2}{R_1 + R_2(1 - \alpha)} \qquad 6.8]$$

I_c can now be expressed in terms of S:

$$I_c = S I_{c0} + E_1(S - 1)/R_2 \qquad [6.9]$$

The relations between R_1, R_2, E_1, and E_2 are now

$$E_2 = V_c + R_l I_c + R_2 I_b$$

$$= V_c + I_c\left(R_l + R_2 - \frac{R_2}{\alpha}\right) + \frac{R_2 I_{c0}}{\alpha} \qquad [6.10]$$

From eq. 6.9,

$$E_1 = \frac{R_2(I_c - S I_{c0})}{S - 1} \qquad [6.11]$$

also (from eq. 6.8),

$$R_2 = \frac{R_1(S - 1)}{1 - S(1 - \alpha)} \qquad [6.12]$$

From [6.11] and [6.12] we obtain

$$R_1 = \frac{E_1[1 - S(1 - \alpha)]}{I_c - SI_{c0}} \qquad [6.13]$$

$$R_2 = \frac{E_1(S - 1)}{I_c - SI_{c0}} \qquad [6.14]$$

and

$$P_{\text{d-c}} = E_2 I_c + E_1(I_c - I_{c0})/\alpha \qquad [6.15]$$

where $P_{\text{d-c}}$ = total power consumption. The above equations give the necessary values for the various resistors and battery potentials, in terms of desired operating currents and potentials and for a desired stability factor S. For example, if a transistor has the following properties:

$$\alpha = 0.9 \qquad I_{c0} = 0.05 \times 10^{-3} \text{ amp}$$

and if it is desired to operate with a collector-base voltage, V_c, of 5.0 volts and collector current of 1.0×10^{-3} amp, and have a stability factor S of 3, then:

$$R_1 = 824E_1 \qquad \text{and} \qquad R_2 = 2350E_1$$

Usually either R_1 or R_2 is determined by the resistance of the previous interstage coupling unit. Let us therefore assume that R_2 represents the d-c resistance of the secondary of an audio transformer coupling into the base, with a value of 1000 ohms, and, further, that R_l represents the d-c resistance of the primary of the output transformer, with a resistance of 100 ohms. Under these conditions

$$E_1 = 0.425 \text{ volt} \qquad \text{and} \qquad R_1 = 350 \text{ ohms}$$

Inserting the above values in eq. 6.10, we obtain for E_2 a value of 5.044 volts. Equation 6.15 gives the total power consumption to be approximately 5.5 milliwatts, 92 per cent of which is dissipated in the collector and 8 per cent in the bias network.

The S factor of 3 means that any change in I_{c0} will appear, multiplied three times, in the collector current. I_{c0} is extremely temperature-dependent and may increase to several hundred per cent of its room-temperature value under some conditions of elevated temperature operation. In the example above, this would mean a change in collector current of the order of 10 per cent. Although this is usually not serious, it is easily conceivable that under some conditions where I_{c0} is a larger per cent of I_c and where S is high a considerable drift in I_c with temperature may be noted.

One other equation is valuable to show variation of V_c with I_{c0}, E_1, and E_2. These relationships are of particular interest in battery-operated devices, where the battery potentials decrease materially with life.

Equation 6.7 gave the relationship between I_c and I_{c0} and E_1. Substituting this in eq. 6.10 and solving results in the following equation:

$$V_c = E_2 - \alpha E_1 \left[\frac{R_l - R_2(1 - \alpha)/\alpha}{R_1 + R_2(1 - \alpha)} \right]$$

$$- I_{c0} \left\{ \frac{R_2}{\alpha} + \left[R_l - \frac{R_2(1 - \alpha)}{\alpha} \right] \frac{R_1 + R_2}{R_1 + R_2(1 - \alpha)} \right\} \quad [6.16]$$

From eq. 6.9 and the above equation we obtain, for the values chosen in our example,

$$I_c = 2E_1 \times 10^{-3} + 3I_{c0}$$

$$= 0.85 + 0.15 \text{ milliampere}$$

$$V_c = E_2 + 0.022E_1 - 1078I_{c0}$$

$$= 5.044 + 0.009 - 0.053 \text{ volt}$$

These equations indicate that, for the above example, the collector current is primarily determined by E_1 and to a lesser degree by I_{c0}, whereas the collector voltage is comparatively unaffected by any factor other than E_2. The reader should be cautioned that this is not always true. Under certain conditions, particularly where the resistance in the collector circuit is high, V_c may vary greatly with battery potential or with I_{c0}, and may even drop to zero, or reverse polarity if battery potential drops appreciably. This comes about by the unique fact that junction transistors ordinarily maintain their collector current at essentially the same value right down to the zero voltage axis.

Summary of Equations. To summarize the equations for separate emitter and collector batteries, knowing α, I_{c0}, V_c, I_c, and R_l:

$$P_{\text{d-c}} = E_2 I_c + E_1(I_c - I_{c0})/\alpha$$

$$R_1 = E_1 \left[\frac{1 - S(1 - \alpha)}{I_c - SI_{c0}} \right]$$

$$R_2 = \frac{E_1(S - 1)}{I_c - SI_{c0}} = \frac{\alpha E_1 - R_1(I_c - I_{c0})}{I_c(1 - \alpha) - I_{c0}}$$

$$S = \frac{R_1 + R_2}{R_1 + R_2(1 - \alpha)}$$

$$E_2 = V_c + I_c R_l - R_2[I_c(1 - \alpha) - I_{c0}]/\alpha$$

Knowing α; I_{c0}; R_1, R_2, R_l, S; E_1, E_2:

$$I_c = SI_{c0} + \frac{\alpha E_1}{R_1 + R_2(1 - \alpha)} = SI_{c0} + E_1(S - 1)/R_2$$

$$V_c = E_2 - \alpha E_1 \left[\frac{R_l - R_2(1 - \alpha)/\alpha}{R_1 + R_2(1 - \alpha)} \right]$$

$$- I_{c0} \left\{ \frac{R_2}{\alpha} + \left[R_l - \frac{R_2(1 - \alpha)}{\alpha} \right] \frac{R_1 + R_2}{R_1 + R_2(1 - \alpha)} \right\}$$

$$= E_2 - \frac{R_2 I_{c0}}{\alpha} - I_c \left(R_l + R_2 - \frac{R_2}{\alpha} \right)$$

6.3   Single-Battery Supply

Figure 6.2 shows an arrangement for obtaining the emitter current and collector potential from the same battery. The same three basic

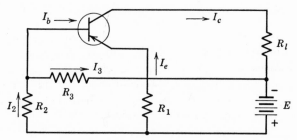

Fig. 6.2   Single-battery bias connections.

assumptions are made here as in the case of separate supplies. Under these conditions, we have the following relationships:

$$I_2 R_2 = I_e R_1 = E - I_3 R_3 \qquad\qquad [6.17]$$

$$I_c = I_b + I_e \qquad\qquad [6.1]$$

$$I_b = I_2 - I_3 \qquad\qquad [6.18]$$

$$I_c = I_{c0} + \alpha I_e \qquad\qquad [6.4]$$

Solving the mesh equations we obtain

$$I_c = \frac{I_{c0}(1 + R_1/R_2 + R_1/R_3) + \alpha E/R_3}{1 - \alpha + R_1/R_2 + R_1/R_3} \qquad\qquad [6.19]$$

$$I_e = (I_c - I_{c0})/\alpha \qquad\qquad [6.5]$$

as before, and

$$I_b = [I_{c0} - I_c(1 - \alpha)]/\alpha \qquad [6.6]$$

Note that I_b will be zero when

$$I_c = I_{c0}/(1 - \alpha)$$

At lower values of I_c, $I_e < I_c$; for higher values of I_c, $I_e > I_c$. Also,

$$I_2 = \frac{(R_1/R_2)(I_{c0} + E/R_3)}{1 - \alpha + R_1/R_2 + R_1/R_3} \qquad [6.20]$$

$$I_3 = \frac{(E/R_3)(1 - \alpha + R_1/R_2) - (I_{c0}R_1/R_3)}{1 - \alpha + R_1/R_2 + R_1/R_3} \qquad [6.21]$$

By differentiating I_c with respect to I_{c0} we derive the stability factor, S, representing the ratio of change in I_c to that in I_{c0}.

$$S = \frac{\partial I_c}{\partial I_{c0}} = \frac{1 + R_1/R_2 + R_1/R_3}{1 - \alpha + R_1/R_2 + R_1/R_3} \qquad [6.22]$$

For stable operation, the numerical value of the stability factor S should be as low as possible while maintaining a reasonable value of battery voltage E and power dissipation in the stabilizing resistances.

Expressing I_c in terms of S,

$$I_c = SI_{c0} + (E/R_3)(S - 1) \qquad [6.23]$$

For a desired operating collector-base voltage V_c,

$$I_e = \frac{E - I_c R_l - V_c}{R_1} \qquad [6.24]$$

By substitution in eqs. 6.5 and 6.23 we derive

$$R_1 = \frac{\alpha(E - R_l I_c - V_c)}{I_c - I_{c0}} \qquad [6.25]$$

$$R_3 = \frac{E(S - 1)}{I_c - SI_{c0}} \qquad [6.26]$$

$$R_2 = \frac{R_1 R_3(S - 1)}{R_3 S \alpha - (S - 1)(R_1 + R_3)} \qquad [6.27]$$

By using the expressions for R_1 and R_3 in eqs. 6.25 and 6.26, substituting R_1/R_3 as derived from eq. 6.22, and solving, we obtain the following equation for E in terms of R_1/R_2:

$$E = \frac{\alpha(V_c + R_l I_c)(I_c - SI_{c0})}{(I_c - I_{c0})[(R_1/R_2)(S - 1) + S(1 - \alpha) - 1] + \alpha(I_c - SI_{c0})}$$

[6.28]

Substituting this in eq. 6.26,

$$R_3 = \frac{\alpha(V_c + R_l I_c)}{(R_1/R_2)(I_c - I_{c0}) + I_c(1 - \alpha) - I_{c0}}$$

[6.29]

All the above values are expressible in terms of E:

$$R_1 = \frac{\alpha(E - V_c - R_l I_c)}{I_c - I_{c0}}$$

[6.25]

$$R_2 = \frac{S - 1}{\dfrac{(1 - S + \alpha S)(I_c - I_{c0})}{\alpha(E - V_c - R_l I_c)} - \dfrac{I_c - SI_{c0}}{E}}$$

[6.30]

$$R_3 = \frac{E(S - 1)}{I_c - SI_{c0}}$$

[6.26]

Thus, for any desired operating point, V_c, I_c (I_{c0} known), load resistance R_l, and desired stability S, the necessary stabilizing resistances may be calculated for any available battery E, or if one of the resistances is known, the necessary battery E and other stabilizing resistors may be calculated.

6.3.1 Power Dissipated

The total power dissipated, $P_{\text{d-c}} = E(I_c + I_3)$. Substituting the value of EI_3 from eqs. 6.21 and 6.26, this becomes

$$P_{\text{d-c}} = \frac{I_c - SI_{c0}}{S - 1}[V_c + I_c(R_3 + R_l)]$$

[6.31]

Expressed in terms of E

$$P_{\text{d-c}} = EI_c + \frac{(V_c + R_l I_c)(I_c - SI_{c0})}{S - 1}$$

$$= E\left[\frac{I_c}{\alpha}\left(1 + \frac{R_1}{R_2}\right) + I_{c0}\left(\frac{R_1}{\alpha R_3} - \frac{S}{S - 1}\right)\right]$$

[6.32]

6.3.2 Examples of Single-Battery Operation

Figures 6.3 and 6.4 give values of R_1, R_2, R_3, and $P_{\text{d-c}}$ versus E for two typical transistor applications. The range of voltages E was chosen such that the total power dissipation $P_{\text{d-c}}$ in the stabilized circuit would not exceed $5V_cI_c$, that is, that 80 per cent of the battery power would be dissipated in the stabilizing network. In these examples, it has been assumed that $\alpha = 0.9$; $I_{c0} = 0.05 \times 10^{-3}$ amp.

Figure 6.3 illustrates the conditions for a resistance-coupled low-level amplifier with $V_c = 1.5$ volts, $I_c = 0.25 \times 10^{-3}$ amp, and $R_l = 10,000$ ohms. Figure 6.4 illustrates a higher-powered application with $V_c = 20$ volts, $I_c = 5 \times 10^{-3}$ amp, and $R_l = 200$ ohms.

In a typical application, the determining items will be the d-c resistances of the coupling network and the available voltage. For example, assume that we are coupling into the emitter with an audio transformer having a d-c resistance of 1000 ohms, in the case illustrated in Fig. 6.4. R_1 therefore $= 1000$ ohms. This determines that $E = 26.5$ volts. If we can allow a stability factor S of 3, we obtain $R_2 = 3800$ ohms, $R_3 = 11,000$ ohms, and $P_{\text{d-c}} = 184$ mw.

This indicates that we insert 3800 ohms in the base lead and 11,000 ohms from the battery also to the base.

Using the equations of Sec. 6.2, for tapped-battery operation, knowing $R_1 = 1000$ ohms, and again using $S = 3$, we find that $E_1 = 6.93$ volts, $R_2 = 2.86$ kilohms, and $E_2 = 23.6$ volts. $P_{\text{d-c}} = 156$ mw. Thus, approximately 30 mw is the net price of using the single battery in this case. Also, note that $E < (E_1 + E_2)$.

In base injection, another factor to consider is the loading effect of R_3 across the input. It may be necessary to keep R_3 higher than the minimum necessary for stabilization, and to increase R_1 and R_2 correspondingly.

Summary of Equations. Knowing α, I_{c0}, V_c, I_c, and R_l,

$$P_{\text{d-c}} = EI_c + (V_c + R_lI_c)(I_c - SI_{c0})/(S - 1)$$

$$R_1 = \frac{\alpha(E - V_c - R_lI_c)}{I_c - I_{c0}}$$

$$R_2 = \frac{S - 1}{\dfrac{(1 - S + \alpha S)(I_c - I_{c0})}{\alpha(E - V_c - R_lI_c)} - \dfrac{I_c - SI_{c0}}{E}}$$

$$R_3 = \frac{E(S - 1)}{I_c - SI_{c0}}$$

$$S = \frac{1 + R_1/R_2 + R_1/R_3}{1 - \alpha + R_1/R_2 + R_1/R_3}$$

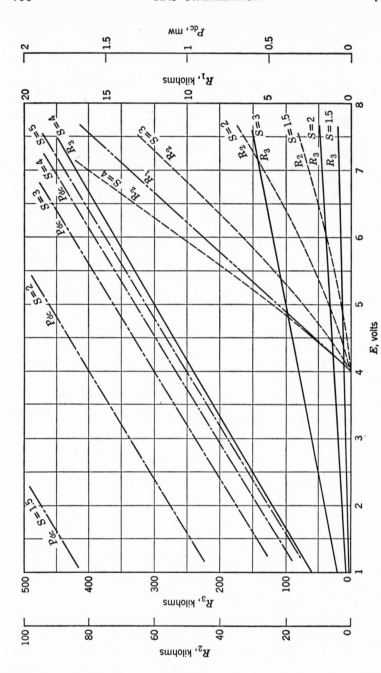

Fig. 6.3 Bias resistances and power dissipation for $V_c = 1.5$ volts, $I_c = 0.25$ ma, $R_l = 10$ kilohms.

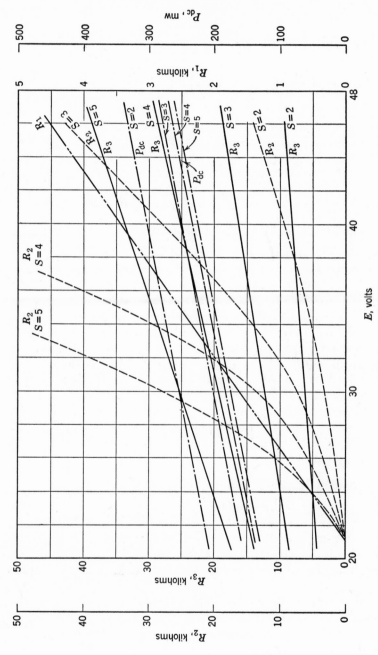

Fig. 6.4 Bias resistances and power dissipation for $V_c = 20$ volts, $I_c = 5$ ma, $R_l = 200$ ohms.

Knowing α; I_{c0}; R_1, R_2, R_3, R_l; and E,

$$I_c = SI_{c0} + E(S - 1)/R_3$$

$$V_c = E\left[1 - \frac{S - 1}{R_3}\left(\frac{R_1}{\alpha} + R_l\right)\right] - I_{c0}\left[\frac{R_1(S - 1)}{\alpha} + SR_l\right]$$

The same precautions are in order here as in Sec. 6.2; i.e., care must be taken in the design of transistor amplifiers that excessive variation in collector current or potential does not occur with variation in battery potential or I_{c0}. The problem is somewhat simplified by there being only one battery; however, now this single battery serves a multiple function, and the effect of variation may be more severe.

6.4   Multistage Stability Considerations

The previous section dealt with the variation of collector current and voltage with I_{c0} and with battery voltage. For multiple transistor amplifiers without blocking capacitors, i.e., direct-coupled, this problem becomes many times more severe, as the variation of collector current of one transistor is passed on to the next transistor, where this variation is amplified and combined with the similar variation due to changes in the second unit. As stages are added the effect is cascaded until finally a very small drift in the first unit may cause the whole chain to become inoperative. This problem is treated in detail in Chapter 8, "Direct-Current Amplifiers." Where the individual stages are isolated by coupling capacitors these variations do not add up, each stage having its own individual stabilization problem. The reader is also referred to Sec. 6.13, describing an incremental method of particular value in multistage analysis.

6.5   Tandem Transistor Operation

In the previous sections the stability conditions for single stages were developed, and it was pointed out that high stability is accompanied by high power dissipation in the stabilizing network. In low-level stages this is usually not serious, and stabilization may usually be accomplished conveniently by use of a moderate amount of resistance in emitter and base leads, occasionally without the added complication of a third resistor to the battery. In the design of power output stages, however, the problem is more severe. The power output from a transistor is primarily limited by the internal heating of the junction; hence there will be an appreciable rise in temperature when the transistor is operating at full output. Since I_{c0} is very temperature-sensitive this means that a considerable increase in the collector current will occur with warm-up unless a high degree of stabilization is achieved. Further, the process may be cumulative, the increase in collector current causing greater internal heating, which, in turn, causes a further increase in I_{c0}. Adequate stabilization, on the other hand, may require dissipation in the bias resistors comparable to the collector dissipation, with the result that the potential high efficiency of the transistor will not be achieved.

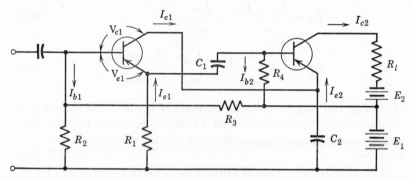

Fig. 6.5   Tandem amplifier.

A tandem transistor arrangement has been developed which uses one transistor to supply constant emitter current to the second transistor, and also to supply power gain. Figure 6.5 shows the basic circuit of this arrangement.

The first transistor is stabilized by resistors R_1, R_2, and R_3 in the manner described in Sec. 6.3. The second transistor derives its emitter current from the collector of the first and supplies collector current to the load R_l. Its base returns to $-E_1$ through resistor R_4.

A-c tandem operation is achieved by grounding the collector of the first transistor and the emitter of the second effectively by bypass capacitor C_2 and connecting the emitter of the first to the base of the second through capacitor C_1. Thus the first stage operates as grounded-collector, the second as grounded-emitter. Alternative arrangements will be described in a later section.

6.6   D-C Relationships in Tandem Amplifiers

Using the designations and directions of currents and voltages as shown in Fig. 6.5, we have the following relationships between currents:

$$I_{e2} = \frac{I_{c2} - I_{c02}}{\alpha_2} \qquad [6.33]$$

$$I_{b2} = \frac{I_{c2}(1 - \alpha_2)}{\alpha_2} - \frac{I_{c02}}{\alpha_2} \qquad [6.34]$$

$$I_{c1} = I_{e2} = \frac{I_{c2} - I_{c02}}{\alpha_2} \qquad [6.35]$$

$$I_{e1} = \frac{I_{c2} - I_{c02}}{\alpha_1 \alpha_2} - \frac{I_{c01}}{\alpha_1} \qquad [6.36]$$

$$I_{b1} = \frac{I_{c2}(1 - \alpha_1)}{\alpha_1 \alpha_2} - \frac{I_{c01}}{\alpha_1} - \frac{I_{c02}(1 - \alpha_1)}{\alpha_1 \alpha_2} \qquad [6.37]$$

where I_{c01} and I_{c02} are collector currents of the first and second transistors, respectively, for zero-emitter current, and α_1 and α_2 are short-circuit current amplifications of the first and second transistors, respectively.

In practically every case of interest for tandem power stages I_{c1} will be considerably greater than $I_{c01}/(1 - \alpha_1)$, I_{c1} usually being somewhat greater than I_{c2}. Therefore, it becomes feasible to eliminate resistor R_2 and use only one resistor R_3, of minimum acceptable value from the standpoint of circuit loading, to supply base current for the first transistor. For the remainder of this analysis R_2 will be neglected.

Using the equations derived in Sec. 6.3, and making the same assumptions, namely, that (1) α is constant over the range under consideration, (2) I_c is independent of V_c, and (3) $V_e \cong 0$, we obtain the following basic relationships:

$$I_{c2} = \frac{\alpha_1 \alpha_2 E_1}{R_1 + R_3(1 - \alpha_1)} + \frac{\alpha_2(R_1 + R_3)I_{c01}}{R_1 + R_3(1 - \alpha_1)} + I_{c02} \qquad [6.38]$$

$$R_3 = \frac{\alpha_1 \alpha_2 V_{c1} + \alpha_1 R_4[I_{c2}(1 - \alpha_2) - I_{c02}]}{I_{c2}(1 - \alpha_1) - \alpha_2 I_{c01} - I_{c02}(1 - \alpha_1)} \qquad [6.39]$$

$$E_1 = V_{c1} + I_{c2}\left[\frac{R_1}{\alpha_1 \alpha_2} + \frac{R_4(1 - \alpha_2)}{\alpha_2}\right]$$

$$- \frac{R_1 I_{c01}}{\alpha_1} - \frac{I_{c02}}{\alpha_2}\left(\frac{R_1}{\alpha_1} + R_4\right) \qquad [6.40]$$

$$V_{c1} = E_1 \left[1 - \frac{R_1 + \alpha_1 R_4(1 - \alpha_2)}{R_1 + R_3(1 - \alpha_1)} \right]$$

$$- I_{c01} \left[\frac{R_1 + R_4(1 - \alpha_2)(1 + R_1/R_3)}{1 - \alpha_1 + R_1/R_3} \right] + R_4 I_{c02}$$

$$[6.41]$$

(E_2 depends upon the desired value of V_{c2} and may be easily calculated. It does not enter the stability problem except as power dissipation affects I_{c02}.) Equation 6.39 gives R_3 as a function of R_4 for any desired I_{c2} and V_{c1}. R_3 and R_4 are chosen as low as permissible from the standpoint of a-c loading, as described later.

Using the chosen values of R_3 and R_4, eq. 6.40 gives E_1 as a function of R_1. In the same manner as described in Sec. 6.3 for a single transistor, a high value of R_1 will produce a high stability but will also require a larger value of E_1 and more power dissipation. However, now we are stabilizing a transistor having comparatively low power dissipation, possibly one-tenth or less of that dissipated in the second transistor; hence, the power required for stabilization will be related to this low level rather than to the output level. This may be visualized by inspection of eq. 6.38, where I_{c02} appears as a very minor item in the total of I_{c2}.

Equations 6.38 and 6.41 may be used to indicate the dependence of I_{c2} and V_{c1} upon E_1, I_{c01} and I_{c02} and to show how much these can vary without serious effects.

Example Let us assume that two identical transistors have $\alpha_1 = \alpha_2 = 0.9$, $I_{c01} = I_{c02} = 0.1$ ma. We desire operation at $I_{c2} = 10.0$ ma and $V_{c1} = 2.0$ volts.

The various currents may be obtained through eqs. 6.33–6.37. This gives

$$I_{b1} = 1.11 \text{ ma} \qquad I_{b2} = 1.00 \text{ ma}$$

$$I_{c1} = 11.00 \text{ ma} \qquad I_{c2} = 10.00 \text{ ma}$$

$$I_{e1} = 12.11 \text{ ma} \qquad I_{e2} = 11.00 \text{ ma}$$

From eq. 6.39 we obtain $R_3 = 1.80 + 0.9R_4$ (all R's in kilohms). If we now assume a minimum acceptable value of R_4 of 20 kΩ then $R_3 = 19.8$ kΩ.

From eq. 6.40 we obtain $E_1 = 22.0 + 12.12R_1$. Let us now further assume that $R_1 = 1.0$ kΩ. This gives $E_1 = 34.1$ volts.

Equation 6.41 can be used to indicate the dependence of V_{c1} upon E_1, I_{c01}, and I_{c02} by substituting the above values. Thus,

$$V_{c1} = 0.060E_1 - 20.6I_{c01} + 20.0I_{c02}$$

Similarly eq. 6.38 shows the constituent parts of I_{c2}:

$$I_{c2} = 0.273E_1 + 6.3I_{c01} + I_{c02}$$

These dependences can be visualized by inserting the given values. Thus,

$$V_{c1} = 2.06 - 2.06 + 2.00 = 2.00$$

$$I_{c2} = 9.3 + 0.6 + 0.1 = 10.0$$

This indicates the considerable degree to which I_{c2} is now stabilized, particularly with respect to I_{c02}. It also indicates certain permissible variations in E_1, I_{c01}, and I_{c02} before excessive change in V_{c1} occurs. Thus V_{c1} will drop to half its original value, to 1.0 volt, if E_1 is halved, I_{c02} halved, or I_{c01} increased by 50 per cent.

This dependence of V_{c1} upon I_{c01} and I_{c02} is dangerous, as it is possible for V_{c1} to drop to zero, or even reverse polarity if these values change excessively. This condition may be improved considerably at the cost of a-c loading (hence loss of gain), by making R_3 and R_4 smaller. For example, if R_3 is reduced to 6.3 kΩ and $R_4 = 5.0$ kΩ, substituting in eq. 6.40 gives $E_1 = 7.0 + 12.12R_1$. For the assumed value of R_1 of 1.0 kΩ, $E_1 = 19.12$ volts. Equations 6.38 and 6.41 now give

$$I_{c2} = 0.496E_1 + 4.0I_{c01} + I_{c02}$$

$$V_{c1} = 0.11E_1 - 6.0I_{c01} + 5.0I_{c02}$$

Substituting the original values,

$$I_{c2} = 9.5 + 0.5 + 0.1 = 10.0$$

$$V_{c1} = 2.1 - 0.6 + 0.5 = 2.0$$

Now an increase in I_{c01} of 165 per cent is required to reduce V_{c1} to 1 volt, compared to 50 per cent before. It should be noted that the changes in V_{c1} due to I_{c01} and I_{c02} are opposing, and hence will tend to cancel if due to a common cause, e.g., ambient temperature change.

6.7 Other Configurations of Tandem Amplifiers

In Figs. 6.6 and 6.7 are shown arrangements whereby the first transistor may be connected as a grounded-emitter stage and connected either to the base of a second grounded-emitter or grounded-collector stage (Fig. 6.6) or to the emitter of a grounded-base stage (Fig. 6.7). This is accomplished by insertion of one or more resistors between the collector of the first transistor and the emitter of the second and appropriate bypassing and coupling as shown.

In all these arrangements (Fig. 6.6) the only d-c variation from that shown in Fig. 6.5 consists of insertion of a resistor R_5 in the series con-

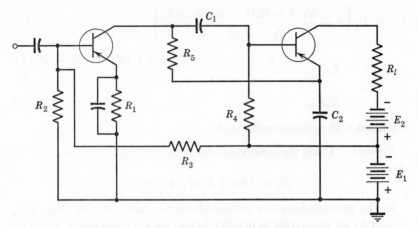

Fig. 6.6   Grounded-emitter, grounded-emitter tandem arrangement.

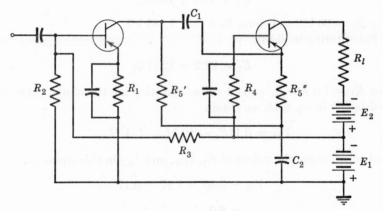

Fig. 6.7   Grounded-emitter, grounded-base tandem arrangement.

nection.   Thereupon the basic equations change to

$$R_3 = \frac{\alpha_1\alpha_2 V_{c1} + I_{c2}[\alpha_1 R_5 + \alpha_1 R_4(1 - \alpha_2)] - \alpha_1 I_{c02}(R_4 + R_5)}{I_{c2}(1 - \alpha_1) - \alpha_2 I_{c01} - I_{c02}(1 - \alpha_1)} \quad [6.42]$$

$$E_1 = V_{c1} + I_{c2}\left[\frac{R_1}{\alpha_1\alpha_2} + \frac{R_4(1 - \alpha_2)}{\alpha_2} + \frac{R_5}{\alpha_2}\right] - \frac{R_1 I_{c01}}{\alpha_1}$$

$$- I_{c02}\left(\frac{R_1}{\alpha_1\alpha_2} + \frac{R_4}{\alpha_2} + \frac{R_5}{\alpha_2}\right) \quad [6.43]$$

$$V_{c1} = E_1 \left[1 - \frac{R_1 + \alpha_1 R_4(1 - \alpha_2) + \alpha_1 R_5}{R_1 + R_3(1 - \alpha_1)} \right]$$

$$- I_{c01} \left[\frac{R_1 + R_4(1 - \alpha_2)(1 + R_1/R_3) + (R_5/R_3)(R_1 + R_3)}{1 - \alpha_1 + R_1/R_3} \right]$$

$$+ R_4 I_{c02} \qquad\qquad\qquad\qquad [6.44]$$

Equation 6.38 remains unchanged.

Example. Using the same values as in the previous example, eq. 6.42 gives

$$R_3 = 1.80 + 0.9R_4 + 9.9R_5$$

In the grounded-emitter grounded-emitter configuration (Fig. 6.6), R_4 and R_5 are effectively in parallel; hence, a good relationship would be to make $R_4 = R_5$. Now:

$$R_3 = 1.80 + 10.8R_4$$

For $R_3 = 20$ kΩ, as before, R_4 is now 1.685 kΩ.
Substituting in [6.43]:

$$E_1 = 22.2 + 12.11R_1$$

For $R_1 = 1.0$ kΩ, $E_1 = 34.3$ volts. Substituting the above values of resistances in eq. 6.44, we obtain

$$V_{c1} = 0.11E_1 - 19.7I_{c01} + 1.7I_{c02}$$

and substituting the values of E_1, I_{c01}, and I_{c02} in this equation,

$$V_{c1} = 3.80 - 1.97 + 0.17$$

$$= 2.0$$

V_{c1} will drop to 1.0 volt if E_1 decreases by 27 per cent, or if I_{c01} increases by 50 per cent. The effect of I_{c02} has been reduced very markedly.

Thus the effect of R_5 is to increase the voltage effect, reducing the permissible battery decay, but it has no appreciable effect on I_{c01} and it greatly reduces the effect of I_{c02}. Although coupling in these circuits is accomplished by RC networks it is obvious that transformers may also be used, maintaining the series d-c connection. For example, in the circuit of Fig. 6.7 resistors R_5' and R_5'' may be replaced by primary and secondary, respectively, of a transformer, with the common junction bypassed by C_2 and with C_1 omitted. This permits better impedance match.

6.8   Push-Pull Tandem Amplifiers

While two tandem strings may be operated in push-pull from either a transformer or phase inverter, it is also possible to utilize the stabilizing transistor as the phase inverter. This is illustrated in Fig. 6.8. The output of the first transistor is divided between R_1 and R_5 (R_5' and R_5'' effectively in parallel), and the voltage across R_1 is coupled to the base of one output transistor, the voltage across R_5 to the other. The emitters of the two output transistors are supplied in parallel from the collector of the first.

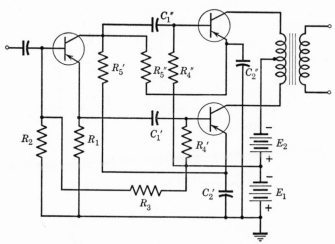

Fig. 6.8   Push-pull tandem amplifier.

6.9   A-C Analysis of Tandem Amplifiers

Figure 6.9 shows the a-c connections including generator and load terminations. Also shown is an idealized approximation, neglecting shunt and coupling capacitances, and external emitter impedances.

Let r_{i1} = input resistance of the first transistor, and r_{i2} = input resistance of the second transistor. The current into the first transistor is

$$i_0 = e_g/(r_g + r_{i1}) \qquad [6.45]$$

The current amplification of the first stage is

$$A_{i1} = \frac{r_{c1}}{r_{c1}(1 - a_1) + r_{e1} + r_{i2}} \cong \frac{1}{1 - a_1} \qquad [6.46]$$

where $a_1 = r_{m1}/r_{c1} \cong \alpha_1$; similarly $a_2 \cong \alpha_2$.

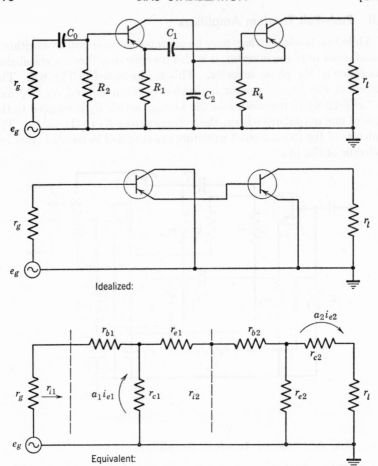

Fig. 6.9   A-c connections for tandem amplifier.

The current amplification of the second stage is

$$A_{i2} = \frac{a_2 r_{c2} - r_{e2}}{r_{c2}(1 - a_2) + r_{e2} + r_l}$$

$$\cong \frac{a_2 r_{c2}}{r_{c2}(1 - a_2) + r_l} \qquad [6.47]$$

The transducer gain of the tandem arrangement (power into the load divided by power available from the generator) is

$$G_t = \frac{4i_{c2}{}^2 r_l r_g}{e_g{}^2} = \frac{4r_l r_g}{(r_g + r_{i1})^2} A_{i1}{}^2 A_{i2}{}^2$$

$$\cong \frac{4r_l r_g}{(r_g + r_{i1})^2} \left(\frac{1}{1 - a_1}\right)^2 \left(\frac{a_2 r_{c2}}{r_{c2}(1 - a_2) + r_l}\right)^2 \qquad [6.48]$$

For a small load, $r_l \ll r_{c2}(1 - a_2)$, this becomes

$$G_t \cong \frac{4r_l r_g}{(r_g + r_{i1})^2} \left(\frac{b_2}{1 - a_1}\right)^2 \qquad [6.49]$$

where $b_2 = a_2/(1 - a_2)$. For a matched load $r_l = r_{c2}(1 - a_2)$,

$$G_t \cong \frac{r_g r_{c2}}{(r_g + r_{i1})^2} \cdot \frac{a_2 b_2}{(1 - a_1)^2} \qquad [6.50]$$

For most power applications the load resistance is considerably less than $r_{c2}(1 - a_2)$ and eq. 6.49 will apply most closely. (A fair approximation for best load resistance at any operating point V_{c2}, I_{c2} is $r_l \cong V_{c2}/I_{c2}$.)

6.9.1 Effect of r_g

With very small r_g, $r_g \ll r_{i1}$, and using the approximation $r_{i1} = r_{i2}/(1 - a_1)$,

$$G_t \cong \frac{4r_l r_g}{r_{i2}{}^2} \left(\frac{a_2 r_{c2}}{r_{c2}(1 - a_2) + r_l}\right)^2 \qquad [6.51]$$

An analysis of the transducer gain of the second stage alone gives the same equation, leading to the conclusion that no insertion gain results from the first stage when operated from a very low-impedance source.

For r_g between r_{i2} and $r_{i2}/(1 - a_1)$ some insertion gain will result from the first stage.

For large r_g, $r_g \gg r_{i2}$,

$$G_t \cong \frac{4r_l}{r_g} \left(\frac{1}{1 - a_1}\right)^2 \left(\frac{a_2 r_{c2}}{r_{c2}(1 - a_2) + r_l}\right)^2 \qquad [6.52]$$

For low values of r_l, as commonly used, this may be approximated to

$$G_t \cong \frac{4r_l (b_1 + 1)^2 b_2{}^2}{r_g} \qquad [6.53]$$

6.9.2 Effects of Shunt Resistors

There are several shunt resistors in the circuit of Fig. 6.5 which reduce the a-c gain. Resistors R_1 and R_4 effectively parallel r_{i2} and R_2 and R_3 parallel r_{i1}.

If the net parallel resistance of R_1 and R_4 equals $8r_{i2}$ there will be 1 db loss; 2 db, if they equal $4r_{i2}$.

Likewise, 1 db loss will result if the parallel resistance of R_2 and R_3 (or R_3 where R_2 is not used, as in this analysis) equals $8r_{i1}$ or $8r_{i2}/(1 - a_1)$; 2 db, for $4r_{i1}$ or $4r_{i2}/(1 - a_1)$.

6.9.3 Effects of Capacitors

Coupling capacitor C_1 will attenuate those frequencies at which its impedance is comparable to r_{i2}. There will be 3 db attenuation where

$$C_1 = \frac{1}{\omega_0 r_{i1}(1 - a_1)} = \frac{1}{\omega_0 r_{i2}}$$

The effect of C_2, the bypass capacitor, is more complex, since it is common to two loops. As an approximation it may be considered to act as a capacitor $C_2/b_1 b_2$ in series with r_{i1}; hence 3 db will result at $C_2 = b_1 b_2/\omega_0 r_g$.

6.9.4 Values of r_{i1}, r_{i2}

Chapter 4 indicated that the input resistance of a grounded-emitter amplifier is of the order of 500-1000 ohms for most transistors, with a low value of load resistance. This is true only for small signals. As the output amplitude is increased the input resistance will drop considerably, owing to non-linearity of the emitter characteristic. See Chapters 1 and 3. For typical operation as an output stage an input resistance of 100–200 ohms is more nearly normal.

We can, therefore, make the following approximations for output stages:

$$r_l = V_{c2}/I_{c2} \qquad r_{i2} = 100 \text{ ohms} - 200 \text{ ohms}$$

Example. Considering the same two transistors, of $a_1 = a_2 = 0.9$, $I_{c01} = I_{c02} = 0.1$ ma with operating points as below:

$$I_{c2} = 10.0 \text{ ma} \qquad V_{c1} = 2.0 \text{ volts}$$

$$V_{c2} = 50 \text{ volts}$$

let $r_l = 5000$ ohms and assume $R_{i2} = 200$ ohms; $b_1 = b_2 = 9$. Also assume a generator impedance of 10 kΩ. From (6.53),

$$G_t = 13{,}100 \equiv 41 \text{ db}$$

The shunt equivalent of R_1 and R_4 may be as low as 800 ohms for 2 db loss, and R_3 may be as low as 8000 ohms for an additional loss of 2 db. Thus the combination of resistances used in the previous example, i.e., $R_1 = 1.0$ kΩ, $R_3 = 6.3$ kΩ, $R_4 = 5.0$ kΩ, will result in about 6 db loss or an overall transducer gain of 35 db.

For 6 db attenuation at 50 cycles,

$$C_1 = \frac{10^6}{2\pi 50 \times 200} = 16 \ \mu f$$

$$C_2 = \frac{81 \times 10^6}{2\pi 50 \times 10,000} = 26 \ \mu f$$

This indicates the order of magnitude of capacitances required at low audio frequencies, due to the low impedances of transistor circuits.

E_2 may be calculated readily, since

$$E_{b2} = E_1 - i_{b2} R_4$$

$$= 19.12 - 5.00 = 14.12 \text{ volts} \quad \text{(negative with respect to ground)}$$

Assuming that the d-c resistance of the output load is 100 ohms,

$$E_2 = 14.12 + 50.0 + 1.0 - 19.12 = 46.0 \text{ volts}$$

Now assuming a power efficiency of 48 per cent in the output stage

$$P_{\text{out}} = 0.48 \times V_{c2} \times I_{c2} = 240 \text{ mw}$$

Total d-c battery power is

$$19.12 \ (12.11) + 46.0 \ (10.0) = 692 \text{ mw}$$

and overall efficiency $= 35$ per cent.

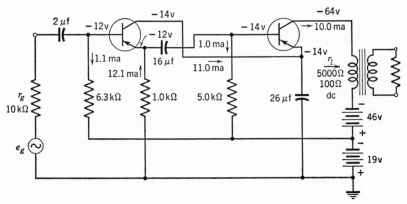

Fig. 6.10 Complete circuit of tandem amplifier.

In passing, it should be emphasized that this efficiency could never be realized with the same stability by the conventional methods described in Sec. 6.3.

Figure 6.10 gives the complete circuit with all values as derived above.

6.10 Practical Examples of Tandem Amplifiers

Figures 6.11 and 6.12 are schematics of two amplifiers incorporating the above principles. Figure 6.11 shows a single-ended n-p-n transistor amplifier with an output power of 5 mw and an overall power gain of

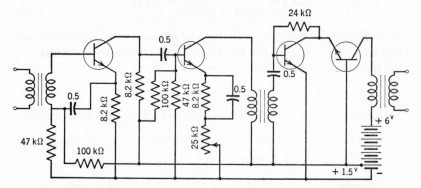

Fig. 6.11   Four-stage amplifier with tandem output arrangement.

90 db. This amplifier requires a total battery power of 15 mw. Figure 6.12 shows a push-pull p-n-p transistor amplifier producing 300 mw class A for 1400 mw of power consumption. For both amplifiers voltage and current stability with time and temperature were excellent.

Push-pull class A and B power amplifiers are discussed in detail in Chapter 7.

6.11 Degenerative Tandem Amplifier

A variation of the preceding employs a degenerative feedback version of stabilization with one of the base resistors returned to the collector. A simplified version of this circuit using only one base resistor R_3 is shown in Fig. 6.13.

The basic equations for this circuit are given below, for transistors of α_1, α_2, I_{c01}, and I_{c02}, and for desired operating points V_{c1}, V_{c2}, and I_{c2}.

$$R_3 = \frac{\alpha_2 V_{c1}}{(I_{c2} - I_{c02})(1 - \alpha_1) - \alpha_2 I_{c01}} \qquad [6.54]$$

$$E_1 = V_{c1} + (I_{c2}/\alpha_2)[R_1 + R_4(1 - \alpha_2)] - (I_{c02}/\alpha_2)(R_1 + R_4) \qquad [6.55]$$

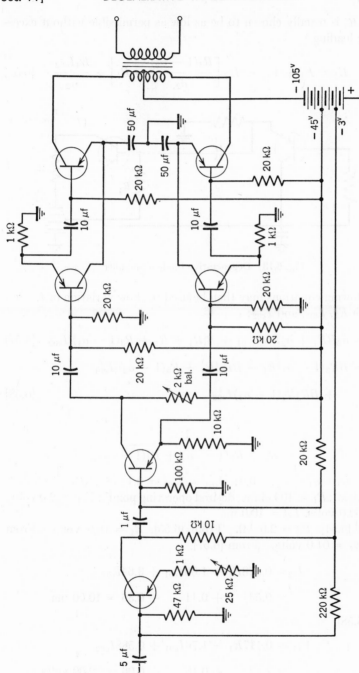

Fig. 6.12   Four-stage amplifier with push-pull tandem output arrangements.

(Note: R_4 is usually chosen to be as low as permissible without excessive a-c loading.)

$$E_2 = E_1 + V_{c2} - I_{c2}\left[\frac{R_4(1 - \alpha_2)}{\alpha_2} - R_l\right] + \frac{R_4 I_{c02}}{\alpha_2} \quad [6.56]$$

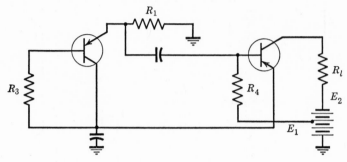

Fig. 6.13   Degenerative tandem amplifier.

The following equations may then be used to show variation of I_{c2} and V_{c1} with E_1, I_{c01}, and I_{c02}:

$$I_{c2} = \alpha_2 B E_1 + \alpha_2 B R_3 I_{c01} + B[R_1 + R_4 + R_3(1 - \alpha_1)]I_{c02} \quad [6.57]$$

$$V_{c1} = BR_3(1 - \alpha_1)E_1 - BR_3[R_1 + R_4(1 - \alpha_2)]I_{c01}$$

$$+ BR_3 R_4(1 - \alpha_1)I_{c02} \quad [6.58]$$

where

$$B = \frac{1}{R_1 + R_3(1 - \alpha_1) + R_4(1 - \alpha_2)}$$

Example. $\alpha_1 = \alpha_2 = 0.9$; $I_{c01} = I_{c02} = 0.1$ ma; $R_4 = 5.0$ kΩ; $R_1 = 1.0$ kΩ; $R_l = 100$ ohms; desired operating points: $V_{c1} = 2.0$ volts, $V_{c2} = 50.0$ volts, $I_{c2} = 10.0$ ma.

From [6.54], $R_3 = 2.0$ kΩ. From [6.55], $E_1 = 18.0$ volts. From [6.56], $E_2 = 64.0$ volts. From [6.57],

$$I_{c2} = 0.528 E_1 + 1.06 I_{c01} + 3.64 I_{c02}$$

$$= 9.53 \quad + 0.11 \quad + 0.36 = 10.00 \text{ ma}$$

From [6.58],

$$V_{c1} = 0.117 E_1 - 1.76 I_{c01} + 0.588 I_{c02}$$

$$= 2.12 \quad - 0.18 \quad + 0.06 = 2.00 \text{ volts}$$

A variation of the circuit of Fig. 6.13 for grounded-base operation of the second transistor is shown in Fig. 6.14. Now,

$$R_3 = \frac{\alpha_2 V_{c1}}{(I_{c2} - I_{c02})(1 - \alpha_1) - \alpha_2 I_{c01}} \qquad [6.59]$$

$$E_1 = V_{c1} + \frac{(I_{c2} - I_{c02})}{\alpha_2}(R_1 + R_5) \qquad [6.60]$$

$$E_2 = E_1 + V_{c2} + R_l I_{c2} \qquad [6.61]$$

$$I_{c2} = \frac{\alpha_2 E_1}{R_1 + R_3(1 - \alpha_1) + R_5} + \frac{\alpha_2 R_3 I_{c01}}{R_1 + R_3(1 - \alpha_1) + R_5}$$
$$+ I_{c02} \qquad [6.62]$$

$$V_{c1} = \frac{R_3(1 - \alpha_1)E_1}{R_1 + R_3(1 - \alpha_1) + R_5} - \frac{R_3(R_1 + R_5)I_{c01}}{R_1 + R_3(1 - \alpha_1) + R_5} \qquad [6.63]$$

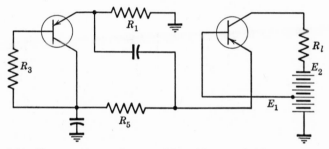

Fig. 6.14   Degenerative tandem amplifier with grounded-base second stage.

Note that all equations are the same as previously with substitution of $(R_1 + R_5)$ for R_1 and setting $R_4 = 0$. Also note that E_1 will be larger than before, but, in compensation, variations in I_{c02} have little effect on I_{c2} and none on V_{c1}. This method, therefore, is most promising for stabilization.

6.12   Transformer-Coupled Tandem-Stabilized Amplifiers

The above variations are particularly adaptable to transformer-coupled tandem amplifiers where R_1, R_3, R_4, and R_5 may represent the d-c resistances of the various transformer windings. Figures 6.15, 6.16, and 6.17 illustrate some configurations utilizing impedance-matching transformers in various portions of the circuit. In Fig. 6.15, transformers are used to couple into the first transistor and out of the second; in Fig. 6.16 a third transformer is used between the two transistors. In both these circuits the first transistor is grounded-collector for a-c signals, the second being grounded-emitter in the first circuit, grounded-base in the second. In Fig. 6.17 the first transistor is

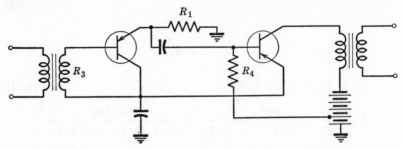

Fig. 6.15 Transformer-coupled input and output connections.

grounded-emitter, transformer-coupled to the second, which is grounded-base. Other combinations are possible, as long as the series connection of first collector to second emitter is maintained for direct current. It

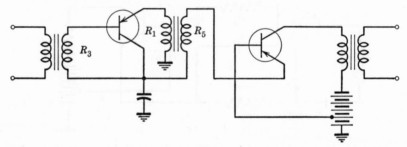

Fig. 6.16 Transformer coupling between stages, grounded-collector, grounded-base combination.

should be borne in mind that the d-c resistances of all windings may not satisfy the above relationships and it may be necessary to add external resistance and possibly bypass it to avoid degeneration.

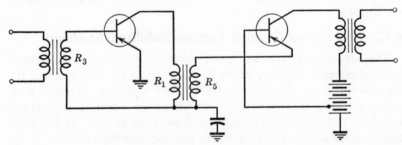

Fig. 6.17 Grounded-emitter, grounded-base transformer-coupled tandem combination.

6.13   Incremental Method of Analysis

At the beginning of this chapter three conditions were stipulated, namely, that the collector current be independent of collector voltage, the current amplification remain constant, and the effective emitter voltage be zero. Although these conditions are approximated in practice, very often such assumptions are not valid. The following method of analysis permits proper evaluation of the effects of variations from

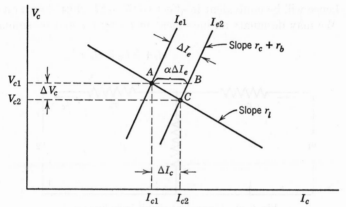

Fig. 6.18   Expanded portion of V_c-I_c characteristics.

the above conditions. It also provides a handy tool for calculation of cascaded effects in d-c amplifiers. It should be remembered, however, that the method described above is adequate and necessary for determination of operating points.

Refer now to Fig. 6.18, which shows an expanded view of a portion of a static V_c-I_c family.

The initial operating point is indicated as point A, with V_{c1}, I_{e1}, and I_{c1} as initial values. Owing to a change of emitter current, ΔI_e, the operating point would shift to B, were it not for the slopes of the V_c-I_c characteristic and the load line. The operating point thus shifts to point C. From eqs. 3.6 and 3.14 we have the slope of the V_c-I_c characteristic given as $r_c + r_b$.

Solving the above-illustrated relationship, we obtain for the net change in collector current:

$$\Delta I_c = \alpha \Delta I_e - \Delta I_c r_l / (r_c + r_b)$$

whence

$$\Delta I_c = \frac{\alpha \Delta I_e (r_c + r_b)}{r_c + r_b + r_l}$$

Now, designating ΔI_c by i_c and ΔI_e by i_e,

$$i_c = \frac{\alpha i_e(r_c + r_b)}{r_c + r_b + r_l} \qquad [6.64]$$

Note that for $r_l = 0$ this reduces to $i_c = \alpha i_e$, which agrees with the definition of α as the short-circuit current amplification.

The effect of a change in I_{c0} will be to shift the V_c-I_c curves to the right, hence will be equivalent in effect to the $\alpha \Delta I_e$ shift shown on Fig. 6.18. We may designate an increment in I_{c0} by i_{c0}, and by similarity

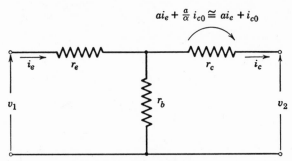

Fig. 6.19   Equivalent circuit including i_{c0}.

between its effect and that due to αi_e derive the following expression:

$$i_c = \frac{\alpha i_e(r_c + r_b)}{r_c + r_b + r_l} + \frac{i_{c0}(r_c + r_b)}{r_c + r_b + r_l} \qquad [6.65]$$

The ability to show the effect of i_{c0} as the equivalent of αi_e now permits us to utilize the equivalent circuits derived in Chapter 3 to show the effect of i_{c0}. Thus Fig. 3.5, which gives the current-generator equivalent of the grounded-base configuration, may be modified to the form shown in Fig. 6.19.

Note that in the above circuit $i_{c0}\, a/\alpha$ is taken as comparable to αi_e where i_{c0} would be comparable to αi_e.

This indicates the effect of zero-emitter collector current drift as a current generator i_{c0} in series with the original current generator αi_e.

Using the relationship $i_b = i_c - i_e$, we can solve eq. 6.65 to obtain i_c in terms of i_b and i_{c0}. This yields

$$i_c = \frac{\alpha i_b(r_c + r_b) - i_{c0}(r_c + r_b)}{(r_c + r_b)(\alpha - 1) - r_l} \qquad [6.66]$$

for $r_l = 0$ this reduces to

$$i_c = \frac{-\alpha i_b}{1 - \alpha} + \frac{i_{c0}}{1 - \alpha} \tag{6.67}$$

$$\cong -b i_b + i_{c0}(b + 1)$$

where $b = a/(1 - a) \cong \alpha/(1 - \alpha)$.

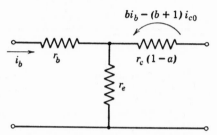

Fig. 6.20   Grounded-emitter equivalent circuit.

This permits us to use the following circuits for the grounded-emitter and grounded-collector configurations.   (See Figs. 6.20 and 6.21.)

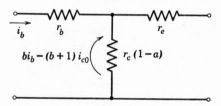

Fig. 6.21   Grounded-collector equivalent circuit.

In using these incremental values of r_e, r_b, etc., it must be remembered that they include all external resistances in addition to the internal resistances of the transistor.

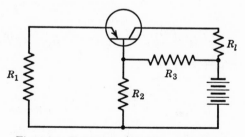

Fig. 6.22   Transistor with bias connections.

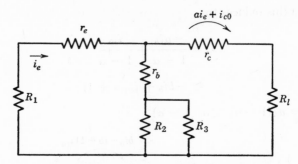

Fig. 6.23   Equivalent circuit of Fig. 6.22.

As an example of the application of this method, consider the circuit of Fig. 6.22, and its equivalent, Fig. 6.23.   For simplicity of analysis let

$$R_1' = R_1 + r_e$$

$$R_2' = r_b + R_2 R_3/(R_2 + R_3)$$

Figure 6.23 can now be redrawn as shown in Fig. 6.24.

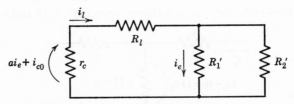

Fig. 6.24   Simplified version of Fig. 6.22

The portion of $(ai_e + i_{c0})$ flowing through R_1' is

$$i_{(R_1')} = i_e = \frac{r_c R_2'(ai_e + i_{c0})}{R_1'R_2' + (R_1' + R_2')(r_c + R_l)} \qquad [6.68]$$

Solving eq. 6.68 for i_e,

$$i_e = \frac{r_c R_2' i_{c0}}{R_1'R_2' + (R_1' + R_2')(r_c + R_l) - a r_c R_2'} \qquad [6.69]$$

Solving for i_l ($= i_e + i_e R_1'/R_2'$),

$$i_l = i_c = \frac{r_c(R_1' + R_2')i_{c0}}{R_1'R_2' + (R_1' + R_2')(r_c + R_l) - a r_c R_2'} \qquad [6.70]$$

Using the letter S, as before, to designate $\partial I_c/\partial I_{c0}$ (or i_c/i_{c0}) we now have a rigorous expression:

$$S = \cfrac{r_c[R_1 + r_e + r_b + R_2R_3/(R_2 + R_3)]}{\left[\begin{array}{c}(R_1 + r_e)\left(r_b + \dfrac{R_2R_3}{R_2 + R_3}\right) + \\[2mm] \left(r_e + r_b + R_1 + \dfrac{R_2R_3}{R_2 + R_3}\right)(r_c + R_l) - ar_c\left(r_b + \dfrac{R_2R_3}{R_2 + R_3}\right)\end{array}\right]}$$

$$[6.71]$$

It is interesting to note that, if we neglect r_b, r_e, and R_l, and consider r_c infinite, eq. 6.71 reduces to

$$S = \frac{1 + R_1/R_2 + R_1/R_3}{1 - a + R_1/R_2 + R_1/R_3}$$

which is identical with eq. 6.22 (using a for α).

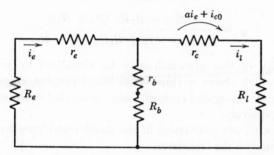

Fig. 6.25 Complete equivalent circuit, grounded-base configuration.

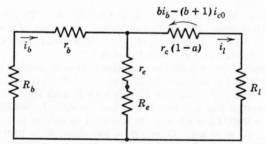

Fig. 6.26 Complete equivalent circuit, grounded-emitter configuration.

We can now redraw Figs. 6.19, 6.20, and 6.21 as shown in Figs. 6.25, 6.26, and 6.27, respectively.

In Figs. 6.25 and 6.26 we have the incremental load current i_l, due to an incremental i_{c0}, as follows:

$$i_l = Si_{c0}$$

where S has the value given in eq. 6.71.

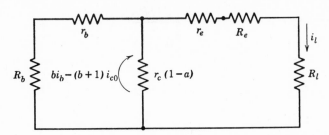

Fig. 6.27   Complete equivalent circuit, grounded-collector configuration.

In Fig. 6.27 we have $i_l = i_e = S'i_{c0}$, where S' is now derived from eq. 6.69 and is

$$S' = -SR_2'/(R_1' + R_2') \qquad [6.72]$$

$$= \frac{-S[r_b + R_2R_3/(R_2 + R_3)]}{R_1 + r_e + r_b + R_2R_3/(R_2 + R_3)}$$

The utility of this approach may be visualized by reference to Fig. 6.28, which shows a three-stage direct-coupled amplifier using grounded-base, grounded-emitter, and grounded-collector configurations, respectively.

R_{e1}, R_{b1}, etc., are resistances in the emitter and base leads respectively, external to the transistor.

6.14   Problems

1. In the circuit of Fig. 6.1, given: $E_1 = 1.5$ volts, $E_2 = 20$ volts, $R_l = 1000$ ohms, $R_2 = 10,000$ ohms. It is desired to operate a transistor of $\alpha = 0.95$, $I_{c0} = 0.05$ ma, at $I_c = 2.0$ ma. Find V_c, S, R_1, $P_{\text{d-c}}$. How does I_c vary with I_{c0}? with E_1? How does V_c vary with E_2? with E_1? with I_{c0}?

2. In the circuit of Fig. 6.2, for the same transistor as in problem 1, and for the same operating V_c and I_c and same R_1, R_l, and S, find E, R_2, R_3, $P_{\text{d-c}}$. How does I_c vary with I_{c0}? with E? How does V_c vary with E? with I_{c0}?

3. In the circuit of Fig. 6.5, transistor 1 has $\alpha = 0.95$, $I_{c0} = 0.05$ ma. Transistor 2 has $\alpha = 0.80$, $I_{c0} = 0.1$ ma. It is desired to operate at $V_{c1} = 1.0$ volt, $V_{c2} = 20$ volts, $I_{c2} = 10$ ma. Given: $R_l = 100$ ohms, $R_1 = 1000$ ohms, $R_4 = 10,000$ ohms. Find E_1, E_2, R_2, R_3, S, and $P_{\text{d-c}}$. How does I_{c2} vary with I_{c01}, I_{c02}, E_1, and E_2? How does V_{c1} vary with I_{c01}, I_{c02}, E_1, and E_2?

4. In problem 3, if the two transistors are interchanged, what readjustments must be made to restore the original operating points? Which arrangement is most stable?

5. Draw the circuit of a degenerative tandem-stabilized amplifier with transformer-coupled input into a grounded-base first stage, which, in turn, is transformer-coupled to a grounded-base second stage, which has transformer-coupled output.

6. Solve for i_l in Fig. 6.28.

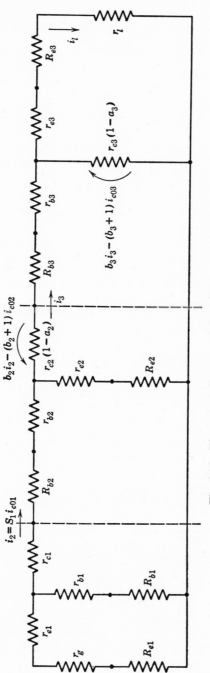

Fig. 6.28   Three-stage direct-coupled amplifier equivalent circuit.

Chapter 7

Power Amplifiers

7.1 Introduction

In the field of portable electronic equipment the transistor has many advantages over the vacuum tube. Extremely rugged, with a life expectancy many times that of its predecessor, the vacuum tube, this device has the further important advantage of requiring no heater power. As an example to illustrate the savings in power obtained by the use of transistors, consider a typical present-day portable radio output stage. Such a stage requires about 450 milliwatts of plate power and 150 milliwatts of filament power. The mere replacement of vacuum tubes by transistors would result in a saving of about $33\frac{1}{3}$ per cent of this battery power by elimination of the filament supply. Further savings also result since the collector efficiency of transistors is well in excess of the plate efficiency obtained with vacuum tubes.

The purpose of this chapter is to discuss the design and performance of audio amplifiers using transistors. Emphasis will be on the output stage, since its high operating level brings with it the attendant problems of heat dissipation, peak inverse voltage, and distortion. These problems are for the main part either absent or unimportant in low-level stages. The performance of these low-level stages has been fully discussed in Chapters 4 and 5.

The choice between junction transistors and point-contact transistors is an easy one to make. The permissible collector dissipation of point-contact transistors is limited to about 50 milliwatts, and this, coupled with the lack of linearity of their collector characteristics, is enough to make us decide on junction transistors for the output stage. There is not much basis for choice between *p-n-p* and *n-p-n* types, as their behaviors are very similar. To avoid possible confusion, we will consider the use of *p-n-p* types exclusively, except where another type is specifically mentioned.

132

7.2 Methods of Operation

Consider a single-ended transistor stage as shown in Fig. 7.1. Let

i_1 be the input current due to the signal
I_1 be the input bias current

Let the input current be sinusoidal, of value

$$i_1 = \hat{\imath}_1 \sin \omega t \qquad\qquad [7.1]$$

Then the instantaneous current in the input circuit is

$$I_1 + \hat{\imath}_1 \sin \omega t$$

Now the input of the transistor in any configuration includes the emitter-to-base diode. It is possible to drive the input circuit in such a

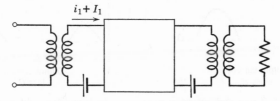

Fig. 7.1   Single-ended amplifier stage.

manner that this diode is either conducting over the entire cycle or non-conducting over a part of the cycle.

When the input signal is sinusoidal and of such an amplitude compared to the bias current that the transistor is conducting over the entire cycle, the transistor is said to be operating class A. In this mode of operation, the output current waveform is ideally a replica of the input wave, and is a complete sinusoid (excluding the effects of distortion).

When the input signal is such that the emitter-to-base diode is cut off over exactly one-half of the cycle, the transistor is said to be operating class B. Under this condition, the output waveform is again a replica of the input wave but now consists of a series of half-sinusoids. Intermediate between class A and class B are various forms of operation designated by the symbol AB with a subscript such as AB_1 or AB_2 to indicate the extent of the cut-off region.

Class C operation is said to occur when the transistor is so biased that it is non-conducting over more than one-half cycle. Figure 7.2 shows typical waveforms for input and output current in the circuit of Fig. 7.1.

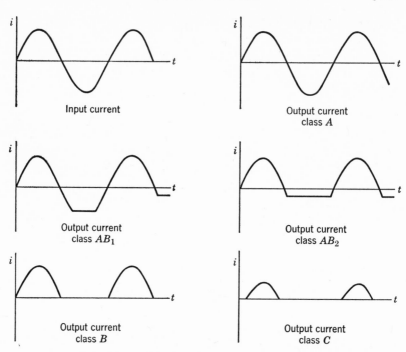

Fig. 7.2 Input and output currents in a single-ended amplifier stage.

Since the entire waveform is transferred to the output circuit in class A operation, this form of operation is possible either using one transistor "single ended," or two transistors in push-pull, as in Fig. 7.3. For class B operation, it is essential to use the push-pull connection where one transistor operates during the positive half of the cycle and a second

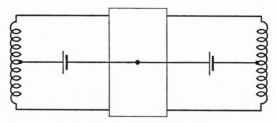

Fig. 7.3 Push-pull amplifier stage.

transistor operates during the negative half. This is true for operation in class AB also. Class C operation introduces much distortion inherently and can be definitely rejected for audio amplifiers.

7.3   Choice of Circuit Configuration

Equations for power gain of a transistor have been derived in Chapter 4. In the approximate form these equations may be summarized as follows.   Power gain for grounded-base:grounded-emitter:grounded-collector as

$$aA_v : \frac{aA_v}{1-a} : \frac{1}{1-a} \qquad [7.2]$$

where A_v is the voltage amplification. This comparison is true for class A operation, since this form of operation is essentially the same as that

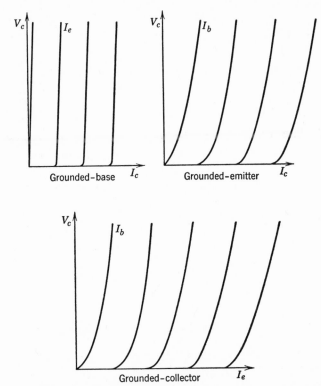

Fig. 7.4   Output characteristics for the different transistor configurations.

used in driving low-level stages. The comparison for class B operation is more simply made by a graphical analysis.

Figure 7.4 shows the output characteristics for a typical transistor in each of its configurations. From this figure we see that the characteristics for grounded-base are extremely linear and evenly spaced, and have a very small sharp knee at their break point. On the other hand, characteristics for the grounded-emitter and grounded-collector circuits show considerable non-linearity and unevenness, and also a large, well-rounded knee at the break point.

Class A operation is generally used when extremely low distortion is required. Power gain is thus of secondary importance, and our choice is dictated by linearity considerations. With these considerations in mind, the grounded-base circuit is considerably superior for class A operation. For higher power outputs and higher efficiencies we must go to the class B form of operation with its attendant higher distortion. In the succeeding sections the grounded-base circuit is the only circuit considered for class A operation. All configurations must be studied, however, in the discussion of class B operation. The performance in class AB operation falls somewhere between class A and B; it will serve no real purpose to make any attempts to analyze this type of operation here.

7.4 Class A Amplifiers

7.4.1 Input Circuit Distortion

The parameters of the present-day transistor are, in general, invariant with frequency over the audio-frequency range. The input impedance is therefore resistive in character, and, for a grounded-base transistor, is shown to be given by

$$r_i = r_e + r_b \cdot \frac{r_l + r_c(1 - a)}{r_l + r_b + r_c} \qquad [7.3]$$

For output stages where

$$r_c \gg r_b \qquad r_c(1 - a) \gg r_l \qquad [7.4]$$

$$r_i \cong r_e + r_b(1 - a) \qquad [7.5]$$

A study of the variation of parameters indicates that, whereas a is reasonably independent of I_e within the limits of operation, both r_e and r_b vary approximately inversely with I_e. Hence, a very close approximation for the curve of input resistance as a function of emitter current is a rectangular hyperbola. A typical experimental curve of this relationship is given as Fig. 7.5. This figure shows the input resistance for a short-circuited output as well as for a 10-kilohm load. Both curves follow a rectangular hyperbola very closely. The curves also show that this resistance is reasonably independent of the output load. The hyperbola is shown for comparison by means of a dashed line. If E_e and

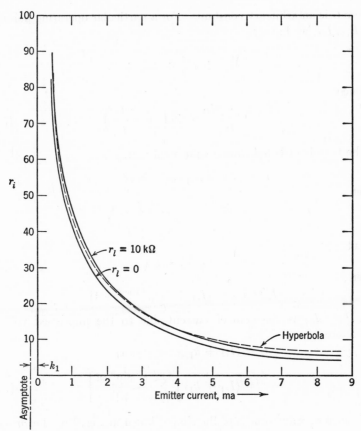

Fig. 7.5 Input resistance as a function of emitter current for a load resistance of 10,000 ohms and for a short-circuited load.

I_e are the d-c values of emitter voltage and current, then the input resistance measured on a small-signal basis, defined as

$$r_i = \frac{dE_e}{dI_e} \qquad [7.6]$$

is related to I_e by the equation

$$\frac{dE_e}{dI_e} = \frac{k_2}{k_1 + I_e} \qquad [7.7]$$

where k_1, k_2 are constants. Then, solving the equation, we have

$$\frac{E_e}{k_2} = \ln (k_1 + I_e) + C \qquad [7.8]$$

where C is an arbitrary constant. For a particular operating point set by E_{e1}, I_{e1}, we have

$$\frac{E_{e1}}{k_2} = \ln (k_1 + I_{e1}) + C \qquad [7.9]$$

whence

$$\frac{E_e - E_{e1}}{k_2} = \ln \left(\frac{k_1 + I_e}{k_1 + I_{e1}} \right) \qquad [7.10]$$

If the transistor is fed from a sinusoidal voltage,

$$E_e - E_{e1} = \hat{v}_i \sin \omega t$$

Then

$$\frac{v_i \sin \omega t}{k_2} = \ln \left(\frac{k_1 + I_e}{k_1 + I_{e1}} \right)$$

Let

$$\hat{v}_i/k_2 = k \qquad [7.11]$$

Then

$$I_e - I_{e1} = (I_{e1} + k_1)[e^{k \sin \omega t} - 1]$$

But $I_e - I_{e1}$ is the emitter current due to the impressed voltage. Therefore

$$i_i = (I_{e1} + k_1)[e^{k \sin \omega t} - 1]$$

$$= (I_{e1} + k_1) \left[\sum_{n=1}^{n=\infty} \frac{k^n \sin^n \omega t}{n!} \right] \qquad [7.12]$$

This current waveform is of the shape shown in Fig. 7.6. Let us consider the effect of inserting a fixed resistance r in series with the emitter.

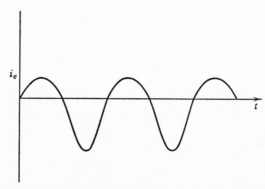

Fig. 7.6 Emitter current in a class A output stage driven from a zero-impedance sinusoidal voltage generator.

In this case

$$dE_e/dI_e = r + k_2/(k_1 + I_e) \qquad [7.13]$$

Then

$$E_e = rI_e + k_2 \ln (k_1 + I_e) + C \qquad [7.14]$$

Using the same conditions as before, we have

$$k \sin \omega t - ri_i/k_2 = \ln [(k_1 + I_e)/(k_1 + I_{e1})] \qquad [7.15]$$

whence

$$e^{k \sin \omega t - ri_i/k_2} - 1 = i_i/(k_1 + I_{e1}) \qquad [7.16]$$

This equation may be solved in series form, to obtain i_i. The resulting expression is very unwieldy; the effect of r is best studied by a graphical representation of the result. This is shown in Fig. 7.7. We see that the

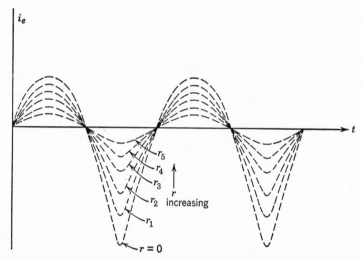

Fig. 7.7   Effect of increasing the source resistance on the emitter current waveform.

insertion of a resistance in series with the emitter results in considerable improvement of the emitter current waveform. If the transistor is fed from a high-impedance source such as another transistor, this condition is already met.

If the driver is transformer-coupled to the output stage it is advisable to mismatch at this point so that the source presents a reasonably high impedance. Typical experimental results are shown in Fig. 7.8 for the emitter current of a transistor as a function of the source impedance. The effect of a resistance in the emitter circuit is a decrease in the overall

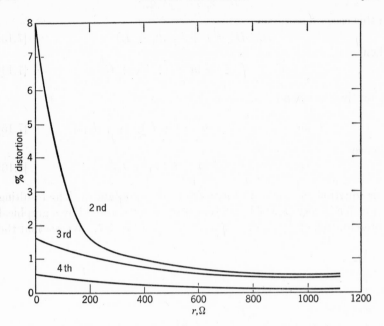

Fig. 7.8   Curve showing input circuit distortion as a function of source impedance.

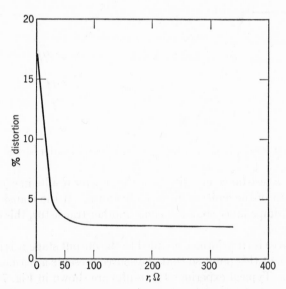

Fig. 7.9   Curve showing total distortion in the output as a function of source impedance

power gain from the value obtained when the driver is matched to the input. This is, however, of secondary importance in class A amplifiers. Figure 7.9 shows an experimentally obtained curve of output distortion for a transistor amplifier with different values of source impedance, for constant power output. This curve shows the increase in distortion caused by the reduction of r. This increase is due to distortion in the input side, since output conditions were maintained constant.

7.4.2 Output Circuit Distortion

A study of the collector characteristics of the grounded-base junction transistor indicates that, except for very large values of collector cur-

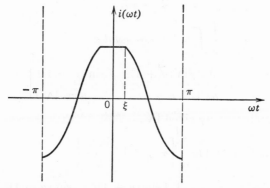

Fig. 7.10   Sinusoidal current wave with hard clipping on one side.

rent, the curves are linear and evenly spaced. Even if these characteristics are plotted after the transistor has reached its operating temperature, they exhibit only very slight curvature. Consequently it is possible to predict that output distortion for small signals will be very low in class A amplifiers. If the signal swing is large, it is possible to overdrive the transistor. Under this condition, clipping will occur at one or both ends of the swing. If clipping is the result of conduction in the collector diode due to reversal of current in the collector circuit, the clipping is extremely sharp and is termed hard clipping. If clipping is due to cut-off at the knee of the collector curve, i.e., due to operation in the high-current region, the crowding of the collector family in this region will result in a slightly rounded, or soft, clipping. Let us analyze the effects of hard clipping on the output current waveform. See Fig. 7.10. Let the current waveform be

$$i_o = \hat{i}_o \cos \omega t \qquad [7.17]$$

and let it be clipped over the region where $-\xi \leq t \leq \xi$. Let

$$i(\omega t) = i_o/\hat{\imath}_o \qquad [7.18]$$

Then

$$i(\omega t) = \cos \omega t \qquad -\pi \leq t \leq -\xi$$

$$i(\omega t) = \cos \xi \qquad -\xi \leq t \leq \xi \qquad [7.19]$$

$$i(\omega t) = \cos \omega t \qquad \xi \leq t \leq \pi$$

The harmonic analysis will only contain cosine terms if the origin is taken as shown. Then

$$i(\omega t) = \frac{a_0}{2} + \sum_{n=1}^{n=\infty} a_n \cos n\omega t \qquad [7.20]$$

where

$$a_n = \frac{1}{\pi} \int_{-\pi}^{\pi} i(\omega t) \cos n\omega t \, d\omega t \qquad [7.21]$$

$$= \frac{1}{n\pi} \left[\frac{\sin (n+1)\xi}{n+1} - \frac{\sin (n-1)\xi}{n-1} \right] \qquad [7.22]$$

Then the amplitudes are given by

$$\text{Fundamental} = \frac{1}{\pi} \left[\pi - \xi + \frac{\sin 2\xi}{2} \right] \qquad [7.23]$$

$$n\text{th harmonic} = \frac{1}{n\pi} \left[\frac{\sin (n+1)\xi}{n+1} - \frac{\sin (n-1)\xi}{n-1} \right] \qquad [7.24]$$

Consider a numerical case where $\xi = 20°$; we have

2nd harmonic   0.86%

3rd harmonic   0.805%

4th harmonic   0.735%

and so on. Thus we see that the distortion due to hard clipping is such that the magnitudes of the harmonics fall off very slowly as their order increases. In practice, no clipping is as hard as that mathematically indicated here, and the slightest softening in this clipping will result in decreasing the higher-order harmonics considerably.

When clipping occurs by the same amount on both sides of the output current wave, the resultant harmonic analysis shows that the even harmonics are eliminated and the odd harmonics doubled in magnitude. In practice, owing to the difference in degree of hardness of clipping at the two extremes of the current swing, some third harmonic will still remain. Though it would then be considered best to set the operating point so that the clipping is exactly the same at both extremes, such a circuit is extremely critical in its adjustment, especially if it is to operate with replaceable transistors.

Typical experimental results for a transistor operating with 0.1-watt output at a collector efficiency of 49% are

2nd harmonic	2.1%	5th harmonic	0.6%
3rd harmonic	2.0%	6th harmonic	0.1%
4th harmonic	0.34%	7th harmonic	0.1%

This serves to show that the predictions of the analysis are reasonable. Figure 7.11 shows a curve for the overall distortion of the transistor as

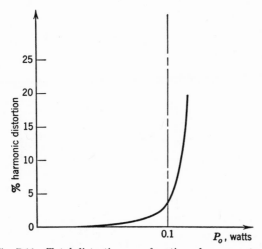

Fig. 7.11   Total distortion as a function of power output.

a function of the power output. It is seen that the overall distortion is low until clipping occurs. At this point, distortion increases very rapidly. The curve was taken with the transistor driven from a constant-current source. As such, it is representative of distortion in the output circuit of the transistor.

7.4.3   Static Characteristic Analysis of Class A Operation

Figure 7.12 shows the collector characteristics for a typical transistor. On this curve, in dotted line, is also shown the curve for maximum collector power dissipation. This curve is a rectangular hyperbola; any choice of operating point above it is not permissible. If the transistor is to be operated at this value of collector dissipation, the operating point must be chosen to lie on this dotted curve. This would imply that there is an infinite number of choices for the load line. This is not so, however, since two more restrictions must be made. First, the collector voltage swing is limited by the peak inverse voltage of the transistor. In the region of this peak inverse voltage, the back current of the diode increases very rapidly as the diode breaks down, and transistor action ceases. Second, the collector current is limited by the fact

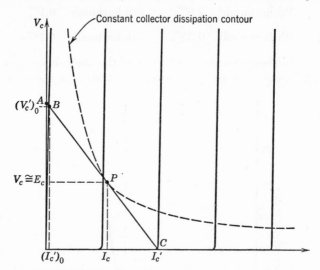

Fig. 7.12 Static characteristics for class A operation.

that, beyond a certain point, the α of the transistor begins to fall off, resulting in a crowding of the collector characteristics. Operation in this region can lead to considerable distortion.

Neglecting the effect of the back diode collector current, a load line corresponding to highest permissible load resistance may be constructed graphically as follows. Setting the point A at the permissible peak inverse voltage, draw the load line tangential to the hyperbola. This fixes the operating point as the point of tangency, and the limits of swing at $(V_c')_0$ and I_c'. If I_c' is less than the permissible peak current, this is an acceptable load line. It is to be emphasized that this is just *one* possible load line. In general, any line drawn within the limits of peak voltage and current, and tangential to the hyperbola, is a permissible load line, and the point of tangency a permissible operating point. A little adjustment will now be necessary to correct for the value of $(I_c')_0$, such that

$$I_c' - I_c = I_c - (I_c')_0 \qquad [7.25]$$

whereupon the positive and negative current swings are of equal magnitude.

$$\text{Maximum a-c power output} \quad P_o \cong \frac{[I_c - (I_c')_0]E_c}{2} \qquad [7.26]$$

$$\text{D-c battery power} \quad P_{\text{d-c}} = E_c I_c \qquad [7.27]$$

Then collector efficiency, η, is given as

$$\frac{P_o}{P_{\text{d-c}}} = \frac{E_c[I_c - (I_c')_0]}{2E_c I_c} \qquad [7.28]$$

$$= 50\left[\frac{I_c - (I_c')_0}{I_c}\right]\% \qquad [7.29]$$

If

$$(I_c')_0 \ll I_c, \qquad \eta \cong 50\% \qquad [7.30]$$

Thus the maximum possible efficiency of a transistor operating in class A depends on the peak value of the back diode current. For transistors where this current is very small, efficiencies as high as 49 per cent are easily attained with low distortion.

The computations for power gain have been given in Chapter 4, and they may be used for class A output stages since the resistance in the input circuit (inclusive of the resistance r) is approximately linear.

7.4.4 Taylor Series Analysis of Class A Operation

It is possible, by means of a theoretical analysis of the transistor characteristics, to obtain some idea of the magnitude of the distortion in the output circuit. Consider the transistor circuit of Fig. 7.13. Let

$$V_e(t) = E_{e1} + v_e(t) \qquad [7.31]$$

$$V_c(t) = E_{c1} + v_c(t) \qquad [7.32]$$

$$I_e(t) = I_{e1} + i_e(t) \qquad [7.33]$$

$$I_c(t) = I_{c1} + i_c(t) \qquad [7.34]$$

where E_{e1}, I_{e1}, E_{c1}, and I_{c1} are the voltages and currents associated with the emitter and collector power supplies respectively, and $v_e(t)$, $i_e(t)$, $v_c(t)$, and $i_c(t)$ are the signal voltage and current in the emitter and collector circuits respectively. Then

$$I_c(t) = f[V_c(t), I_e(t)] \qquad [7.35]$$

and

$$I_e(t) = f[V_e(t), I_c(t)] \qquad [7.36]$$

These expressions may be expanded in a Taylor series. Since the fourth and higher harmonics are small in comparison to the second and third harmonics, we may safely neglect terms of the fourth and higher orders. Though terms of the third order cannot be neglected, they contribute to only the fundamental and the third harmonic. Thus only a small error will result in the second harmonic if terms of the third order are also

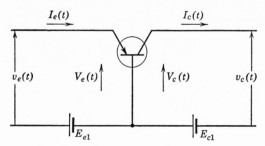

Fig. 7.13   Grounded-base output stage.

neglected, since the small contribution of the third-order term to the fundamental is neglected. Then

$$I_c(t) = I_{c1} + i_c(t) = f[E_{c1} + v_c(t); I_{e1} + i_e(t)] \qquad [7.37]$$

Expanding about the operating point determined by E_{c1}, I_{e1},

$$I_{c1} + i_c(t) = f[V_c(t), I_e(t)]_{E_{c1},I_{e1}} + v_c(t)\left[\frac{\partial I_c(t)}{\partial V_c(t)}\right]_{E_{c1},I_{e1}}$$

$$+ i_e(t)\left[\frac{\partial I_c(t)}{\partial I_e(t)}\right]_{E_{c1},I_{e1}} + \frac{[v_c(t)]^2}{2}\left\{\frac{\partial^2 I_c(t)}{[\partial V_c(t)]^2}\right\}_{E_{c1},I_{e1}}$$

$$+ \frac{[i_e(t)]^2}{2}\left\{\frac{\partial^2 I_c(t)}{\partial[I_e(t)]^2}\right\}_{E_{c1},I_{e1}} + v_c(t)i_e(t)\left[\frac{\partial^2 I_c(t)}{\partial V_c(t)\,\partial I_e(t)}\right]_{E_{c1},I_{e1}} \qquad [7.38]$$

Therefore

$$i_c(t) = v_c(t)\left[\frac{\partial I_c(t)}{\partial V_c(t)}\right]_{E_{c1},I_{e1}} + i_e(t)\left[\frac{\partial I_c(t)}{\partial I_e(t)}\right]_{E_{c1},I_{e1}}$$

$$+ \frac{[v_c(t)]^2}{2}\left\{\frac{\partial^2 I_c(t)}{\partial[V_c(t)]^2}\right\}_{E_{c1},I_{e1}} + \frac{i_e(t)^2}{2}\left\{\frac{\partial^2 I_c(t)}{\partial[I_e(t)]^2}\right\}_{E_{c1},I_{e1}}$$

$$+ v_c(t)i_e(t)\left[\frac{\partial^2 I_c(t)}{\partial V_c(t)\,\partial I_e(t)}\right]_{E_{c1},I_{e1}} \qquad [7.39]$$

In like manner, expanding $I_e(t)$ about E_{e1}, I_{c1}, we obtain

$$i_e(t) = v_e(t)\left[\frac{\partial I_e(t)}{\partial V_e(t)}\right]_{E_{e1},I_{c1}} + i_c(t)\left[\frac{\partial I_e(t)}{\partial I_c(t)}\right]_{E_{e1},I_{c1}}$$

$$+ \frac{[v_e(t)]^2}{2}\left\{\frac{\partial^2 I_e(t)}{\partial[V_e(t)]^2}\right\}_{E_{e1},I_{c1}} + \frac{i_c(t)^2}{2\cdot}\left\{\frac{\partial^2 I_e(t)}{\partial[I_c(t)]^2}\right\}_{E_{e1},I_{c1}}$$

$$+ v_e(t)i_c(t)\left[\frac{\partial^2 I_e(t)}{\partial V_e(t)\,\partial I_c(t)}\right]_{E_{e1},I_{c1}} \qquad [7.40]$$

Now

$$\left[\frac{\partial I_c(t)}{\partial V_c(t)}\right]_{E_{c1},I_{e1}} \cong \frac{1}{r_c} = g_c \qquad [7.41]$$

as determined at the operating point.

$$\left(\frac{\partial I_c}{\partial I_e}\right)_{E_{c1},I_{e1}} = \alpha \cong a \qquad [7.42]$$

as determined at the operating point. Furthermore, a is invariant with changes in operating voltage and current, to a close approximation, whence

$$i_c(t) = v_c(t)g_c + ai_e(t) + \frac{[v_c(t)]^2}{2}\left[\frac{\partial g_c}{\partial V_c(t)}\right]_{E_{c1},I_{e1}} \qquad [7.43]$$

and

$$i_e(t) = v_e(t)g_e + \frac{1}{a}\cdot i_c(t) + \frac{[v_e(t)]^2}{2}\left[\frac{\partial g_e}{\partial V_e(t)}\right]_{E_{c1},I_{c1}} \qquad [7.44]$$

If the load impedance is r_l,

$$v_c(t) = i_c(t)r_l \qquad [7.45]$$

and

$$i_c(t) = i_c(t)r_l g_c + ai_e(t) + \frac{[i_c(t)]^2}{2}r_l^2\left[\frac{\partial g_c}{\partial V_c(t)}\right]_{E_{c1},I_{e1}} \qquad [7.46]$$

The solution of this equation yields $i_c(t)$ as a function of $i_e(t)$. If the transistor is fed from a high resistance source the emitter current is sinusoidal, and thus the second harmonic in $i_c(t)$ may be computed as equal, approximately, to

$$\frac{ar_l^2}{2(r_l g_c - 1)^2}\left(\frac{\partial g_c}{\partial V_c(t)}\right)_{E_{c1},I_{e1}} \times 100\% \qquad [7.47]$$

Equation 7.44 may be used in conjunction with equation 7.46 to compute the value of the second harmonic for source resistances other than zero. The solution is best obtained for specific cases by the inclusion of numerical values.

7.4.5   Class A Operation in Push-Pull

The analysis for push-pull class A operation will be discussed very briefly, since the results of such an analysis may be directly obtained from the analysis for single-ended class A amplifiers.

The main advantage of using push-pull operation for class A amplifiers is that a cancellation is effected for the even-order harmonics. This cancellation occurs only if there is an equal amount of phase shift in the transistors, at all frequencies. The easiest way to meet this condition is for both transistors to have *no* phase shift over the frequency range in question. However, it should be remembered that the phase shift in the α of a transistor is over 6° at frequencies as low as one-tenth the α cut-off frequency.

7.5   Class B Amplifiers

The permissible power dissipation of available junction transistors is relatively low; this makes the use of class B operation, with its inherent high efficiency, an extremely attractive proposition. As explained earlier, class B operation implies biasing the transistor so that it is cut off over either the positive or the negative part of the cycle. Under this condition, the current swing on the load line of the output circuit occurs for only one-half of the cycle. The operating point may thus be set at either end of the load line, at points of low power dissipation. Thus one may (*a*) operate at low output current and high output voltage, or (*b*) operate at high output current and low output voltage.

In general, the second method is not used for two reasons: first, under no-signal conditions, high current operation gives rise to considerable reduction in α; and, second, to obtain a low collector voltage at zero signal implies a power loss in a dropping resistance connected to the bias source, with consequent low standby efficiency.

When comparing class B operation of vacuum tubes to class B operation of transistors, some major points of difference arise. The vacuum tube is a device which ordinarily has a harmonic content that is small for the third and higher harmonics. Further, it is a device with substantially no phase shift over a frequency band that is many decades wider than the audio-frequency band. Under these conditions even-order harmonics are completely canceled in class B operation. Since they constitute the greater part of the entire harmonic content, this permits a considerable increase in power output for a given distortion. From the discussion of push-pull class A operation, it is evident that this may not occur with transistors. In class B operation, especially when grounded-emitter and grounded-collector configurations are considered, with their effective cut-off frequencies lowered by the factor $1/(1 - a)$, push-pull operation usually does not lead to a complete cancellation of even-order harmonics.

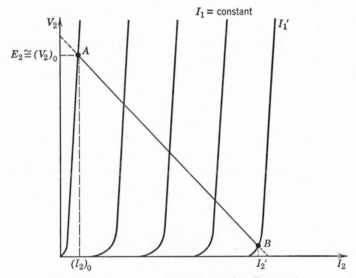

Fig. 7.14   Output characteristics for class B operation.

7.5.1   Static Characteristic Analysis of Class B Operation

In discussing the three configurations, it is advantageous to use a general circuit and later to supply it with various interpretations. Let the subscript 2 denote the output circuit, and the subscript 1 the input circuit, and let the output circuit battery voltage be designated by E_2.

Figure 7.14 shows a set of output characteristics for a transistor. The lines are drawn for constant I_1, and the load line, designated by AB, covers that part of the operating region where the characteristics are reasonably linear and evenly spaced. The operating point may now be set at A or at B. We choose the point A, however, since under this condition the standby current drain of the supply is at a minimum, designated by $(I_2)_0$.

Two major considerations limit the maximum power output: the permissible peak inverse voltage, and the permissible average power dissipation. With transformer coupling, the peak inverse voltage applied to each transistor is twice the value of $(V_2)_0$.

Since $(V_2)_0 \cong E_2$, this sets the value for the maximum supply voltage. In computing the power dissipation the input circuit dissipation is neglected, as it is usually considerably less than the output circuit dissipation. With the operating point set at A,

Zero signal output circuit dissipation per transistor $\cong (V_2)_0(I_2)_0$ [7.48]

$$\cong E_2(I_2)_0 \qquad [7.49]$$

Under maximum signal conditions, the signal in the output consists of a series of half sinusoids of peak value $[I_2' - (I_2)_0]$. This results in an average direct current of $(1/\pi)[I_2' - (I_2)_0]$. Then the increase in supply current per transistor due to the signal is

$$\frac{1}{\pi}[I_2' - (I_2)_0] \qquad [7.50]$$

Therefore, the supply power per transistor for maximum signal

$$\cong \frac{E_2}{\pi}[I_2' - (I_2)_0] + E_2(I_2)_0$$

$$\cong \frac{E_2}{\pi}[I_2' + (I_2)_0(\pi - 1)] \qquad [7.51]$$

A-c power contribution per transistor

$$\cong \frac{E_2[I_2' - (I_2)_0]}{4} \qquad [7.52]$$

Whence output circuit efficiency

$$\eta = 78\left[\frac{I_2' - (I_2)_0}{I_2' + (I_2)_0(\pi - 1)}\right]\% \qquad [7.53]$$

If $(I_2)_0$ is negligible compared to I_2',

$$\eta \cong 78\% \qquad [7.54]$$

The maximum signal collector dissipation per transistor is the difference between the supply power and the output power. Whence

$$P_D \cong (E_2/\pi)[I_2' + (I_2)_0(\pi - 1)] - (E_2/4)[I_2' - (I_2)_0]$$

$$\cong 0.068E_2I_2' + 0.932E_2(I_2)_0 \qquad [7.55]$$

The effect of the second term can be quite appreciable when the transistor is operated at low current and high voltage. The value of the load resistance may now be computed

$$r_l \cong E_2/I_2' \qquad [7.56]$$

From eq. 7.55

$$I_2' = \frac{P_D - 0.932E_2(I_2)_0}{0.068E_2} \qquad [7.57]$$

Whence

$$r_l/\text{transistor} = \frac{0.068E_2{}^2}{P_D - 0.932E_2(I_2)_0} \qquad [7.58]$$

To obtain the total primary impedance of the output transformer for push-pull operation, this value of r_l must be multiplied by 4. For a typical transistor with a peak inverse voltage of 100, and a power dissipation of 0.5 watt, the load resistance is about 350 ohms per transistor. The total primary impedance of the output transformer is, therefore, about 1400 ohms. The input resistance and power gain of the transistor may now be computed. Since we may not know whether this input resistance is non-linear or linear, the following analysis will be confined to computing the peak value of the input resistance and the peak value of the power gain. This forms a satisfactory basis for comparison of the configurations and is of special value since a large number of laboratory-type a-c voltmeters are peak-reading instruments. Let

$$\text{Peak input voltage} = V_1'$$

$$\text{Peak input current} = I_1'$$

Then

$$\text{Peak input resistance per transistor} = V_1'/I_1' \qquad [7.59]$$

$$\begin{aligned}\text{Secondary peak load impedance} \\ \text{of input transformer} \qquad = 4V_1'/I_1' \qquad [7.60]\end{aligned}$$

$$\text{Peak output power} \cong E_2[I_2' - (I_2)_0] \qquad [7.61]$$

$$\text{Peak input power} \cong V_1'I_1' \qquad [7.62]$$

Then

$$\text{Peak power gain} \cong \frac{E_2[I_2' - (I_2)_0]}{V_1'I_1'} \qquad [7.63]$$

If the transistor is operated such that $(I_2)_0 \ll I_2'$, the various equations are simplified considerably. The results under this condition are summarized as follows, for a pair of transistors:

$$\text{A-c power output} \cong E_2 I_2'/2 \tag{7.64}$$

$$\text{D-c supply power} \cong 2E_2 I_2'/\pi \tag{7.65}$$

$$\text{Output circuit } \eta \cong 78\% \tag{7.66}$$

$$\text{Load resistance} \cong 4E_2/I_2' \tag{7.67}$$

$$\text{Peak input resistance per transistor} \cong V_1'/I_1' \tag{7.68}$$

$$\text{Peak a-c power output} \cong E_2 I_2' \tag{7.69}$$

$$\text{Peak a-c power input} \cong V_1' I_1' \tag{7.70}$$

$$\text{Peak power gain} \cong E_2/V_1' \times I_2'/I_1' \tag{7.71}$$

It is for us now to interpret these various terms for the different transistor configurations.

7.5.2   Discussion of the Results

Figure 7.15 shows the various circuit configurations, with the values of v_1, v_2, i_1, and i_2 given in terms of the peak transistor voltages and currents as obtained from the appropriate static characteristics. Remembering that

$$I_c' \cong a I_e' \tag{7.72}$$

and

$$I_c' \cong [a/(1 - a)] \cdot I_b' \tag{7.73}$$

the performance of the three circuits may now be compared as tabulated for a push-pull pair.

	Grounded-Base	Grounded-Emitter	Grounded-Collector
A-c power output	$\dfrac{aE_c I_e'}{2}$	$\dfrac{aE_c I_e'}{2}$	$\dfrac{E_c I_e'}{2}$
D-c power	$\dfrac{2aE_c I_e'}{\pi}$	$\dfrac{2aE_c I_e'}{\pi}$	$\dfrac{2E_c I_e'}{\pi}$
$\eta, \%$	78	78	78
Load resistance	$\dfrac{4E_c}{aI_e'}$	$\dfrac{4E_c}{aI_e'}$	$\dfrac{4E_c}{I_e'}$
Peak input resistance per transistor	$\dfrac{V_e'}{I_e'}$	$\dfrac{V_e'}{I_e'(1 - a)}$	$\dfrac{E_c}{I_e'(1 - a)}$
Peak a-c power out	$aE_c I_e'$	$aE_c I_e'$	$E_c I_e'$
Peak a-c power in	$V_e' I_e'$	$V_e' I_e'(1 - a)$	$E_c I_e'(1 - a)$
Peak power gain	$\dfrac{aE_c}{V_e'}$	$\dfrac{a}{1 - a}\left(\dfrac{E_c}{V_e'}\right)$	$\dfrac{1}{1 - a}$

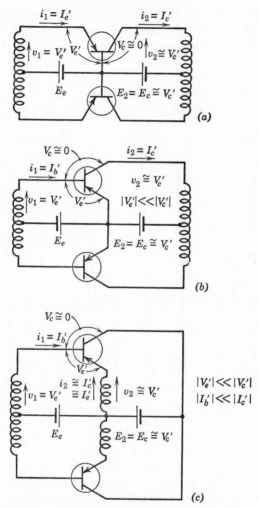

Fig. 7.15 Relationships for the three configurations.

Figure 7.16 shows the V_c vs. I_c characteristics for a transistor, drawn in full line for I_e = constant and in dashed line for I_b = constant. As can be seen from the results of Fig. 7.15, the curves for I_e constant can be used for the grounded-base configuration, and the curves for I_b constant must be used for the grounded-emitter or grounded-collector configuration. Comparison shows that the curves for constant I_b have considerable curvature, and also that the curve for $I_b = 0$ gives a much larger minimum current than that for $I_e = 0$. Both these statemenst arise from the fact that the curves for I_b = constant are essentially

$1/(1 - a)$ times those for $I_e = $ constant. The consequence is that the operating point for the grounded-base connection may be set at A, whereas that for the other configurations lies somewhere between A and B, depending on the d-c resistances of the base and emitter as well as of the driving source. Also, if low distortion is required, the peak current swing may be to the point D for the grounded-base but is limited to C for the other configurations. The comparative performance will now

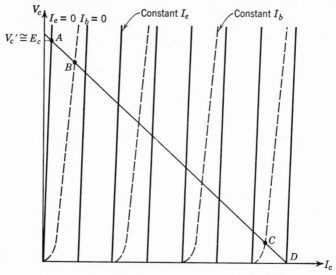

Fig. 7.16 Comparison of output characteristics and load lines for the various configurations.

be discussed. Peak power output (where distortion rises rapidly): Nearly alike in all cases, possibly somewhat higher for the grounded-base stage, since the permissible swings may be a little higher. Owing to better linearity the power output of the grounded-base stage will be highest for equal distortion at reduced driving signal. Zero signal supply power: Owing to the $1/(1 - a)$ effect in the $I_b = $ constant curves, the operating point for the grounded-base configuration may require less supply current than for the other configurations. Efficiency: In class B amplifiers, the efficiency, since it depends upon the driving signal, will be greatest at peak output, at which value the efficiency will be nearly alike in all three cases. At reduced output, the distortion will normally be considerably lower for the grounded-base configuration, owing to better linearity. Consequently the efficiency will be highest for this configuration on an equal distortion basis. Power gain: From eq. 7.71, the peak power gain is given by the product of the peak voltage amplification times the peak current amplification. If the distortion is not too great, we can consider this gain as representative of actual power gain when making comparative statements.

The current amplifications of the three configurations are a for the grounded-base, $a/(1 - a)$ for the grounded-emitter, and $1/(1 - a)$ for the grounded-collector. The corresponding approximate voltage amplifications as given in Chapter 4 are respectively

$$\frac{ar_l}{r_e + r_b(1 - a)} \qquad \frac{ar_l}{r_e + r_b(1 - a)} \qquad \text{and} \qquad \text{Unity}$$

Then power gains for the three configurations are $\dfrac{a^2 r_l}{r_e + r_b(1 - a)}$, $\dfrac{a^2 r_l}{(1 - a)[r_e + r_b(1 - a)]}$, and $\dfrac{1}{1 - a}$ for the grounded-base, grounded-emitter, and grounded-collector respectively. In the first two configurations, power gain is a function of r_l. Thus, under operation where r_l is large, the power gain of the grounded-emitter is the highest, and that of the grounded-collector is the lowest. Under low-voltage high-current operation, r_l may be very small, and in this case, the grounded-collector may have a power gain comparable to, or in excess of, that of the other configurations. An example will illustrate this point:

Consider a transistor with a collector dissipation of 0.2 watt, peak inverse voltage 100 volts, $a = 0.9$, $r_e = 20$ ohms, $r_b = 100$ ohms. Neglecting the back diode current, from eq. 7.55,

$$P_D \cong 0.068 E_2 I_2' \qquad \qquad [7.74]$$

from eq. 7.56

$$r_l \cong E_2/I_2' \qquad \qquad [7.75]$$

Let us choose

$$E_2 = 50 \text{ volts} \qquad 10 \text{ volts} \qquad 3 \text{ volts}$$

Then

$$I_2' = \quad 5.88 \text{ ma} \qquad 29.4 \text{ ma} \qquad 98.5 \text{ ma}$$

For one transistor

$$r_l = 8500 \text{ ohms} \qquad 340 \text{ ohms} \qquad 30.5 \text{ ohms}$$

A_v (grounded-base)
and (grounded-emitter) = 254   10.2   0.91
Power gain
  (grounded-base)   = 228   9.2   0.82
  (grounded-emitter)   = 2280   92   8.2
  (grounded-collector)   =   10   10   10

The peak input resistance for the grounded-emitter stage is $1/(1 - a)$ times that of the grounded-base. The input resistance of the grounded-collector stage is the highest. Furthermore, it is linear whereas that of the grounded-base and grounded-emitter is non-linear. The average input resistance for the grounded-base and grounded-emitter is found to be in practice about 1.25 to 1.5 times the peak value.

7.5.3   Class B Operation with *p-n-p* and *n-p-n* Transistors

The use of both *p-n-p* and *n-p-n* transistors in class B amplifiers is interesting in that it affords a simple method of eliminating the need for a separate phase inverter and for a push-pull output transformer. The

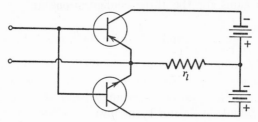

Fig. 7.17   Class B operation with *p-n-p* and *n-p-n* transistors.

circuit is extremely simple, consisting of the parallel combination of a *p-n-p* and an *n-p-n* transistor (see Fig. 7.17). It is seen that the *p-n-p* unit will pass and amplify the negative part of the input signal whereas the *n-p-n* transistor will pass and amplify the positive part. In this manner phase inversion is automatically accomplished. The process of recombining the positive and negative parts to form the whole signal is effected by connecting the two outputs together.

7.6   Driver Considerations

Next to the output stages, the driver operates at a higher level than the other transistor stages. The power that the driver is called upon to deliver to the output stage will be, ordinarily, of such a magnitude that more care must be taken in its design than is necessary for the design of the low-level stages preceding it. These preceding stages have already been discussed in Chapter 5.

A comparison of the various output stage configurations shows that under high-voltage low-current operation the grounded-base and grounded-emitter have much higher power gains than the grounded-collector. In high-current low-voltage operation, the power gain of the grounded-base and grounded-emitter falls so as to be comparable to that of the grounded-collector. As has been pointed out in Chapter 6, some degree of d-c bias stabilization is necessary for all stages, its extent depending on the power level of the stage. Considerable stabilization is required therefore for a driver feeding a low-voltage high-current output stage. If the driver is required to operate into a grounded-base or grounded-emitter output stage, the use of stepdown transformer coupling is advantageous as it increases the effective power gain of the driver. With class B output stages it is possible to operate at a reasonably close match † to the input resistance. With class A, it is better to

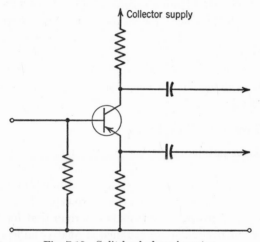

Fig. 7.18   Split-load phase inverter.

mismatch somewhat since it is desirable to have the source resistance larger than the input resistance. When a grounded-collector output stage is to be driven, it is often unnecessary to use a stepdown transformer, since the input resistance is high. In fact, since the input voltage swing of the output stage is approximately equal to the collector voltage, the driver must be capable of handling large voltages, and it may even be necessary to use a step-up transformer.

Phase inversion is most conveniently done by means of a transformer—a split-load transistor phase inverter may be used as an alternative. Figure 7.18 illustrates such a phase inverter. If the design is such that the operating level of the driver is low, its stabilization may be economically effected as described in Sec. 6.3. Under this condition the stabilized driver could be used in a tandem arrangement wherein

† It must be remembered that, for large signals, the input resistance is non-linear. Mathematically speaking, a match would imply a similar source resistance, but foi practical purposes it is sufficient to match to the average input resistances.

the stability of the output stage is largely dictated by that of the driver stage. Circuits using this arrangement have been shown in Figs. 6.5 to 6.7. The a-c performance of these circuits has been analyzed in Sec. 6.9. Figure 6.8 shows a practical tandem amplifier driven by a phase inverter, and Fig. 6.12 shows a complete amplifier using a push-pull tandem arrangement.

7.7 High-Temperature Operation

The basic problems of miniaturization and high-temperature operation go hand in hand, since a reduction of the available space results in elevated temperatures. Moreover, there are a large number of applications for transistors which call for their operation at temperatures of the order of 100° C. It is the purpose of this section to look into some of the problems affecting the behavior of transistor audio amplifiers under these conditions.

7.7.1 Parameter Variation

The subject of parameter variation with temperature has been discussed in Chapter 3. A study of this behavior shows that the a of neither n-p-n rate-grown nor p-n-p diffused-junction types exceeds unity at elevated temperatures. Of these two types the parameter variation of n-p-n rate-grown transistors is less than that for the diffused-junction type; of particular importance is relative independence of a with temperature for the n-p-n rate-grown type. It is thus clear that the n-p-n rate-grown transistor is perhaps the best of these types to choose for high-temperature operation. For this transistor, we have the following behavior: (a) I_{c0} rises with temperature; (b) a is independent of temperature; (c) r_c falls with temperature; (d) r_e rises with temperature; and (e) r_b rises with temperature. Under these conditions, it is possible to get some idea of the behavior of input resistance and current amplification as a function of temperature.

For a typical transistor, we have:

	$-55°$ C	$+100°$ C
a	0.95	0.95
r_e	30 ohms	50 ohms
r_b	100 ohms	500 ohms
r_c	10^6 ohms	10^5 ohms
I_{c0}	Negligible	0.5 ma

For these parameters, we have at two temperature extremes and for different load resistances:

$-55°$ C	$r_l = 100 \ \Omega$	$r_l = 1000 \ \Omega$	$r_l = 10,000 \ \Omega$
r_i	698 Ω	687 Ω	605 Ω
A_i	19.0	18.5	15.8

$+100°$ C	$r_l = 100 \ \Omega$	$r_l = 1000 \ \Omega$	$r_l = 10,000 \ \Omega$
r_i	1498 Ω	1335 Ω	865 Ω
A_i	18.4	15.7	6.3

Thus the input resistance rises and the current amplification falls with increasing temperature.

7.7.2   Input Stage

Consider an input stage fed from a source resistance of r_g. Then the power gain of the stage is given by

$$G = \frac{A_i^2 r_i}{r_g + r_i} \tag{7.76}$$

under the assumption that the stage feeds another stage of equal input resistance r_i. Since, as shown above, A_i and r_i vary with temperature it is possible to adjust the resistance r_g to equalize the power gain at two temperatures. These temperatures may be chosen so as to keep the overall variation of power gain to a minimum.

7.7.3   Intermediate Stages

Since intermediate stages having an input resistance of r_i feed into transistors which likewise have a resistance of r_i, the power gain is

$$G = A_i^2 r_i / r_i = A_i^2 \tag{7.77}$$

For grounded-emitter stages, this indicates a loss in gain of about 2 db per stage, due to the above variation in temperature.

7.7.4   Output Stage

Here, gain is given by

$$G = A_i^2 r_l / r_i \tag{7.78}$$

Since A_i falls with temperature and r_i rises with temperature, the loss in gain will be considerably in excess of that for the intermediate stage. Furthermore, the effect of temperature change is very pronounced, since a shift in operating point may severely limit the power output and linear operation of the amplifier.

Figure 7.19 shows the static characteristics for a transistor at 27° C and 85° C. We see that: (*a*) The $I_e = 0$ line is considerably displaced owing to the increased back diode current at high temperatures.

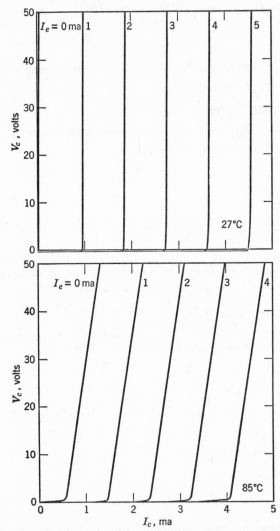

Fig. 7.19   Comparative characteristics at room and elevated temperatures.

(*b*) The slope of the lines is considerably lessened, owing to the fall in r_c.   (*c*) The curves are a little more closely spaced, owing to the slight change of a. Since this last change is about 2 per cent at most, it may be neglected.

7.7.5   Static Characteristic Analysis of High-Temperature Operation

Figure 7.20 shows idealized V_c-I_c characteristics of a transistor for which only the lines for $I_e = 0$ are drawn for both temperature extremes. Solid lines are for normal operation; dashed lines and primed quantities for elevated temperatures. Since $(I_c)_0$ is $\ll (I_c')_0$, it may

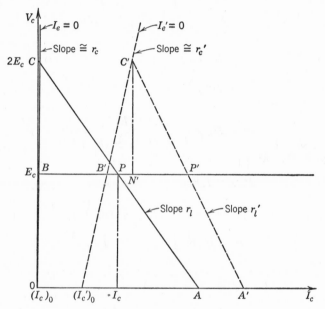

Fig. 7.20   Load line analysis of high-temperature operation.

be neglected. At high temperature, the increase in back diode current, given by BB', is equal to $(I_c')_0 + (E_c/r_c')$. If the d-c resistance in the transformer winding is very much less than r_c', the effect of this increased current on the collector voltage can be neglected, and the operating point is moved to P', i.e., to a current equal to

$$I_c + (I_c')_0 + (E_c/r_c')$$

At this operating point, maximum efficiency and power output will result if the dynamic load line is such that the swing extends to a peak voltage that is twice the battery voltage, i.e., if $C'P'A'$ is the load line. Then

$$CC' = (I_c')_0 + 2E_c/r_c' \qquad\qquad [7.79]$$

Therefore

$$P'N' = P'B - CC' \qquad [7.80]$$

$$= I_c - (E_c/r_c') \qquad [7.81]$$

Whence load resistance (hot)

$$r_l' = \frac{2E_c - E_c}{I_c - (E_c/r_c')} = \frac{E_c}{I_c - (E_c/r_c')} \qquad [7.82]$$

and

$$r_l = E_c/I_c \qquad [7.83]$$

$$\eta = 50\% \qquad [7.84]$$

$$\eta' = 50 \times \frac{I_c - (E_c/r_c')}{I_c + (I_c')_0 + (E_c/r_c')} \qquad [7.85]$$

(see eq. 7.29). Also

$$P_{\text{d-c}} = I_c E_c \qquad [7.86]$$

$$P_{\text{d-c}}' = E_c[I_c + (I_c')_0 + (E_c/r_c')] \qquad [7.87]$$

$$P_o = E_c I_c/2 \qquad [7.88]$$

$$P_o' = \frac{E_c[I_c - (E_c/r_c')]}{2} \qquad [7.89]$$

By way of an example, consider the following transistor

$$(I_c)_0 = 10 \ \mu a \qquad (I_c')_0 = 600 \ \mu a$$

$$r_c = 570 \ k\Omega \qquad r_c' = 57 \ k\Omega$$

$$E_c = 30 \ \text{volts}$$

$$I_c = 4.7 \ \text{ma}$$

Then

$$E_c/r_c' = 0.544 \ \text{ma}$$

whence

$$r_l' = 30,000/(4.7 - .544) = 30,000/4.156 = 7220 \ \Omega$$

and

$$r_l = E_c/I_c = 30{,}000/4.7 = 6383 \ \Omega$$

$$\eta \cong 50\%$$

$$\eta' \cong 50 \times (4.156/5.844) \cong 35.5\%$$

$$P_{\text{d-c}} = 30 \times 4.7 = 141 \ \text{mw}$$

$$P_{\text{d-c}}' = 30 \times 5.844 = 175 \ \text{mw}$$

$$P_o = \frac{30 \times 4.7}{2} = 70 \ \text{mw}$$

$$P_o' = \frac{30 \times 4.156}{2} = 62.2 \ \text{mw}$$

It will be noted from the above that collector current rises while the power output and efficiency fall as the temperature is increased. Also a higher value of load resistance is needed. It is best to design, then, for the high-temperature case, since dissipation is at the maximum for this condition. If such a transistor is now operated at normal temperatures, it is not possible to swing the collector current to its maximum extent. Thus, the emitter current swing should be reduced and the transistor operated at reduced collector efficiency. Also, if constant power output is required over the entire temperature range, some means must be provided to reduce the signal swing at low temperatures.

7.8   Problems

1. Given a transistor with $\alpha = 0.95$, $r_c = 1$ MΩ, a permissible peak inverse voltage of 90 volts, and a maximum permissible dissipation of 250 mw. What is the maximum value of load resistance required for a single-ended class A amplifier? What is the efficiency?

2. What is the efficiency if the back diode current at 90 volts is (a) 100 μa, (b) 500 μa, (c) 1.5 ma?

3. What is the value of the primary impedance of an output transformer for a push-pull class A amplifier using the transistor of problem 1?

4. Repeat problem 1 for a push-pull class B amplifier.

5. Repeat problem 2 for a push-pull class B amplifier.

6. Given a transistor whose parameters at room temperature are $r_c = 1$ MΩ, $\alpha = 0.95$, permissible peak inverse voltage 90 volts, $I_{c0} = 10\mu$a at 90 volts. What is the maximum value of load resistance for a power output of 200 mw? The parameters at 100° C are $r_c = 100$ kΩ, $\alpha = 0.94$, permissible peak inverse voltage 90 volts, $I_{c0} = 1$ ma. What is the maximum load resistance for the same power output? What is the efficiency?

7.9   Bibliography

R. F. Shea, "Transistor Power Amplifiers," *Electronics*, *25*, 106–108 (September, 1952).

Chapter 8

Direct-Current
Amplifiers

8.1   Direct-Coupled Amplifier Circuits

Direct-coupled amplifiers are commonly used in a wide variety of applications. In many of these applications the signal may contain a d-c component as well as low-frequency components. Signals of this type are encountered in biology, medicine, cathode-ray techniques, square-wave testing, electronic switching techniques, and in many

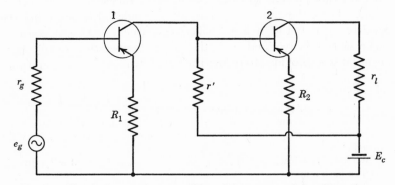

Fig. 8.1   Simple d-c transistor amplifier with two grounded-emitter stages.

instruments and apparatus. Consequently this type of amplifier requires direct coupling between the stages without the use of coupling condensers.

Figure 8.1 shows one possible arrangement of this type consisting of two grounded-emitter stages in which the signal developed across the load resistance r' of the first transistor is applied directly to the base of the second transistor.

For proper operation of such an amplifier the d-c voltage drop across resistance r' must be sufficient to maintain the emitter of the second transistor slightly positive with respect to the base.

An alternative arrangement consisting of a tandem connection of grounded-base and grounded-emitter stages, where the input resistance of the second stage serves as a load to the first stage, is shown in Fig. 8.2.

Still other arrangements can be devised, and the number of cascaded stages can be increased to provide higher gain.

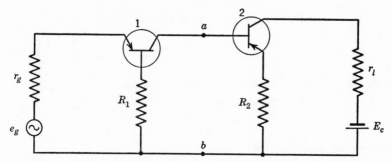

Fig. 8.2   Grounded-base, grounded-emitter d-c transistor amplifier.

8.2   Basic Relationships

The analysis of the d-c transistor amplifier, as far as gain and impedances are concerned, follows the general pattern of the audio amplifier.

In order to avoid unnecessary duplication, a number of equations will be quoted directly from Chapter 4, modified slightly to meet d-c and very low-frequency requirements.

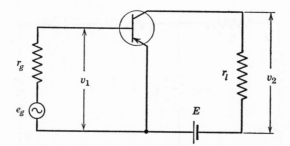

Fig. 8.3   Single-stage grounded-emitter amplifier.

Figure 8.3 shows a single-stage grounded-emitter amplifier, and Fig. 8.4 its equivalent circuit.   The input resistance

$$r_i = r_b + r_e \left[\frac{r_c + r_l}{r_c - r_m + r_e + r_l} \right] \qquad [8.1]$$

The output resistance

$$r_o = r_c - r_m + r_e \left[\frac{r_g + r_b + r_m}{r_g + r_b + r_e} \right] \qquad [8.2]$$

The voltage amplification

$$A_v = \frac{v_2}{v_1} = - \frac{r_l(r_m - r_e)}{r_b(r_c - r_m + r_e + r_l) + r_e(r_c + r_l)}$$

$$\cong - \frac{ar_l}{r_e + r_b(1 - a)} \qquad [8.3]$$

or for an iterative multistage amplifier, assuming $r_i = r_l$; $r_i \cong r_b + r_e/(1 - a)$, and the voltage amplification per stage will be

$$A_v \cong a/(1 - a) \qquad [8.4]$$

The current amplification

$$A_i = - \frac{r_m - r_e}{r_c - r_m + r_e + r_l} \cong - \frac{ar_c}{(1 - a)r_c + r_l} \qquad [8.5]$$

The power gain

$$G = \frac{r_i}{r_l} A_v{}^2 \qquad [8.6]$$

From these equations it can be seen that, as far as the gain of a d-c amplifier is concerned, the a of the transistor is one of the most important parameters and consequently should be as high as possible.

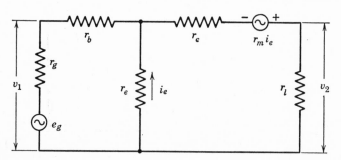

Fig. 8.4   Equivalent diagram of the grounded-emitter amplifier stage.

Negative feedback as used in amplifiers usually improves their frequency response, linearity, and stability, and therefore its use in the d-c amplifier is especially desirable.   Figure 8.5 shows a very common arrangement of feedback, obtained by means of the resistance R in the emitter circuit of the transistor, and Fig. 8.6 its equivalent circuit.

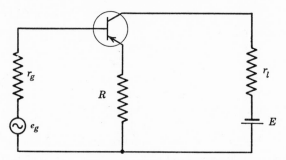

Fig. 8.5 A single-stage grounded-emitter amplifier with negative feedback.

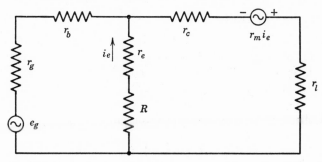

Fig. 8.6 Equivalent circuit of a grounded-emitter amplifier with negative feedback.

The effect of an external emitter resistance R may be determined by substituting $r_e + R$ for r_e in eqs. 8.1–8.6. If we neglect $r_e + R$, r_g, r_b, and r_l as compared to $r_c(1 - a)$ we get:

The input resistance

$$r_i \cong r_b + \frac{r_e + R}{1 - a} \tag{8.7}$$

The output resistance

$$r_o \cong r_c(1 - a) + \frac{ar_c(r_e + R)}{r_g + r_b + r_e + R} \tag{8.8}$$

The voltage amplification

$$A_v \cong -\frac{ar_l}{r_e + R + r_b(1 - a)} \tag{8.9}$$

The current amplification

$$A_i \cong -\frac{a}{1 - a} \tag{8.10}$$

The power gain

$$G \cong \frac{a^2 r_l}{(1 - a)[r_e + R + r_b(1 - a)]} \tag{8.11}$$

These equations, used in conjunction with the analysis of the RC-coupled amplifier in Chapter 5, may be used for the basic design of d-c transistor amplifiers. Another, and very important, factor enters into the design of d-c amplifiers, namely, the drift of output current.

This effect occurs even when the input terminal is connected directly to ground and therefore cannot be attributed to thermal noise produced in an input resistor. Negative feedback cannot entirely eliminate this drift since it acts as if it were due to input signal variations, hence cannot be distinguished from the signal itself. The following material will, therefore, be devoted primarily to the problem of drift in d-c amplifiers and to the methods of design for minimizing its effect.

8.3   Problem of Drift

In d-c transistor amplifiers, drift is caused primarily by random changes of temperature. In Chapter 3 it was shown that all parameters vary with temperature, particularly the collector impedance r_c and the diode back current I_{c0} (see below). The current amplification A_i is therefore very sensitive to temperature change.

The collector current of the transistor can be expressed by

$$I_c = \alpha I_e + I_{c0} \qquad [8.12]$$

where I_{c0} is the collector current for zero-emitter current.

Figure 8.7 shows the variation of the current I_{c0} with temperature for several junction transistors.

From these curves it can be seen that the current I_{c0} may be expressed approximately as

$$I_{c0} = I_s e^{0.05T} \qquad [8.13]$$

where I_s is the current at $0°$ C, and T the temperature in degrees Centigrade. Hence:

$$dI_{c0}/dT = 0.05 I_s e^{0.05T} = 0.05 I_{c0} \qquad [8.14]$$

The incremental change of this current can be written as

$$i_{c0} = 0.05 I_{c0} \Delta T \qquad [8.15]$$

where ΔT is the temperature change in degrees Centigrade.

In general the temperature coefficient for I_{c0} is about 5–10 per cent per degree Centigrade. In view of this, temperature compensation of the d-c transistor amplifier becomes a serious problem.

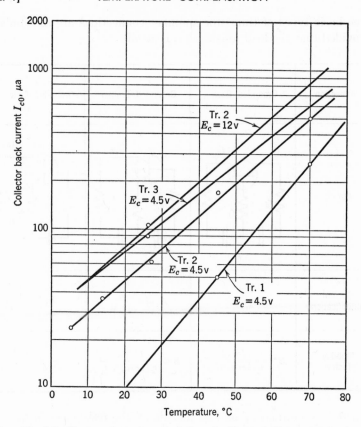

Fig. 8.7   Temperature characteristics of collector back current I_{c0}.

8.4   Temperature Compensation of D-C Amplifiers

One of the methods which may be employed is based on proper selection of the characteristics of the various transistors employed in the d-c amplifier. Let us consider the effect of temperature on collector current in a transistor amplifier. The principal increment of the output current of an amplifier due to the temperature change of the transistor is that due to change in the zero-emitter collector current and is given by

$$i_o = Si_{c0} \qquad [8.16]$$

where i_{c0} is the increment of current I_{c0} and S is the stability factor of the amplifier stage as defined in Sec. 6.13.

The expressions for S and A_i, the current amplification factor, for three basic types of transistor amplifier connections are as tabulated (provided that the load resistance r_l is small).

Connection	Grounded–Base	Grounded–Emitter	Grounded–Collector
Circuit			
Current amplification	$A_i \cong a$	$A_i \cong -\dfrac{a}{1-a}$	$A_i \cong \dfrac{1}{1-a}$
Stability factor	$S = \dfrac{r_1' + r_g'}{r_1'(1-a) + r_g'}$	$S = \dfrac{r_1' + r_g'}{r_g'(1-a) + r_1'}$	$S = -\dfrac{ar_g'}{(1-a)r_g' + r_1'}$

In these equations r_1' and r_g' include all the resistances in their respective circuits, internal as well as external to the transistor. For example, in the grounded-base configuration $r_1' = r_1 + r_b$. In a two-stage amplifier the incremental current change of the first stage i_o is amplified by A_{i2}, the current amplification of the second stage. Therefore, the net incremental change in output current of a two-stage amplifier due to changes in I_{c01} and I_{c02} is

$$i_l = A_{i2}S_1 i_{c01} + S_2 i_{c02} \qquad [8.17]$$

In order to obtain temperature compensation, the current i_l must be equal to zero for any temperature range of interest, thus:

$$A_{i2}S_1 i_{c01} + S_2 i_{c02} = 0 \qquad [8.18]$$

This can be accomplished if one of the following four conditions is satisfied, provided that the currents i_{c01} and i_{c02} have the same sign:

$$A_{i2} < 0 \qquad S_1 > 0 \qquad S_2 > 0 \qquad\qquad [8.19]$$

$$A_{i2} < 0 \qquad S_1 < 0 \qquad S_2 < 0 \qquad\qquad [8.20]$$

$$A_{i2} > 0 \qquad S_1 > 0 \qquad S_2 < 0 \qquad\qquad [8.21]$$

$$A_{i2} > 0 \qquad S_1 < 0 \qquad S_2 > 0 \qquad\qquad [8.22]$$

Temperature compensation may also be achieved if i_{c01} and i_{c02} have opposite signs, as with an amplifier employing one p-n-p type and one n-p-n type transistor. Still other arrangements can be devised to satisfy eq. 8.18. If both transistors are of the same type (n-p-n or p-n-p), only the following five connections can be used for temperature compensation of the amplifier:

1. Grounded-emitter grounded-emitter.
2. Grounded-base grounded-emitter.
3. Grounded-base grounded-collector.
4. Grounded-emitter grounded-collector.
5. Grounded-collector grounded-base.

The other four connections of all nine possible combinations are not suitable for temperature compensation (see problem 1). These four non-suitable combinations are:

1. Grounded-base grounded-base.
2. Grounded-emitter grounded-base.
3. Grounded-collector grounded-emitter.
4. Grounded-collector grounded-collector.

Depending on the requirements, any of the first five connections mentioned above can be used for temperature compensation. For example, if input resistance of the amplifier must be very low, connections 2 or 3

Fig. 8.8 Block diagram of a two-stage amplifier.

will be most desirable, whereas, in order to have very high input resistance, connection 5 would be preferable. Let us consider now in detail a two-stage amplifier, a block diagram of which is shown in Fig. 8.8.

The equivalent circuit of this amplifier, assuming that both stages are of the grounded-emitter configuration, is shown in Fig. 8.9.

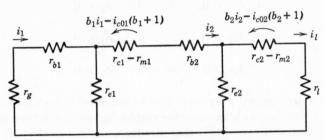

Fig. 8.9 Equivalent circuit of the two-stage grounded-emitter, grounded-emitter amplifier.

In this diagram the current increment (due to the change in I_{c0}) through the load is approximately

$$i_l \cong A_{i2}i_2 + i_{c02}S_2 \qquad [8.23]$$

and current i_2 is given by

$$i_2 \cong i_{c01}S_1 \qquad [8.24]$$

Thus, the current through the load

$$i_l \cong A_{i2}S_1 i_{c01} + i_{c02}S_2 \qquad [8.25]$$

where i_{c01} and i_{c02} are increments of the currents I_{c01} and I_{c02} due to the change of temperature of the transistors, and

$$A_i \cong -\frac{a}{1-a} \qquad S \cong \frac{r_e + r_g'}{r_g'(1-a) + r_e} \qquad [8.26]$$

From eq. 8.25 it can be seen that the current through the load (i_l) will be independent of i_{c01} and i_{c02}, if

$$A_{i2}S_1 i_{c01} = -i_{c02}S_2 \qquad [8.27]$$

Now, if $S_1 \cong S_2$, then

$$i_{c02} \cong -A_{i2}i_{c01} \qquad [8.28]$$

From this equation it can be seen that for given A_{i2} a pair of transistors can be so selected that the values of i_{c01} and i_{c02} will satisfy eq. 8.28 for a restricted region of temperature variations. Or, for any given value of i_{c01}, A_{i2} can be selected in accordance with eq. 8.28. Note, however, that the condition $S_1 = S_2$ implies that r_{g1}' and r_{g2}' be nearly equal. This may require an additional resistor across the input of the second stage.

In general, this method requires use of a transistor with small value of I_{c0} in the first stage, and with a large value of I_{c0} in the second stage. A small degree of mismatch between the transistors can be corrected by

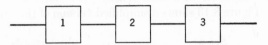

Fig. 8.10 Block diagram of a three-stage amplifier.

adjusting the magnitudes of negative feedbacks in both stages of amplifiers.

Let us now consider a three-stage grounded-emitter amplifier. Figure 8.10 shows a block diagram of such an amplifier, and Fig. 8.11,

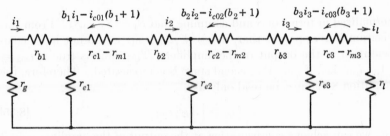

Fig. 8.11 Equivalent circuit of three-stage amplifier.

its equivalent circuit. In this diagram

$$i_2 = i_{c01}S_1 \qquad [8.29]$$

$$i_3 = A_{i2}i_2 + i_{c02}S_2 = A_{i2}i_{c01}S_1 + i_{c02}S_2 \qquad [8.30]$$

(remembering that A_i is negative in this connection).

$$i_l = A_{i3}i_3 + i_{c03}S_3 = A_{i3}A_{i2}i_{c01}S_1 + A_{i3}i_{c02}S_2 + i_{c03}S_3 \qquad [8.31]$$

The amplifier will be temperature-stabilized if

$$A_{i3}A_{i2}i_{c01}S_1 + i_{c03}S_3 = -A_{i3}i_{c02}S_2 \qquad [8.32]$$

or, assuming that $S_1 \cong S_2 \cong S_3$, the condition for stabilization will be

$$A_{i3}A_{i2}i_{c01} + i_{c03} = -i_{c02}A_{i3} \qquad [8.33]$$

If we now ignore i_{c03} as compared to $A_{i3}A_{i2}i_{c01}$, then

$$i_{c02} \cong -A_{i2}i_{c01} \qquad [8.34]$$

which indicates that the transistor with smallest I_{c0} should be placed in the first stage. The same note as above concerning equality of S also applies here.

Let us now refer to Fig. 8.12, which presents all the currents of interest in the amplifier, with their relative directions at the outputs of each stage. Figure 8.13 shows a simplified version of the same diagram,

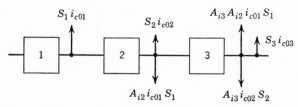

Fig. 8.12 Relative direction of the currents in the three-stage amplifier.

normalized in terms of S and assuming that $S_1 = S_2 = S_3$. From this diagram it is apparent that, if $i_{c02} < |A_{i2}| i_{c01}$, we do not have compensation in the output of the amplifier. The same is true if $i_{c02} = |A_{i2}| i_{c01}$, i.e., if only the second stage is compensated. Therefore, the condition 8.32 must be read only as

$$i_{c02} > |A_{i2}| i_{c01} \qquad [8.35]$$

i.e., we can achieve compensation at the output of the amplifier only if the preceding (second) stage is overcompensated. The amount of

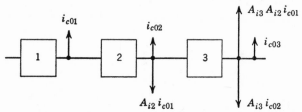

Fig. 8.13 Simplified version of diagram of Fig. 8.12, when S_1, S_2, S_3 are equal.

overcompensation necessary will depend on the characteristic (i_{c03}) of the transistor in the last stage. Transistors with small i_{c03} in the output stage will require less overcompensation in the second stage, and vice versa. The "current direction" method of stabilization described above, which was based on linear operation of the amplifier and on the assumption that other parameters of the transistors are not affected by temperature, is a very simple one. However, it is not entirely practical, since it requires transistors of the particular characteristics in each stage.

Figure 8.14 shows another arrangement which may be used for temperature stabilization of the amplifier. A resistance R_3 is placed in series with the base of the second transistor, and, therefore, the current increment i_1 due to the change of temperature of the first transistor is

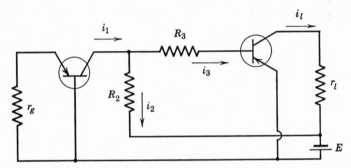

Fig. 8.14   Circuit arrangement for temperature stabilization of a d-c amplifier.

divided into currents i_2 and i_3 flowing through resistances R_2 and R_3 respectively.

Owing to current increment i_3, a current increment will appear (with phase reversed) on the collector side of the second transistor. The ratio between R_2 and R_3 may be so chosen that this current increment will compensate the current increment which is due to the change of

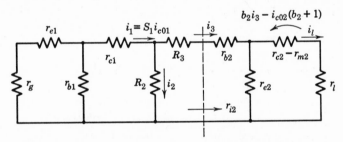

Fig. 8.15   The equivalent diagram of the circuit of Fig. 8.14.

temperature of the second transistor, resulting in the net increment i_l becoming zero.

Figure 8.15 shows an equivalent diagram of this arrangement. In this diagram, the current i_3

$$i_3 = S_1 i_{c01} R_2 / (R' + R_2) \qquad [8.36]$$

where $R' = R_3 + r_{i2}$ and S_1 is the stability factor as before.

i_3 will appear amplified in the output of the last transistor as i_l'.

$$i_l' = i_{c01} S_1 \times A_{i2} \left[\frac{R_2}{R' + R_2} \right] \qquad [8.37]$$

The current increment in i_l due to i_{c02} is

$$i_l'' \cong i_{c02}(A_{i2} + 1) \qquad [8.38]$$

For temperature compensation, $i_l' = i_l''$ or

$$i_{c02}(A_{i2} + 1) \cong i_{c01} S_1 \times A_{i2} R_2 / (R' + R_2) \qquad [8.39]$$

Now, if $A_{i2} \gg 1$, the condition for temperature compensation will be

$$i_{c02} \cong i_{c01} S_1 R_2 / (R' + R_2) \qquad [8.40]$$

Figure 8.16 shows another way of stabilizing a d-c amplifier. A feed back resistance R_3 is placed in series with the load resistance r_l. The analysis of this circuit, which is very similar to that shown in Fig. 8.14, shows that, depending on the characteristics of the transistors, the

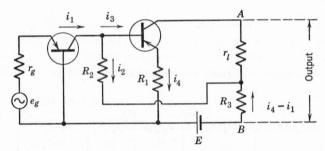

Fig. 8.16   Method of temperature stabilization of a d-c amplifier.

values of resistances R_1, R_2, and R_3 may be chosen such that current increments due to i_{c01} will be compensated by current increments due to i_{c02} and consequently the output voltage between points A and B will be independent of change of ambient temperature.

The methods described above, based on proper selection of transistor characteristics, are not entirely practical, since they are good for restricted regions of temperature change and depend critically on the characteristics of the individual transistors. From this point of view, the next method of temperature compensation, which is based on the use of temperature-sensitive elements (such as a junction diode, for example), is much superior. This method does not require the selection of transistors with specific characteristics and can be applied to any pair of transistors with standard characteristics.

8.5 Temperature Compensation by Non-Linear Elements

In Fig. 8.1 (Sec. 8.1) a diagram of a simple d-c transistor amplifier was shown. Unless this amplifier is compensated against temperature effects the output current may vary as much as 100 per cent for a variation of ambient temperature of only 15° C. However, this effect can be reduced practically to zero if the load resistance of the first stage, r', is made temperature-sensitive. By proper choice of the characteristic of this resistance, it will automatically adjust the bias of the second transistor so that the d-c collector current of this transistor remains constant as the ambient temperature varies.

Since the temperature affects almost all the parameters of transistors, as well as all external "permanent" resistors employed in the amplifier circuit, it would be very difficult to take into account all the factors that are due to temperature in order to calculate the proper characteristic of the compensating temperature-sensitive resistance mentioned above. Therefore, for simplicity (and greater accuracy also), this characteristic may be determined experimentally for any pair of transistors in the amplifier circuit. The procedure is as follows:

In the circuit of Fig. 8.1, the resistance r' is replaced by a variable resistance. Then, for any given ambient temperature, the value of this resistance is adjusted so that the output current of the amplifier, I_o, remains constant. The plot of these values of resistance against temperature will then represent the desired temperature characteristic of the temperature-sensitive resistance. This means that a resistance having this temperature characteristic, being substituted for r', will maintain the output current I_o constant as the ambient temperature is changed. Figure 8.17 shows such a characteristic obtained experimentally for the two-stage amplifier consisting of one grounded-base stage and one grounded-emitter stage shown in Fig. 8.2. The variable resistance r' was placed between the points a and b. The parameters of the p-n-p junction transistors employed in the amplifier were as tab-

	α	r_c	r_b	r_e	I_{c0}
Transistor 1	0.96	1 MΩ	600 Ω	20 Ω	6 μa
Transistor 2	0.94	140 kΩ	340 Ω	32 Ω	40 μa

ulated. The first set of curves (solid lines) was obtained with transistor 1 used in the first stage and transistor 2 in the second stage. The second set of curves (dotted lines) represents the case where the transistors are interchanged. In each set the characteristics were taken for two constant values of output current I_o, 1 ma and 3 ma.

After the curves of the compensating resistance have been obtained, a suitable temperature-sensitive element must be found to replace resistor r' in Fig. 8.1 or 8.2. A "suitable" resistance should not only have the required temperature characteristic, but also the same thermal time-constant as the transistors used in the amplifier. If the last requirement is not satisfied, the chosen resistor will not respond to tem-

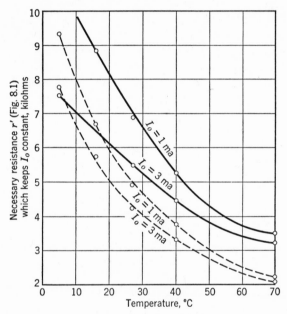

Fig. 8.17 Temperature characteristics of the load resistance r' for constant output.

perature changes simultaneously with the transistors and therefore the amplifier will not be truly compensated.

In the realization of the proposed method of temperature compensation, a number of temperature-sensitive elements may be used, among them (a) special types of ceramic resistors, (b) temperature-sensitive paints, (c) thermistors, (d) germanium diodes, and (e) transistors.

Despite the fact that all the different types of temperature-sensitive resistors mentioned above offer a great variety of characteristics, it is impossible to select among them a particular one which would have exactly the same shape as required for complete temperature compensation of an amplifier (curves in Fig. 8.17). Therefore, for a practical application, the temperature-sensitive element must be used in the amplifier circuit in conjunction with a special "shaping" network of series and parallel resistances, which will change the characteristic of the temperature-sensitive resistance to that which is required for compensation.

Figure 8.18 shows a modification of the circuit of Fig. 8.14 which makes use of the non-linear element (e.g., a junction diode) in conjunction with resistors R_2 and R_3 to compensate for the current increments.

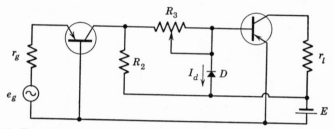

Fig. 8.18 Two-stage temperature stabilized d-c amplifier with low input resistance.

8.6 Operating Characteristics of a Temperature-Compensated D-C Amplifier

A two-stage d-c transistor amplifier employing a junction diode as a temperature-stabilized element is illustrated in Fig. 8.19. The char-

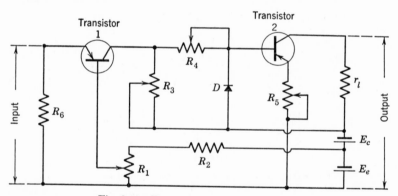

Fig. 8.19 Two-stage transistor amplifier.

acteristics of this amplifier are shown in Table 8.1

Table 8.1 Characteristics of the D-C Amplifier Shown in Fig. 8.19

1. No. 1, No. 2	G.E., *p-n-p* junction transistors	9. R_2	1000 Ω
2. Diode D	G.E. junction diode	10. R_3	15,000 Ω
3. E_c	12 volts	11. R_5	500 Ω
4. E_e	1.5 volts	12. R_6	100 Ω
5. I_{c1}	0.43 ma	13. ΔV_1 min	0.5 mv
6. I_{c2}	2 ma	14. V_1 max	50 mv
7. R_1	100 Ω	15. Dynamic range 100 ÷ 1 = 40 db
8. R_4	1000 Ω	16. Overall power gain = 23 db
			(for $r_l = 1$ kΩ)

Input resistance of amplifier   50 Ω

Figure 8.20 shows the temperature characteristics of this amplifier. Curve 1 corresponds to the compensated amplifier; curve 2 represents the temperature characteristic of the non-compensated amplifier with diode D removed and the values of the resistors changed to maintain I_o at its original value.

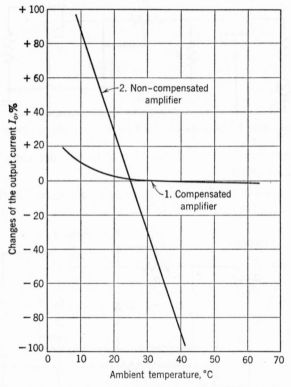

Fig. 8.20   Characteristics of the amplifier of Fig. 8.19.

Note the extreme change of output current I_o with temperature for the non-compensated amplifier: a temperature variation of less than $\pm 20°$ C is enough to produce $\pm 100\%$ change in output current I_o.

The curve representing the compensated amplifier is still far from ideal, but with some readjustment of the shaping networks, as well as by choosing a particular diode, the temperature characteristic of the amplifier may be further improved.

The lower limit of the dynamic range of this amplifier is limited by the noise figure of the transistors, which is very high at low frequencies (see Fig. 20.5).

The upper limit of the dynamic range is limited by the characteristic of the first transistor. In the arrangement shown in Fig. 8.19, the collector voltage of the first transistor is 0.5 volt while the second transistor has a collector voltage of 10 volts. The collector voltage of the first transistor may be increased by increasing the negative feedback resistance R_5, which will, however, reduce the gain of the amplifier.

The collector voltage of the first stage may be increased also by reducing the value of resistance R_3, which will also drop the gain of the amplifier and will increase the collector current of the second transistor I_{c2}, causing larger power consumption from the batteries. However, there is another reason for not increasing the collector voltage of the first transistor. From Fig. 20.7, it may be seen that, for most transistors, a large V_c means a large noise figure, therefore, if there is no special requirement for a large dynamic range, the collector voltage of the first transistor, which contributes largely to the noise, should be low.

8.7   Stability of Power Supplies and General Design Features

Practical performance of any d-c amplifier is also affected by the stability of the power supply.

In a transistor d-c amplifier, which generally requires relatively small power consumption from the power supply (low voltages, low currents), this stability is fairly easy to achieve by means of batteries. However, it is still necessary to consider the temperature effect on the batteries. The temperature coefficient of a typical dry-cell battery is $+0.0016$ volt per degree per cell in the range of 15° C to 20° C. Thus, a 10-volt battery will have a temperature coefficient of the order of $+11$ mv per °C. To minimize this effect, it is desirable to operate the d-c amplifier from a low-voltage power source.

Wherever ac-dc power supply is used, good regulation of this supply is almost always required. Otherwise, special arrangements such as balanced circuits which provide self-stabilization are necessary.

In addition to the specific effect of transistor and battery temperature, the temperature coefficients of other components of the amplifier must be taken into consideration. In d-c transistor amplifiers, the only components besides transistors are resistors. Figure 8.21 shows the temperature characteristics of typical fixed-composition resistors and wire-wound resistors. As may be seen, fixed-composition resistors have comparatively negligible temperature coefficient within the temperature range of 20° C–60° C. However, wire-wound resistors are generally preferable because composition resistors generally produce noise, which, like transistor noise, is most serious at low frequencies.

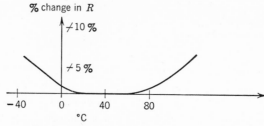

Fixed-composition resistors

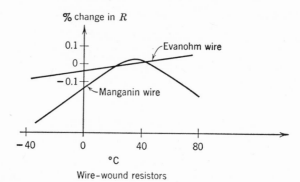

Wire-wound resistors

Fig. 8.21   Temperature characteristics of two types of resistors.

8.8   Problems

1. Prove that in a two-stage d-c transistor amplifier, with temperature compensation based only on proper selection of the I_{c0} of transistors, none of the following four connections can be used: (1) Grounded-base, grounded-base; (2) grounded-emitter, grounded-base; (3) grounded-collector, grounded-collector; (4) grounded-collector, grounded-emitter.

2. Derive the condition for temperature compensation in terms of the current increments and stability factors for the circuit shown in Fig. 8.18.

3. For the circuit shown in Fig. 8.19 calculate the power gain of the amplifier for three different temperatures 10° C, 25° C, and 40° C. For the temperature curves for the diode D, use the curves in Fig. 8.7. The circuit and transistor parameters are given in Table 8.21. Assume $R_5 = 0$, but take into account the temperature effect on all the resistances, which are made from Evanohm wire (Fig. 8.21). Assume also that collector voltage V_c of the first transistor is 4.5 volts and that all parameters of the transistors remain constant for the given temperature change.

Chapter 9

Transistors as High-Frequency Circuit Elements

9.1 The Validity of the Low-Frequency Equivalent Circuit of the Transistor at High Frequencies

It was shown in Chapter 3 that the properties of a transistor at low frequencies can be represented by the static characteristics

$$V_e = F_1(I_e, I_c) \qquad V_c = F_2(I_e, I_c) \qquad [9.1]$$

And the small a-c voltages v_e and v_c produced by small a-c currents i_e and i_c are

$$v_e = \frac{\partial F_1}{\partial I_e} i_e + \frac{\partial F_1}{\partial I_c} i_c \qquad [9.2]$$

$$v_c = \frac{\partial F_2}{\partial I_e} i_e + \frac{\partial F_2}{\partial I_c} i_c \qquad [9.3]$$

At low frequencies the four terms $\partial F_1/\partial I_e$, $\partial F_1/\partial I_c$, $\partial F_2/\partial I_e$, and $\partial F_2/\partial I_c$ are resistive, and so we can write

$$v_e = r_{11}i_e + r_{12}i_c \qquad [9.4]$$

$$v_c = r_{21}i_e + r_{22}i_c \qquad [9.5]$$

In terms of a three-terminal equivalent network, we have, for the grounded-base configuration, the circuit shown in Fig. 9.1:

$$r_{11} = r_e + r_b \qquad [9.6]$$

$$r_{12} = r_b \qquad [9.7]$$

$$r_{21} = r_m + r_b \qquad [9.8]$$

$$r_{22} = r_b + r_c \qquad [9.9]$$

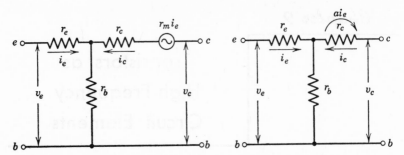

Fig. 9.1   The low-frequency equivalent circuit, grounded-base.

Solving the above four equations, we have the equivalent circuit parameters

$$r_e = r_{11} - r_{12} \tag{9.10}$$

$$r_b = r_{12} \tag{9.11}$$

$$r_c = r_{22} - r_{12} \tag{9.12}$$

$$r_m = r_{21} - r_{12} \tag{9.13}$$

$$\alpha = r_{21}/r_{22} \tag{9.14}$$

Since at low frequencies r_{11}, r_{12}, r_{21}, and r_{22} are resistive, the parameters of the equivalent circuit, r_e, r_b, r_c, and r_m, will be resistive and α will be a real number.   This fact greatly simplifies the numerical calculations at low frequencies.   The input and output impedances

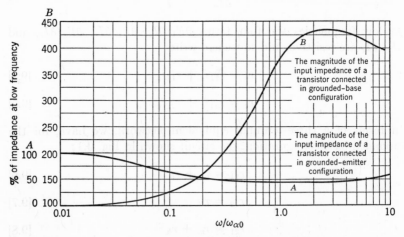

Fig. 9.2   The variation of the magnitude of the input impedance of a transistor amplifier with frequency.

will be resistive if a resistive load is used. The voltage amplification and the power gain can be found by simple arithmetic equations.

However, it has been observed that the properties of a transistor change when the signal frequency increases. The effect of changing properties of a transistor with signal frequency can be observed clearly by measuring the input and the output impedances for a given resistive load for different signal frequencies. Figure 9.2 is a plot of the absolute value of input impedance of a typical junction transistor against signal frequency, and Fig. 9.3 shows the variation of the ab-

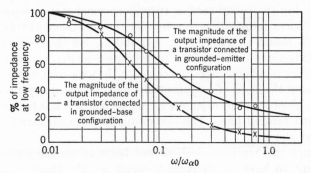

Fig. 9.3   The variation of the magnitude of the output impedance of a transistor amplifier with frequency.

solute value of the output impedance of a junction transistor with frequency. † Besides the variation of the magnitude of these impedances with frequency, the input impedance of a transistor is inductive for a grounded-base configuration, capacitive for a grounded-emitter configuration. However, the output impedances of both the grounded-base and the grounded-emitter connections are capacitive.

Examining the equations which were derived at low frequency for the input and output resistance, we see that they involve all the parameters of the equivalent circuit. Naturally, before we know which parameter or parameters contributed to the changes, we will assume that all these parameters of the equivalent circuit are changing with frequency.

Mathematically the above phenomena mean that we have to write

$$V_e = F_1{}' \, (I_e, I_c, \omega) \qquad\qquad [9.15]$$

$$V_c = F_2{}' \, (I_e, I_c, \omega) \qquad\qquad [9.16]$$

† The signal frequency is normalized with respect to the α cut-off frequency, $f_{\alpha 0}$, which is defined as the frequency at which $|\alpha|$ is 3 db below its low-frequency value α_0. The angular α cut-off frequency $\omega_{\alpha 0} = 2\pi f_{\alpha 0}$.

Namely, V_e, V_c are not only a function of I_e, I_c but also a function of frequency. The small signal a-c equations will be, for a given frequency,

$$\mathbf{v}_e = \frac{\partial F_1{}'}{\partial I_e} \, \mathbf{i}_e + \frac{\partial F_1{}'}{\partial I_c} \, \mathbf{i}_c = z_{11}\mathbf{i}_e + z_{12}\mathbf{i}_c \qquad [9.17]$$

$$\mathbf{v}_c = \frac{\partial F_2{}'}{\partial I_e} \, \mathbf{i}_e + \frac{\partial F_2{}'}{\partial I_c} \, \mathbf{i}_c = z_{21}\mathbf{i}_e + z_{22}\mathbf{i}_c \qquad [9.18]$$

where z_{11}, z_{12}, z_{21}, and z_{22} are complex numbers.

In the low-frequency case, a two-dimensional static characteristic gives sufficient information to construct the equivalent circuit parameters. As shown above, r_{11}, r_{12}, r_{21}, and r_{22} are the slopes of these static characteristic curves. At high frequencies z_{11}, z_{12}, z_{21}, and z_{22} are complex numbers. We can consider that the real component of each z gives the slope of a tangent line and the imaginary component of each z gives the slope of another tangent line which is perpendicular to the first tangent line. The two mutually perpendicular lines form a tangent plane.

Although this mathematical concept helps to see the problem it is convenient to have an equivalent circuit for the transistor at high frequency. This point will be studied in the next section.

The physical reasons accounting for the change of properties of a transistor are given in Chapter 1. In this chapter only two of the important effects are summarized. (1) The transit time effect plays a very important role in the decreasing value of the current amplification factor α. If all holes followed paths of equal length from emitter to collector, and took the same time, the current generator in the collector circuit would be a faithful but delayed replica of the input signal. If, however, holes travel in unequal paths, then the hole current at the collector will represent an average of the emitter currents at various previous times. If the spread of times is comparable to one cycle of an a-c input signal, there will be a great deal of cancellation and the gain will be reduced. (2) The collector-base voltage is essentially concentrated across the barrier layer at the collector end and is of the order of 5 volts for the junction type and 25 volts for the point-contact-type transistor. The capacitive effect for this layer becomes important at high frequencies.

9.2 Transistor Equivalent Circuits at High Frequency

Since high frequencies represent a very important field of transistor application, it is advisable to have an equivalent circuit useful for the circuit design calculation. It is preferable, in the first place, to have an equivalent circuit which has a simple configuration. Secondly, the high-frequency equivalent circuit should have approximately the same form as the low-frequency equivalent circuit. Consequently the equivalent circuits of a transistor at high frequencies may assume the following forms.

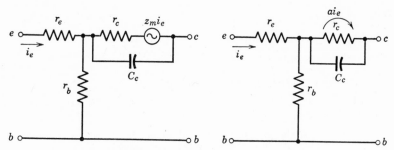

Fig. 9.4   The high-frequency grounded-base configurations.

9.2.1   Grounded-Base Configuration

The high-frequency equivalent circuits assume the T form with r_e and r_b branches and a third branch in which a capacitor C_c is shunted across r_c and the voltage-generator for the voltage-generator equivalent circuit. The capacitor C_c is in parallel with r_c for the case of the current-generator equivalent circuit as shown in Fig. 9.4.

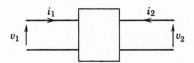

Fig. 9.5   A four-terminal network.

The output short-circuit vector current ratio $\mathbf{A}_i$ can be obtained as follows: Referring to Fig. 9.5, we have

$$v_1 = i_1 z_{11} + i_2 z_{12} \qquad [9.19]$$

$$v_2 = i_1 z_{21} + i_2 z_{22} \qquad [9.20]$$

For $v_2 = 0$

$$i_2/i_1 = -z_{21}/z_{22} \qquad [9.21]$$

In the grounded-base configuration, we have

$$z_{21} = r_b + jx_c z_m/(r_c + jx_c) \qquad [9.22]$$

$$z_{22} = r_b + jx_c r_c/(r_c + jx_c) \qquad [9.23]$$

where $x_c = -1/2\pi f C_c$. The output short-circuit current ratio $\mathbf{A}_i$ will be

$$\mathbf{A}_i = -\frac{r_b + jx_c z_m/(r_c + jx_c)}{r_b + jx_c r_c/(r_c + jx_c)} \qquad [9.24]$$

The negative sign in the above equation is due to the assumed i_2 direction in Fig. 9.5.

When $r_b \ll$ real component of $jx_c z_m/(r_c + jx_c)$ and also $\ll$ real component of $jx_c r_c/(r_c + jx_c)$, eq. 9.24 can be simplified to

$$\mathbf{A}_i \cong z_m/r_c = a \qquad [9.25]$$

The above expression has the same form as that of the expression of a_0 in the approximate low-frequency equivalent circuit. The difference is that a_0 is a real number and a is a complex quantity.

9.2.2   Grounded-Emitter Configuration

The grounded-emitter configuration is similar to the grounded-base configuration, a T circuit with the branches r_b and r_e interchanged with reference to the ground point, as shown in Fig. 9.6.

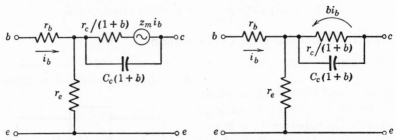

Fig. 9.6   The high-frequency grounded-emitter configuration.

For this configuration we can derive the output short-circuit current ratio $\mathbf{A}_i$ as follows:

$$z_{21} = r_e - jx_c z_m/(r_c + jx_c) \qquad [9.26]$$

$$z_{22} = r_e + \frac{jx_c r_c}{r_c + jx_c} - \frac{jx_c z_m}{r_c + jx_c}$$

$$= r_e + \frac{jx_c(r_c - z_m)}{r_c + jx_c} \qquad [9.27]$$

We get

$$\mathbf{A}_i = \frac{jx_c z_m/(r_c + jx_c) - r_e}{r_e + [(r_c - z_m)jx_c]/(r_c + jx_c)} \qquad [9.28]$$

When $r_e \ll$ real component of $\dfrac{jx_c z_m}{r_c + jx_c}$ or $\dfrac{(r_c - r_m)jx_c}{r_c + jx_c}$ then

$$\mathbf{A}_i \cong \frac{z_m}{r_c - z_m} \qquad [9.29]$$

This term has the same form as that of b_0 at low frequencies. Therefore we define b at high frequencies as

$$b = z_m/(r_c - z_m) = a/(1 - a) \qquad [9.30]$$

9.2.3 Grounded-Collector Configuration

Figure 9.7 shows the equivalent circuits of the grounded-collector configuration. The output short-circuit current ratio can be calculated as follows:

$$z_{21} = jx_c r_c/(r_c + jx_c) \qquad [9.31]$$

$$z_{22} = r_e + [jx_c r_c/(r_c + jx_c)] - [jx_c z_m/(r_c + jx_c)]$$

$$= r_e + [(r_c - z_m)jx_c]/(r_c + jx_c) \qquad [9.32]$$

The current ratio will be

$$\mathbf{A}_i = \frac{jx_c r_c/(r_c + jx_c)}{r_e + [(r_c - z_m)jx_c]/(r_c + jx_c)} \qquad [9.33]$$

Neglecting r_e, we have

$$\mathbf{A}_i \cong r_c/(r_c - z_m) = 1/(1 - a) = 1 + b \qquad [9.34]$$

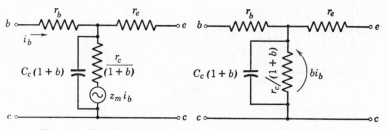

Fig. 9.7   The high-frequency grounded-collector configuration.

9.3   The Variation of α and b

According to definition the current-amplification factor α is

$$\alpha = \left(\frac{\partial I_c}{\partial I_e}\right)_V$$

From the above section, eq. 9.24 gives

$$\alpha = \frac{z_{21}}{z_{22}} = \frac{r_b + jx_c z_m/(r_c + jx_c)}{r_b + jx_c r_c/(r_c + jx_c)} \qquad [9.24]$$

When r_b is small,

$$\alpha \cong a = z_m/r_c \qquad [9.25]$$

The term b was defined as

$$b = a/(1 - a) \qquad [9.30]$$

The two terms a and b are very useful since they give approximately the output short-circuit current amplification for the grounded-base and the grounded-emitter configurations, respectively.

9.3.1   The Variation of α with Frequency

The value of α of a transistor has been found to vary considerably with the signal frequency. For a given operating point, the magnitude of α of a transistor is practically constant at low frequencies.

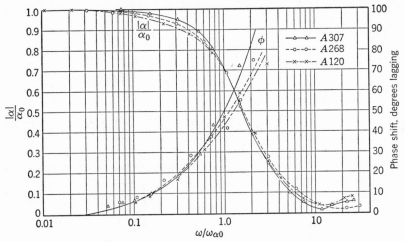

Fig. 9.8   The variation of α with frequency for three typical transistors.

When the signal frequency increases, the magnitude of α decreases at first slowly and then sharply until it reduces to a value of the order of a few per cent of the original value. At this low value the rate of attenuation becomes less and less and the $|\alpha|$ curve becomes flat or rises slightly, as shown in Fig. 9.8.

Besides the variation of the magnitude of α with frequency, there is a phase shift of α. At low frequencies α is a real number, but at high frequencies α is a complex number. The phase shift of α is very small and almost linear with frequency at the beginning as the signal frequency increases and then rises fairly rapidly. See Fig. 9.8.

(Note: the α cut-off frequency $f_{\alpha 0}$ has been defined as the frequency at which $|\alpha|$ is 3 db below its low-frequency value α_0.)

Since the magnitude of α of a given transistor in general is different from the magnitude of α of another transistor (this is true for the present-day techniques of making transistors), for the purpose of simplifying the process of analyzing the variation of α with frequency it is convenient to use the normalized term, that is, $|\alpha|/\alpha_0$ instead of $|\alpha|$. It is also convenient to plot $|\alpha|/\alpha_0$ against $\omega/\omega_{\alpha 0}$ instead of against the actual value of frequency for a particular transistor.

It has been found by measuring different transistors of both the point-contact and the junction types that there exists no single curve that can be applied to every transistor to give a theoretically accurate result for the variation of α with frequency. Nevertheless many experimental results have shown that, when $|\alpha|/\alpha_0$ is plotted against $\omega/\omega_{\alpha 0}$ for different transistors, all the curves follow a definite pattern fairly closely as shown in Fig. 9.8. For the convenience of circuit design at high frequencies, considerable effort has been devoted to obtaining an analytical expression which can be used to calculate the value of α at high frequency.

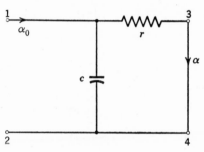

Fig. 9.9 A simple minimum-phase-shift network.

Two analytical expressions have been used. One is a simple minimum phase-shift network as shown in Fig. 9.9. With terminals 3 and 4 shorted, the current α will be

$$\alpha = \frac{\alpha_0(1/r)}{(1/r) + j\omega c}$$

$$= \frac{\alpha_0}{1 + j\omega cr} \qquad [9.31]$$

Letting $cr = 1/\omega_{\alpha 0}$, we have

$$\alpha = \frac{\alpha_0}{1 + j(\omega/\omega_{\alpha 0})} \qquad [9.32]$$

If we plot

$$\frac{\alpha}{\alpha_0} = \frac{1}{\sqrt{1 + (\omega/\omega_{\alpha 0})^2}} e^{-j \tan^{-1}(\omega/\omega_{\alpha 0})}$$

we get a curve as shown in Fig. 9.10.

Comparing Figs. 9.8 and 9.10, we see that for a value of $\omega/\omega_{\alpha 0}$ less than 1 this analytical expression gives a fairly close representation of the variation of α with frequency for both the magnitude and the angle of the phase shift. However, when $\omega/\omega_{\alpha 0}$ is larger than 1, the deviation between the measured and the calculated results becomes considerable. The magnitude of α calculated by means of this ana-

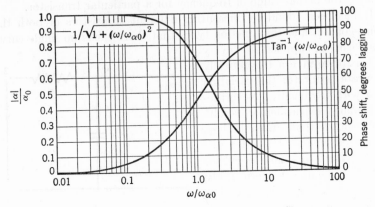

Fig. 9.10   The analytical expression $\alpha = \dfrac{\alpha_0}{1 + j\omega/\omega_{\alpha 0}}$.

lytical expression is larger than the measured value, and the calculated angle of phase shift is smaller than the measured value.†

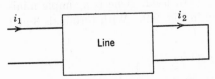

Fig. 9.11   A short-circuited transmission line.

The second analytical expression is obtained from the conception that the attenuation and the phase shift of this current amplification factor is due to the effect of a transmission line through which the current $\alpha_0 i_e$ has to pass before it reaches the outside circuit. In Fig. 9.11 is shown an output short-circuited transmission line. Let the constants of this line be

z = the series impedance per unit length

$\quad = r + j\omega l$

y = the shunt admittance per unit length

$\quad = g + j\omega c$

† A theoretical analysis of the variations of α with frequency, based on the diffusion equation, is given in Chapter 17.

The telegrapher's formula for the short-circuit output current is †

$$i_2 = i_1/\cosh \sqrt{zya^2} \qquad [9.33]$$

where a = the length of the line.

Now suppose that we feed α_0 to the transmission line; the current at the short-circuited output will be α

$$\alpha = \alpha_0/\cosh \sqrt{ZY} \qquad [9.34]$$

where $Z = za$ and $Y = ya$.

In general the product YZ is a complex number in which both the real and the imaginary components are dependent upon the signal frequency. In order to simplify the study of eq. 9.34, several simple cases are taken as follows.

Case 1. $Z = j\omega L; Y = j\omega C$. The shunt conductance and the series resistance of the line are assumed to be zero. The product $YZ = \omega^2 LC$. And $\cosh j\omega \sqrt{LC} = \cos \omega \sqrt{LC}$. It is evident that this case cannot represent the variation of α with frequency.

Case 2. $Z = R; Y = j\omega C$. The series inductance and the shunt conductance of the line are assumed to be zero. Here we have

$$\cosh \sqrt{YZ} = \cosh \sqrt{j\omega RC}$$

$$= \cosh (\sqrt{\omega RC}\, e^{j\pi/4})$$

$$= \cosh \sqrt{\omega RC/2} \quad \cos \sqrt{\omega RC/2}$$

$$+ j \sinh \sqrt{\omega RC/2} \quad \sin \sqrt{\omega RC/2} \qquad [9.35]$$

For our purpose, if eq. 9.34 can be used to represent the variation of α with frequency, then the magnitude of the expression $1/\cosh \sqrt{j\omega RC}$ has to be 3 db down at $\omega = \omega_{\alpha 0}$. This condition requires that $\omega_{\alpha 0} RC = 2.43$ or

$$\omega_{\alpha 0} = 2.43/RC \qquad [9.36]$$

Using the constant $\omega_{\alpha 0} RC = 2.43$ and plotting the variation of the expression $1/\cosh \sqrt{j\omega RC}$ against $\omega/\omega_{\alpha 0}$ we get the curves shown in Fig. 9.12.

Examining Fig. 9.12 and Fig. 9.8 we see that the magnitude of this expression $1/\cosh \sqrt{j\omega RC}$ represents the variation of the magnitude of α with frequency fairly well for the value of $\omega/\omega_{\alpha 0}$ up to 10. But

† F. E. Terman, *Radio Engineer's Handbook*, McGraw-Hill, 1943, p. 172.

the angle of phase shift given by this expression appears to be larger than the measured value when $\omega/\omega_{\alpha 0}$ is larger than 1. However, the phase shift of this expression does not limit it to a certain value as does eq. 9.31. This indicates that eq. 9.34 gives a better approximation of the variation of α with frequency.

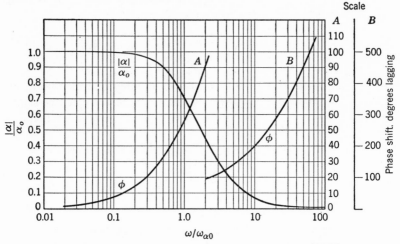

Fig. 9.12   The analytical expression $\alpha = \alpha_0/\cosh \sqrt{j\omega RC}$.

Case 3. $Z = j\omega L$; $Y = G$. The series resistance and the shunt capacitance are assumed to be zero. We have

$$\cosh \sqrt{YZ} = \cosh \sqrt{j\omega LG} \qquad [9.37]$$

and

$$\alpha/\alpha_0 = 1/\cosh \sqrt{j\omega LG} \qquad [9.38]$$

The similarity existing between eqs. 9.35 and 9.37 indicates that, if we let $\omega_{\alpha 0}LG = 2.43$, we get the same curves as shown in Fig. 9.12.

Either one of the last two simple transmission-line concepts can be used to represent the variation of α with frequency. However, the RC transmission-line concept appears to be more desirable for the reason explained in Sec. 9.4.

9.3.2   The Variation of b with Frequency

It was shown in Sec. 9.2.2 that, for a grounded-emitter configuration, the short-circuit current ratio

$$\mathbf{A}_i \cong z_m/(r_c - z_m) = a/(1 - a)$$

The term b was also defined as

$$b = a/(1 - a) \qquad [9.30]$$

When the parameter r_b of the equivalent circuit of a transistor is negligible in the α expression, we have $\alpha \cong a$ and

$$b \cong \alpha/(1 - \alpha) \qquad [9.39]$$

It has been shown in Sec. 9.3.1 that at high frequencies the magnitude of α decreases, and consequently the magnitude of $1/(1 - \alpha)$ may decrease quite rapidly. Of more importance, however, is the

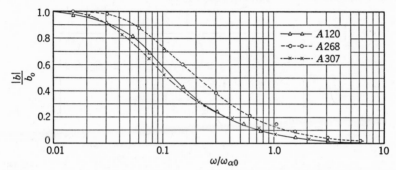

Fig. 9.13 Normalized variation of b vs. frequency for three typical transistors.

fact that the phase shift associated with α may cause a substantial decrease in the magnitude of $1/(1 - \alpha)$ at frequencies for which the magnitude of α has not decreased appreciably from its low-frequency value. This is illustrated in Fig. 9.13.

In general the current-amplification factor α can be written as a function of angular frequency ω:

$$\alpha = A(\omega)e^{jB(\omega)}$$

$$= \alpha_r + j\alpha_i \qquad [9.40]$$

where $A(\omega)$ and $B(\omega)$ are functions of ω. Substituting eq. 9.40 in eq. 9.39, and using A and B for $A(\omega)$ and $B(\omega)$ for simplicity, we have

$$b = \frac{Ae^{jB}}{(1 - A\cos B) - jA\sin B} \qquad [9.41]$$

At very low frequencies

$$\alpha = \alpha_0 \qquad b_0 \cong \alpha_0/(1 - \alpha_0) \qquad [9.42]$$

Using eq. 9.32 for α, we have

$$A(\omega) = \alpha_0/\sqrt{1 + (\omega/\omega_{\alpha 0})^2} \qquad [9.43]$$

$$B(\omega) = -\tan^{-1}(\omega/\omega_{\alpha 0}) \qquad [9.44]$$

When the signal frequency is still low, the value $(\omega/\omega_{\alpha 0})^2$ is much smaller than 1. Equation 9.40 can be written

$$\alpha \cong \alpha_0 \left[1 - \frac{1}{2}\left(\frac{\omega}{\omega_{\alpha 0}}\right)^2 \right] \left\{ \left[1 - \frac{1}{2}\left(\frac{\omega}{\omega_{\alpha 0}}\right)^2 \right] - j\left[\frac{\omega}{\omega_{\alpha 0}}\right] \right\} \qquad [9.45]$$

Substitution of eq. 9.45 in eq. 9.39 yields

$$|b| \cong \frac{\alpha_0[1 - \frac{1}{2}(\omega/\omega_{\alpha 0})^2]}{\left| \left\{ 1 - \alpha_0 \left[1 - \frac{1}{2}\left(\frac{\omega}{\omega_{\alpha 0}}\right)^2 \right] \left[1 - \frac{1}{2}\left(\frac{\omega}{\omega_{\alpha 0}}\right)^2 \right] \right\} - j\alpha_0 \left[1 - \frac{1}{2}\left(\frac{\omega}{\omega_{\alpha 0}}\right)^2 \right] \left[\frac{\omega}{\omega_{\alpha 0}} \right] \right|}$$

$$\cong \frac{\alpha_0/(1 - \alpha_0)}{\left| 1 + \frac{(\omega/\omega_{\alpha 0})^2}{(1 - \alpha_0)} \left[\frac{1}{2} + \frac{\alpha_0}{2} \right] - j\frac{\alpha_0}{1 - \alpha_0}\left(\frac{\omega}{\omega_{\alpha 0}}\right) \right|} \qquad [9.46]$$

The angular frequency at which the magnitude of b is 3 db below the value of b_0 can be found by letting the magnitude of the denominator in eq. 9.46 be 1.414 and solving for $\omega/\omega_{\alpha 0}$. The result gives

$$\frac{\omega_{b0}}{\omega_{\alpha 0}} \cong \left\{ \left(\frac{\alpha_0}{1 - \alpha_0}\right)^2 + \frac{1 + \alpha_0}{1 - \alpha_0} \right\}^{-\frac{1}{2}}$$

$$\cong \left\{ \frac{1}{(1 - \alpha_0)^2} \right\}^{-\frac{1}{2}}$$

$$\cong 1 - \alpha_0 \qquad [9.47]$$

This result shows that the frequency at which the magnitude of the grounded-emitter current ratio is down 3 db from its low-frequency value is of the order of $(1 - \alpha_0)$ times the frequency at which the magnitude of the current-amplification factor is 3 db below its low-frequency value. (See Fig. 9.13.) Hence, when α_0 is very close to unity, the grounded-emitter amplifier may cut off at a fairly low frequency, even though the α cut-off frequency may be relatively high. It should be noted that the 3-db decrease in the magnitude of b at frequency ω_{b0} is caused predominantly by the phase shift of α. Thus, if it were assumed that the amplitude of α decreased with no accompanying phase shift, then in eq. 9.45

$$\alpha \cong \alpha_0[1 - \tfrac{1}{2}(\omega/\omega_{\alpha0})^2]$$

and

$$b \cong \frac{\alpha_0}{1 + \tfrac{1}{2}(\omega/\omega_{\alpha0})^2 - \alpha_0}$$

$$\cong \frac{b_0}{1 + \tfrac{1}{2}\dfrac{(\omega/\omega_{\alpha0})^2}{1 - \alpha_0}}$$

The cut-off frequency would be

$$\frac{\omega_{b0}}{\omega_{\alpha0}} \cong \sqrt{2(\sqrt{2} - 1)(1 - \alpha_0)} \qquad [9.48]$$

When α_0 is close to unity, this frequency would be considerably higher than that given by eq. 9.47 when the phase shift of α is not neglected.

9.4 Variation of Other Parameters of the Equivalent Circuit

It is found that the change of properties with frequency at the terminals of a transistor cannot be explained by the variation of the current-amplification factor α alone. Results of measurements on several junction-type transistors indicate that besides the variation of α there are definite indications of variations of other parameters of the equivalent circuit.† This demands that either the high-frequency equivalent circuits have to be modified or the parameters have to be functions of frequency.

In Fig. 9.14 are shown the variations of r_c and C_c against $\omega/\omega_{\alpha0}$ for three junction transistors. Here the values of $1/r_c$ in μmhos are plotted against $\omega/\omega_{\alpha0}$ instead of r_c in ohms. The value of $1/r_c$ increases very rapidly when the frequency increases to near and beyond the value $f_{\alpha0}$. When $\omega/\omega_{\alpha0}$ goes from 1 to 10, the $1/r_c$ value has approximately a ratio of 1 to 5. However, the variation of C_c with frequency is less. A variation of $\omega/\omega_{\alpha0}$ from 0.1 to 10 gives approximately a ratio of C_c of 2 to 1.

† For point-contact transistors, measurements have indicated that parameters r_e, r_b, r_c, and C_c are essentially independent of frequency for frequencies up to 10 megacycles per second. See J. A. Becker and J. N. Shive, "The Transistor—A New Semiconductor Amplifier," *Elec. Eng.*, *68*, No. 3, p. 221 (March, 1949); or J. Bardeen and W. H. Brattain, "Physical Principles Involved in Transistor Action," *Phys. Rev.*, *75*, No. 8, pp. 1215–1216 (15 April, 1949); also in *Bell Sys. Tech. J.*, *28*, No. 2, p. 258 (April, 1949).

In order to relate these higher-frequency measurements to the normal low-frequency behavior of the transistor, analytical expressions are required. The two expressions discussed in Sec. 9.3 will be examined to see what significance they give to the variations of r_c and C_c with frequency.

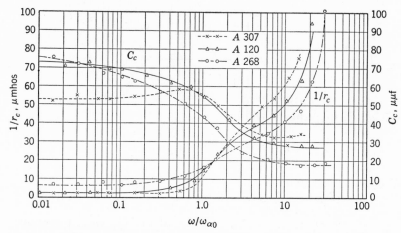

Fig. 9.14 The variation of r_c and C_c with frequency for three typical junction transistors.

According to the discussion in Sec. 9.3 we can construct an equivalent circuit including a passive four-terminal device inserted into the current generator $\alpha_0 i_e$ circuit to give the value of αi_e at high frequencies as shown in Fig. 9.15. The first four-terminal passive device discussed in Sec. 9.3 is a low-pass network as shown in Fig. 9.9. In-

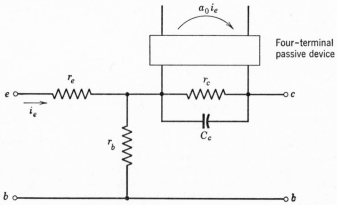

Fig. 9.15 General form of a modified equivalent circuit for high frequencies.

serting this network into the current generator circuit, the modified high-frequency equivalent circuit is shown in Fig. 9.16. With terminals e and b open, the open-circuit admittance measured at terminals c and b is the open-circuit collector-base admittance. The value

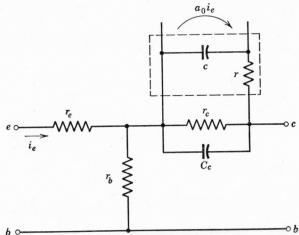

Fig. 9.16　A modified high-frequency equivalent circuit, including a low-pass network.

of r_b is usually of the order of several hundred ohms for junction transistors. The admittance measured at terminals c and b with terminals e and b open will be predominantly the admittance of r_c, C_c, and the low-pass network. Therefore we can write

$$y_c = 1/z_{22} \cong (1/r_c) + j\omega C_c + y \qquad [9.49]$$

where

$y =$ the admittance of the network

$$= \frac{\omega^2 c^2 r}{1 + (\omega c r)^2} + \frac{j\omega c}{1 + (\omega c r)^2} \qquad [9.50]$$

Now we see that both components of y_c are functions of frequency. Thus

$$g = \frac{1}{r_c} + \frac{\omega^2 c^2 r}{1 + (\omega c r)^2} \qquad [9.51]$$

and

$$b = \omega C_c + \frac{\omega c}{1 + (\omega c r)^2}$$

$$= \omega \left[C_c + \frac{c}{1 + (\omega c r)^2} \right] \qquad [9.52]$$

Examining eq. 9.50 by plotting $y/\omega c$ against $\omega/\omega_{\alpha 0}$ using $\omega_{\alpha 0} cr = 1$, we have Fig. 9.17. The two curves appear to be symmetrical with respect to the line $\omega/\omega_{\alpha 0} = 1.0$ on the semi-log scale. At small values

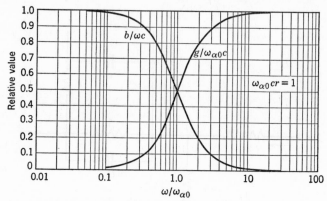

Fig. 9.17   The variation of the admittance $y = j\omega c/(1 + j\omega cr)$.

of $\omega/\omega_{\alpha 0}$, the conductance of y is very small; and at large values of $\omega/\omega_{\alpha 0}$, the susceptance of y is very small. Hence we can write at small values of $\omega/\omega_{\alpha 0}$

$$y_c \cong (1/r_c) + j\omega(C_c + c) \qquad [9.53]$$

At larger values of $\omega/\omega_{\alpha 0}$

$$y_c \cong (1/r_c) + (1/r) + j\omega C_c \qquad [9.54]$$

The value of C_c in eq. 9.54 can either be found from the high-frequency measurement of y_c, or it can be found directly by measuring the collector-base capacitance with the emitter current zero.

The accuracy of the approximate eq. 9.49 is good for a $\omega/\omega_{\alpha 0}$ value below 1.

The second four-terminal passive device discussed in Sec. 9.3 is an RC transmission line. Inserting this RC line in the current-generator circuit, we get a modified equivalent circuit as shown in Fig. 9.18. Using the same notation as in Sec. 9.3, the admittance of an open-circuit RC transmission line is †

$$y = g + jb = \sqrt{Y/Z}\,\tanh\sqrt{ZY}$$
$$= \sqrt{j\omega C/R}\,\tanh\sqrt{j\omega RC} \qquad [9.55]$$

† F. E. Terman, *Radio Engineering*, McGraw-Hill, 1947, p. 94.

A condition required for the value of RC is

$$\omega_{a0}RC = 2.43 \qquad [9.36]$$

Since this admittance y is effectively in parallel with r_c and C_c, the combined admittance is

$$y_c \cong (1/r_c) + j\omega C_c + y \qquad [9.56]$$

At low frequencies where $\omega RC/2 \ll 1$, eq. 9.55 can be written as

$$y \cong \sqrt{j\omega C/R}\ \sqrt{j\omega RC} = j\omega C \qquad [9.57]$$

This means that, at low frequencies, the series resistance of the line is negligible, and the line behaves as a simple capacitance. On the

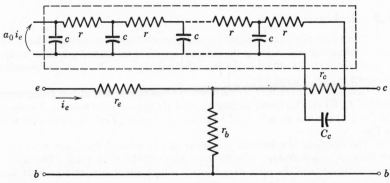

Fig. 9.18   The modified high-frequency equivalent circuit, RC transmission line.

other hand, for higher frequencies, the admittance of the line has equal real and imaginary parts which increase in magnitude as the square root of the frequency. Consequently, the effective capacitance of the line decreases as the square root of the frequency at higher frequencies.

Figure 9.19 shows the relative conductance $g/\omega_{a0}C$ and the relative capacitance $b/\omega C$ of the RC line as functions of ω/ω_{a0}, with the condition $\omega_{a0}RC = 2.43$.

Equation 9.56 indicates that the real part of the admittance y_c will be equal to $1/r_c$ at low frequencies and will increase as the square root of ω at high frequencies. On the other hand, the total effective collector-base capacitance will be equal to $(C_c + C)$ at low frequencies and will decrease toward C_c as the square root of ω for high frequencies. The accuracy of eq. 9.56 used to represent the variation of y_c is good for ω/ω_{a0} values up to 10.

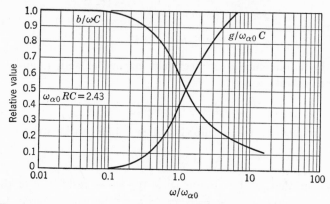

Fig. 9.19   The variation of the admittance y of the transmission line.

9.5   Problems

1. Prove that, for grounded-emitter and grounded-collector configurations, the value of shunting capacitance in the collector branch of the current-generator equivalent circuit is $(1 + b)$ times larger than that for the grounded-base configuration as shown in Figs. 9.6 and 9.7.

2. Given the magnitude of α of a junction transistor as 0.91 at low frequencies, and the $f_{\alpha 0}$ for this transistor as 1.03 mc, find the approximate b cut-off frequency f_{b0}. At 1.03 mc, the magnitude of b is found to be 0.9. Find the phase shift of α at $f_{\alpha 0}$.

3. The constants of a junction transistor at 1 kc are as follows: $\alpha = 0.95$, $r_c = 870$ kilohms, $r_b = 430$ ohms, $r_e = 25$ ohms, $f_{\alpha 0} = 220$ kc, $C_c = 18\mu\mu f$. The capacitance obtained from the open-circuit collector-base admittance at 1 kc is 51 $\mu\mu f$. Find the complex value of α at $f = 455$ kc.

4. Using the constants given in problem 3, find the open-circuit collector-base admittance y_c at $f = 455$ kc.

9.6   Bibliography

1. J. A. Becker and J. N. Shive, "The Transistor—a New Semiconductor Amplifier," *Elec. Eng.*, *68*, No. 3, p. 221 (March, 1949).

2. J. Bardeen and W. H. Brattain, "Physical Principles Involved in Transistor Action," *Phys. Rev.*, *75*, No. 8, pp. 1215–1216 (April, 1949).

3. Ryder and Kircher, "Some Circuit Aspects of the Transistor," *Bell Sys. Tech. J.*, *28*, 367–400 (July, 1949).

4. C. B. Brown, "Magnetically Biased Transistors," *Phys. Rev.*, *76*, 1736–1737 (December, 1950).

5. Wallace, Schimpf, and Dickten, "A Junction Tetrode for High Frequency Use," *Proc. IRE*, *40*, No. 11, pp. 1395–1400 (November, 1952).

6. J. M. Early, "Effects of Space-Charge Layer Widening in Junction Transistor," *Proc. IRE*, *40*, No. 11, pp. 1401–1406 (November, 1952).

7. E. L. Steele, "Theory of Alpha for *p-n-p* Diffused Junction Transistor," *Proc. IRE*, *40*, No. 11, pp. 1424–1428 (November, 1952).

8. R. L. Pritchard, "Frequency Variations of Current Amplification Factor for Junction Transistors," *Proc. IRE*, *40*, No. 11, pp. 1476–1480 (November, 1952).

Chapter 10

Basic Principles of High-Frequency Operation

In Chapter 9 the equivalent circuit of the transistor at high frequencies was discussed. Certain parameters of the equivalent circuit were shown to be functions of frequency. Analytical expressions were derived from which circuits may be designed. In this chapter the high-frequency equivalent circuit will be used to derive and study formulas useful in circuit design. Either the voltage-generator or the current-generator equivalent circuit can be used, however, as the current-generator equivalent circuit generally describes the behavior of a transistor better than the voltage equivalent circuit, it will be used in the following sections. Since the power gain of a transistor amplifier drops rapidly with increasing frequency, as we shall see later, we shall limit the discussion of the amplifier stage in this chapter to frequencies below the α cut-off frequency $f_{\alpha 0}$. We shall also assume that r_e and r_b are real and frequency-invariant.

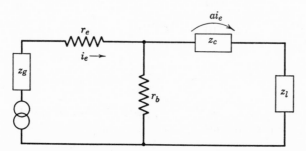

Fig. 10.1 A grounded-base equivalent circuit.

10.1 The Grounded-Base Amplifier

A grounded-base equivalent circuit is shown in Fig. 10.1. The impedance z_c is the total effective impedance in the collector circuit, z_l is the load impedance, and z_g is the signal source impedance as seen by the transistor. As has been shown in Chapter 9, a and z_c are functions of frequency. The analytical expressions discussed in Chapter 9 can be used; however, only the general symbols a and z_c will be used in the following discussion for the purpose of simplifying the derivation of the equations.

10.1.1 The Input and Output Impedances

The equations relating the input and output voltages and currents are

$$v_1 = i_1 z_{11} + i_2 z_{12} \quad [10.1]$$

$$v_2 = i_1 z_{21} + i_2 z_{22} \quad [10.2]$$

From Fig. 10.1 we have

$$z_{11} = r_e + r_b \quad [10.3]$$

$$z_{22} = r_b + z_c \quad [10.6]$$

$$z_{12} = r_b \quad [10.4]$$

$$v_2 = -i_2 z_l \quad [10.7]$$

$$z_{21} = r_b + a z_c \quad [10.5]$$

Substituting eq. 10.7 into eq. 10.2, and solving for i_2, yields

$$i_2 = \frac{-z_{21}}{z_l + z_{22}} i_1 \quad [10.8]$$

Combining eqs. 10.1 and 10.8, and solving for the input impedance,

$$z_i = v_1/i_1 = z_{11} - z_{12}z_{21}/(z_l + z_{22}) \quad [10.9]$$

Substituting eqs. 10.3, 10.4, 10.5, and 10.6 into eq. 10.9, and simplifying, yields

$$z_i = r_e + r_b \left[\frac{z_c(1 - a) + z_l}{r_b + z_c + z_l} \right] \quad [10.10]$$

Similarly, the output impedance $z_o = v_2/i_2$ as seen by the load impedance z_l can be obtained

$$z_o = z_c + r_b \left[\frac{r_e + z_g - a z_c}{r_e + r_b + z_g} \right] \quad [10.11]$$

In order to analyze the variation of z_i and z_o with frequency as a consequence of the variation of a and z_c with frequency, let us use the low-pass network concept for the variation of z_c and a with frequency as discussed in Chapter 9. We have

$$a = \frac{a_0}{1 + j\omega/\omega_{\alpha 0}} = \frac{a_0}{\sqrt{1 + (\omega/\omega_{\alpha 0})^2}} e^{-j \tan^{-1}(\omega/\omega_{\alpha 0})} \qquad [10.12]$$

and

$$1 - a = \sqrt{\frac{(1 - a_0)^2 + (\omega/\omega_{\alpha 0})^2}{1 + (\omega/\omega_{\alpha 0})^2}} \; e^{-j\left\{ \tan^{-1}\left(\frac{\omega}{\omega_{\alpha 0}}\right) - \tan^{-1}\left[\frac{\omega}{\omega_0(1 - a_0)}\right] \right\}}$$

$$[10.13]$$

For a junction transistor the magnitude of a is normally less than 1. Consequently eqs. 10.12 and 10.13 can be represented graphically as in Fig. 10.2.

The usefulness of eq. 10.12 is limited to frequencies below the α cut-off frequency $f_{\alpha 0}$ as discussed in Chapter 9. In Fig. 10.2 the solid

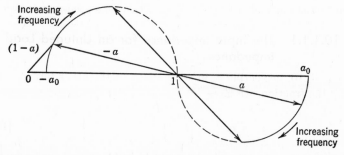

Fig. 10.2   The variation of $(1 - a)$ with frequency for a junction transistor.

curves show the loci of a and $(1 - a)$ for frequencies from zero to $f_{\alpha 0}$. It is clear from Fig. 10.2 that $(1 - a)$ has a phase angle which first increases and then decreases after passing through a maximum value. The value of this maximum phase angle of $(1 - a)$, and the frequency at which this maximum phase angle occurs, depend entirely on the value of a_0. Differentiating the expression

$$-\phi = \tan^{-1}\left(\frac{\omega}{\omega_{\alpha 0}}\right) - \tan^{-1}\left[\frac{\omega}{\omega_{\alpha 0}(1 - a_0)}\right] \qquad [10.14]$$

with respect to ω and setting $d\phi/d\omega = 0$, we have

$$\omega = [\sqrt{1 - a_0}]\omega_{\alpha 0} \qquad [10.15]$$

Equation 10.15 gives the frequency at which the maximum phase angle of $(1 - a)$ occurs. The value of this angle will be

$$\phi_m = \tan^{-1}\frac{1}{\sqrt{1 - a_0}} - \tan^{-1}\sqrt{1 - a_0} \qquad [10.16]$$

In the case of a point-contact transistor, the magnitude of a_0 is normally larger than 1. The vector $(1 - a)$ will therefore have the locus shown in Fig. 10.3.

As frequency increases, the phase angle ϕ of $(1 - a)$ will decrease from π to zero and then go slightly into the negative region.

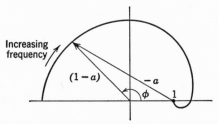

Fig. 10.3   The variation of $(1 - a)$ with frequency for a point-contact transistor.

10.1.1.1   The Input Impedance for an Untuned Load Impedance

In eq. 10.10, neglecting r_b in comparison to the other terms, and re-writing the fraction, we have

$$z_i = r_e + r_b \left[\frac{(1 - a) + (z_l/z_c)}{1 + (z_l/z_c)} \right] \qquad [10.17]$$

When a pure resistance r_l is used as the load the phase angle of r_l/z_c will depend entirely on z_c. For a junction transistor, the variation of z_c with frequency was discussed in Chapter 9. At low frequencies, z_c and a can be considered as real numbers and the input impedance is resistive. At high frequencies, the phase angles of a and z_c must be included.

The vector diagrams for $(1 - a) + (r_l/z_c)$ and $1 + r_l/z_c$ are shown in Fig. 10.4. It is clear that the fraction $\dfrac{(1 - a) + (r_l/z_c)}{1 + (r_l/z_c)}$ will give a positive imaginary term. The input impedance will therefore have an inductive component which increases gradually to a maximum value and then decreases with increasing frequency. Besides the variation of the phase angle of the input impedance with frequency, the magnitude of the input impedance also changes, increasing slowly at first and then more rapidly, finally approaching a value of approximately $r_e + r_b$. The effect of the magnitude of r_l on the input impedance z_i at a given frequency can be studied by noting the effect of the ratio r_l/z_c in the fraction $\dfrac{(1 - a) + (r_l/z_c)}{1 + (r_l/z_c)}$. At any fixed frequency, an increase in the magnitude of the ratio r_l/z_c will give an increase in input impedance and a decrease in phase angle. The

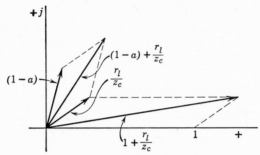

Fig. 10.4   The vector diagram for $(1 - a) + r_l/z_c$ and $(1 + r_l/z_c)$.

variation of input impedance with frequency for a typical junction transistor is shown in Fig. 10.5.

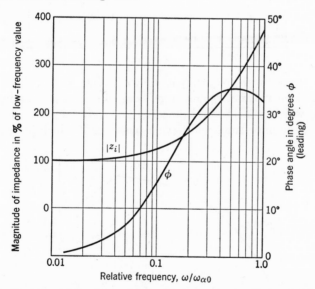

Fig. 10.5   Variation of input impedance with frequency for a grounded-base junction transistor amplifier using resistance as load.

For a point-contact transistor, the components of z_c, r_c, and C_c in parallel are usually assumed to be constant.

$$z_c = -jr_cx_c/(r_c - jx_c) \qquad [10.18]$$

where $x_c = 1/2\pi f C_c$.

Substituting eq. 10.18 into eq. 10.17, and using eq. 10.12 for a, we have

$$z_i = r_e + r_b \left[\frac{\left(1 - \dfrac{a_0}{1 + j\omega/\omega_{\alpha 0}}\right) + \dfrac{r_l(r_c - jx_c)}{-jr_c x_c}}{1 + r_l(r_c - jx_c)/-jr_c x_c} \right] \qquad [10.19]$$

Simplifying eq. 10.19 yields

$$z_i = r_e + r_b \left[\frac{\left[1 - \dfrac{a_0}{1 + (\omega/\omega_{\alpha 0})^2} + \dfrac{r_l}{r_c}\right] + j\left[\dfrac{a_0(\omega/\omega_{\alpha 0})}{1 + (\omega/\omega_{\alpha 0})^2} + \dfrac{r_l}{x_c}\right]}{1 + r_l/r_c + jr_l/x_c} \right]$$

$$[10.20]$$

Since the value of a_0 is normally larger than 1, if r_l/x_c may be considered negligible for a wide range of frequencies below the α cut-off frequency $f_{\alpha 0}$, the fraction becomes

$$\frac{\left[1 + \dfrac{r_l}{r_c} - \dfrac{a_0}{1 + (\omega/\omega_{\alpha 0})^2}\right] + j\left[\dfrac{a_0(\omega/\omega_{\alpha 0})}{1 + (\omega/\omega_{\alpha 0})^2}\right]}{1 + (r_l/r_c)} \qquad [10.21]$$

which will vary with frequency as shown in Fig. 10.6.

For a given value of r_l/r_c a large value of a_0 will give an input impedance which is a low resistance at low frequency. As frequency increases, the impedance will have a phase angle which increases and

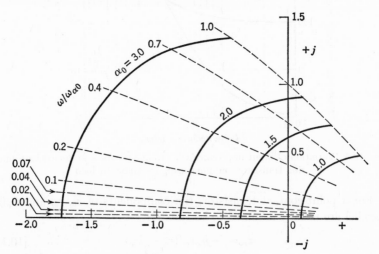

Fig. 10.6   Equation 10.21 for $r_l/r_c = 0.1$.

then decreases after passing through a maximum value. If a_0 is large enough, the input impedance may have a negative resistance component.

10.1.1.2 The Input Impedance for a Tuned Load Impedance

When a tuned LC circuit is used as load as shown in Fig. 10.7, the impedance reflected to the input side of a transistor will depend on the location of the resonant frequency of this tuned circuit relative to the α cut-off frequency, $f_{\alpha 0}$.

If the resonant frequency of this tuned circuit is much lower than the α cut-off frequency $f_{\alpha 0}$, and if the phase angles of a and z_c are small, then the impedance of the tuned circuit will be reflected in the input impedance. At a frequency lower than the reso-

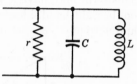

Fig. 10.7 A tuned LC circuit as load.

nant frequency, an inductive impedance component will appear at the transistor input; and when the signal frequency is higher than the resonant frequency of this tuned circuit, a capacitive impedance component will appear at the input.

However, if the resonant frequency of the tuned circuit is comparable to $f_{\alpha 0}$ the phase angles of a and z_c cannot be neglected. The effect of the tuned circuit, in general, will be masked and cannot be seen clearly in the input impedance.

At resonant frequency, r is the effective load. For a fixed value of L and C, the variation of r is the variation of the Q of the tuned circuit. Changing the Q of the load circuit at resonance will, therefore, have the same effect as changing the load resistance, as discussed in Sec. 10.1.1.

10.1.1.3 The Output Impedance of a Grounded-Base Amplifier

Equation 10.11 gives the output impedance of a grounded-base amplifier as

$$z_o = z_c + r_b \left[\frac{r_e + z_g - az_c}{r_e + r_b + z_g} \right] \qquad [10.11]$$

Rewriting eq. 10.11, we have

$$z_o = z_c \left(1 - \frac{ar_b}{r_e + r_b + z_g} \right) + \frac{r_b(r_e + z_g)}{r_b + r_e + z_g} \qquad [10.22]$$

For impedance matching in the input circuits we have

$$z_g = r_e + Kr_b \qquad [10.23]$$

where K represents the fraction in eq. 10.10.

The second term on the right-hand side of eq. 10.22 can be written as

$$r_b \left[\frac{2r_e + Kr_b}{2r_e + (1 + K)r_b} \right] \qquad [10.24]$$

This term may have a value up to r_b. The fraction in the first term on the right-hand side of eq. 10.22 can be written $ar_b/[2r_e + (1 + K)r_b]$, and normally has a value between a and $a/2$.

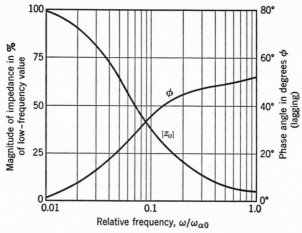

Fig. 10.8 Variation of output impedance with frequency for a grounded-base junction transistor amplifier with resistance in the input circuit.

Since r_b is generally small in comparison with z_c, neglecting the second term on the right-hand side of eq. 10.22 we have

$$z_o \cong z_c \left(1 - \frac{ar_b}{r_e + r_b + z_g} \right) \qquad [10.25]$$

The output impedance will be capacitive since z_c is capacitive. Figure 10.8 shows the variation with frequency of output impedance of a grounded-base amplifier.

10.1.2   The Power Gain of a Grounded-Base Amplifier

The general equation for power gain can be derived from eqs. 10.1, 10.2, 10.7, and 10.9. The input power is

$$P_i = |i_1|^2 (z_i)_R \qquad [10.26]$$

Here $(z_i)_R$ represents the real component of z_i. The output power is

$$P_o = |i_2|^2 (z_l)_R \qquad [10.27]$$

where $(z_l)_R$ represents the real component of z_l. The power gain G will be

$$G = \frac{P_o}{P_i} = \frac{|i_2|^2 (z_l)_R}{|i_1|^2 (z_i)_R} \qquad [10.28]$$

Substituting eqs. 10.8 and 10.9 into eq. 10.28 yields

$$G = \frac{|-z_{21}/(z_l + z_{22})|^2 (z_l)_R}{[z_{11} - z_{12}z_{21}/(z_l + z_{22})]_R} \qquad [10.29]$$

For the grounded-base amplifier, substituting eqs. 10.3 to 10.6 into eq. 10.29 we have

$$G = \frac{|r_b + az_c|^2 (z_l)_R}{|z_l + r_b + z_c|^2 \left\{ r_e + r_b \left[\dfrac{z_c(1 - a) + z_l}{r_b + z_c + z_l} \right] \right\}_R} \qquad [10.30]$$

Letting the load be a resistance r_l and neglecting r_b in comparison with z_c yields

$$G \cong \frac{|az_c|^2 r_l}{|r_l + z_c|^2 \left\{ r_e + r_b \left[\dfrac{z_c(1 - a) + r_l}{z_c + r_l} \right] \right\}_R} \qquad [10.31]$$

Let the power gain at low frequency, that is at $\omega/\omega_{a0} \ll 1$, be G_0; the ratio of power gain at high frequency to that at low frequency will be

$$\frac{G}{G_0} \cong \frac{|az_c|^2}{(a_0 r_c)^2} \frac{(r_l + r_c)^2}{|r_l + z_c|^2} \frac{r_i}{(z_i)_R} \qquad [10.32]$$

where r_c is the value of z_c when $\omega/\omega_{a0} \ll 1$

r_i is the value of z_i when $\omega/\omega_{a0} \ll 1$

when r_l is relatively small in comparison with r_c, then $\left|\dfrac{z_c}{r_c}\right|^2 \left|\dfrac{r_l + r_c}{r_l + z_c}\right|^2$ will be approximately unity. If we consider $r_i/(z_i)_R \cong 1$ as a first approximation, the power gain will be roughly

$$\frac{G}{G_0} \cong \left| \frac{a}{a_0} \right|^2 \qquad [10.33]$$

Using eq. 10.12 for the magnitude of a we have

$$\frac{G}{G_0} \cong \frac{1}{1 + (\omega/\omega_{a0})^2} \qquad [10.34]$$

Let us define a frequency f_{G0} at which the power gain drops 3 db from its low-frequency value as the power cut-off frequency. We have, from eq. 10.34,

$$\frac{G}{G_0} = \frac{1}{2} = \frac{1}{1 + (\omega_{G0}/\omega_{\alpha 0})^2} \qquad [10.35]$$

or

$$\omega_{G0} = \omega_{\alpha 0} \qquad [10.36]$$

Taking into consideration the variation of $(z_i)_R$ with frequency the power cut-off frequency will be lower than that given by eq. 10.36.

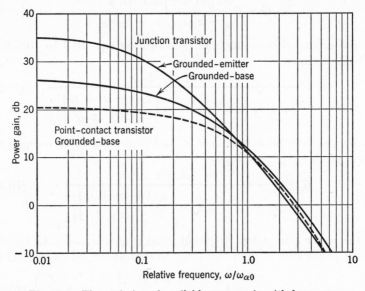

Fig. 10.9   The variation of available power gain with frequency.

For example, a value of $r_i/(z_i)_R = 0.8$ will give an ω_{G0} of about $0.77\omega_{\alpha 0}$. A power cut-off frequency of only a few per cent of the α cut-off frequency is not unusual. The variation of power gain with frequency for a grounded-base amplifier is shown in Fig. 10.9.

10.1.3   The Voltage Amplification of a Grounded-Base Amplifier

The voltage ratio in vector form is

$$\mathbf{A}_v = \frac{v_2}{v_1} = \frac{i_1 z_{21} + i_2 z_{22}}{i_1 z_{11} + i_2 z_{12}}$$

$$= \frac{z_{21} + z_{22}(i_2/i_1)}{z_{11} + z_{12}(i_2/i_1)} \qquad [10.37]$$

Substituting eqs. 10.3, 10.4, 10.5, 10.6, and 10.8 into eq. 10.37 yields

$$\mathbf{A}_v = \frac{(r_b + az_c)z_l}{r_e(z_l + z_c) + r_b(r_e + z_l + z_c - az_c)} \qquad [10.38]$$

Neglecting r_b in the numerator, and r_e in the second bracket in the denominator, eq. 10.38 can be regrouped to give

$$\mathbf{A}_v = \frac{az_l}{r_e[1 + (z_l/z_c)] + r_b[(z_l/z_c) + 1 - a]} \qquad [10.39]$$

Equation 10.39 gives both the magnitude and the phase angle of the voltage ratio of a grounded-base amplifier.

The voltage amplification of a grounded-base amplifier will be the magnitude of eq. 10.39

$$A_v = \left| \frac{az_l}{r_e\left(1 + \dfrac{z_l}{z_c}\right) + r_b\left(\dfrac{z_l}{z_c} + 1 - a\right)} \right| \qquad [10.40]$$

Let the voltage amplification at low frequency be A_{v0}

$$A_{v0} = \frac{a_0 r_l}{r_e\left(1 + \dfrac{r_l}{r_c}\right) + r_b\left(\dfrac{r_l}{r_c} + 1 - a_0\right)} \qquad [10.41]$$

where r_l is the low-frequency value of z_l. The ratio of the voltage amplification at high frequency to that at low frequency will be

$$\frac{A_v}{A_{v0}} = \left| \frac{az_l}{a_0 r_l} \right| \left| \frac{r_e\left(1 + \dfrac{r_l}{r_c}\right) + r_b\left(\dfrac{r_l}{r_c} + 1 - a_0\right)}{r_e\left(1 + \dfrac{z_l}{z_c}\right) + r_b\left(\dfrac{z_l}{z_c} + 1 - a\right)} \right| \qquad [10.42]$$

When the load is a resistance, the ratio A_v/A_{v0} will be approximately $|a/a_0|$ multiplied by a fraction which depends on the load resistance. If we define a voltage amplification cut-off frequency f_{A0} as a frequency at which the voltage amplification is 3 db down from its low-frequency value, we can see from eq. 10.42 that the cut-off frequency f_{A0} is lower than f_{a0}. The effect of the value of r_l upon the cut-off frequency f_{A0} is relatively slight. However, since the voltage amplification of a grounded-base amplifier does depend on the load it is possible to compensate the voltage amplification at high frequencies. The variation of voltage amplification of a grounded-base amplifier with load resistance is shown in Fig. 10.10.

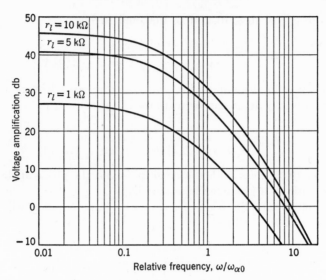

Fig. 10.10   The variation of voltage amplification with frequency.

10.2   The Grounded-Emitter Amplifier

Figure 10.11 shows a grounded-emitter equivalent circuit with z_l as load impedance and z_g as the source impedance.   The four impedances z_{11}, z_{12}, z_{21}, and z_{22} will be

$$z_{11} = r_b + r_e \qquad [10.43]$$

$$z_{12} = r_e \qquad [10.44]$$

$$z_{21} = r_e - az_c \qquad [10.45]$$

$$z_{22} = r_e + z_c/(1 + b) \qquad [10.46]$$

and

$$v_2 = -i_2 z_l$$

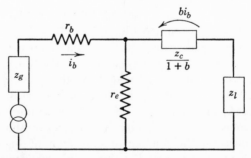

Fig. 10.11   A grounded-emitter equivalent circuit.

10.2.1   The Input and Output Impedances

The input impedance of a grounded-emitter amplifier can be derived immediately from eq. 10.9 and eqs. 10.43 to 10.46.   The input impedance of a grounded-emitter amplifier is

$$z_i = r_b + r_e \left[\frac{z_l + z_c}{r_e + z_l + (1 - a)z_c} \right] \qquad [10.47]$$

Neglecting r_e in the denominator, and rewriting the fraction, we obtain

$$z_i \cong r_b + r_e \left[\frac{1 + (z_l/z_c)}{(1 - a) + (z_l/z_c)} \right] \qquad [10.48]$$

When $\left| z_l/z_c \right| \ll \left| 1 - a \right|$, eq. 10.48 becomes

$$z_i \cong r_b + r_e(1 + b) \qquad [10.49]$$

We have seen that b decreases rapidly with frequency.   Equation 10.49 shows that the input impedance of a grounded-emitter amplifier has a magnitude which decreases with increasing frequency and approaches the value $r_b + r_e$ when the signal frequency is high.   For a given frequency, z_i decreases as the ratio z_l/z_c increases.   When the load is a pure resistance, the input impedance of a grounded-emitter amplifier is capacitive.   The phase angle of the input impedance increases with frequency, and then decreases after passing through a maximum point.   This maximum point will occur at a frequency near the frequency at which $(1 - a)$ has a maximum phase angle.

When a parallel tuned circuit as shown in Fig. 10.7 is used as a load, the characteristics of a parallel tuned circuit will appear clearly at the input side of the amplifier only when the resonant frequency of this tuned circuit is much lower than the α cut-off frequency $f_{\alpha 0}$.

10.2.1.1   The Output Impedance of a Grounded-Emitter Amplifier

Using the same method as in deriving the input impedance, the output impedance of a grounded-emitter amplifier is found to be

$$z_o = (1 - a)z_c + r_e \left[\frac{(r_b + z_g + az_c)}{z_g + r_b + r_e} \right] \qquad [10.50]$$

In order to study the variation of z_o with frequency, let us neglect $r_b + z_g$ in comparison with az_c, and consider $r_e/(z_g + r_b + r_e) = K$, a constant fraction.   We have

$$z_o \cong (1 + Ka - a)z_c \qquad [10.51]$$

Since the point-contact transistor is seldom used as a grounded-emitter amplifier, we will discuss the junction transistor only. The order of

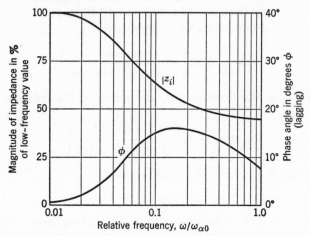

Fig. 10.12   Variation of input impedance with frequency for a grounded-emitter junction transistor amplifier.

magnitude of r_e of a junction transistor is about one-tenth of r_b. If z_g is comparable to r_b, the value of K is about 0.05. Neglecting the Ka term in eq. 10.51 yields

$$z_o \cong (1 - a)z_c \qquad [10.52]$$

Equation 10.52 shows that z_o decreases with frequency owing to the decrease of z_c with frequency. The phase angle of z_o will be ap-

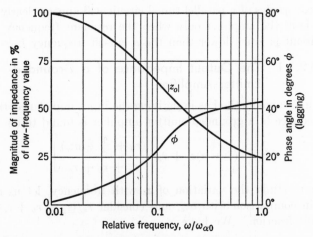

Fig. 10.13   Variation of output impedance with frequency for a grounded-emitter junction transistor amplifier.

proximately the difference of the phase angles of $(1 - a)$ and z_c. The variation of the input and output impedance of a grounded-emitter amplifier using a junction transistor is shown in Figs. 10.12 and 10.13.

10.2.2 The Power Gain of a Grounded-Emitter Amplifier

The equation for power gain of a grounded-emitter amplifier is

$$G = \left| \frac{az_c - r_e}{z_l + r_e + z_c(1 - a)} \right|^2 \frac{(z_l)_R}{(z_i)_R} \qquad [10.53]$$

where $(z_l)_R$ means the real component of z_l, and $(z_i)_R$ means the real component of z_i.

Neglecting r_e in eq. 10.53, and letting $z_l = z_c(1 - a)$ to produce an approximate impedance match, we have

$$G \cong \left| \frac{az_c}{2z_c(1 - a)} \right|^2 \frac{(z_l)_R}{(z_i)_R}$$

$$= \left| b/2 \right|^2 (z_l)_R / (z_i)_R \qquad [10.54]$$

Comparing eqs. 10.54 and 10.31, we see that since b is much larger than a at low frequencies we can get more power gain from a grounded-emitter amplifier than from a grounded-base amplifier using the same junction transistor.

Let the power gain at low frequency of a grounded-emitter amplifier be G_0

$$G_0 \cong \left(\frac{b_0}{2} \right)^2 \frac{r_l}{r_i} \qquad [10.55]$$

where r_l is the value of z_l at low frequency and r_i is the value of z_i at low frequency.

The ratio of power gain at high frequency to that at low frequency is

$$\frac{G}{G_0} \cong \left| \frac{b}{b_0} \right|^2 \frac{(z_l)_R}{r_l} \frac{r_i}{(z_i)_R} \qquad [10.56]$$

For a rough approximation, letting $[(z_l)_R / r_l][r_i / (z_i)_R] \cong 1$, we have

$$\frac{G}{G_0} \cong \left| \frac{b}{b_0} \right|^2 \qquad [10.57]$$

In Chapter 9, we showed the variation of b with frequency. In eq. 9.47 we have

$$\frac{\omega_{b0}}{\omega_{\alpha 0}} \cong 1 - a_0 \qquad [9.47]$$

which says that the b cut-off frequency is much lower than the α cut-off frequency. Consequently eq. 10.57 indicates that the power gain cut-off frequency f_{G0} defined in Sec. 10.1.2 will be lower than the b cut-off frequency and therefore much lower than the α cut-off frequency. The variation of power gain with frequency for a grounded-emitter amplifier using a junction transistor is shown in Fig. 10.9.

10.2.3 The Voltage Amplification of a Grounded-Emitter Amplifier

The equation for the voltage amplification of a grounded-emitter amplifier is

$$A_v = \left| \frac{z_l(az_c - r_e)}{r_b[(1 - a)z_c + r_e + z_l] + r_e[z_c + z_l]} \right| \qquad [10.58]$$

Neglecting the term r_e and rewriting terms of z_l/z_c yields

$$A_v \cong \left| \frac{az_l}{r_b[(1 - a) + (z_l/z_c)] + r_e[1 + (z_l/z_c)]} \right| \qquad [10.59]$$

The term $|\, z_l/z_c\, |$ is usually much less than 1 but may be comparable to $(1 - a)$. If the voltage amplification at low frequency is A_{v0}, then for a rough approximation

$$\frac{A_v}{A_{v0}} \cong \left| \frac{az_l}{a_0 r_l} \right| \left| \frac{(1 - a_0) + r_l/r_c}{(1 - a) + z_l/z_c} \right| \qquad [10.60]$$

The frequency at which the voltage amplification is 3 db down from the low-frequency value will be around the b cut-off frequency. When all the factors in eq. 10.59 are taken into consideration, the voltage amplification cut-off frequency may be less than the b cut-off frequency. However, when an inductive impedance is used as load the actual voltage gain at high frequencies may be increased. The variation of voltage amplification of a grounded-emitter amplifier with load resistance is shown in Fig. 10.10.

10.3 The Grounded-Collector Amplifier

The equivalent circuit of a grounded-collector amplifier is shown in Fig. 10.14.

As before, z_l is the load impedance and z_g is the source impedance. The four impedances z_{11}, z_{12}, z_{21}, and z_{22} will be

$$z_{11} = r_b + z_c \qquad [10.61] \qquad\qquad z_{21} = z_c \qquad [10.63]$$

$$z_{12} = z_c/(1 + b) \qquad [10.62] \qquad\qquad z_{22} = r_e + z_c/(1 + b) \qquad [10.64]$$

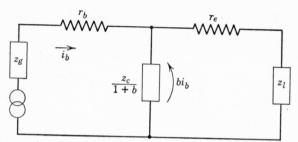

Fig. 10.14   A grounded-collector equivalent circuit.

10.3.1   The Input and Output Impedances of a Grounded-Collector Amplifier

The input impedance of a grounded-collector amplifier can be found by the same method as described in Sec. 10.1.   It is found to be

$$z_i = r_b + z_c \left[\frac{r_e + z_l}{r_e + z_l + z_c/(1+b)} \right] \qquad [10.65]$$

The input impedance is very much dependent on the value of z_l, the load impedance, since it appears in the numerator as the only variable.

When a resistance r_l is used as load, and r_e is much smaller than r_l, we have

$$z_i \cong r_b + z_c \left[\frac{r_l}{r_l + z_c/(1+b)} \right]$$

$$\cong r_b + \frac{r_l}{(r_l/z_c) + 1/(1+b)} \qquad [10.66]$$

Since the output impedance of a grounded-collector amplifier is very low, indicating that r_l should be low, we can neglect r_l/z_c in comparison with $1/(1+b)$.   We have now

$$z_i \cong r_b + (1+b)r_l \qquad [10.67]$$

Equation 10.67 gives a picture of the order of the magnitude and phase angle of the input impedance of a grounded-collector amplifier. The variation of input impedance with frequency is due mainly to the variation of $(1+b)$ with frequency.

If a parallel tuned circuit is used as the load, and if the resonant frequency is low enough that the factor $(1+b)$ has little phase shift, then the characteristics of the parallel tuned circuit will appear in the input impedance clearly.   Otherwise the phase shift of the factor $(1+b)$ will mask the change of the phase angle of the load z_l with frequency.

The equation for the output impedance of a grounded-collector amplifier is

$$z_o = r_e + \frac{z_c}{1 + b}\left(\frac{r_b + z_g}{r_b + z_g + z_c}\right) \qquad [10.68]$$

Simplifying eq. 10.68 by neglecting $r_b + z_g$ in the denominator yields

$$z_o \cong r_e + (r_b + z_g)/(1 + b) \qquad [10.69]$$

Equation 10.69 also shows clearly that the variation of z_o with frequency is due principally to the variation of $(1 + b)$ with frequency.

10.3.2 The Power Gain of a Grounded-Collector Amplifier

The equation for the power gain of a grounded-collector amplifier is

$$G = \left|\frac{z_c}{z_l + r_e + z_c/(1 + b)}\right|^2 \frac{(z_l)_R}{(z_i)_R} \qquad [10.70]$$

where $(z_l)_R$ is the real component of the load z_l, and $(z_i)_R$ is the real component of the input impedance z_i. Let the load be a resistance r_l, and use eq. 10.67 for z_i. Then

$$G = \left|\frac{z_c}{r_l + r_e + z_c/(1 + b)}\right|^2 \frac{r_l}{[r_b + (1 + b)r_l]_R} \qquad [10.71]$$

For a qualitative study, neglecting $r_l + r_e$ and r_b terms, we have

$$G \cong |1 + b| \qquad [10.72]$$

Equation 10.72 gives a good approximation for the power gain of a grounded-collector amplifier. When the terms $r_l + r_e$ and r_b are included, the power gain will be less than that given in eq. 10.72.

10.3.3 The Voltage Amplification of a Grounded-Collector Amplifier

The voltage amplification of a grounded-collector amplifier is

$$A_v = \left|\frac{z_l z_c}{z_c(r_e + z_l) + r_b[z_c/(1 + b) + r_e + z_l]}\right| \qquad [10.73]$$

Simplifying eq. 10.73 by neglecting r_e yields

$$A_v \cong \left|\frac{1}{1 + (r_b/z_l z_c)[z_c/(1 + b) + z_l]}\right| \qquad [10.74]$$

If z_l can be neglected in comparison with $z_c/(1 + b)$, we have

$$A_v \cong \left| \frac{1}{1 + r_b/[z_l(1 + b)]} \right| \qquad [10.75]$$

It is evident from eq. 10.75 that the voltage amplification of a grounded-collector amplifier is less than unity. As the frequency in-

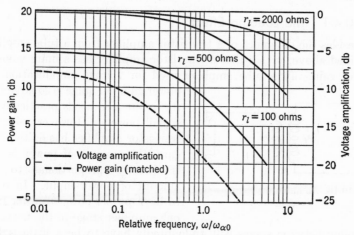

Fig. 10.15 The variation of the available power gain and the voltage amplification of a grounded-collector amplifier.

creases, the voltage amplification drops further owing to the decrease of the value $(1 + b)$.

The variation of the power gain and the voltage amplification of a grounded-collector amplifier using resistance as load is shown in Fig. 10.15.

10.4 Gain-Bandwidth Considerations

The impedances and the power gain of a single-stage transistor amplifier of three different connections were discussed in the previous three sections. Of the many differences existing between a transistor and a tube, one important difference merits our attention here: the relation between the input side and the output side of a transistor amplifier. Unlike the vacuum-tube amplifier of which the input side is practically isolated from the output side, the input impedance of a transistor amplifier is a function of the load impedance as shown in the above three sections.

The problem introduced by the close relation between the input side and the output side impedances of a transistor amplifier appears when several tuned transistor amplifier stages are cascaded. The load impedance of the first stage will depend on the load impedance of the second stage, and the load impedance of the second stage will depend on the load impedance of the third stage, and so on. On the other hand any change of the source impedance of the first amplifier stage will appear at the input side of the second amplifier stage, and so forth.

10.4.1 The Loading Effect

Besides the difference of a transistor amplifier from a tube amplifier outlined above, we see that a transistor amplifier has a finite value of power gain. In a tube amplifier used for voltage amplification the power gain per stage is so large that the input side needs practically no signal power. However, since a transistor amplifier has finite power gain, the amount of power output is directly proportional to the amount of power input. In order to have proper power transfer from one amplifier stage to the next, the coupling between stages will undoubtedly have to be a little tighter than that required for tube amplifiers used as voltage amplifiers.

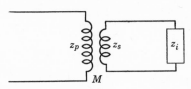

Fig. 10.16   An inductive coupling circuit.

The input impedance of a transistor amplifier is normally smaller than the output impedance for the grounded-base and grounded-emitter circuits. The input impedance is higher than the output impedance for the grounded-collector amplifier.

In order to feed a proper amount of signal power into the second amplifier stage from the output of the first stage, an impedance step-up or step-down is necessary. Let the input impedance be $z_i = r_i + jx_i$, and let the coupling circuit be an inductive one as shown in Fig. 10.16, where z_p is the impedance of the primary coil; z_s is the impedance of the secondary coil; and M is the mutual inductance of the two coils. The reflected impedance in the primary circuit is †

$$\omega^2 M^2/(z_s + z_i) \qquad [10.76]$$

The total impedance in the primary circuit then will be

$$z_1 = z_p + \omega^2 M^2/(z_s + z_i) \qquad [10.77]$$

Let

$$z_p = r_p + j\omega L_p \qquad [10.78]$$

$$z_s = r_s + j\omega L_s \qquad [10.79]$$

† See Terman, *Radio Engineer's Handbook*, McGraw-Hill, 1943, p. 149.

We have

$$z_1 = r_p + j\omega L_p + \frac{\omega^2 M^2}{r_s + r_i + j\omega L_s + jx_i}$$

$$= r_p + j\omega L_p + \frac{\omega^2 M^2}{(r_s + r_i)^2 + (\omega L_s + x_i)^2}[(r_s + r_i) - j(\omega L_s + x_i)]$$

$$= r_p + \frac{\omega^2 M^2}{(r_s + r_i)^2 + (\omega L_s + x_i)^2}(r_s + r_i)$$

$$+ j\left[\omega L_p - \frac{\omega^2 M^2}{(r_s + r_i)^2 + (\omega L_s + x_i)^2}(\omega L_s + x_i)\right]$$

$$= r_1 + jx_1 \hspace{5cm} [10.80$$

The original Q of the primary circuit is $\omega L/r_p$, but, with a secondary impedance z_i, the Q of the primary circuit becomes $Q' = x_1/r_1$, where x_1 and r_1 are given in eq. 10.80. It is clear that the real component of z_i is increased. The imaginary component may be either increased or decreased, depending on the sign of x_i and the relative magnitude of ωL_s and x_i. However, the value Q' in general will be less than the value Q.

An approximation may be used in obtaining the power output by assuming that the output circuit is as shown in Fig. 10.17, where r_c is the inverse of the real component of $1/z_c$. If the Q of the coil is greater than 10, we have the equivalent resistance r across the tank circuit due to r_1 as ap-

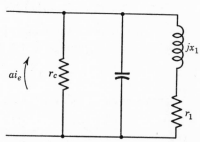

Fig. 10.17 An approximation of the output circuit.

proximately $(Q')^2 r_1$. The output power will be a maximum when $r = r_c$. In eq. 10.80, if we neglect the imaginary component of the reflected impedance and also r_p and r_s we have

$$Q' = \frac{x_1}{r_1} \cong \frac{\omega L_p}{(\omega^2 M^2/|z_i|^2)r_i} \hspace{3cm} [10.81]$$

$$r = (Q')^2 r_1 = \frac{\omega^2 L_p{}^2}{\omega^2 M^2}\frac{|z_i|^2}{r_i}$$

$$= (L_p/M)^2|z_i|^2/r_i \hspace{3cm} [10.82]$$

The condition for maximum power output is

$$r = r_c = (L_p/M)^2 |z_i|^2 / r_i \qquad [10.83]$$

or

$$M = L_p |z_i| / \sqrt{r_c r_i} \qquad [10.84]$$

10.4.2 The Effect of Collector Capacitance

In Chapter 9 we discussed the variation of the collector capacitance with frequency. When a parallel-tuned tank circuit, which is adjusted to resonance at a given frequency, is used as the load in a transistor amplifier stage, the collector capacitance is effectively in parallel with the tank circuit. Consequently the resonant frequency is changed. The resonant frequency may be brought back by either decreasing the capacitance value of the tank circuit or decreasing the inductance value. Decreasing the inductance value of the tank circuit will decrease the Q. However, the limitation on decreasing the value of capacitance of the tank circuit will soon be reached when there is only stray capacitance left. The existence of the collector capacitance imposes a limitation on the bandwidth of an amplifier when the frequency is high.

10.4.3 The Gain Bandwidth

We have discussed the effect of the collector capacitance on the parallel tuned load circuit. For a junction transistor the collector ca-

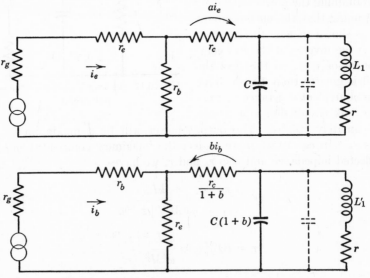

Fig. 10.18 The approximation equivalent circuits.

pacitance is of considerable size. When a junction transistor is connected as a ground-emitter amplifier the effective collector capacitance will increase to $|1 + b|$ times the value when this transistor is connected as a grounded-base amplifier. If, for the given frequency, the tank circuit for a grounded-base amplifier is already designed to have only the stray capacitance left in parallel with the inductance, changing the grounded-base connection to a grounded-emitter connection will mean that the Q of the tank circuit must be decreased.

Assuming that the stray capacitance of the inductor is small in comparison with the effective collector capacitance, then changing the grounded-base amplifier to the grounded-emitter amplifier will mean a decrease of Q of $|1 + b|$ times.

Referring to Fig. 10.18, eq. 10.31 gives the power gain of a grounded-base amplifier

$$G_1 \cong \frac{|az_c|^2 r_l}{|r_l + z_c|^2 \left\{ r_e + r_b \left[\dfrac{z_c(1 - a) + r_l}{z_c + r_l} \right] \right\}_R} \qquad [10.31]$$

Substituting r_c for z_c and $(Q')^2 r$ for r_l in eq. 10.31 yields

$$G \cong \frac{|ar_c|^2}{[(Q')^2 r + r_c]^2} \frac{(Q')^2 r}{\left\{ r_e + r_b \left[\dfrac{r_c(1 - a) + (Q')^2 r}{r_c + (Q')^2 r} \right] \right\}_R} \qquad [10.85]$$

For the grounded-emitter amplifier, eqs. 10.53 and 10.48 give

$$G = \left| \frac{az_c - r_e}{z_l + r_e + z_c(1 - a)} \right|^2 \frac{r_l}{\left\{ r_b + r_e \left[\dfrac{z_l + z_c}{r_e + z_l + (1 - a)z_c} \right] \right\}_R}$$

Using $(Q'')^2 r$ for r_l, r_c for z_c, and assuming r_e to be small, we have

$$G \cong \left| \frac{ar_c}{(Q'')^2 r + r_c/(1 + b)} \right|^2 \frac{(Q'')^2 r}{\left\{ r_b + r_e \left[\dfrac{(Q'')^2 r + r_c}{(Q'')^2 r + r_c/(1 + b)} \right] \right\}_R}$$

$$[10.86]$$

Using the result of the above discussion that

$$Q'' = Q'/|1 + b| \qquad [10.87]$$

where Q' is as in eq. 10.85, and substituting eq. 10.87 into eq. 10.86

for Q'' yields for the grounded-emitter power gain

$$
G = \frac{\left| ar_c \right|^2}{\left| \dfrac{Q'^2 r}{|1+b|^2} + \dfrac{r_c}{(1+b)} \right|^2}
$$

$$
\times \frac{Q'^2 r / |1+b|^2}{\left\{ r_b + r_e \left[\dfrac{[Q'^2/|1+b|^2]r + r_c}{[Q'^2/|1+b|^2]r + r_c/(1+b)} \right] \right\}_R}
\qquad [10.88]
$$

A rough approximation may be obtained for the power gain by assuming that the signal frequency is an order of magnitude or more below the cut-off frequency $f_{\alpha 0}$, and using the low-frequency values a_0 and b_0 for a and b. Under these conditions eq. 10.88 becomes

$$
G \cong \frac{(a_0 r_c)^2}{\left[\dfrac{Q'^2 r}{1+b_0} + r_c \right]^2} \frac{Q'^2 r}{\left\{ r_b + r_e \left[\dfrac{Q'^2 r + r_c(1+b_0)^2}{Q'^2 r + r_c(1+b_0)} \right] \right\}}
\qquad [10.88a]
$$

and eq. 10.85 becomes

$$
G \cong \frac{(a_0 r_c)^2}{[(Q')^2 r + r_c]^2} \frac{(Q')^2 r}{\left\{ r_e + r_b \left[\dfrac{r_c(1-a_0) + (Q')^2 r}{r_c + (Q')^2 r} \right] \right\}}
\qquad [10.85a]
$$

Comparing eqs. 10.85a and 10.88a, we see that the numerator is the same but the denominator of eq. 10.88a is larger than that of eq. 10.85a. This means that the grounded-emitter amplifier using the degraded tank circuit will give less output at the resonant frequency than that of the grounded-base amplifier using a higher-Q circuit.

For a rough estimate, let us assume that $r_b/r_e = 10$, $r_c/Q'^2 r = 10$. The ratio of eqs. 10.85a and 10.88a will be the ratio of the denominators of these two equations. Thus, under the conditions discussed above, we have

$$
\frac{\text{Power gain of grounded-base amplifier}}{\text{Power gain of grounded-emitter amplifier}} = \frac{11 + b_0}{2 + 10/(1+b_0)}
\qquad [10.89]
$$

When b_0 is large, the ratio of the power gain may be quite high. However, this does not necessarily mean that the grounded-emitter amplifier is inferior. When the Q of the tank circuit is decreased the bandwidth of the tank circuit is increased. If the resonant frequency of the tank circuit is lower than $f_{\alpha 0}$ such that the variation of the parameters of the transistor itself with frequency can be neglected, and if we neglect the small variation of the real component of the input impedance in eqs. 10.30 and 10.53, we see that the power gain of either the grounded-base amplifier or the grounded-emitter amplifier will be practically proportional to the real component of the load impedance. Let the frequency at the half-power point be $f_1 = f_0 \pm \Delta f$, and let the bandwidth be $2\Delta f$. The approximate condition for the power gain to drop to the half-power point is that the real component of the tank circuit impedance r' drops to half the value at the resonant frequency f_0. Thus

$$r'/2 = r'x^2/(r'^2 + x^2) \qquad [10.90]$$

where $x = \dfrac{L/C}{(\omega L - 1/\omega C)}$ and $r' = Q^2 r$. Rewriting eq. 10.90, we have

$$r'^2 + (L/C)^2/(\omega L - 1/\omega C)^2 = 2(L/C)^2/(\omega L - 1/\omega C)^2$$

or

$$r'(\omega L - 1/\omega C) = L/C \qquad [10.91]$$

Let us use the subscripts 1 and 2 to distinguish between the grounded-base and grounded-emitter cases,

$$r_1'(\omega_1 L_1 - 1/\omega_1 C_1) = L_1/C_1 \qquad [10.91a]$$

and

$$r_2'(\omega_2 L_2 - 1/\omega_2 C_2) = L_2/C_2 \qquad [10.91b]$$

Following the discussion at the beginning of this section, $C_2 = (1 + b_0)C_1$, $L_2 = L_1/(1 + b_0)$, and $Q_2 = Q_1/(1 + b_0)$, so that eq. 10.91b will become

$$r_1' \frac{1}{(1 + b_0)^2} \left[\omega_2 \frac{L_1}{(1 + b_0)} - \frac{1}{\omega_2(1 + b_0)C_1} \right] = \frac{L_1}{C_1} \frac{1}{(1 + b_0)^2}$$

or

$$r_1' \left[\omega_2 L_1 - \frac{1}{\omega_2 C_1} \right] \frac{1}{(1 + b_0)} = \frac{L_1}{C_1} \qquad [10.92]$$

combining eqs. 10.91a and 10.92 yields

$$\omega_1 L_1 - \frac{1}{\omega_1 C_1} = \frac{1}{(1 + b_0)} \left[\omega_2 L_1 - \frac{1}{\omega_2 C_1} \right] \qquad [10.93]$$

using $\omega_1 = \omega_0 \pm \Delta\omega_1$ and $\omega_2 = \omega_0 \pm \Delta\omega_2$, eq. 10.93 becomes

$$(\omega_0 \pm \Delta\omega_1)L_1 - \frac{1}{(\omega_0 \pm \Delta\omega_1)C_1}$$

$$= \frac{1}{(1 + b_0)}\left[(\omega_0 \pm \Delta\omega_2)L_1 - \frac{1}{(\omega_0 \pm \Delta\omega_2)C_1}\right] \quad [10.94]$$

Equation 10.94 can be simplified by expanding the fraction into a series and neglecting the higher-order terms. Thus

$$(\omega_0 \pm \Delta\omega_1)L_1 - \frac{1}{\omega_0 C_1}\left(1 \mp \frac{\Delta\omega_1}{\omega_0}\right)$$

$$= \frac{1}{(1 + b_0)}\left[(\omega_0 \pm \Delta\omega_2)L_1 - \frac{1}{\omega_0 C_1}\left(1 \mp \frac{\Delta\omega_2}{\omega_0}\right)\right]$$

or

$$\omega_0 L_1\left(1 - \frac{1}{1 + b_0}\right) - \frac{1}{\omega_0 C_1}\left(1 - \frac{1}{1 + b_0}\right) \pm \Delta\omega_1 L_1 \pm \frac{\Delta\omega_1}{\omega_0{}^2 C_1}$$

$$= \frac{1}{(1 + b_0)}\left[\pm \Delta\omega_2 L_1 \pm \frac{\Delta\omega_2}{\omega_0{}^2 C_1}\right] \quad [10.95]$$

But here $\omega_0 L_1 - 1/\omega_0 C_1 = 0$; hence eq. 10.95 becomes

$$\Delta\omega_1 = \frac{\Delta\omega_2}{(1 + b_0)} \quad \text{or} \quad \frac{\Delta\omega_1}{\Delta\omega_2} = \frac{1}{1 + b_0} \quad [10.96]$$

This result indicates that, under the condition assumed, the bandwidth of a grounded-emitter amplifier is approximately $(1 + b_0)$ times that of a grounded-base amplifier. The product of eqs. 10.96 and 10.89 will give roughly the ratio of the gain bandwidth of a grounded-base amplifier to that of a grounded-emitter amplifier. Thus

$$\frac{\text{Gain bandwidth of grounded-base amplifier stage}}{\text{Gain bandwidth of grounded-emitter amplifier stage}}$$

$$\cong \frac{11 + b_0}{2 + 10/(1 + b_0)} \frac{1}{1 + b_0} = \frac{11 + b_0}{12 + 2b_0} \quad [10.97]$$

When the resonant frequency f_0 is of comparable size to the α cutoff frequency $f_{\alpha 0}$, the variation of the parameters of a transistor cannot be neglected. This means that the variation of power gain with frequency with a constant load has to be taken into consideration. Owing to the property of a grounded-emitter amplifier which has a relatively faster rate of decrease in power gain with increasing frequency, the ratio of the gain bandwidth of a grounded-base amplifier stage to that of a grounded-emitter amplifier stage will increase to a value greater than unity.

10.5   The Stability Criterion

Since the transistor is an element which has power gain there are conditions under which a circuit using a transistor will break into oscillation. This is a serious situation for an amplifier stage, not only because it interrupts the amplifying action but also because it may damage the transistor.

10.5.1   The Stability Criterion of a Grounded-Base Amplifier Stage

In Sec. 10.1, the grounded-base amplifier was discussed. The input impedance of a grounded-base amplifier stage is given by eq. 10.10

$$z_i = r_e + r_b \left[\frac{z_c(1 - a) + z_l}{r_b + z_c + z_l} \right] \qquad [10.10]$$

For a junction transistor the current-amplification factor a is normally less than unity. Consequently when the load impedance z_l has no negative resistance the input impedance will have no negative resistance component. However, for a point-contact transistor the value of a is normally larger than unity. A value of a of 2 to 3 is normal. If there is no negative resistance in the load impedance z_l, the input impedance z_i will have a maximum negative resistance value when the frequency is low and the load impedance is small. Thus from eq. 10.20 the maximum negative resistance of the input impedance, $(z_i)_R$,

$$(z_i)_R \cong r_e + r_b \left[1 - \frac{a_0}{1 + (\omega/\omega_{a0})^2} \right]$$

$$\cong r_e + r_b(1 - a_0) \qquad [10.98]$$

The minimum value of load resistance required to compensate for the negative resistance can be found as follows. At low frequency

$$r_i = r_e + r_b \left[\frac{r_c(1 - a_0) + r_l}{r_b + r_c + r_l} \right] \qquad [10.99]$$

Setting r_i to zero and solving for r_l

$$r_l = \frac{r_b r_c(a_0 - 1) - r_e(r_b + r_c)}{r_e + r_b} \qquad [10.100]$$

At high frequencies the load will be

$$z_l = \frac{r_b z_c \left(\dfrac{a_0}{1 + j\omega/\omega_{a0}} - 1 \right) - r_e(r_b + z_c)}{r_e + r_b} \qquad [10.101]$$

In Sec. 10.1.1.3, eq. 10.22 gives the output impedance of a grounded-base amplifier stage as

$$z_o = z_c \left(1 - \frac{ar_b}{r_e + r_b + z_g} \right) + \frac{r_b(r_e + z_g)}{r_b + r_e + z_g} \qquad [10.22]$$

For a junction transistor there is little chance of z_o having negative resistance, but for a point-contact transistor there is a good possibility for $1 - ar_b/(r_e + r_b + z_g)$ to have a negative real term. Let us consider $z_g = r_g$, $z_c \cong r_c$, and $a = a_0/[1 + j\omega/\omega_{a0}]$; the minimum value of r_g required to compensate the negative resistance in z_o will be

$$r_g = \frac{\{a_0/[1 + (\omega/\omega_{a0})^2]\}r_c r_b - (r_e + r_b)r_c - r_b r_e}{r_c + r_b} \qquad [10.102]$$

In Sec. 10.1.2, eq. 10.30 gives the power gain of a grounded-base amplifier. One will notice that in the denominator of eq. 10.30 there is a factor which is the real component of the input impedance of the grounded-base amplifier. When this factor decreases to zero, eq. 10.30 will give an infinite power gain. Therefore, the values given by eqs. 10.100 and 10.101 are not sufficient to insure stable amplifying action. The required load value should be a little larger than that given by eqs. 10.100 and 10.101.

10.5.2 The Stability Criterion of a Grounded-Emitter Amplifier Stage

The input impedance of a grounded-emitter amplifier stage is given by eq. 10.47. If the load z_l is primarily an inductance and the collector impedance z_c can be considered effectively as a capacitance C_c, then the equivalent circuit of this amplifier stage will be as shown in Fig. 10.19.

The input impedance will be

$$z_i = r_b + r_e \left[\frac{j\omega L + 1/j\omega C_c}{r_e + j\omega L + (1 - a)(1/j\omega C_c)} \right] \qquad [10.103]$$

If the r_e term is negligible in the denominator of eq. 10.103, we have

$$z_i \cong r_b + r_e \left[\frac{\omega L - 1/\omega C_c}{\omega L - (1 - a)/\omega C_c} \right]$$ [10.104]

When the frequency is less than $\omega_0 = 1/\sqrt{LC_c}$, the term $\omega L - 1/\omega C_c$ is negative. There is a frequency band within which the difference $\omega L - 1/\omega C_c$ is negative but $\omega L - (1 - a)/\omega C_c$ is positive. This means that, even for a junction transistor which has an a_0 less than unity, there is possibility of oscillation.

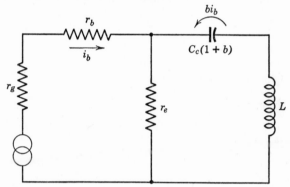

Fig. 10.19   An inductance L as the load of a grounded-emitter amplifier.

For a point-contact transistor even for a resistance load there is possibility that the input impedance will have a negative real component. From eq. 10.47, the value of load resistance r_l which will give zero resistance in the input impedance is approximately

$$r_l \cong \frac{r_c r_b \left[\dfrac{a_0}{1 + (\omega/\omega_{a0})^2} - 1 \right] - r_e(r_b + r_c)}{r_b + r_e}$$ [10.105]

The expression for the output impedance of a grounded-emitter amplifier stage is given by eq. 10.50

$$z_o = (1 - a)z_c + r_e \left(\frac{r_b + z_g + az_c}{z_g + r_b + r_e} \right)$$ [10.50]

There is little chance for a junction transistor to have a negative resistance in eq. 10.50. However, for a point-contact transistor it is possible to have a negative resistance in eq. 10.50.

The power gain is given by eq. 10.53. Since there is possibility for a point-contact transistor to have an input impedance which has no real component, eq. 10.53 will give an infinite gain. Hence, the required value of r_l should be larger than that given by eq. 10.105.

10.5.3   The Stability Criterion of a Grounded-Collector Amplifier Stage

For a grounded-collector amplifier stage without any feedback circuit and using a junction transistor, there is little possibility of having a negative resistance component in either the input impedance z_i or the output impedance z_o. But, when a point-contact transistor is used in a grounded-collector amplifier, it is possible to get negative resistance in the output and input impedances. The method of study of the conditions for stable amplifying operation is the same as in Secs. 10.5.1 and 10.5.2.

The stability problem of an amplifier stage employing feedback is studied in Chapter 16 and will not be repeated here.

10.6   Problems

1. Given a junction transistor which has parameters as following. At 1 kc: r_e = 30 ohms, r_b = 250 ohms, r_c = 500 kilohms, C_c = 40 $\mu\mu$f, α = 0.9, $f_{\alpha 0}$ = 1 mc. Collector-base diode capacitance = 18 $\mu\mu$f. When a parallel-tuned resonant circuit which has a Q of 50 and an effective shunting resistance of 50 kilohms is used as load, study the properties of the input impedances of a grounded-base amplifier for a resonant frequency of 175 kc and 455 kc and a bandwidth of 10 kc.

2. Repeat problem 1 for a grounded-emitter amplifier.

3. Using r_b/r_e = 10, $r_c/(Q')^2 r$ = 10, verify eq. 10.89.

10.7   Bibliography

1. Ryder and Kircher, "Some Circuit Aspects of the Transistor," *Bell Sys. Tech. J.*, *28*, 367–400 (July, 1949).

2. Wallace, Schimpf, and Dickten, "A Junction Transistor Tetrode for High-Frequency Use," *Proc. IRE*, *40*, No. 11, pp. 1395–1400 (November, 1952).

3. D. E. Thomas, "Transistor Amplifier-Cut-off Frequency," *Proc. IRE*, *40*, No. 11, pp. 1481–1483 (November, 1952).

4. H. J. Reich and Others, "Effect of Auxiliary Current on Transistor Operation," *J. Applied Phys.*, *22*, 682–683 (May, 1951).

5. M. J. E. Golay, "Equivalent Circuit of the Transistor," *Proc. IRE*, *40*, 360 (March, 1952).

Chapter 11

High-Frequency
Circuit Design

For vacuum tubes, it is relatively simple to design multistage amplifiers because there is usually little reflection from the output side to the input side of each amplifier stage. However, it is different with transistor amplifiers since the input side and the output side are closely coupled through the transistor. Any change in the final output circuit will be reflected to all the preceding stages. A transistor amplifier differs from a tube amplifier in another respect, namely, in that the input impedance is normally smaller than the output impedance, particularly in a grounded-emitter or a grounded-base transistor amplifier. For a grounded-collector transistor amplifier stage the input impedance is a little larger than for the other two circuit connections, comparable to the output impedance. This input impedance is still very small compared to the input impedance of a tube amplifier.

As a result of these differences, the interstage coupling circuit of a transistor amplifier is different from that of a tube amplifier.

In Chapter 10, the principles of the single amplifier stage were discussed. Equations were given for the input and output impedances, the voltage amplification, and the power gain. In this chapter different interstage coupling networks will be discussed. Tuned amplifier stages and the associated interstage coupling networks will be studied for resonant frequencies below the α cut-off frequency $f_{\alpha 0}$.

11.1 Narrow-Band Tuned Amplifier

By narrow-band tuned amplifiers is meant an amplifier of one or more cascaded stages where the overall bandwidth is only a small percentage of the mean or resonant frequency. If we use Δf to represent the bandwidth at the half-power points on the response curve of the amplifier, and f_0 to represent the mean or resonant frequency, then

$$\text{The effective } Q \text{ of the amplifier} = f_0/\Delta f \qquad [11.1]$$

In this section we will discuss narrow-band tuned amplifiers which have an effective Q much larger than 10. This includes most of the r-f and i-f amplifiers of broadcast and communication receivers.

11.1.1 Series-Resonant Circuit Used as the Interstage Coupling Network

In early application of point-contact transistors to high-frequency amplification the grounded-base configuration was generally used. The principle of duality was applied, and the single-tuned vacuum-tube amplifier circuit was found to correspond to a transistor amplifier employing a series-resonant circuit as the interstage network.†

In using the series-resonant circuit as the interstage coupling network the necessary condition is that the output short-circuit current ratio must be greater than unity. This condition implies that the point-contact transistor should be connected in either the grounded-base connection or the grounded-emitter; however, the junction transistor should use the grounded-emitter connection. The grounded-emitter configuration in point-contact transistors is very unstable and is seldom used at high frequencies.

When the effective Q of a single amplifier stage is known, and if each amplifier stage is so designed that the power gain vs. frequency curves are practically identical, the overall Q of the cascaded amplifier will be larger than the effective Q of each amplifier and will depend on the number of amplifier stages. Thus, let the power gain of each amplifier stage be a function of frequency $G(f)$. At the resonant frequency f_0, the power gain is $G(f_0)$. At the half-power point, for each amplifier stage, we have

$$G(f_1)/G(f_0) = \tfrac{1}{2} \qquad [11.2]$$

For the whole amplifier, we have

$$[G(f_2)/G(f_0)]^n = \tfrac{1}{2}$$

or

$$G(f_2)/G(f_0) = (\tfrac{1}{2})^{1/n} \qquad [11.3]$$

where n is the number of stages in cascade. In eq. 11.3, the frequency f_2 will be much closer to the center frequency f_0 than f_1 in eq. 11.2.

† The principle of duality is discussed in Chapter 14.

In Fig. 11.1 is shown a series-resonant circuit used as an interstage coupling network between two point-contact transistor amplifiers with

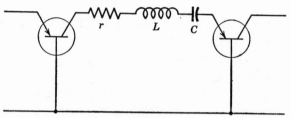

Fig. 11.1   Point-contact transistors using series-resonant circuit as an interstage coupling network.

the d-c bias current circuit not shown.   Let the effective load presented to the first stage be z_l

$$z_l = r + j(\omega L - 1/\omega C) + z_i = z_R + z_i \qquad [11.4]$$

where z_i is the input impedance of the second transistor.   The input impedance of an iterative transistor amplifier with a load as given by eq. 11.4 will be

$$z_i = r_e + r_b \left[\frac{z_c(1 - a) + z_R + z_i}{z_c + r_b + z_R + z_i} \right] \qquad [11.5]$$

Rearranging eq. 11.5 gives

$$(z_i)^2 + z_i(z_c + z_R - r_e) - r_e(z_c + r_b + z_R) - r_b z_c(1 - a) - r_b z_R = 0$$

$$[11.6]$$

For a given transistor and given operating conditions the input impedance of this amplifier stage can be calculated from eq. 11.6.   Since the resonant circuit is in series with the input impedance, the effective Q of this amplifier stage will be modified by z_i.   The power gain per stage will be approximately $|a|^2$.

When a junction transistor is used instead of a point-contact transistor, the junction transistor should be connected in the grounded-emitter configuration.   The input impedance will be

$$z_i \cong r_b + r_e \frac{z_c + z_R + z_i}{[z_c(1 - a) + r_e + z_R + z_i]} \qquad [11.7]$$

Rearranging eq. 11.7 yields

$$(z_i)^2 + z_i[z_R + (1 - a)z_c - r_b]$$

$$- r_b[z_c(1 - a) + r_e + z_R] - r_e(z_c + z_R) = 0 \quad [11.3]$$

Equation 11.6 or 11.8 may be used to calculate the effective Q of each stage. The power gain per stage will be approximately $|b|^2$, where $b = a/(1 - a)$.

11.1.2 Parallel-Resonant Circuit Used as the Interstage Coupling Network

A parallel-resonant circuit can be used as the interstage coupling network. As was shown in Chapter 10 the output impedance of a transistor amplifier of the grounded-base or grounded-emitter connection is larger than the input impedance. In order to maximize the power transfer from one amplifier stage to the next, the output impedance

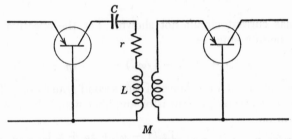

Fig. 11.2   Series-resonant circuit with impedance transformation.

of the first stage must be properly matched to the input impedance of the following stage. Although this can be accomplished by a series-resonant coupling network as shown in Fig. 11.2, the reflected impedance in the primary circuit will decrease the Q of the series resonant circuit appreciably. With the parallel-resonant circuit the loading effect on Q is a little less severe. However, when point-contact transistors are used with a parallel-tuned coupling network, the short-circuit unstable problem appears. Unless the circuit is so designed that there is sufficient positive resistance in the circuit to compensate for the negative resistance component of the input impedance, the amplifier will oscillate.

There are several arrangements for coupling two amplifier stages using a parallel-resonant circuit. We will group them into three classes and discuss them below.

11.1.2.1 Direct Connection

Figures 11.3(a) and (b) show two connections in which the second amplifier stage is directly connected into the parallel-resonant circuit. The input impedance of the second stage is either in series with the inductance or in series with the capacitance. As far as the first stage

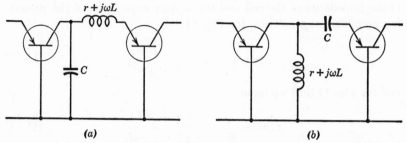

Fig. 11.3 Parallel-tuned circuit with second stage directly connected to the tuned circuit.

is concerned it has a load impedance which is a parallel-resonant circuit. This load impedance is, for Fig. 11.3(a),

$$z_l = \frac{(-j/\omega C)(r + j\omega L + z_i)}{z_i + r + j(\omega L - 1/\omega C)} \qquad [11.9]$$

and for Fig. 11.3(b).

$$z_l = \frac{(z_i - j/\omega C)(r + j\omega L)}{z_i + r + j(\omega L - 1/\omega C)} \qquad [11.10]$$

where z_i is the input impedance of the second amplifier stage.

If these amplifier stages are intended for iterative cascading, the input impedance is the same for each stage. Thus, for the grounded-base amplifier,

$$z_i \cong r_e + r_b \left[\frac{z_c(1 - a) + z_l}{z_c + r_b + z_l}\right] \qquad [11.11]$$

and for the grounded-emitter amplifier

$$z_i \cong r_b + r_e \left[\frac{z_c + z_l}{(1 - a)z_c + r_e + z_l}\right] \qquad [11.12]$$

The load impedance z_l given by eq. 11.9 or eq. 11.10 can be used to solve for the input impedance z_i.

The impedance appearing across the amplifier input is the impedance of the coil in series with the parallel combination of the output impedance of the preceding amplifier stage and the capacitance C, for the circuit shown in Fig. 11.3(a). For the circuit of Fig. 11.3(b) it is the impedance of the condenser in series with the parallel combination of the impedance of the coil and the output impedance of the preceding amplifier stage. Thus, for Fig. 11.3(a),

$$z_g = r + j\omega L + \frac{z_o(-j/\omega C)}{z_o - j/\omega C} \qquad [11.13]$$

and for Fig. 11.3(b) we have

$$z_g = -\frac{j}{\omega C} + \frac{z_o(r + j\omega L)}{z_o + r + j\omega L} \qquad [11.14]$$

The output impedances for the grounded-base amplifier and for the grounded-emitter amplifier are given in Chapter 10. They are, for the grounded-base amplifier,

$$z_o = z_c + r_b \left(\frac{r_e + z_g - a z_c}{r_e + r_b + z_g}\right) \qquad [11.15]$$

and for the grounded-emitter amplifier

$$z_o = (1 - a)z_c + r_e \left(\frac{r_b + z_g + a z_c}{z_g + r_b + r_e}\right) \qquad [11.16]$$

Equations 11.13 and 11.14 can be used for the term z_g in eqs. 11.15 and 11.16. The output impedance z_o obtained from these equations

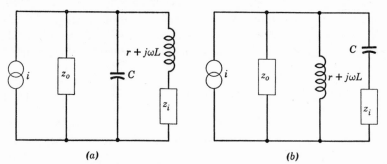

(a)   (b)

Fig. 11.4   Equivalent circuits of Figs. 11.3a and b.

will be the output impedance of an amplifier stage which is designed for cascading with similar stages.

Let the input impedance obtained by substituting z_l from eqs. 11.9 or 11.10 into eq. 11.11 or 11.12, respectively, be $z_i = r_i + jx_i$, and the output impedance z_o obtained by substituting z_g from eq. 11.13 or 11.14 into eq. 11.15 or 11.16, respectively, be $z_o = r_o + jx_o$. We can now study the power-transfer problem using the simplified circuit shown in Figs. 11.4(a) and 11.4(b).

The output impedance z_o can be converted into admittance $y_o = g_o + jb_o$. Thus

$$y_o = \frac{1}{z_o} = \frac{r_o}{r_o^2 + x_o^2} + j\frac{-x_o}{r_o^2 + x_o^2} \qquad [11.17]$$

$$= g_o + jb_o$$

The susceptance of y_o can be combined with that of the parallel-tuned circuit. It has been shown in Chapter 10 that this susceptance is capacitive; therefore, we will combine it with the capacitance of the

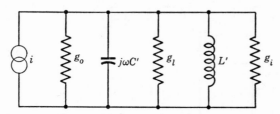

Fig. 11.5   The simplified equivalent circuit of Fig. 11.4a.

parallel circuit. For the circuit in Fig. 11.4(a), let the combined capacitance be C' as shown in Fig. 11.5. The input impedance z_i can be combined with the coil to give $r_i + r + j(\omega L + x_i)$. The Q of this impedance is

$$Q = \frac{\omega L + x_i}{r + r_i} \qquad [11.18]$$

The dynamic resistance of the parallel-resonant circuit is approximately † $Q^2(r_i + r)$ at resonance. This resistance can be converted into two conductances g_l and g_i

$$g_l = r/(\omega L + x_i)^2 \qquad [11.19]$$

and

$$g_i = r_i/(\omega L + x_i)^2 \qquad [11.20]$$

The condition required for maximum power transfer at resonance from the preceding amplifier stage through the interstage coupling network to the following amplifier stage is

$$g_i = g_l + g_o \qquad [11.21]$$

g_l corresponds to the resistive component of the interstage coupling network and decreases the available power. The ratio of available

† For $Q > 10$.

power with the coupling network connected, to the available power without it is a power-loss factor F_p.

$$F_p = \frac{g_o}{g_o + g_l} = \frac{1}{1 + (g_l/g_o)} \qquad [11.21a]$$

11.1.2.2 Capacitive Coupling

In Fig. 11.6 is shown a coupling circuit in which the second stage is connected to the junction of two capacitors. These two capacitors

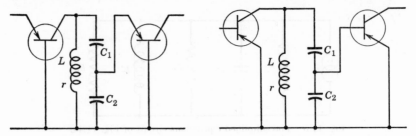

Fig. 11.6   Parallel resonant circuit with capacitive coupling.

are also the elements of the parallel-tuned resonant circuit. Let the input impedance of the second transistor be z_i. The effective input impedance across the resonant circuit is z_i', where

$$z_i' = \frac{z_i - j\dfrac{1}{\omega(C_1 + C_2)}}{[C_1/(C_1 + C_2)]^2} \qquad [11.22]$$

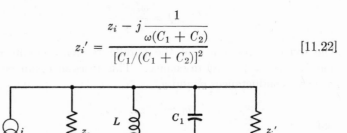

Fig. 11.7   The equivalent circuit of Fig. 11.6.

(See Fig. 11.7.) The load impedance z_l as seen by the first stage is

$$z_l = \frac{(r + j\omega L)\left(-j\dfrac{1}{\omega C}\right)z_i'}{(r + j\omega L)\left(-j\dfrac{1}{\omega C}\right) + z_i'\left[r + j\left(\omega L - \dfrac{1}{\omega C}\right)\right]} \qquad [11.23]$$

where $C = C_1 C_2 / (C_1 + C_2)$. By combining eq. 11.23 with eq. 11.11 or 11.12 the input impedance of an amplifier stage designed for iterative cascading may be obtained.

The source impedance z_g as seen by the following stage is

$$z_g = \frac{\left(-j\dfrac{1}{\omega C_2}\right)\left[\dfrac{z_o(r + j\omega L)}{z_o + r + j\omega L} - j\dfrac{1}{\omega C_1}\right]}{\dfrac{z_o(r + j\omega L)}{z_o + r + j\omega L} - j\dfrac{1}{\omega C_1} - j\dfrac{1}{\omega C_2}} \qquad [11.24]$$

where z_o is the output impedance of the preceding stage, which is given in eqs. 11.15 and 11.16. Substituting the proper expression for z_o in eq. 11.24 and solving will give z_g in terms of the circuit

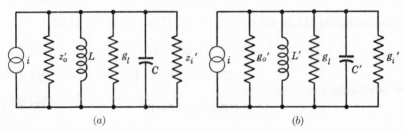

(a)   (b)

Fig. 11.8   The simplified equivalent circuits.

constants and the transistor parameters. We will now study the power-transfer problem together with the bandwidth problem. In Fig. 11.8(a) is shown a parallel-tuned circuit which has a conductance $g_l = 1/rQ_0^2$, where Q_0 is the Q of the coil at the resonant frequency, $\omega_0 = 2\pi f_0$. The capacitance C is the resultant of C_1 and C_2. The impedance z_o' is the effective output impedance of the preceding amplifier stage. (The original output impedance z_o, as obtained from eq. 11.15 or 11.16, may have to be stepped up or down to give z_o'.) The impedance z_i' is the effective input impedance of the following stage as given in eq. 11.22. Since impedances z_o' and z_i' generally contain imaginary terms, it is more convenient to convert these two impedances into conductances, and susceptances. In Fig. 11.8(b) are shown the conductance components g_o' and g_i' corresponding to z_o' and z_i' respectively. The susceptances are combined into either L or C to give L' and C'. The effective Q of such an amplifier stage will be determined by the total conductance and the inductance or the capacitance. Thus at resonant frequency ω_0:

$$Q = \frac{\omega_0 C'}{g_o' + g_l + g_i'} = \frac{\omega_0}{\Delta\omega} \qquad [11.25]$$

where $\Delta\omega$ is the bandwidth at the half-power points on the selectivity curve of this amplifier stage. The condition for maximum power transfer at resonance to the following stage is

$$g_i' = g_o' + g_l \qquad [11.26]$$

Let the original Q of the parallel-tuned circuit at frequency ω_0 be Q_0

$$Q_0 \cong \omega_0 C'/g_l = \omega_0/\Delta\omega_0 \qquad [11.27]$$

Combining eqs. 11.25, 11.26, and 11.27 to solve the required impedance-matching condition and at the same time satisfy the required bandwidth, we have, from eq. 11.25,

$$\Delta\omega = (g_o' + g_l + g_i')/C' \qquad [11.28]$$

Substituting eq. 11.26 for g_i' and eq. 11.27 for g_l, in eq. 11.28,

$$\Delta\omega = (2/C')(g_o' + g_l)$$

$$= 2[(g_o'/C') + \Delta\omega_0] \qquad [11.29]$$

or solving for g_o',

$$g_o' = [(\Delta\omega/2) - \Delta\omega_0]C' \qquad [11.30]$$

Also, from eqs. 11.26 and 11.28

$$g_i' = (\Delta\omega/2)C' \qquad [11.31]$$

The power-loss factor F_p, as discussed in the last section, is

$$F_p = \frac{1}{1 + (g_l/g_o')} \qquad [11.21a]$$

The interstage network normally takes the form shown in Fig. 11.9. Both the output impedance of the preceding amplifier stage and the input impedance of the following amplifier stage are stepped up in order to satisfy the narrow-band requirement.

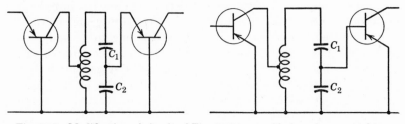

Fig. 11.9   Modification of circuit of Fig. 11.6 to provide impedance matching.

11.1.2.3 Inductive Coupling

Figure 11.10 shows two inductively coupled circuits with the grounded-base connection. It should be understood that the grounded-emitter connection can also be used. The inductively coupled circuits shown in Figs. 11.10(a) and (b) have only one tuned circuit. The secondary is untuned. Owing to the requirements of impedance match-

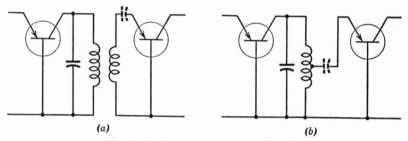

(a)   (b)

Fig. 11.10   Inductively coupled circuits.

ing, the secondary will normally have a small inductance. However, the secondary circuit also can be made into a series-tuned circuit by inserting a capacitor into the secondary circuit in series with the coil. An example of an untuned secondary circuit is discussed in Chapter 10 in showing the effect of load on the value of Q. This parallel-tuned inductively coupled interstage network will be studied further.

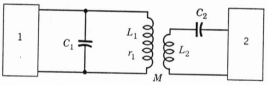

Fig. 11.11   The general inductively coupled circuit.

In Fig. 11.11 the transistors are represented by two blocks 1 and 2. Let the input impedance of the second stage be z_i and the resistance of the secondary coil be negligible in comparison with z_i. The reflected impedance of the secondary in the primary coil is

$$\frac{\omega^2 M^2}{z_i + j\left(\omega L_2 - \dfrac{1}{\omega C_2}\right)} \qquad [11.32]$$

The impedance of the primary circuit as viewed by transistor 1 will be

$$z_l = \frac{\left[r_1 + \dfrac{\omega^2 M^2}{z_i + j\left(\omega L_2 - \dfrac{1}{\omega C_2}\right)} + j\omega L_1 \right]\left(-j\dfrac{1}{\omega C_1}\right)}{r_1 + \dfrac{\omega^2 M^2}{z_i + j\left(\omega L_2 - \dfrac{1}{\omega C_2}\right)} + j\left(\omega L_1 - \dfrac{1}{\omega C_1}\right)}$$ [11.33]

When another impedance step-down circuit is used between transistor 1 and z_l, then eq. 11.33 should be modified by this impedance ratio. The input impedance z_i of a transistor amplifier designed for cascading with other, similar stages can be obtained by substituting z_l as found from eq. 11.33 in either eq. 11.11 or 11.12. The output impedance z_o of such an amplifier stage can be obtained by first finding the impedance z_g appearing at the input of transistor 2 in Fig. 11.11 when the output impedance of transistor 1 is also z_o. Then the output impedance is found with z_g as the signal source impedance.

When the input impedance z_i and the output impedance z_o are known, the processes of studying the problem of impedance match and bandwidth is the same as described in the last section. Thus, let the input impedance be

$$z_i = r_i + jx_i$$ [11.34]

The secondary should be tuned so that at the resonant frequency ω_0

$$z_i + j(\omega_0 L_2 - 1/\omega_0 C_2) = r_i$$ [11.35]

Referring to Figs. 11.8(b) and 11.11, we have

$$g_l = r_1(\omega_0 C')^2 = C' \Delta\omega_0$$ 11.36]

and

$$g_i' = \frac{\omega_0{}^2 M^2/r_i}{(\omega_0 L')^2}$$

$$= (M/L')^2(1/r_i)$$ [11.37]

Conditions given by eqs. 11.25, 11.26, and 11.27 can be used together with eqs. 11.36 and 11.37 to design the required interstage network.

The secondary circuit of the interstage coupling network of Fig. 11.11 can also be a parallel-tuned resonant circuit as shown in Fig. 11.12. In order to preserve the Q of both the primary and secondary coils, the output circuit of the first transistor amplifier is connected to a tap on the primary coil, and the input side of the second transistor is capacitive-coupled to the secondary coil. This circuit can be studied in the same manner as before.

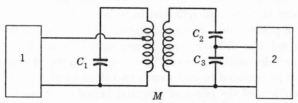

Fig. 11.12   The double-tuned inductively coupled circuit.

11.1.3   The Effect of Reflected Impedances

In the above sections the interstage coupling circuits are discussed with the assumptions that the transistors used in the cascading amplifier are identical and that the interstage coupling circuit is so designed that the input impedance of each stage is the same, as is also the output impedance (see Fig. 11.13).   Therefore when each single

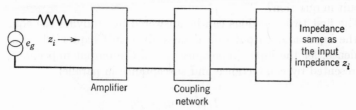

Fig. 11.13   The effect of reflected impedance.

stage is designed to work into an impedance which is the same as its input impedance z_i, when tuned to the required resonant frequency, these stages can be cascaded without further tuning of the resonant circuit.   However, there is considerable variation between transistors; hence the necessary requirement of exact duplication of impedance is difficult to achieve.

If the interstage coupling circuit is tuned to resonance with a resistive load, the resonant frequency will change slightly when the input impedance of a transistor amplifier is substituted.   This detuning effect may be cumulative as the number of amplifier stages is increased. Consequently the problem of alignment of a narrow-band-tuned amplifier with more than two stages may become very tedious.

The problem of reducing the effect of reflected impedances on the tuned amplifier has been studied quite extensively.   Different decoupling circuits have been proposed. The objective is to make the input impedance of the transistor amplifier relatively constant and resistive at least over the pass band. This aim may be achieved, e.g., by inserting a resistance in series with the next amplifier stage. In so doing the effect of reflected impedances is reduced at the cost of a loss of power gain. Since the alignment of two cascaded amplifier stages is not too difficult, two stages may be considered as a unit without any decoupling network between the stages. Decoupling networks will be required between such two-stage units, however.

The problem of the effect of reflected impedances can be studied a little further and from the practical point of view by first asking the following questions: (a) What is the percentage variation of the input impedance of an amplifier for a given percentage variation of the load impedance? (b) What is the percentage variation of the output impedance of an amplifier for a given percentage variation of the generator impedance? (c) What kind of interstage coupling network will fulfill the requirement of selectivity, low loss, and reduced sensitivity to variation of the input and output impedances? (d) What kind of transistor circuit configuration is most suitable for the coupling circuit in question?

The first two questions can be answered by studying the equations of the input and output impedances given in Chapter 10. For convenience, let the input impedance z_i and the output impedance z_o be represented by conductance and susceptance in parallel

$$1/z_i = g_i + jb_i \qquad\qquad [11.38]$$

$$1/z_o = g_o + jb_o \qquad\qquad [11.39]$$

Let z_g be the generator impedance and z_l the load impedance, and the value of z_g and z_l be approximately the order of the input and output impedances respectively. The variation of output impedance z_o due to the variation of z_g for a typical junction transistor in the grounded-base configuration is as follows: a 100 per cent variation of the conductance of z_g gives about 15 per cent variation of the conductance of z_o and practically no variation of susceptance; a 100 per cent variation of the susceptance of z_g gives less than 4 per cent variation of the susceptance of z_o and about 6 per cent variation of the conductance of z_o. The variation of z_i due to the variation of z_l for a typical junction transistor is as follows: a 100 per cent variation of the conductance of z_l gives about 10 per cent variation of the conductance of z_i and about 60 per cent variation of the susceptance of z_i; a 100 per cent variation of the susceptance of z_l gives about 20 per cent variation of the sus-ceptance of z_i and little variation of the conductance of z_i. The over-all picture is that the load impedance z_l has more effect on the input impedance z_i than the generator impedance z_g has on the output impedance z_o. This indicates that the best procedure for aligning a narrow-band amplifier consisting of several cascaded stages is to start with the alignment of the last stage and then align stage by stage progressively toward the first stage.

The third question concerns the interstage coupling network. Its answer is a parallel-tuned resonant circuit having a relatively low L/C ratio, but with a high Q in order to decrease the loss of this coupling circuit.

The fourth question concerns the best transistor connection in an amplifier circuit. From the power-gain point of view the grounded-base and the grounded-emitter configurations have, in general, a little more power gain than the grounded-collector configuration. Further, as shown in Chapter 10, the input impedance of a grounded-base transistor amplifier with a resistive load is inductive at high frequencies; the input impedance of a grounded-emitter transistor amplifier with resistive load is capacitive. The output impedance for both is capacitive. When the interstage coupling circuit is tuned to the resonant frequency, the load appearing on the preceding stage is practically resistive. Hence the properties of the input impedances just described are preserved. When a parallel-tuned resonant circuit is used for interstage coupling, the capacitive susceptance of the output impedance z_o will be modified by the proper impedance ratio and added to the capacitance of the resonant circuit. The inductive susceptance of the input impedance z_i of a grounded-base amplifier will also be modified by the proper impedance ratio and will appear in parallel with the inductance of the resonant circuit. The combined result is an increase of capacitance and decrease of inductance of the resonant circuit. If a grounded-emitter amplifier is used instead of a grounded-base amplifier, the capacitive susceptance of its input impedance will be modified by the impedance ratio and added to the capacitance of the resonant circuit. The combined result is an increase of capacitance and no change of inductance of the resonant circuit.

From the above considerations it appears that, in order to make alignment of the resonant circuit less sensitive to variation of the input and output impedances, the ratio L/C of this resonant circuit should be relatively small so that the input and output capacitances are only a small percentage of the total capacitance, and inductance of the resonant circuit will not be changed too much by the reactive component of z_i.

11.1.4 Narrow-Band Tuned Amplifier Circuits

The principles described in the above discussion are illustrated in the amplifier circuits shown in Figs. 11.14 to 11.20 inclusive. Although for each amplifier two stages are shown, the number of stages is by no means limited to two. In these figures transistors are shown con-

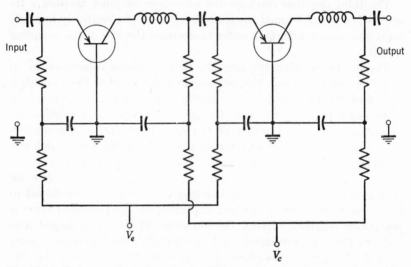

Fig. 11.14 Series-tuned coupling circuit. Point-contact transistors can be used in the grounded-base connection, and junction transistors in the grounded-emitter connection.

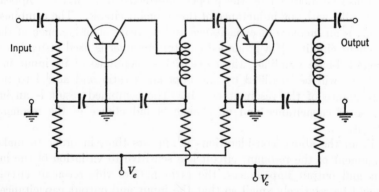

Fig. 11.15 Parallel-tuned direct-coupled circuit. Either grounded-base or grounded-emitter connections can be used.

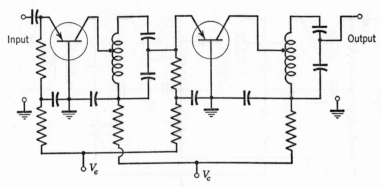

Fig. 11.16　Single-tuned capacitive-coupled circuit. Any one of the three transistor connections can be used.

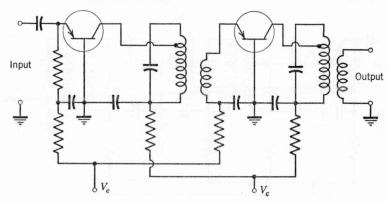

Fig. 11-17　Single-tuned inductive-coupled circuit. Any one of the three transistor connections can be used.

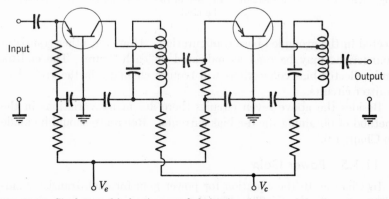

Fig. 11.18　Single-tuned inductive-coupled circuit. Any one of the three transistor connections can be used.

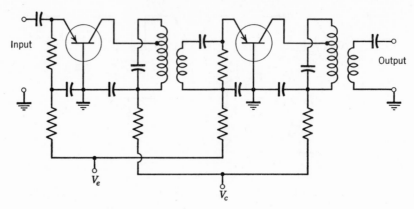

Fig. 11.19 Double-tuned circuit. Any one of the three transistor connections can be used.

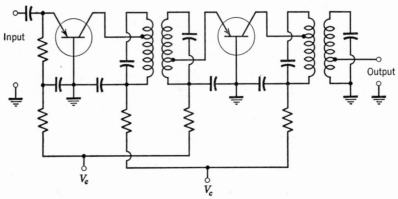

Fig. 11.20 Double-tuned circuit. Any one of the three transistor connections can be used.

nected in the grounded-base configuration. However, other transistor connections may be used as indicated on each figure. The emitter and collector bias connections will require changing in the grounded-emitter circuits.

Besides the above seven circuits there are many variations in the method of obtaining the d-c bias currents. Reference should be made to Chapter 6.

11.1.5 Power Gain

In Chapter 10 the equation for power gain for each transistor amplifier stage is given. Thus, for the grounded-base configuration, we have from Sec. 10.1.2

$$G = \frac{|r_b + az_c|^2(z_l)_R}{|z_l + r_b + z_c|^2(z_i)_R}$$

For the grounded-emitter configuration it is

$$G = \left| \frac{az_c - r_e}{z_l + r_e + z_c(1 - a)} \right|^2 \frac{(z_l)_R}{(z_i)_R} \qquad [10.53]$$

and for the grounded-collector configuration it is

$$G = \left| \frac{z_c}{z_l + r_e + [z_c/(1 + b)]} \right|^2 \frac{(z_l)_R}{(z_i)_R} \qquad [10.70]$$

The load impedance z_l in the above three equations is the load appearing directly on the output side of the amplifier. This load is the input impedance of the next stage together with the interstage coupling network. At the resonant frequency eqs. 11.25, 11.26, and 11.27 give the conditions for impedance match and bandwidth for each stage. The input impedance of the next stage will be stepped up by a proper ratio.

Let the impedance step-up ratio be n^2, and let the interstage coupling network be a single-tuned circuit as shown in Fig. 11.17. The transformed z_i appearing in parallel with the resonant circuit is $n^2 z_i = z_i'$. The impedance of the parallel combination of L, C, and g_l, as shown in Fig. 11.8(a), is

$$z_l = \frac{1}{g_l + j\omega C + 1/j\omega L} \qquad [11.40]$$

The combined impedance of this circuit and z_i' is

$$z_l' = \frac{1}{g_l + j\omega C + 1/j\omega L + 1/n^2 z_i} \qquad [11.41]$$

Let the second impedance transformation ratio be m^2. The load impedance applied to the output terminals of the amplifier stage will be

$$z_l'' = \frac{z_l'}{m^2} = \frac{1}{m^2} \left(\frac{1}{g_l + j\omega C + 1/j\omega L + 1/n^2 z_i} \right) \qquad [11.42]$$

Using eq. 11.42 for z_l'', the power gain per stage can be found by solving the power-gain equations given above. The same principle is applicable for the other interstage coupling network.

11.2　Wide-Band Tuned Amplifiers

In this section tuned transistor amplifiers which have a relatively large bandwidth with respect to the resonant frequency will be discussed. In terms of effective Q, this type of amplifier has a Q value of about 10 or less. In this category are i-f amplifiers such as are used in television and radar receivers.

The problems encountered in designing a wide-band tuned amplifier using transistors are essentially the same as for the narrow-band amplifier, with the additional requirement that, within the wide pass band, the gain shall be reasonably flat.

When the center frequency is considerably below the α cut-off frequency, $f_{\alpha 0}$, so that the upper extreme of the amplifier pass band is less than the frequency at which the available power gain of the transistor drops rapidly, the problem of obtaining a wide bandwidth with a transistor amplifier becomes similar to that encountered with a vacuum-tube amplifier. It is clear that a multistage amplifier consisting of a number of stages using single-tuned coupling circuits, all resonant at the same frequency, will have a pass band which becomes narrower with increasing number of stages. In the double-tuned coupling circuit, the coefficient of coupling plays an important role. If the coupling is equal to or below critical coupling the overall bandwidth will become less when the number of stages is increased. If it is over-coupled, the mid-band "valley" will increase with increasing number of stages. Staggered tuning of successive stages has been found to provide a practicable method for obtaining a relatively flat, wide-band response curve.

11.2.1　Staggered-Tuned Amplifier

The principle of a staggered-tuned transistor amplifier is the same as for the staggered-tuned tube amplifier. The wide band is obtained by detuning each stage slightly about the desired center frequency. The resonant circuit of each stage can be single-tuned or double-tuned. In this section we will discuss the single-tuned resonant circuit; however, the principle can be applied to the double-tuned resonant circuit.

In Sec. 11.1 the problem of reflected impedance was discussed for a stage designed to cascade with a similar stage. When the individual stages are resonant at different frequencies the problem of reflected impedances becomes a little more complicated. The effect of reflected impedance on one stage will depend on the resonant frequency of this stage and on the resonant frequency of the stage which produces the reflected impedance. The effect, to a large degree, is dependent upon the α cut-off frequency. If the resonant frequency of the preceding or the following stage is much smaller than the α cut-off frequency the reflected impedance may clearly bear the properties of the impedances. Let the first stage be resonant at f_1 and the second stage be resonant at $f_2 = f_1 + \Delta f$ as shown in Figs. 11.21(a) and (b). When the signal frequency is at f_1 the resonant circuit following the second stage will present an inductive load to the second stage. The property of the impedance reflected to the input side of the second stage will depend on the connection of the transistor and the relative magnitude of f_1 and $f_{\alpha 0}$. The input impedance of the second stage will combine with the impedance of the resonant circuit of the first stage to resonate at frequency f_1. When the signal frequency is at f_2 the resonant circuit

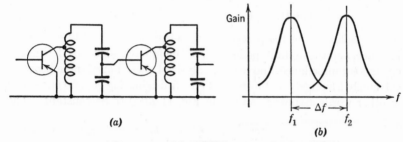

(a)

(b)

Fig. 11.21   Staggered-tuned amplifier.

of the first stage will present a capacitive source impedance to the second stage. This source impedance will be reflected into the output impedance of the second stage, and the resonant frequency of the resonant circuit of the second stage will be affected. Thus the resonant frequency of each stage is affected by the immediately preceding and following stages.

As a result of the coupling between input and output circuits, inherent in the transistor amplifier, changing the impedance of one element in the whole amplifier, in general, will affect every stage in the amplifier. Fortunately the effect of reflected impedance is not cumulative from stage to stage. If the interstage coupling network is properly designed this effect of reflected impedance will gradually disappear as it goes from stage to stage. Consequently we can limit our study to those stages immediately preceding and following the resonant circuit.

Let the resonant circuit of each stage be the type shown in Fig. 11.22. The theory to be described is applicable to the other common forms of coupling. Let the resonant frequency of this circuit be f_0, as determined by the values of L, C_1, C_2, and the imaginary components of the input impedance of the following stage, z_i, and the output impedance of the preceding stage, z_o. The impedance seen by the following stage at any frequency will, of course, be a function of the Q of the resonant circuit and the output impedance z_o. The impedance seen by the preceding stage will also be a function of the Q of the resonant circuit and the input impedance z_i. Theoretically, since the out-

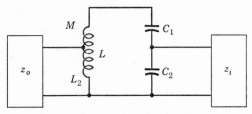

Fig. 11.22   The coupling circuit of one stage.

put impedance z_o of the preceding stage is dependent on its source impedance, and the input impedance z_i of the following stage is dependent on its load impedance, the exact analysis of these impedances becomes extremely involved. Let us neglect effects originating beyond one stage, in other words assume z_1 and z_2 in Fig. 11.23(a) to be constant. The

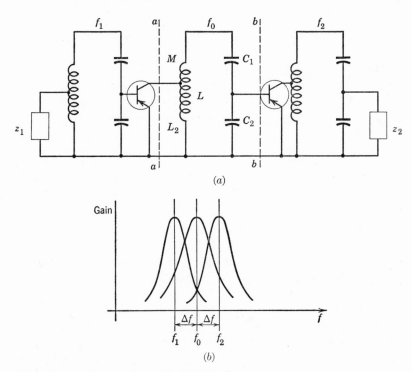

(a)

(b)

Fig. 11.23   Staggered-tuned amplifier.

impedance z_o in Fig. 11.22 is the impedance seen to the left of the line a–a, and the impedance z_i in Fig. 11.22 is the impedance seen to the right of the line b–b. The impedances z_1 and z_2 can be the output impedance of the preceding stage at frequency f_1 and the input impedance of the following stage at f_2 respectively. The values of z_o and z_i in Fig. 11.22, then, can be calculated for frequency f_0 by using the impedance formulas given in Chapter 10.

As far as each individual stage is concerned, it is a narrow-band tuned amplifier. If the values of z_o and z_i are known the resonant circuit can be designed, following the principle discussed in Sec. 11.1. The sharpness of the slope of the selectivity curve will be controlled by the Q of each individual stage and the number of stages which are tuned to the same frequency.

The power gain per stage can be calculated in the same manner as for the narrow-band tuned amplifier. The overall power gain in decibels will be the sum of the power gains of each stage. Since stages are tuned to different frequencies the overall power gain will be less than for the narrow-band tuned amplifier for the same number of stages but the bandwidth will be increased.

11.3 Problems

1. Given a transistor which has the following parameters at 1000 cps: $\alpha = 0.9$; $r_c = 250$ kilohms; $r_b = 200$ ohms; $r_e = 30$ ohms; $f_{\alpha 0} = 1$ mc; $C_c = 50$ $\mu\mu$f; collector-base-diode capacitance = 15 $\mu\mu$f. This transistor is to be used in a 455-kc i-f amplifier using the grounded-base connection. Find the input impedance of this stage if the interstage coupling circuit used is as shown in Fig. 11.6, with $C_1/C_2 = \frac{1}{10}$ and a coil having $Q = 100$, $L = 1$ millihenry.

2. Find the output impedance of the amplifier stage of problem 1. Find the effective Q of this amplifier stage.

3. Given the resonant frequency $f_0 = 455$ kc, the effective Q of each amplifier stage as 20, and the original Q of the resonant circuit in Fig. 11.9 as 100. If the inductance of the coil is taken as 0.5 millihenry, find the ratio C_1/C_2 if the input impedance of the next stage is $300\underline{/-15°}$ ohms. Find the tap required on the inductance for matching an output impedance $z_o = 14\underline{/-25°}$ kilohm.

11.4 Bibliography

1. C. B. Brown, "High Frequency Operation of Transistors," *Electronics*, *23*, 81–83 (July, 1950).

2. Wallace, Schimpf, and Dickten, "A Junction Transistor Tetrode for High-Frequency Use," *Proc. IRE*, *40*, No. 11, pp. 1395–1400 (November, 1952).

3. L. L. Karos and R. F. Schwartz, "Transistor Frequency Modulator Circuit," *Electronics*, *24*, 130–132 (July, 1951).

4. G. Raisbeck, "Transistor Circuit Design," *Electronics*, *24*, No. 12, pp. 128–132 (December, 1951).

5. G. S. Epstein and others, "Transistorizing Communication Equipment," *Electronics*, *25*. 98–102 (May, 1952).

Chapter 12

Video Amplifiers

12.1 Introduction

The term video-frequency amplifier is used with the same meaning as for tube amplifiers, i.e., an amplifier passing a band of frequencies from 60 cps or lower to 4 mc or higher. The requirements of this kind of amplifier have been well established for vacuum tubes.[1,2] The frequency response characteristic and the total time delay must be reasonably uniform over the frequency range of interest.

The problems encountered in using transistors as elements of a video-frequency amplifier can be divided into two groups. The first group comprises those contributed by the circuit components other than the transistors. With transistors having α cut-off frequencies much higher than the highest frequency of a video amplifier and power gain flat over the video-frequency band, the problems encountered in using these transistors for video amplifiers are similar to those encountered in the design of a video amplifier using tubes.

The second group of problems is contributed by the characteristics of transistors. In Chapter 9 the variation of current-amplification factors α and b with frequency are shown, and in Chapter 10 the variation of power gain, voltage amplification, and impedances with frequency are discussed for different circuit configurations. It is evident that, with transistors having a cut-off frequency $f_{\alpha 0}$ only slightly larger than or equal to the high-frequency end of the video-frequency band, the high-frequency characteristics of such transistors introduce additional problems. The attenuation and phase shift due to the transistor itself must be compensated by circuit elements in the amplifier.

The simplest method of obtaining such a wide pass band is to employ resistance coupling together with compensation networks. This is similar to the tube amplifier principle. However, there are distinct differences between a video amplifier using transistors and one using tubes. It has been shown in the preceding chapters that the transistor is essentially a power-amplification device in the sense that it requires a certain amount of signal power input to give an amplified power output. It is unlike the tube amplifier used for voltage amplification, which needs practically no input signal power. It was also shown in Chapter 10 that the input impedances of a grounded-base and a grounded-emitter transistor amplifier are smaller than the output impedances of these two amplifiers. The input impedance of a grounded-collector transistor is larger than its output impedance. However, when a grounded-base or a grounded-emitter amplifier is used as the load, this input impedance is still smaller than the output impedance of a grounded-base or a grounded-emitter amplifier used to drive it. Therefore, in general, a certain degree of mismatch exists with the consequence of increasing the number of stages to achieve the required gain.

These characteristics, low input impedance of the grounded-base and grounded-emitter amplifier and high output impedance, indicate that, for junction transistors, certain connections cannot be cascaded with resistance coupling as will be shown below, and for point-contact transistors the grounded-base configuration is required.

12.2 The Configurations of Cascaded Stages

Owing to the wide frequency band involved, compensated resistance-coupled amplifier stages appear to be the practical solution. This implies that impedance matching cannot be obtained and power gain must be sacrificed to secure the required bandwidth. This is similar in some respects to the practice with tube amplifiers where voltage amplification is sacrificed to obtain bandwidth. However, because of the high output impedance and low input impedance of grounded-base

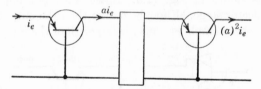

Fig. 12.1   Two grounded-base transistors in cascade.

and grounded-emitter transistor amplifiers there are restrictions on the transistor connections that can be used for cascaded stages in a video-frequency amplifier.

When a junction transistor is used in the grounded-base configuration, the short-circuit current-amplification factor α is less than unity, and the input impedance is much smaller than the output impedance. Consequently, when a junction transistor connected in the grounded-base configuration with resistive coupling is cascaded with a similar unit as shown in Fig. 12.1, there will be no gain. If the second transistor in Fig. 12.1 is changed to a grounded-emitter connection, as shown in Fig. 12.2, there will be practically no current amplification in the first stage but there will be power gain since the input impedance of a

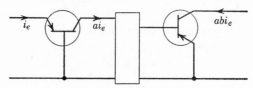

Fig. 12.2   A grounded-base transistor followed by a grounded-emitter stage.

grounded-emitter stage is larger than the input impedance of the grounded-base stage. The grounded-emitter stage will have considerable current amplification, approximately equal to $b = a/(1 - a)$; hence, the grounded-base grounded-emitter pair will have an overall current amplification and power gain of approximately $a^2/(1 - a)$.

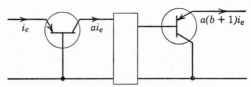

Fig. 12.3   A grounded-base stage followed by a grounded-collector stage.

Let a grounded-collector amplifier stage be preceded by a grounded-base stage as shown in Fig. 12.3. Since the input impedance of a grounded-collector stage, although smaller than the output impedance of a grounded-base amplifier stage, is larger than the input impedance

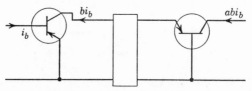

Fig. 12.4   A grounded-emitter stage followed by a grounded-base stage.

of the other two circuit configurations, the grounded-base stage is now able to give a certain amount of power gain.

When a grounded-emitter amplifier is followed by a grounded-base amplifier with resistance coupling as shown in Fig. 12.4, the grounded-base amplifier stage will contribute power gain only when its load resistance is appreciably greater than its input impedance. When two

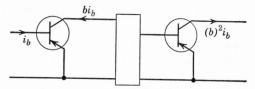

Fig. 12.5   Two grounded-emitter stages in cascade.

grounded-emitter amplifiers are cascaded with resistance coupling as shown in Fig. 12.5, power gain will be contributed by both stages.

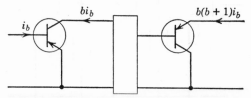

Fig. 12.6   A grounded-emitter stage followed by a grounded-collector stage.

In Fig. 12.6 is shown a grounded-emitter stage followed by a grounded-collector stage with resistance coupling. Power gain is contributed by

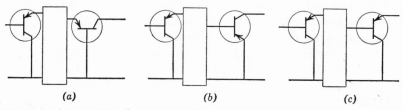

(a)   (b)   (c)

Fig. 12.7   A grounded-collector stage followed by one of the three different circuit configurations.

both stages. Any of the three different circuit configurations can be used to follow a grounded-collector amplifier as shown in Fig. 12.7(a), (b), and (c).

12.3   Low-Frequency Considerations

In the last section different transistor circuit configurations were presented which are usable for video-frequency amplifiers. The interstage circuit is not shown. Although it is described as resistance coupling and shown as a four-terminal network it may be either a four-terminal or a two-terminal network, and may consist of resistances, capacitances, and inductances. The components are so designed in the network that the frequency response of each amplifier stage is properly compensated for amplitude and phase angle over the wide band required.

The transistors themselves present no serious problems at low frequency. The parameters of the equivalent circuit are real and constant as shown in Chapter 4. The input and output resistances can be easily calculated. When the load resistance is small the current amplification is approximately equal to α for the grounded-base point-contact transistor, b for the grounded-emitter junction transistor, and $(b + 1)$

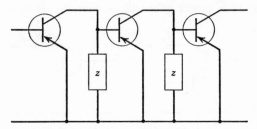

Fig. 12.8   A direct-coupled amplifier.

for the grounded-collector junction transistor. However, since transistors require d-c bias supplies, the bias current circuits may affect the low-frequency response of the amplifier. In Fig. 12.8 is shown a direct-coupled amplifier. The two-terminal coupling network z may be a combination of L, R, and C. Such an amplifier will extend down to direct current. Two major problems are encountered here, however: the method of supplying the necessary bias currents, and the problem of stabilizing against drift. These are covered in detail in Chapters 6 and 8.

The d-c bias circuits can be isolated by a blocking condenser C as shown in Fig. 12.9. R is the effective resistance of the d-c bias circuit

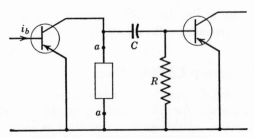

Fig. 12.9   An R-C coupled amplifier.

of the last stage. The network between points a–a will consist of L, R, and C for proper frequency compensation. The low-frequency response is, of course, effected by the blocking condenser. The method of compensating is well known from the art of video amplifiers using tubes. Thus, the preceding amplifier stage will be considered as a constant-current generator which supplies a current bi_b. This current

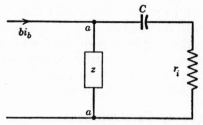

Fig. 12.10   Low-frequency equivalent circuit of Fig. 12.9.

bi_b will flow into the network as shown in Fig. 12.10, where C is the blocking condenser and r_i is the input resistance of the next stage (which is usually smaller than R and therefore the effect of R is neglected). The network between points a–a should be so designed that the current flowing in r_i will be practically the same for all low signal frequencies within the required frequency band, together with the condition that

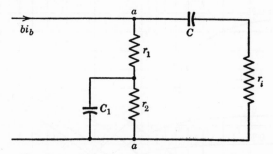

Fig. 12.11   Low-frequency compensating circuit.

a d-c path should be available for the bias current of the preceding stage. The solution is shown in Fig. 12.11. A resistance r_1 is connected in series with a parallel combination of C_1 and r_2. The condition for constant current flowing in r_i at low frequencies is

$$\frac{r_1 + r_2/(1 + \omega^2 C_1^2 r_2^2)}{r_i} = \frac{\omega C}{(1 + \omega^2 C_1^2 r_2^2)/(r_2^2 \omega C_1)} \qquad [12.1]$$

When r_2 is much larger than $1/\omega C_1$ for the frequencies concerned and is comparable to r_1, eq. 12.1 becomes

$$r_1/r_i \cong C/C_1 \qquad [12.2]$$

The input resistance of a grounded-emitter stage is about 1000 ohms at low frequency. The value of r_1 will be determined by the gain at medium frequency. In general, the smaller the value r_1 the greater the loss in the circuit. As the input resistance r_i is low compared to that of a tube amplifier, the coupling capacitance C must be many times the value usually employed for vacuum-tube video amplifiers. Fortunately transistors are able to work at low voltages, thus permitting a lower rating, and hence smaller physical size, for the coupling capacitors.

12.4   High-Frequency Considerations

The upper limit of frequency response of a transistor amplifier is controlled principally by the transistor itself. In addition, as was shown in Sec. 12.2, for junction transistors the grounded-emitter configuration and grounded-collector configurations are the most profitable transistor connection for video amplifiers. The high-frequency response will thus be greatly affected by the value of $b\ [= a/(1 - a)]$.

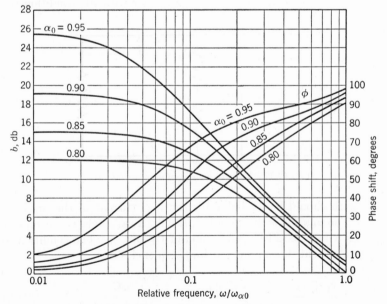

Fig. 12.12   The variation of b with frequency.

It was shown in Chapter 9 that the short-circuit current gain b for the grounded-emitter circuit has a cut-off frequency much lower than the α cut-off frequency $f_{\alpha 0}$. Using the expressions given in Chapter 9 for α and b,

$$\alpha = \alpha_0/\cosh\sqrt{j\omega RC} \qquad \omega_{\alpha 0}RC = 2.43 \qquad \text{and} \qquad b \cong \alpha/(1-\alpha)$$

the variation of b with frequency for $\alpha_0 = 0.95$, 0.90, 0.85, and 0.80 is plotted in Fig. 12.12. If the load impedance of a grounded-emitter amplifier stage is low the power gain is approximately proportional to the current amplification $|b|$ squared. The curves of Fig. 12.12 show that, in a video amplifier, the upper frequency of which approaches the α cut-off frequency $f_{\alpha 0}$, a transistor having an $\alpha_0 = 0.8$ is as good as one having an $\alpha_0 = 0.95$. The curves of Fig. 12.12 indicate approximately the required α cut-off frequency of transistors to be used in the video amplifier. The requirements are also a function of the gain in decibels required per stage. For instance, if 10-db current amplification is required per stage, then the high-frequency end will be at approximately $0.2f_{\alpha 0}$. For frequencies below $f_{\alpha 0}$ let us use the expression $\alpha = \alpha_0/(1 + j\omega rc)$ given in Chapter 9. If $rc = 1/\omega_{\alpha 0}$ we have

$$b \cong \alpha/(1-\alpha)$$

$$\cong \cfrac{1}{\left(\cfrac{1}{\alpha_0} - 1\right) + j\left(\cfrac{1}{\alpha_0}\cfrac{\omega}{\omega_{\alpha 0}}\right)} \qquad [12.3]$$

At high frequencies we can neglect the reactances of C and C_1 of Fig. 12.11, but the high-frequency input impedance should be used instead of the resistance r_i. Figure 12.11 changes to Fig. 12.13 in which r_i is replaced by z_i. The stray capacitance and the capacitive susceptance

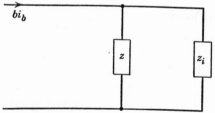

Fig. 12.13   High-frequency equivalent circuit.

of the output impedance are combined into z. The input impedance of a grounded-emitter amplifier stage has been shown to be capacitive at high frequencies and to vary with frequency. Let us represent the input impedance z_i by the circuit shown in Fig. 12.14, where r_3, r_4, and C_3 are all fictitious, but chosen to simulate the input impedance z_i for frequencies up to the α cut-off frequency $f_{\alpha0}$. Thus

$$z_i \cong r_3 + \frac{r_4}{1 + j\omega C_3 r_4} \qquad [12.4]$$

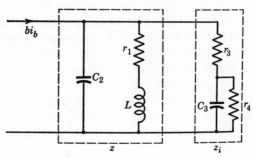

Fig. 12.14 A simple high-frequency compensating circuit employing shunt peaking.

For a number of junction transistors it was found that a reasonable approximation is

$$r_3 = r_4 \qquad [12.5]$$

and

$$\omega_{\alpha0} C_3 r_4 = 10$$

or

$$C_3 r_4 = 10/\omega_{\alpha0} \qquad [12.6]$$

Hence, we can rewrite eq. 12.4 to give

$$z_i = r_3 + \frac{r_3}{1 + j(10\omega/\omega_{\alpha0})} \qquad [12.7]$$

12.4.1 Shunt Peaking

The simplest two-terminal high-frequency compensation circuit is shown in Fig. 12.14. An inductance L is in series with r_1. The stray capacitance and the capacitive susceptance of the output impedance are represented by C_2. The object is to find that value of L which will maintain constant signal current flowing into z_i for all the high frequencies within the required band.

The impedance z in Fig. 12.14 is given by

$$z = \frac{r_1 + j\omega L}{1 + j\omega C_2(r_1 + j\omega L)} \qquad [12.8]$$

The current flowing into z_i is

$$i_b' = b i_b z / (z + z_i) \qquad [12.9]$$

The expression for b is given by eq. 12.3. The condition for flat response is

$$i_b'/i_b = \text{constant} = bz/(z + z_i) \qquad [12.10]$$

Since eq. 12.10 is in vector form, the word "constant" means constant magnitude and linear variation of phase angle with frequency.

Substituting eqs. 12.3, 12.7, and 12.8 for b, z_i, and z in eq. 12.10 yields the magnitude of current amplification

$$|A_i| = \sqrt{\frac{r_1^2 + \omega^2 L^2}{A^2 + B^2}} \times \frac{1}{\sqrt{[(1/\alpha_0) - 1]^2 + [(1/\alpha_0)(\omega/\omega_{\alpha 0})]^2}} \qquad [12.11]$$

and the phase angle

$$\phi = \tan^{-1}\left(\frac{\omega L}{r_1}\right) - \tan^{-1}\left(\frac{\omega/\omega_{\alpha 0}}{1 - \alpha_0}\right) - \tan^{-1}\left(\frac{B}{A}\right) \qquad [12.12]$$

where

$$A = r_1 + r_3 \left(\frac{1}{1 + (10\omega/\omega_{\alpha 0})^2}\right)$$

$$\times \left[2 - 2\omega^2 C_2 L + (1 - \omega^2 C_2 L)\left(\frac{10\omega}{\omega_{\alpha 0}}\right)^2 + r_1 C_2 \omega \frac{10\omega}{\omega_{\alpha 0}}\right]$$

$$B = \omega L + \omega r_3 \left[\frac{1}{1 + (10\omega/\omega_{\alpha 0})^2}\right]$$

$$\times \left[2 C_2 r_1 + C_2 r_1 \left(\frac{10\omega}{\omega_{\alpha 0}}\right)^2 + \left(\frac{10\omega}{\omega_{\alpha 0}}\right)\omega C_2 L - \frac{10}{\omega_{\alpha 0}}\right]$$

At low frequency $\omega \ll \omega_2$ (where ω_2 is the amplifier cut-off frequency) the magnitude of the current amplification is $[r_1/(r_1 + 2r_3)][\alpha_0/(1 - \alpha_0)]$. At frequency ω_2 the magnitude of the current amplification will depend on the ratio $\omega_2/\omega_{\alpha 0}$. Let us study several cases as follows:

Case 1: $\omega_2/\omega_{\alpha 0} = 0.1$.

The above eqs. 12.11 and 12.12 reduce to

$$|A_i| = \sqrt{\frac{r_1^2 + \omega_2^2 L^2}{A^2 + B^2}} \times \frac{1}{\sqrt{[(1/\alpha_0) - 1]^2 + (1/10\alpha_0)^2}} \qquad [12.13]$$

$$\phi = \tan^{-1}\left(\frac{\omega_2 L}{r_1}\right) - \tan^{-1}\left(\frac{1}{10 - 10\alpha_0}\right) - \tan^{-1}\left(\frac{B}{A}\right) \qquad [12.14]$$

and now

$$A = r_1 + r_3[\tfrac{3}{2} - \tfrac{3}{2}\omega_2{}^2 C_2 L + \tfrac{1}{2} r_1 C_2 \omega_2]$$

$$B = \omega_2 L + \omega_2 r_3[\tfrac{3}{2} C_2 r_1 + \tfrac{1}{2}\omega_2 C_2 L - (1/2\omega_2)]$$

Equating eq. 12.13 to $\left| A_i \right|$ at $\omega \ll \omega_2$, we have

$$\sqrt{\frac{r_1{}^2 + \omega_2{}^2 L^2}{A^2 + B^2}} \left\{ \frac{1}{\sqrt{[(1/\alpha_0) - 1]^2 + (1/10\alpha_0)^2}} \right\} = \left(\frac{r_1}{r_1 + 2r_3} \right) \frac{\alpha_0}{1 - \alpha_0}$$

[12.15]

For a given α_0, the ratio of

$$\frac{b_0}{\left| b \right|_{(\omega_2)}} = \frac{\alpha_0 \sqrt{[(1/\alpha_0) - 1]^2 + (1/10\alpha_0)^2}}{1 - \alpha_0} = k$$

can be calculated. This value is shown in Fig. 12.15. Substituting this value of k, eq. 12.15 becomes

$$\sqrt{\frac{r_1{}^2 + \omega_2{}^2 L^2}{A^2 + B^2}} = \frac{r_1}{r_1 + 2r_3} k$$

[12.16]

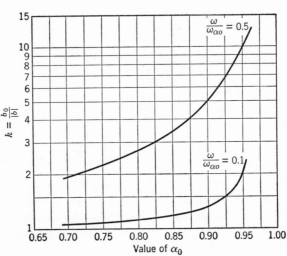

Fig. 12.15 The value of k vs. α_0.

The value of r_1 in eq. 12.16 will determine the current amplification over the pass band. In a typical case the relations between C_2, r_1, and r_3 might be as follows

$$r_1 = 2r_3$$

[12.17]

and

$$\omega_2 C_2 = 1/4r_3$$

[12.18]

Using the relation given by eqs. 12.17 and 12.18, the expressions A and B can be simplified to give

$$A = \tfrac{15}{4}r_3 - \tfrac{3}{8}\omega_2 L \qquad \text{and} \qquad B = \tfrac{1}{4}r_3 + \tfrac{9}{8}\omega_2 L$$

Equation 12.16 now becomes

$$\sqrt{\frac{(2r_3)^2 + (\omega_2 L)^2}{A^2 + B^2}} = \frac{1}{2}k$$

or

$$4 + \left(\frac{\omega_2 L}{r_3}\right)^2 = \frac{1}{4}k^2\left[\left(\frac{15}{4} - \frac{3}{8}\frac{\omega_2 L}{r_3}\right)^2 + \left(\frac{1}{4} + \frac{9}{8}\frac{\omega_2 L}{r_3}\right)^2\right]$$

$$= \frac{1}{4}k^2\left[\frac{113}{8} - \frac{9}{4}\frac{\omega_2 L}{r_3} + \frac{45}{32}\left(\frac{\omega_2 L}{r_3}\right)^2\right]$$

or

$$\left(\frac{1}{4}k^2\frac{45}{32} - 1\right)\left(\frac{\omega_2 L}{r_3}\right)^2 - \frac{1}{4}k^2\frac{9}{4}\left(\frac{\omega_2 L}{r_3}\right) + \frac{1}{4}k^2\frac{113}{8} - 4 = 0$$

$$[12.19]$$

For a given value of k, $\omega_2 L$ can be solved in terms of r_3. As an example, for $\alpha_0 = 0.9$, we have $k = 1.312$ at $\omega_2/\omega_{a0} = 0.1$. Equation 12.19 becomes

$$0.395(\omega_2 L/r_3)^2 + 0.966(\omega_2 L/r_3) - 2.07 = 0 \qquad \text{or} \qquad \omega_2 L = 1.37r_3$$

The relative magnitude of current amplification $|A_i|$ and the time delay $t = \phi/\omega$ of this example are plotted in Fig. 12.16. The magni-

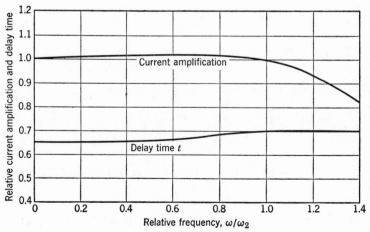

Fig. 12.16   Frequency response of circuit of Fig. 12.14.

tude of current amplification A_i rises to about 1.02 times its low-frequency value at $0.6\omega_2$ and passes through 1.0 again at ω_2. The delay time is about $0.04(1/\omega_2)$ from $\omega = 0$ to $\omega = \omega_2$.

Case 2: $\omega_2/\omega_{\alpha 0} = 0.5$.

If we make the ratio $\omega_2/\omega_{\alpha 0}$ a little higher we will expect a little less gain per stage than was obtained before. Using $\omega_2 = 0.5\,\omega_{\alpha 0}$, eq. 12.11 becomes

$$A_i = \sqrt{\frac{r_1{}^2 + \omega_2{}^2 L^2}{A^2 + B^2}} \times \frac{1}{\sqrt{[(1/\alpha_0) - 1]^2 + (1/2\alpha_0)^2}} \quad [12.20]$$

and eq. 12.12 becomes

$$\phi = \tan^{-1}\left(\frac{\omega_2 L}{r_1}\right) - \tan^{-1}\left(\frac{1}{2 - 2\alpha_0}\right) - \tan^{-1}\left(\frac{B}{A}\right) \quad [12.21]$$

where $A = r_1 + r_3[\frac{27}{26} - \frac{27}{26}\omega_2{}^2 C_2 L + \frac{5}{26}r_1\omega_2 C_2]$

$$B = \omega_2 L + \omega_2 r_3 \left[\frac{27}{26} C_2 r_1 + \frac{5}{26} \omega_2 C_2 L - \frac{5}{26\omega_2}\right]$$

Let us set up the relations between ω_2, C_2, r_1, and r_3 as follows

$$\omega_2 C_2 = 1/4r_3 \quad [12.18]$$

and

$$r_1 = r_3 \quad [12.22]$$

The expressions for A and B reduce to

$$A = \tfrac{217}{104}r_3 - \tfrac{27}{104}\omega_2 L \qquad B = \tfrac{7}{104}r_3 + \tfrac{109}{104}\omega_2 L$$

Substituting above results into eq. 12.16, we have

$$1 + \left(\frac{\omega_2 L}{r_3}\right)^2 = \frac{1}{9} k^2 \left[\left(\frac{217}{104} - \frac{27}{104}\frac{\omega_2 L}{r_3}\right)^2 + \left(\frac{7}{104} + \frac{109}{104}\frac{\omega_2 L}{r_3}\right)^2\right]$$

$$= \tfrac{1}{9}k^2[4.35 - 0.963(\omega_2 L/r_3) + 1.168(\omega_2 L/r_3)^2]$$

or

$$(0.13k^2 - 1)(\omega_2 L/r_3)^2 - 0.107k^2(\omega_2 L/r_3) + 0.483k^2 - 1 = 0 \quad [12.23]$$

The value $\omega_2 L/r_3$ can be solved for a given value of k. However, it should be noticed that, since $(\omega_2 L/r_3)$ has to be a real number, there is an upper limit for the value of k. This is the consequence of setting up the relations given by eqs. 12.18 and 12.22. The largest value of k which can be used in eq. 12.23 is given by

$$(0.107k^2)^2 - 4(0.13k^2 - 1)(0.483k^2 - 1) = 0 \qquad [12.24]$$

or

$$k = 2.87 \qquad [12.24a]$$

This value of k corresponds to an α_0 of about 0.815. If we decrease the value of r_1 relative to r_3, the limitation of eq. 11.65 will be removed, but little advantage can be obtained in this case by using a large value of k, corresponding to junction transistors of high α_0. Decreasing the value

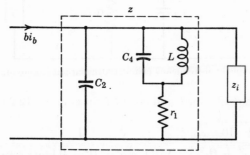

Fig. 12.17 A high-frequency compensating circuit employing modified shunt peaking.

of r_1 or using transistors of low α_0 gives the same result of less gain per stage.

The applications of two-terminal high-frequency compensation circuits using two or more compensating elements for tube amplifiers are described in many television books.[3] Those circuits can also be used for high-frequency compensation of a transistor amplifier. Figure 12.17 shows a simple circuit using L and C_4 as compensating elements. Equation 12.10 or 12.27 is still the required condition for designing z. It is not quite as straightforward as with the tube amplifiers since the relations between r_1, C_2, C_4, and L depend upon the values of b, $\omega_2/\omega_{\alpha 0}$, and z_i. Therefore they cannot be solved by simply considering the m-derived type half-T section of low-pass filter. However, the principle employed in studying the high-frequency compensation circuit given above can still be used to study the more complicated circuit.

12.4.2 Series Peaking

If the inductance L in Fig. 12.14 is connected in series with the second stage, it forms a series circuit as shown in Fig. 12.18. The signal current flowing into the second stage is

$$i_b' = bi_b \frac{r_1/(1 + j\omega C_2 r_1)}{(z_i + j\omega L) + r_1/(1 + j\omega C_2 r_1)} \qquad [12.25]$$

or

$$\frac{i_b'}{i_b} = b \frac{r_1}{r_1 + (1 + j\omega C_2 r_1)(z_i + j\omega L)}$$

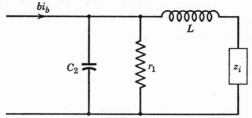

Fig. 12.18 A simple high-frequency compensating circuit employing series peaking.

Substituting eq. 12.3 for b and eq. 12.7 for z_i in eq. 12.25 yields

$$A_i = \frac{r_1 \sqrt{1 + (10\omega/\omega_{\alpha 0})^2}}{\sqrt{A_1{}^2 + B_1{}^2}} \frac{1}{\sqrt{[(1/\alpha_0) - 1]^2 + [(1/\alpha_0)(\omega/\omega_{\alpha 0})]^2}} \qquad [12.26]$$

and

$$\phi = \tan^{-1}\left(\frac{10\omega}{\omega_{\alpha 0}}\right) - \tan^{-1}\left(\frac{\omega/\omega_{\alpha 0}}{1 - \alpha_0}\right) - \tan^{-1}\left(\frac{B_1}{A_1}\right) \qquad [12.27]$$

where

$$A_1 = r_1 + 2r_3 - (10\omega/\omega_{\alpha 0})(\omega C_2 r_1 r_3 + \omega L) - \omega^2 L C_2 r_1$$

$$B_1 = \omega L + r_3 \omega \left(2C_2 r_1 + \frac{10}{\omega_{\alpha 0}}\right) + \frac{10\omega}{\omega_{\alpha 0}} r_1 (1 - \omega^2 C_2 L)$$

At low frequencies A_i will be

$$A_i = [r_1/(r_1 + 2r_3)]b_0 \qquad [12.28]$$

Equating eq. 12.26 to 12.28, and simplifying, yields

$$\sqrt{\frac{1 + (10\omega/\omega_{\alpha 0})^2}{A_1{}^2 + B_1{}^2}} = \frac{1}{r_1 + 2r_3} k \qquad [12.29]$$

where the constant k is the same as in eq. 12.16. There is also a limitation of the value of k which can be used in eq. 12.29 for the given relations between r_1, r_3, and ω_2C_2.

As an example, let us assume that $\omega_2/\omega_{a0} = 0.1$, $\omega_2C_2 = 1/4r_3$. and $r_1 = 2r_3$. We have

$$A_1 = \tfrac{7}{2}r_3 - \tfrac{3}{2}\omega_2L \qquad B_1 = 4r_3 + \tfrac{1}{2}\omega_2L$$

and from eq. 12.29

$$32 = k^2 \left[\left(\frac{7}{2} - \frac{3}{2}\frac{\omega_2L}{r_3} \right)^2 + \left(4 + \frac{1}{2}\frac{\omega_2L}{r_3} \right)^2 \right]$$

or

$$2.5k^2 \left(\frac{\omega_2L}{r_3} \right)^2 - 6.5k^2 \left(\frac{\omega_2L}{r_3} \right) + (28.25k^2 - 32) = 0$$

The maximum value of k which will give a real value of ω_2L/r_3 is $k = 1.155$. This value of k corresponds to a value of $\alpha_0 = 0.825$. Under the above conditions, the value of ω_2L/r_3 is 1.3, or $\omega_2L = 1.3r_3$.

12.4.3 Series-Shunt Peaking

Combining the principles of the above two sections we have a four-terminal high-frequency compensation network. One of the simplest

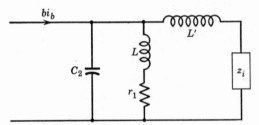

Fig. 12.19 A simple high-frequency compensating circuit employing series-shunt peaking.

circuits is shown in Fig. 12.19. The signal current flowing into z_i is

$$i_b' = bi_b \frac{\dfrac{r_1 + j\omega L}{1 + j\omega C_2(r_1 + j\omega L)}}{(z_i + j\omega L') + \dfrac{r_1 + j\omega L}{1 + j\omega C_2(r_1 + j\omega L)}}$$

or

$$\frac{i_b'}{i_b} = b \frac{r_1 + j\omega L}{(r_1 + j\omega L) + (z_i + j\omega L')[1 + j\omega C_2(r_1 + j\omega L)]} \qquad [12.30]$$

Substituting eq. 12.3 for b and eq. 12.7 for z_i in eq. 12.30 yields

$$A_i = \frac{\sqrt{r_1^2 + (\omega L)^2}\ \sqrt{1 + (10\omega/\omega_{\alpha 0})^2}}{\sqrt{A_2^2 + B_2^2}} \frac{1}{\sqrt{\left(\dfrac{1}{\alpha_0} - 1\right)^2 + \left(\dfrac{1}{\alpha_0}\dfrac{\omega}{\omega_{\alpha 0}}\right)^2}}$$

[12.31]

$$\phi = \tan^{-1}\left(\frac{\omega L}{r_1}\right) + \tan^{-1}\left(\frac{10\omega}{\omega_{\alpha 0}}\right) - \tan^{-1}\left(\frac{\omega/\omega_{\alpha 0}}{1 - \alpha_0}\right) - \tan^{-1}\left(\frac{B_2}{A_2}\right)$$

[12.32]

where

$$A_2 = r_1 + 2r_3 - \omega^2(2r_3 C_2 L + r_1 C_2 L')$$

$$+ \frac{10\omega}{\omega_{\alpha 0}}(\omega^3 C_2 L L' - \omega C_2 r_1 r_3 - \omega L - \omega L')$$

$$B_2 = \omega(L + L') + 2\omega C_2 r_1 r_3 - \omega^3 C_2 L L'$$

$$+ \frac{10\omega}{\omega_{\alpha 0}}(r_1 + r_3 - \omega^2 C_2 L r_3 - \omega^2 C_2 L' r_1)$$

Equating eq. 12.31 to its low-frequency value, we have

$$\frac{\sqrt{r_1^2 + (\omega L)^2}\sqrt{1 + (10\omega/\omega_{\alpha 0})^2}}{\sqrt{A_2^2 + B_2^2}} = \frac{r_1}{r_1 + 2r_3}k$$

[12.33]

where k has the same meaning as in eq. 12.16.

The above principle of compensating the frequency response of a transistor video amplifier can be applied to different compensation networks used in modern video amplifiers using tubes.

12.5 Problems

1. The principle of compensation of the frequency response of a video amplifier can be applied directly to high-fidelity audio amplifiers using transistors of relatively low α cut-off frequency. Given a transistor having parameters at 1000 cps as follows: $\alpha_0 = 0.95$, $r_c = 500$ kilohms, $r_b = 250$ ohms, $r_e = 40$ ohms, $f_{\alpha 0} = 150$ kc, $C_c = 40$ $\mu\mu f$, $r_l = 1000$ ohms, $r_g = 500$ ohms, find the compensating network for one amplifier stage using resistance r_l as load. The required frequency response is 3 db down at 10 cps and at 50 kc, with essentially flat response for the pass band. Find the power gain for this stage.

2. Since many video stages will be cascaded to give the required overall gain, while the higher-frequency compensation given in Fig. 12.16 is satisfactory for one stage, it may be found needing further improvement. Find the value of $\omega_2 L/r_3$ which will give practically constant delay time t.

3. The high-frequency compensating circuit shown in Fig. 12.17 has two compensating elements L and C_4. Following the principle discussed in Sec. 12.4.1 derive equations for designing C_4 and L.

4. In Fig. 12.7, using the relations $L' = \frac{1}{10}L$, $r_1 = 3r_3$, $\omega_2 C_2 = 1/4r_3$, $\omega_2/\omega_{a0} = 0.2$, find the maximum value of k. Using this value of k, calculate the value of $\omega_2 L/r_3$ and plot the relative current amplification and time delay.

12.6 Bibliography

1. Scott Helt, *Practical Television Engineering*, Rinehart, 1950.

2. Sid Deutsch, *Theory and Design of Television Receivers*, McGraw-Hill, 1951.

3. R. B. Dome, *Television Principles*, McGraw-Hill, 1951.

4. D. E. Thomas, "Transistor Amplifier—Cut-off Frequency," *Proc. IRE, 40*, No. 11, pp. 1481–1483 (November, 1952).

Chapter 13

Oscillators

13.1 Introduction

In many respects electron-tube circuits and transistor circuits are similar. One of the main differences is that electron tubes are normally operated as voltage amplifiers whereas transistors are normally operated as current amplifiers. This makes some changes in circuits necessary; for example, voltage feedback must be replaced by current feedback. In spite of a number of other differences, the similarity permits transistor amplifiers and oscillators to be discussed along somewhat the same lines as their vacuum-tube counterparts.

The most important part of every oscillator is an element of amplification; to be more precise, this element must be capable of translating small variations of input power into larger variations of output

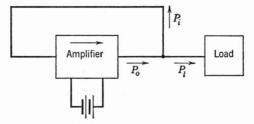

Fig. 13.1   Typical oscillator.

power. Given such an element, it is usually quite easy to build an oscillator around it. All that is required is a path that feeds back all or a part of the output power to the input in the proper phase, and a source of d-c power. In addition are needed a non-linear element to limit the amplitude of the oscillation and usually resonant elements to produce the desired waveform.

Figure 13.1 shows the schematic of an oscillator, consisting of an amplifier, a feedback path, and a load. The input and output powers of the transistor amplifier are related by

$$P_o = GP_i$$

where P_o is the output power, P_i the input power, and G the gain of the amplifier. The output power is related to the d-c power fed into the transistor by

$$P_o = \eta P_{\text{d-c}}$$

where η is the efficiency of the amplifier.

The power into the load is

$$P_l = P_o - P_i = P_o(G - 1)/G$$

This power is smaller than the output power of the amplifier. For example, if the amplifier has a maximum power output of 1 watt we will get less than 1 watt of power from the corresponding oscillator.

Similarly, we have

$$P_l = \frac{G - 1}{G} \eta P_{\text{d-c}}$$

The efficiency of the oscillator is therefore less than that of the corresponding amplifier.

A study of amplifiers, therefore, gives us knowledge about the upper limits for oscillators. For example, a transistor amplifier cannot be made to oscillate if the maximum available power gain is less than unity.

In the following sections the basic principles of a number of transistor oscillator circuits will be developed.

13.2   Negative-Impedance Oscillators

The input and output impedances of point-contact transistor † amplifiers can usually be made negative by proper choice of source and load impedances and possibly by inserting an additional resistance in series with the grounded electrode. For example, in the grounded-emitter configuration the input resistance (eq. 4.29) is

$$r_i = r_b + r_e \left[\frac{r_c + r_l}{r_c(1 - a) + r_e + r_l} \right] \qquad [13.1]$$

† $\alpha > 1$.

This resistance is negative if

$$r_b + r_e \left[\frac{r_c + r_l}{r_c(1 - a) + r_e + r_l} \right] < 0$$

Since for point-contact transistors a is usually greater than 2, this condition is readily satisfied for small r_b and r_l. If a resistance r_e' is inserted in series with the emitter lead (Fig. 13.2), and if $r_e' \gg r_e$, then the input resistance is

$$r_i \cong r_b + r_e' \left[\frac{r_c + r_l}{r_c(1 - a) + r_e' + r_l} \right] \qquad [13.2]$$

Figure 13.3 shows qualitatively the variation of r_i as a function of

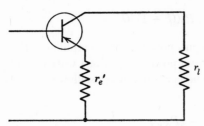

r_l for two different values of r_e', 100 ohms and 200 ohms. It may be seen that by a proper choice of r_e' and r_l any desired value of input resistance may be obtained.

At high frequencies, the input impedance will become capacitive or inductive. For example, the input impedance of the grounded-emitter stage will become capaci-

Fig. 13.2 The grounded-emitter configuration.

tive if r_l is small. This was shown in Chapter 9.

The input impedance is negative only for a limited range of d-c operating points. For example, in the grounded-base circuit of Fig. 13.4 it will be negative only as long as the emitter-base diode remains conducting and the collector-base diode non-conducting. The emitter-

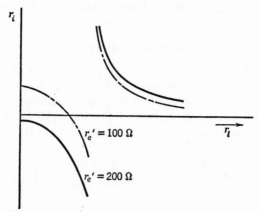

Fig. 13.3 The input resistance vs. load resistance.

base diode is reversed as the d-c emitter current changes its direction, the collector-base diode is reversed as the collector voltage is reversed. In Fig. 13.5 the relation between input current and voltage is shown. In region II the emitter diode is conducting and the collector diode

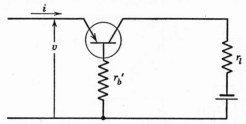

Fig. 13.4   The grounded-base stage.

non-conducting. We have, therefore, normal transistor action, and the input resistance is negative. In region I the emitter diode is reversed, and in region III the collector diode is reversed. The reader is referred to Chapter 18 for a detailed analysis of the negative resistance characteristic.

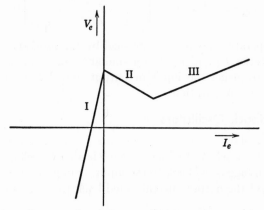

Fig. 13.5   Current-voltage characteristic for the circuit of Fig. 13.4.

The d-c input resistance of the grounded-base stage as shown in Fig. 13.5 is always positive for positive I_e. However, the a-c input resistance is negative in region II. In an oscillator the operating point must therefore be selected in this region, preferably at its center. This may be done, for example, by means of a battery in series with a large resistance.

Given a negative resistance, it is relatively easy to construct a sinusoidal oscillator by adding a resonant circuit (series, parallel, or mixed) across the negative resistance. The resonant circuit should not provide a d-c path that would change the d-c operating point of the transistor.

Figure 13.6 shows an oscillator using a point-contact transistor in the grounded-emitter configuration. It is assumed that all losses of the resonant circuit are concentrated in r_o. If the negative input resist-

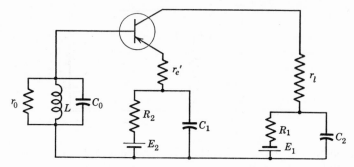

Fig. 13.6   Negative impedance oscillator.

ance at the d-c operating point is r_i, then oscillations will start if $r_o > -r_i$ or, eq. 13.2,

$$r_o > -\left\{ r_b + r_e' \left[\frac{r_c + r_l}{r_c(1 - a) + r_e' + r_l} \right] \right\} \qquad [13.3]$$

The d-c operating point is established by the resistances R_1 and R_2 and the batteries E_1 and E_2. In a similar manner oscillators may be constructed by using the input or output impedances of any of the three amplifier configurations.

13.3   Feedback Oscillators

Figure 13.7 shows an oscillator using a junction transistor with an external feedback path. In vacuum-tube feedback oscillators a part of the output voltage is fed back to the input. Similarly, with transistors a part or all of the output current is fed back to the input.

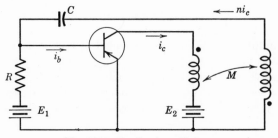

Fig. 13.7   Feedback oscillator.

In the oscillator of Fig. 13.7 the current i_b is amplified by the transistor in the grounded-emitter configuration. The collector current i_c is approximately

$$i_c \cong -[a/(1 - a)]i_b \qquad [13.4]$$

The minus sign indicates a reversal of the phase. The transformer, with turns ratio n, changes the amplitude of the current and changes its phase by an additional 180° so that it is fed back to the input in the proper phase. The current in the secondary of the transformer is fed back through the capacitance C to the input, where it passes to ground through the emitter electrode. The d-c operating point is established by the resistance R in series with the battery E_1 (which controls the emitter current) and the battery E_2 (which largely determines the collector voltage).

The current amplification of the transistor is approximately $a/(1 - a)$. For a turns ratio n and coupling $k = 1$, the current in the secondary of the transformer is n times the collector current, so that the total current amplification is $na/(1 - a)$. Oscillations will occur if this amplification is greater than unity, and therefore we have as starting conditions

$$n[a/(1 - a)] > 1 \qquad \text{or} \qquad n > (1 - a)/a \qquad [13.5]$$

13.3.1 Conditions for Self-Excitation in Transistor Feedback Oscillation

It was stated earlier that the transistor is essentially a current amplifier, therefore requiring a current feedback path. Figure 13.8 shows the general network for current feedback.

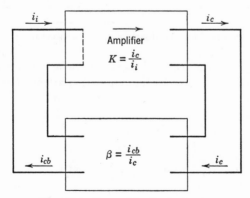

Fig. 13.8   General feedback circuit.

The amplifier of this figure is assumed to have zero input impedance, a short-circuit current amplification of A_i, and an output impedance z_o. It is unilateral.

The feedback network has, for short-circuited output, an input impedance z_i and a current amplification β. The current amplification of the amplifier, when working into the input impedance z_i of the feedback network, is

$$K = A_i z_o / (z_o + z_i)$$

The starting condition for oscillation is that the total current amplification be unity

$$K\beta = A_i[z_o/(z_o + z_i)]\beta = 1$$

or

$$\beta = (1/A_i)(z_o + z_i)/z_o \qquad [13.6]$$

A practical transistor amplifier does not have zero input impedance. However, by absorbing the resistances r_e and r_b into the feedback network it is possible to use eq. 13.6. Figure 13.9 shows how r_e and r_b

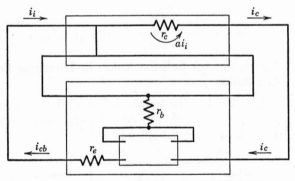

Fig. 13.9   Feedback oscillator networks.

may be included in the feedback network for a grounded-base stage. The amplifier of this figure has the required zero impedance input, the short-circuit current gain is a, the output impedance is r_c, and the starting condition is therefore

$$\beta = (1/a)(r_c + z_i)/r_c$$

$$= (1/a) + (1/a)(z_i/r_c) \qquad [13.7]$$

or approximately

$$\beta \cong 1/a \qquad [13.8]$$

Similarly, for the grounded-emitter stage we have

$$\beta = -[(1 - a)/a][r_c(1 - a) + z_i]/r_c(1 - a)$$

$$= -(1 - a)/a - z_i/ar_c \qquad\qquad [13.9]$$

or approximately

$$\beta \cong -(1 - a)/a \qquad\qquad [13.9a]$$

At high frequencies, a and r_c become complex, and so β must also be complex to satisfy the starting conditions. At high frequencies, there-

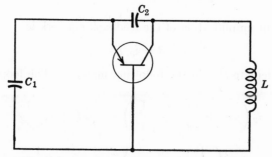

Fig. 13.10   Circuit similar to Colpitts oscillator.

fore, the coupling network has to provide a phase shift that may have any value from $0°$ to $360°$.

In the following the starting condition for a simple oscillator, resembling the Colpitts oscillator, will be calculated (see Fig. 13.10).

The equivalent circuit of this oscillator is shown in Fig. 13.11.

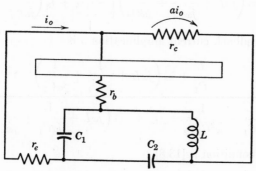

Fig. 13.11   The equivalent circuit for oscillator of Fig. 13.10.

Figure 13.12 shows the feedback network.

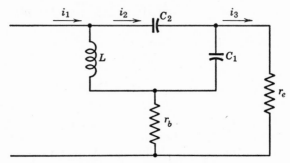

Fig. 13.12   The feedback network.

The current amplification of the feedback network is

$$\beta = i_3/i_1$$

We shall calculate this in the following manner.   The loop equations
are

$$i_2\left(j\omega L + \frac{1}{j\omega C_1} + \frac{1}{j\omega C_2}\right) = i_1 j\omega L + i_3\frac{1}{j\omega C_1}$$

$$i_3\left(\frac{1}{j\omega C_1} + r_e + r_b\right) = i_1 r_b + i_2\frac{1}{j\omega C_1}$$

The current i_2 may be eliminated

$$\frac{1}{j\omega C_1}\left(i_1 j\omega L + i_3\frac{1}{j\omega C_1}\right)$$

$$= \left(j\omega L + \frac{1}{j\omega C_1} + \frac{1}{j\omega C_2}\right)\left[-i_1 r_b + i_3\left(\frac{1}{j\omega C_1} + r_e + r_b\right)\right]$$

whence the feedback current amplification β is

$$\beta = \frac{i_3}{i_1} = \frac{\dfrac{L}{C_1} + r_b\left(j\omega L + \dfrac{1}{j\omega C_1} + \dfrac{1}{j\omega C_2}\right)}{\dfrac{L}{C_1} - \dfrac{1}{\omega^2 C_1 C_2} + (r_e + r_b)\left(j\omega L + \dfrac{1}{j\omega C_1} + \dfrac{1}{j\omega C_2}\right)} \qquad [13.10]$$

The starting condition is [13.8]

$$\beta \cong 1/a$$

this condition is satisfied if the real and imaginary parts of eq. 13.10 are related by $1/a$, whence

$$aL/C_1 = L/C_1 - 1/\omega^2 C_1 C_2$$

and

$$ar_b\left(j\omega L + \frac{1}{j\omega C_1} + \frac{1}{j\omega C_2}\right) = (r_e + r_b)\left(j\omega L + \frac{1}{j\omega C_1} + \frac{1}{j\omega C_2}\right)$$

These two equations in turn can only be satisfied if the total of the reactances is zero, from which

$$\omega^2 = (1/L)[(1/C_1) + (1/C_2)]$$

$$C_2 = C_1 a/(1 - a)$$

[13.11]

The frequency of the oscillator of Fig. 13.10 is therefore determined by a resonant circuit consisting of the inductance L in series with the capacitances C_1 and C_2. Oscillations will start if capacitance of C_2 is $a/(1 - a)$ times the capacitance of C_1.

A feedback oscillator based on the "dual" of the vacuum-tube Colpitts oscillator is discussed in Chapter 14.

13.4 Crystal Oscillators

In order to improve the frequency stability and waveform it may be desirable to use a crystal as the frequency-controlling element in a tran-

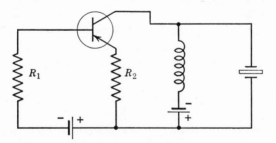

Fig. 13.13   Crystal oscillator with crystal in collector circuit.

sistor oscillator. The oscillator can be of either the negative-impedance or the feedback type.

Figures 13.13 and 13.14 show two such oscillators. In Fig. 13.13 the negative output impedance of the grounded-emitter stage for point-contact transistors is used. In the oscillator of Fig. 13.14 the crystal is connected to the emitter. In order to obtain a large input impedance, a parallel-resonant circuit is connected in series with the base. D-c bias current is provided through resistances R_1 and R_2.

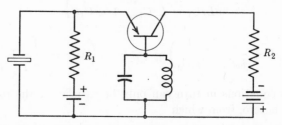

Fig. 13.14   Crystal oscillator with crystal in emitter circuit.

13.5   Linearity Considerations

For a thorough investigation of an oscillator, not only the linear but also the non-linear components of the circuit should be considered. As stated earlier, a linear analysis determines the frequency of oscillation and the starting conditions; a non-linear analysis determines the amplitude of oscillation, the waveform, and the stability of frequency and amplitude.

Practical oscillators are never absolutely linear. One of the reasons for this is that in a linear oscillator the amplitude would increase indefinitely. Only non-linearity can limit the amplitude of oscillation, and, therefore, every oscillator must contain some non-linearity. Besides limiting the amplitude, this will distort the waveform and cause a slight shift in the frequency of oscillation.

As a rule, it is desirable that the waveform of an oscillator be as nearly sinusoidal as possible. The opposite is true, however, for a number of applications, for example for harmonic generators and for frequency multiplication and division.

Physically, a transistor consists of two diodes: the emitter-base diode and the collector-base diode. Amplification occurs only if the emitter-base diode is operating in its conducting region and the collector-base diode in the non-conducting region. No amplification is ordinarily possible if both diodes are either conducting or non-conducting.

As long as signal amplitudes remain small, transistors are quite linear. Serious non-linearity occurs only if the polarity of either one of the two diodes is reversed. For point-contact and p-n-p transistors, non-linearity occurs if (a) the emitter becomes highly negative with respect to the base, (b) the collector becomes positive with respect to the base. For n-p-n transistors, these polarities are reversed.

Figure 13.15 shows a typical transistor oscillator of the feedback type. The effects of the non-linearity on the operation will be investigated for this oscillator. The d-c bias connections have been omitted.

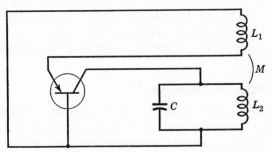

Fig. 13.15   Transistor oscillator employing inductive feedback.'

Oscillations will start in a region in which the emitter-base diode is conducting, the collector-base diode non-conducting. As the amplitude increases, however, one or the other of the two diodes will change its polarity during some part of the cycle. This will have one of the

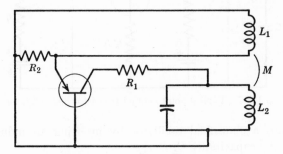

Fig. 13.16   Reduction of waveform distortion.

following effects: (a) If the collector becomes positive, the collector-base diode will then become conducting and will effectively short-circuit the resonant circuit. (b) If the emitter becomes negative, the emitter-base diode will then become non-conducting, leading to a surge in the voltage across inductance L_1 and, because of the inductive coupling, across L_2. Both these effects will lead to a relatively poor waveform.

Figure 13.16 shows a method for compensating for these two effects for the oscillator of Fig. 13.15 by inserting resistances in series with the collector and in parallel with the inductance, L_1.

In this circuit, the resistance R_1, in series with the collector, will effectively eliminate the short circuit mentioned earlier, and the resistance R_2 will reduce the surge of voltage across L_1.

Another type of non linearity occurs in transistors: the transit time depends considerably on the collector voltage. In most high-frequency oscillators, the frequency of oscillation varies with the collector voltage. A stable oscillator, therefore, requires a well-stabilized power supply.

13.6 Transistor Multivibrators

Sinusoidal oscillators and multivibrators are not essentially different. Indeed, a sinusoidal oscillator can often be changed into a multivibrator by simply changing the resonant elements and increasing the feedback.

Figure 13.17 shows a typical transistor multivibrator based on the negative input impedance of the point-contact transistor. It can be

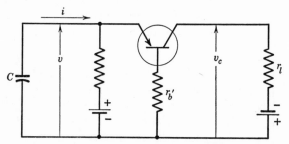

Fig. 13.17   Typical point-contact transistor multivibrator.

changed into a sinusoidal oscillator by inserting an inductance in series with the capacitance C.

In order to understand the operation of this multivibrator it is important that the relation between current and voltage across the input be studied (Fig. 13.18). This figure is identical with Fig. 13.5 except that the abscissa is now the difference between the total emitter current and bias current, the ordinate being the instantaneous emitter voltage.

For $i = 0$ the input impedance is negative as indicated by the negative slope of the i-v characteristic.

The transistor acts as an amplifier only as long as the emitter-base diode is conducting and the collector-base diode non-conducting. If one of these two diodes reverses, amplification will cease, the result being a passive network with positive input impedance (regions I and

III of Fig. 13.18).   In region I, the current i is so strongly negative that the emitter current is reversed.   The input resistance is now positive and very large, since the transistor consists of two non-conducting diodes.   Similarly, as the emitter current increases, the collector voltage will decrease because of the additional voltage drops in r_l and r_b due to increases in collector and base currents.   For some value of i the collector voltage will become zero, and now the transistor consists of two conducting diodes.   Consequently the input re-

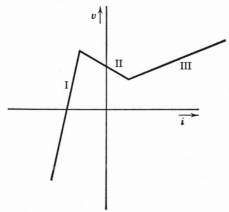

Fig. 13.18   Current-voltage relationship for circuit of Fig. 13.17.

sistance is now positive, but relatively small, as indicated in region III of Fig. 13.18.

In order to obtain a multivibrator, a capacitance should be connected between emitter and ground as shown in Fig. 13.17.   The current i passing through the capacitance and the voltage across it are related by the equation

$$dv/dt = -Ci \qquad [13.12]$$

Physically this means that a current flowing out of the capacitance will decrease the voltage across it.   The voltage v is constant only if $i = 0$.   For all other values of i, v must either increase or decrease with time.   The direction in which v changes is indicated by arrows on Fig. 13.19.

At a given time, the system is characterized by its current i and voltage v and therefore by a point on Fig. 13.19.   Equation 13.12 shows that this point will remain at the same place only for $i = 0$.   For all other values it must move in the direction of the arrows.   The point must, of course, stay on the curve.

Of particular interest are points A and C. There the point representing the system must "jump" to another part of the characteristic
since it cannot continue beyond A or C. This jump occurs almost
instantaneously. As the charge on the capacitance, proportional to

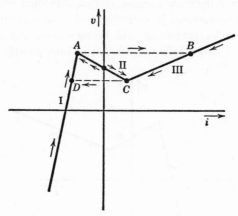

Fig. 13.19   The variation of i and v for circuit of Fig. 13.17.

v, cannot be changed instantaneously, we must assume the voltage v
remains essentially constant during this jump. The "representative
point" moves, therefore, along the dotted lines from A to B and from
C to D. In its steady-state operation, the point representing the sys-

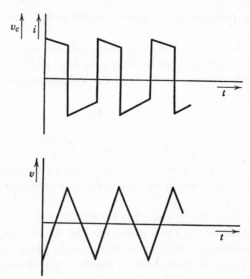

Fig. 13.20   Variation with time of v, v_c, and i for circuit of Fig. 13.17.

tem will move from D to A, jump to B, move to C, and jump again to D. Figure 13.20 shows the waveforms of i, v, and the collector voltage, $v_c \cong a i_e r_l$, as a function of time. The voltage across the capacitance is approximately a sawtooth wave; the voltage across the load resistance, approximately a square wave.

Figure 13.21 shows a multivibrator using two junction transistors, in the grounded-emitter configuration, connected to form a direct-coupled amplifier. The impedance presented by this amplifier between

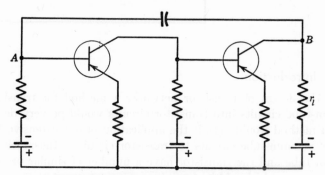

Fig. 13.21   Junction transistor multivibrator.

points A and B is negative. It will become positive, however, if the emitter or collector diode of one of the transistors is reversed. The relation between i and v of Fig. 13.21 is quite similar to that shown in Fig. 13.18. Connecting a capacitor between points A and B will give us a multivibrator. The voltage across r_l is approximately a square wave.

13.7   Problems

1. Calculate the starting conditions for a point-contact transistor oscillator in the grounded-emitter configuration with a series-resonant circuit across the output.

2. Calculate the approximate frequency of the multivibrator shown in Fig. 13.17.

3. Calculate the starting conditions for the oscillator of Fig. 13.7 by the method explained in Sec. 13.3.1.

13.8   Bibliography

D. E. Thomas, "Low Drain Transistor Audio Oscillator," *Proc. IRE, 40,* 1385 (1952).

G. E. McDuffie, "Pulse Duration and Repetition Rate of a Transistor Multivibrator," *Proc. IRE, 40,* 1487 (1952).

E. A. Oser, R. O. Enders, and R. P. Moore, Jr., "Transistor Oscillators," *RCA Rev., 13,* 369 (1952).

Chapter 14

Circuit Design
by Duality

14.1 Introduction

For the design of transistor networks a method for transforming vacuum-tube circuits into transistor circuits would be very desirable. Such a method would permit the application of our extensive knowledge of vacuum-tube circuits to transistor circuits. Inasmuch as the vacuum tube and the transistor have a number of similar properties, such an approach should be feasible.

A method of this general nature has been proposed by R. L. Wallace and G. Raisbeck.[1] Although the transistor circuits so obtained are not always realizable with practical circuit elements, they may indicate the general nature of the solution.

Circuit design employing the principles of duality is generally of limited scope, and is most useful in the design of systems. The various existing methods for solving such problems as detection, modulation, and automatic gain control with vacuum tubes may readily be transformed by means of dual methods to transistors. The circuits that are best suited for vacuum tubes are, of course, not necessarily the duals of the best for transistors. On the other hand, a method that is of only academic interest for vacuum tubes may have a dual for transistors which is entirely practical.

14.2 Duality in Electrical Networks

In order to explain this method it is first necessary to introduce briefly the principle of duality as applied to electrical networks. The principle will be only outlined here; for a more detailed presentation it may be desirable to consult one of the numerous textbooks on network analysis.[2,3]

In general, an electrical network contains a number of currents and voltages. Of these, only a limited number may be chosen independently.   For example, choosing the currents in the resistances r_1, r_2, r_3, and r_4 of the circuit of Fig. 14.1(a) will determine uniquely all the other currents and voltages of the network.   Commonly the sets of variables used for circuit analysis are the loop currents and the node

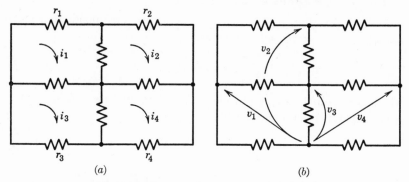

(a)   (b)

Fig. 14.1   Loop currents and node voltages.

voltages (Fig. 14.1).   It is assumed that the reader is sufficiently familiar with these concepts.

We can now define duality simply: Two networks are dual if to every loop current i_j in one network there corresponds a node voltage $v_j = ri_j$ in the other (and vice versa).   For the two networks, r is the

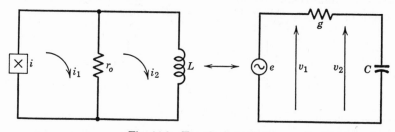

Fig. 14.2   Two dual circuits.

"transformation resistance," a constant with the dimension of a resistance.

Figure 14.2 illustrates a simple example of two circuits which are dual to each other.   The square box represents a current generator.

The two networks are dual by definition if

$$v_1 = ri_1 \qquad v_2 = ri_2 \qquad\qquad [14.1]$$

These equations hold if

$$e = ri \qquad g = r_o/r^2 \qquad C = L/r^2 \qquad [14.2]$$

From such examples a number of simple rules for the design of dual networks can be obtained. For an exact derivation of these rules one of the textbooks mentioned earlier may be consulted.

14.2.1 The Duals of Single Elements

As seen from Fig. 14.2, a current generator i corresponds to a voltage generator $e = ir$, and vice versa.

$$i \leftrightarrow e = ir \qquad [14.3]$$

where the symbol $\leftrightarrow$ is used to denote "is the dual of." A resistance r_1 corresponds to another resistance $r_2 = r^2/r_1$

$$r_1 \leftrightarrow r_2 = r^2/r_1 \qquad [14.4]$$

An inductance L corresponds to a capacitance $C = L/r^2$

$$L \leftrightarrow C = L/r^2 \qquad [14.5]$$

$$C \leftrightarrow L = r^2C \qquad [14.6]$$

Another relation not indicated in Fig. 14.2 is: A current generator which is proportional to a loop current $i = ki_j$ is the dual of a voltage generator proportional to the corresponding node voltage $v = kv_j$;

$$[14.7]$$

These relations will be sufficient for the purpose of this chapter.

We have now to establish rules for the design of the duals of more complicated circuits. In order to simplify these rules we shall represent single elements (batteries, current generators, resistors, capacitors, etc.) by arrows and numbers:

$$[14.8]$$

The arrow on the left with the number 2 can, for example, represent a battery, and the arrow on the right a current generator; similarly the arrow on the left may be a capacitor, that on the right an inductance. Using these symbols the circuits of Fig. 14.2 may be redrawn as in Fig. 14.3. The direction of the arrow is meaningful only for current generators or voltage generators.

The relation represented in Fig. 14.3 will hold regardless of the type of single element represented by arrows 1, 2, and 3. They may, for

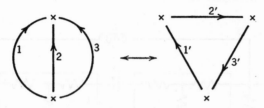

Fig. 14.3 Simplified circuits.

example, be all capacitors or voltage generators, or combinations of elements.

14.2.2 The Duals of Multielement Networks

A general rule for the design of duals of complicated networks is illustrated in Fig. 14.4.

Figure 14.4(a) shows a network with three meshes. We propose to find its dual. As a first step we select points A, B, and C inside the

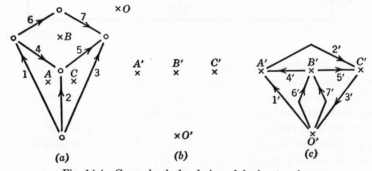

(a)   (b)   (c)

Fig. 14.4 General rule for design of dual networks.

three meshes and a point O outside the meshes. These points will correspond to the node points of the dual network. We therefore start out with the dual network by choosing four node points A', B', C', and O', Fig. 14.4(b). The next step is to find the single elements connecting these points. We find these by connecting points O, A, B, and C by single lines in such a way that any line intersects only one arrow. For example, the line between O and A intersects only arrow

1; that between A and C, arrow 2. Between O and B two lines are possible, intersecting arrows 6 and 7. The rule for the design is now: If the line between two such points intersects a single element, then the dual of this single element connects the two corresponding node points. For example: the line between A and C intersects arrow 2.

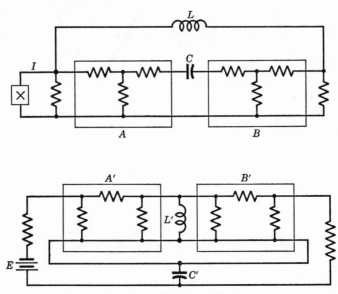

Fig. 14.5   Circuit and dual.

Arrow $2'$ therefore will connect points A' and C' of the dual circuit, Fig. 14.4(b). Figure 14.4(c) shows the complete dual circuit.

The basic elements need not necessarily be single elements; sometimes four-terminal networks are more desirable. Figure 14.5 shows, for example, a circuit containing two four-terminal networks and its dual. The four-terminal elements and their duals are designated by letters A and A', B and B', respectively.

The easiest way to construct such general dual circuits is by assuming simple networks, for example, resistive T networks for the four-terminal networks, and then obtaining the dual circuit. The elements dual to the T networks of A and B then constitute A' and B'. The duality relation of Fig. 14.5 holds independent of the type of four-terminal network used; A and B may, for example, be transistors or band-pass filters.

Figure 14.6 shows a simple transistor amplifier using the grounded-emitter configuration. The connections for providing d-c bias are

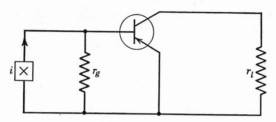

Fig. 14.6   Transistor amplifier.

omitted from this circuit and will be discussed separately. Figure 14.7 shows the equivalent circuit, and Fig. 14.8 the dual of this equivalent circuit as constructed by the methods described above.

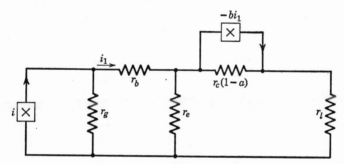

Fig. 14.7   The equivalent circuit.

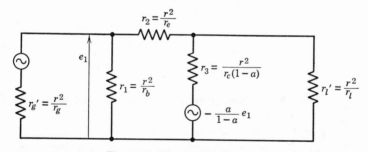

Fig. 14.8   The dual of Fig. 14.7.

14.3   Vacuum-Tube Duals of Transistors

The circuit of Fig. 14.8 may be realized by a vacuum tube together with two resistances (Fig. 14.9). For small values of r_e and r_b, resistances r_1 and r_2 of Fig. 14.8 are very large so that in the first approximation they can be neglected.

The circuits of Figs. 14.8 and 14.9 are identical if

$$r^2 = r_p r_c (1 - a) \qquad \mu = a/(1 - a)$$

The first condition restricts the duality relation to junction transistors, since, for $a > 1$, r would become imaginary. Normally r has a

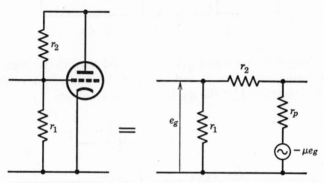

Fig. 14.9   The exact dual of a transistor.

value of about 30 kilohms.   The second condition holds quite well for triodes and junction transistors.   We find, therefore, that the triode is the approximate dual of the grounded-emitter junction transistor (Fig. 14.10).

Fig. 14.10   The duality between transistors and vacuum tubes.

For the grounded-base configuration a similar relation may be found incorporating a 1:1 transformer for phase reversal (Fig. 14.11).

This relationship is considerably less practical than the one of Fig. 14.10, but it is the only one available for point-contact transistors.

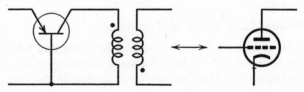

Fig. 14.11   Duality between point-contact transistors and vacuum tubes.

Figure 14.12 shows a triode with its normal bias connections, and the dual transistor circuit. The transistor bias circuits are also the duals of the tube circuits.

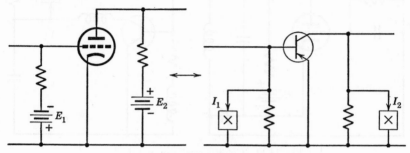

Fig. 14.12   The bias connections.

In Fig. 14.13 the current generators in parallel with resistances have been replaced by batteries in series with resistances (by Thévenin's theorem). This figure shows the normal bias connections for

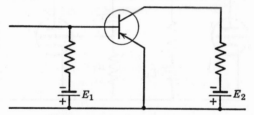

Fig. 14.13   D-c bias connections.

the grounded-emitter stages. Bias connections therefore also obey duality. (For *n-p-n* transistors all bias voltages must, of course, be reversed.)

14.4   Examples

In this section the duals of two common vacuum-tube circuits are shown. Figure 14.14 shows a Colpitts oscillator and its dual.

It can be seen that the original parallel-resonant circuit is now transformed to a series-resonant circuit. The voltages across the parallel-resonant circuits were applied to the three electrodes of the vacuum tubes. Similarly, the currents of the series-resonant circuit pass through the electrodes of the transistor. Of considerable interest is the *rL* self-biasing network of the transistor circuit. It prevents the base-emitter diode from becoming non-conducting over an apprecia-

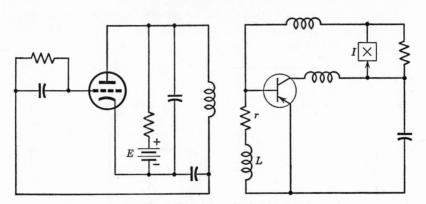

Fig. 14.14   Colpitts oscillator and dual.

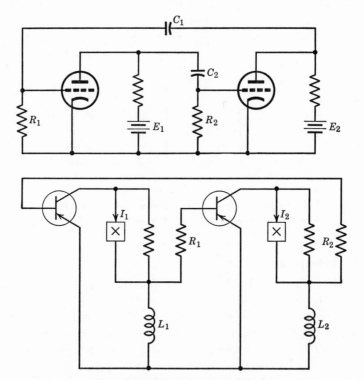

Fig. 14.15   Multivibrator and dual.

ble part of the cycle. The current source may again be transformed
into a battery by Thévenin's theorem.

Figure 14.15 shows a multivibrator and its dual. Capacitors C_1
and C_2 in the vacuum-tube circuit discharge through the resistances
R_1 and R_2. Similarly the inductances L_1 and L_2 will store a direct
current through R_1 and R_2 and the input diodes of the transistors.
This will limit the lowest frequency at which the transistor circuit can
operate since the LR time constants cannot be made as large as the
RC time constants, with present-day circuit elements. In Fig. 14.16

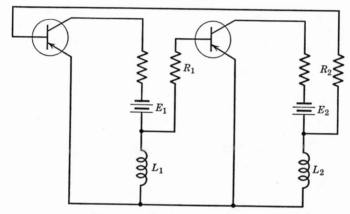

Fig. 14.16   Dual to multivibrator.

the current generators have been replaced by batteries. These circuits are not readily realizable for a number of reasons: (a) the d-c
bias connections are not practical because neither end of the batteries
is at ground; (b) the time constants that can be obtained from short-
circuited inductances are much smaller than those obtained from open-
circuited capacitances (this is important for self-biasing arrangements,
multivibrators, etc.); (c) the values of capacitances and inductances
obtained from eqs. 14.5 and 14.6 may not be practical.

In spite of these limitations, dual circuits may frequently serve as a
guide towards the construction of practical circuits and are often very
useful for the understanding of the mechanism of a specific circuit.

The reader is also referred to Sec. 15.6.5, in which the application
of matrix methods to dual networks is covered.

14.5   Problems

1. Find the dual of a Hartley oscillator. Calculate the values of all parameters
for a typical oscillator.

2. Find the dual of a tuned-plate oscillator.

3. Find the dual of a three-stage RC-coupled triode amplifier.

14.6   References

1. R. L. Wallace and G. Raisbeck, "Duality as a Guide in Transistor Circuit Design," *Bell Sys. Tech. J.*, April, 1951.

2. Guillemin, *Communication Networks*, Vol. 2, p. 246, John Wiley & Sons, 1935.

3. Gardner and Barnes, *Transients in Linear Systems*, Vol. 1, p. 46, John Wiley & Sons, 1942.

Chapter 15

Matrix Methods
of Circuit Analysis

15.1 Introduction

Perhaps the behavior of a transistor departs most significantly from that of a vacuum tube in that, whereas there is a considerable degree of isolation between the input and the output of a vacuum tube, such isolation does not exist with the transistor. Any change of circuit conditions at the output of a transistor is reflected in a change in circuit behavior at the input terminals. Consequently, any analysis of a transistor amplifier on a stage-by-stage basis is at best a rude approximation to the problem.

In this chapter we will present a very powerful approach to the solution of just such a problem. The method was first applied for the purpose by F. Strecker and R. Feldtkeller, and was published in the *Elektrische Nachrichten Technik* in 1929. In 1932, H. G. Baerwald added many refinements to the theory, notably in the direction of validity tests.

In the United States, Guillemin, Le Corbeiller, and Kron have done much work along these lines, but the method has attained far more popularity outside the United States.

15.2 The Four-Terminal Network Approach to Engineering Problems

By far the largest percentage of the problems encountered in engineering are of the cause-and-effect type; i.e., we have a cause and would like to study its effect, or we have an effect the reason for which is to be studied. All other details of the problem, as well as all intermediate steps, are essentially a means to an end and are of secondary interest. For example, take a device such as an electromechanical transducer. At one end, we feed in the "cause"—a voltage and a current. At the other end, we obtain the "effect"—a force and a displacement. Conversely, we may begin with a force and a displacement, and be required to obtain information about the current and voltage.

In an electrical circuit, the input is a voltage and a current, as is the output. In all these problems, the emphasis is again and again centered on the four terminals, the input pair and the output pair. As far as we are concerned, these terminals belong to the proverbial "black box," and our interest does not lie in what is in this box but rather in what features define the behavior of this box.

In circuit problems, such a box with its input and output terminals is known as a four-terminal network. A more correct term is a two-terminal pair, since each set comprises a pair of terminals.

15.3   The Transistor as a Four-Terminal Network

Consider a single transistor, in any particular configuration. Such a device is, from the device point of view, an extremely complex object, whose approximate behavior may be formulated in terms of a

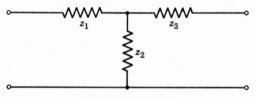

Fig. 15.1   T network.

large number of basic parameters. From the engineering point of view, as far as the application of the device is concerned, it is a four-terminal network, characterized in its behavior by four quantities.

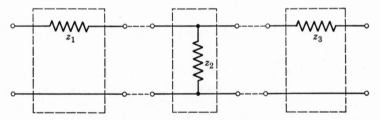

Fig. 15.2   Elements of T network.

Before such a device can be characterized by four quantities, it is necessary to make the tacit assumptions that these quantities are interrelated, and that the interrelation can be expressed by one or more linear differential equations. For any fixed operating point under small-signal operation, these assumptions are justified.

A complex circuit involving active and passive elements can always be broken up into simple units each of which is a four-terminal network. Under certain conditions, these units may be connected in a variety of ways. How simple the networks will be is entirely dependent on the experience of the worker. Thus a simple network like that in Fig. 15.1, which is ordinarily handled as a single unit, may, if needed, be split up into sections connected in cascade as shown in Fig. 15.2.

The transistor itself is usually considered as one unit. A complex circuit may be broken up into a series of separate four-terminal networks connected in various configurations.

15.4 Matrix Methods

By way of an introduction to the application of matrix methods to transistor circuits, a working knowledge of matrix algebra is required. The subject is reviewed briefly in Appendix I.

15.4.1 Matrix Algebra of the Four-Terminal Network

Figure 15.3 shows a four-terminal network, more correctly known as a two-terminal pair. Unfortunately, no definite convention has been set for the current and voltage. The one described here is in common use in the United States.

Fig. 15.3 Four-terminal network.

In this convention, the terminal markings for the two ends are labeled $1'$, 1 and $2'$, 2. No attempt is made to mark either side as the input or the output, in order to preserve the generality of the treatment. Currents i_1 and i_2 are defined as positive when flowing as indicated, into the network. Voltages e_1 and e_2 are defined as positive when the terminals $1'$ and $2'$ are at a higher potential than 1 and 2 respectively.

The behavior of such a network may be expressed in terms of the four quantities indicated. Further, the behavior of any two quantities may be given in terms of the other two. Our only requirement on the network is that it is linear, so these relations will take the form of linear transformations and may be set up in matrix form as follows:

$$\begin{bmatrix} e_1 \\ e_2 \end{bmatrix} = \begin{bmatrix} z_{11} & z_{12} \\ z_{21} & z_{22} \end{bmatrix} \begin{bmatrix} i_1 \\ i_2 \end{bmatrix} \quad \text{and} \quad \begin{bmatrix} i_1 \\ i_2 \end{bmatrix} = \begin{bmatrix} y_{11} & y_{12} \\ y_{21} & y_{22} \end{bmatrix} \begin{bmatrix} e_1 \\ e_2 \end{bmatrix}$$

[15.1]
and
[15.2]

$$\begin{bmatrix} e_1 \\ i_2 \end{bmatrix} = \begin{bmatrix} h_{11} & h_{12} \\ h_{21} & h_{22} \end{bmatrix} \begin{bmatrix} i_1 \\ e_2 \end{bmatrix} \quad \text{and} \quad \begin{bmatrix} i_1 \\ e_2 \end{bmatrix} = \begin{bmatrix} g_{11} & g_{12} \\ g_{21} & g_{22} \end{bmatrix} \begin{bmatrix} e_1 \\ i_2 \end{bmatrix}$$

[15.3]
and
[15.4]

$$\begin{bmatrix} e_1 \\ i_1 \end{bmatrix} = \begin{bmatrix} a_{11} & a_{12} \\ a_{21} & a_{22} \end{bmatrix} \begin{bmatrix} e_2 \\ -i_2 \end{bmatrix} \quad \text{and} \quad \begin{bmatrix} e_2 \\ i_2 \end{bmatrix} = \begin{bmatrix} b_{11} & b_{12} \\ b_{21} & b_{22} \end{bmatrix} \begin{bmatrix} e_1 \\ -i_1 \end{bmatrix}$$

[15.5]
and
[15.6]

The last pair are written in power work as

$$\begin{bmatrix} e_1 \\ i_1 \end{bmatrix} = \begin{bmatrix} A & B \\ C & D \end{bmatrix} \begin{bmatrix} e_2 \\ -i_2 \end{bmatrix} \quad \text{and} \quad \begin{bmatrix} e_2 \\ i_2 \end{bmatrix} = \begin{bmatrix} A' & B' \\ C' & D' \end{bmatrix} \begin{bmatrix} e_1 \\ -i_1 \end{bmatrix}$$

[15.7]
and
[15.8]

Note that

$$[y] = [z]^{-1} \tag{15.9}$$

$$[h] = [g]^{-1} \tag{15.10}$$

but

$$[a] \neq [b]^{-1} \tag{15.11}$$

Given the terms of any one matrix, the terms of any of the matrices may be computed by reverting to the algebraic form. Since this process is a very common one in matrix manipulations, a table of the various interrelations is presented at the end of the chapter; a table of determinant relations is also given.

15.4.2 Significance of the Circuit Parameters

A study of the matrix equations will serve to indicate the significance of the various parameters involved. Take for example the z matrix. We have

$$z_{11} = e_1/i_1 \quad \text{when } i_2 = 0 \tag{15.12}$$

$$z_{12} = e_1/i_2 \quad \text{when } i_1 = 0 \tag{15.13}$$

$$z_{21} = e_2/i_1 \quad \text{when } i_2 = 0 \tag{15.14}$$

$$z_{22} = e_2/i_2 \quad \text{when } i_1 = 0 \tag{15.15}$$

Thus, z_{11} and z_{22} may be interpreted as input and output impedances, with open-circuit conditions on the output and input, respectively. In like manner, z_{12} and z_{21} are reverse and forward transfer impedances with the input and output respectively open-circuited.

In like manner, the y matrix parameters are y_{11}, y_{22}, the input and output admittances with short-circuit conditions on the output and input, respectively, and y_{12}, y_{21}, the reverse and forward transfer admittances with the input and output respectively short-circuited. It may be mentioned here that, as a direct consequence of the reciprocity theorem, z_{12} equals z_{21} and $y_{12} = y_{21}$ for any linear passive network involving reciprocal elements. A further point of interest is that the determinant of the a matrix for this type of circuit is equal to unity, since

$$\Delta^a = z_{12}/z_{21} \qquad [15.16]$$

The terms of the other matrix forms may be interpreted in like manner.

15.4.3 Setting Up of Matrix Forms

Given a reasonably simple network configuration, any of its matrix forms may be set up by inspection. An example will serve to illustrate this.

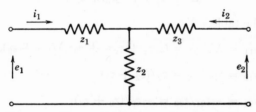

Fig. 15.4   T network showing convention of signs.

Example.   Derive the h matrix for the circuit of Fig. 15.4.   Let

$$\begin{bmatrix} e_1 \\ i_2 \end{bmatrix} = \begin{bmatrix} h_{11} & h_{12} \\ h_{21} & h_{22} \end{bmatrix} \begin{bmatrix} i_1 \\ e_2 \end{bmatrix} \qquad [15.17]$$

Then

$$h_{11} = e_1/i_1 \qquad \text{when } e_2 = 0 \qquad [15.18]$$

$$h_{11} = z_1 + \frac{z_2 z_3}{z_2 + z_3} = \frac{z_1 z_2 + z_2 z_3 + z_3 z_1}{z_2 + z_3} \qquad [15.19]$$

$$h_{12} = e_1/e_2 \qquad \text{when } i_1 = 0 \qquad [15.20]$$

$$h_{12} = \frac{z_2}{z_2 + z_3} \qquad [15.21]$$

$$h_{21} = i_2/i_1 \qquad \text{when } e_2 = 0 \qquad [15.22]$$

$$h_{21} = - \frac{z_2}{z_2 + z_3} \qquad [15.23]$$

Finally,

$$h_{22} = i_2/e_2 \quad \text{when } i_1 = 0 \qquad [15.24]$$

$$h_{22} = 1/(z_2 + z_3) \qquad [15.25]$$

and all the terms are obtained.

An easier and much quicker method is to write down the mesh or nodal equations for the circuit. These are the z or y matrices respectively, and with the aid of the table of matrix interrelations they can be converted to any other forms.

Referring to the last example, the z matrix equation is immediately written down as

$$\begin{bmatrix} e_1 \\ e_2 \end{bmatrix} = \begin{bmatrix} z_1 + z_2, & z_2 \\ z_2, & z_2 + z_3 \end{bmatrix} \begin{bmatrix} i_1 \\ i_2 \end{bmatrix} \qquad [15.26]$$

The determinant of the matrix,

$$\Delta^z = z_1 z_2 + z_2 z_3 + z_3 z_1 \qquad [15.27]$$

Then, from the table,

$$h_{11} = \Delta^z/z_{22} = (z_1 z_2 + z_2 z_3 + z_3 z_1)/(z_2 + z_3) \qquad [15.28]$$

$$h_{12} = z_{12}/z_{22} = z_2/(z_2 + z_3) \qquad [15.29]$$

$$h_{21} = -z_{21}/z_{22} = -z_2/(z_2 + z_3) \qquad [15.30]$$

$$h_{22} = 1/z_{22} = 1/(z_2 + z_3) \qquad [15.31]$$

With active elements, it is usually easier to obtain the matrix by means of the mesh or nodal equations. For any multiloop two-terminal pair, the mesh or nodal equations result in a matrix of the form

$$\begin{bmatrix} e_1 \\ e_2 \\ 0 \\ 0 \\ \cdot \\ \cdot \\ \cdot \\ 0 \end{bmatrix} = \begin{bmatrix} z_{11} & z_{12} & \cdots & z_{1n} \\ z_{21} & z_{22} & \cdots & z_{2n} \\ & & & \\ & & & \\ & \cdot & \cdot & \cdot \\ & \cdot & \cdot & \cdot \\ & \cdot & \cdot & \cdot \\ z_{n1} & z_{n2} & \cdots & z_{nn} \end{bmatrix} \begin{bmatrix} i_1 \\ i_2 \\ i_3 \\ i_4 \\ \cdot \\ \cdot \\ \cdot \\ i_n \end{bmatrix} \qquad [15.32]$$

or of the corresponding y form. This may be reduced to a matrix with two rows and two columns as follows:

Split the matrix as shown in eq. 15.33

$$
\begin{bmatrix} e_1 \\ e_2 \\ \hline 0 \\ 0 \\ \cdot \\ \cdot \\ \cdot \\ 0 \end{bmatrix} = \begin{bmatrix} z_{11} & z_{12} & \cdots & z_{1n} \\ z_{21} & z_{22} & \cdots & z_{2n} \\ \hline & & & \\ & \cdot & \cdot & \cdot \\ & \cdot & \cdot & \cdot \\ & \cdot & \cdot & \cdot \\ z_{n1} & z_{n2} & \cdots & z_{nn} \end{bmatrix} \begin{bmatrix} i_1 \\ i_2 \\ \hline i_3 \\ i_4 \\ \cdot \\ \cdot \\ \cdot \\ i_n \end{bmatrix}
$$

[15.33]

into the submatrices

$$
\begin{bmatrix} E \\ 0 \end{bmatrix} = \begin{bmatrix} Z_{11} & Z_{12} \\ Z_{21} & Z_{22} \end{bmatrix} \begin{bmatrix} I_A \\ I_B \end{bmatrix}
$$

[15.34]

where each of the terms E, Z, I are matrices themselves. Then

$$
E = Z_{11}I_A + Z_{12}I_B
$$

[15.35]

$$
0 = Z_{21}I_A + Z_{22}I_B
$$

[15.36]

Premultiplying eq. 15.36 by $Z_{12}Z_{22}^{-1}$ and subtracting this from eq. 15.35, gives

$$
E = (Z_{11} - Z_{12}Z_{22}^{-1}Z_{21})I_A
$$

[15.37]

$$
= ZI_A
$$

[15.38]

or

$$
\begin{bmatrix} e_1 \\ e_2 \end{bmatrix} = [Z] \begin{bmatrix} i_1 \\ i_2 \end{bmatrix}
$$

[15.39]

where $[Z]$ is a matrix of order $(2, 2)$. An example will illustrate the use of this theorem.

Example.   Given a two-terminal pair, where

$$
\begin{bmatrix} e_1 \\ e_2 \\ \hline 0 \end{bmatrix} = \begin{bmatrix} z_{11} & z_{12} & z_{13} \\ z_{21} & z_{22} & z_{23} \\ \hline z_{31} & z_{32} & z_{33} \end{bmatrix} \begin{bmatrix} i_1 \\ i_2 \\ \hline i_3 \end{bmatrix}
$$

[15.40]

It is required to reduce this to the simplest form.   Let

$$
Z_{11} = \begin{bmatrix} z_{11} & z_{12} \\ z_{21} & z_{22} \end{bmatrix}
$$

[15.41]

$$
Z_{12} = \begin{bmatrix} z_{13} \\ z_{23} \end{bmatrix}
$$

[15.42]

$$
Z_{21} = \begin{bmatrix} z_{31} & z_{32} \end{bmatrix}
$$

[15.43]

$$
Z_{22} = \begin{bmatrix} z_{33} \end{bmatrix}
$$

[15.44]

Then

$$Z_{22}{}^{-1} = \left[\frac{1}{z_{33}}\right] \tag{15.45}$$

$$Z_{12}Z_{22}{}^{-1}Z_{21} = \left[\begin{matrix} z_{13} \\ z_{23} \end{matrix}\right] \left[\frac{1}{z_{33}}\right] [z_{31} \quad z_{32}] \tag{15.46}$$

$$= \left[\begin{matrix} z_{13} \\ z_{23} \end{matrix}\right] \left[\begin{matrix} \dfrac{z_{31}}{z_{33}} & \dfrac{z_{32}}{z_{33}} \end{matrix}\right] \tag{15.47}$$

$$= \left[\begin{matrix} \dfrac{z_{13}z_{31}}{z_{33}} & \dfrac{z_{13}z_{32}}{z_{33}} \\[2mm] \dfrac{z_{23}z_{31}}{z_{33}} & \dfrac{z_{23}z_{32}}{z_{33}} \end{matrix}\right] \tag{15.48}$$

Then

$$\left[\begin{matrix} e_1 \\ e_2 \end{matrix}\right] = \left\{ \left[\begin{matrix} z_{11} & z_{12} \\ z_{21} & z_{22} \end{matrix}\right] - \left[\begin{matrix} \dfrac{z_{13}z_{31}}{z_{33}} & \dfrac{z_{13}z_{32}}{z_{33}} \\[2mm] \dfrac{z_{23}z_{31}}{z_{33}} & \dfrac{z_{23}z_{32}}{z_{33}} \end{matrix}\right] \right\} \left[\begin{matrix} i_1 \\ i_2 \end{matrix}\right] \tag{15.49}$$

By way of comparison, a direct approach would be as follows.

$$\left[\begin{matrix} e_1 \\ e_2 \\ 0 \end{matrix}\right] = \left[\begin{matrix} z_{11} & z_{12} & z_{13} \\ z_{21} & z_{22} & z_{23} \\ z_{31} & z_{32} & z_{33} \end{matrix}\right] \left[\begin{matrix} i_1 \\ i_2 \\ i_3 \end{matrix}\right] \tag{15.50}$$

from which

$$\left[\begin{matrix} i_1 \\ i_2 \\ i_3 \end{matrix}\right] = \left[\begin{matrix} z_{11} & z_{12} & z_{13} \\ z_{21} & z_{22} & z_{23} \\ z_{31} & z_{32} & z_{33} \end{matrix}\right]^{-1} \left[\begin{matrix} e_1 \\ e_2 \\ 0 \end{matrix}\right] \tag{15.51}$$

$$= \left[\begin{matrix} y_{11} & y_{12} & y_{13} \\ y_{21} & y_{22} & y_{23} \\ y_{31} & y_{32} & y_{33} \end{matrix}\right] \left[\begin{matrix} e_1 \\ e_2 \\ 0 \end{matrix}\right] \tag{15.52}$$

whence

$$\left[\begin{matrix} i_1 \\ i_2 \end{matrix}\right] = \left[\begin{matrix} y_{11} & y_{12} \\ y_{21} & y_{22} \end{matrix}\right] \left[\begin{matrix} e_1 \\ e_2 \end{matrix}\right] \tag{15.53}$$

and

$$\left[\begin{matrix} e_1 \\ e_2 \end{matrix}\right] = \left[\begin{matrix} y_{11} & y_{12} \\ y_{21} & y_{22} \end{matrix}\right]^{-1} \left[\begin{matrix} i_1 \\ i_2 \end{matrix}\right] \tag{15.54}$$

Thus the direct approach would involve two matrix inversion processes, one on a three-row three-column matrix, and the other on a two-row, two-column matrix.

15.4.4 The Transistor Matrix

Given the transistor parameters r_e, r_b, r_c, r_m, the matrix equations for the various configurations may be set up. As mentioned earlier, Kirchhoff's equations are perhaps the easiest to set up, and they give the z matrix for the transistor.

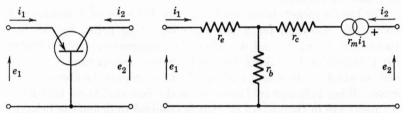

Fig. 15.5   Grounded-base transistor and its equivalent circuit.

Example.   Obtain the matrix equation for a grounded-base transistor as shown in Fig. 15.5.   The relations are

$$\begin{bmatrix} e_1 \\ e_2 - r_m i_1 \end{bmatrix} = \begin{bmatrix} r_e + r_b, & r_b \\ r_b, & r_b + r_c \end{bmatrix} \begin{bmatrix} i_1 \\ i_2 \end{bmatrix} \qquad [15.55]$$

$$\begin{bmatrix} e_1 \\ e_2 \end{bmatrix} = \begin{bmatrix} r_e + r_b, & r_b \\ r_b + r_m, & r_b + r_c \end{bmatrix} \begin{bmatrix} i_1 \\ i_2 \end{bmatrix} \qquad [15.56]$$

This is the z matrix equation for a grounded-base transistor.

For the transistor, α is defined by the equation

$$\alpha = \left(\frac{\partial I_c}{\partial I_e} \right)_{V_c} = \frac{r_m + r_b}{r_c + r_b} \qquad [15.57]$$

and a is defined by

$$a = r_m / r_c \qquad [15.58]$$

$$r_m = a r_c \qquad [15.59]$$

For most present-day transistors,

$$r_m \gg r_b \qquad [15.60]$$

$$r_c \gg r_b \qquad [15.61]$$

Therefore

$$\alpha \cong a \qquad [15.62]$$

Note that in this active circuit, as in all active circuits, $z_{12} \neq z_{21}$. The other matrix forms may be easily obtained with the aid of the table of matrix interrelations at the end of the chapter. A table of matrix interrelations for the transistor is also given there. For all circuit configurations, the determinant of the transistor z matrix is equal to

$$r_e r_b + r_c \{r_e + r_b(1 - a)\} \qquad [15.63]$$

It is only natural that this quantity appears very often in the analysis of transistor circuits.

For low-frequency linear operation, the behavior of a transistor is completely specified, for a particular operating point, by the four parameters r_e, r_b, r_c, and a. These four parameters are determined for a transistor by taking four independent measurements, the results of which are necessary and sufficient to compute the above parameters. What is important, however, is the fact that these four measurements are in themselves all that is required to define the behavior of the transistor without the necessity of converting to the parameters of a hypothetical equivalent circuit.

A common method of junction transistor parameter measurement, described in Chapter 22, employs for its four measurements: (a) the input impedance, with the output shorted; (b) the backward voltage ratio with the input open; (c) the forward current ratio with the output shorted; and (d) the output admittance with the input open.

A study of the h matrix will show that h_{11}, h_{12}, $-h_{21}$, and h_{22} are the results of the above measurements. Definition of the circuit parameters in terms of the h matrix accordingly has the advantage that the solution can be expressed in terms of these coefficients, which are the result of direct measurement, without the intermediate steps of developing an equivalent circuit, only later to recombine its many terms to obtain the final solution. A numerical example will illustrate this point.

Example. Measurements on a grounded-emitter transistor give $h_{11} = 10^3$ ohms; $h_{12} = 9 \times 10^{-4}$; $h_{21} = 19$; $h_{22} = 2 \times 10^{-5}$ mho. Find the voltage amplification for a load of 10^4 ohms.

Solution.   (a) Using equivalent circuit parameters,

$$h_{12} = \frac{r_e}{r_e + r_c(1 - a)} = 9 \times 10^{-4} \qquad [15.64]$$

$$h_{22} = \frac{1}{r_e + r_c(1 - a)} = 2 \times 10^{-5} \qquad [15.65]$$

Therefore

$$r_e = 45\ \Omega \qquad\qquad [15.66]$$

and

$$r_c(1 - a) \cong 5 \times 10^4 \qquad\qquad [15.67]$$

$$h_{21} = 19 \cong a/(1 - a) \qquad\qquad [15.68]$$

$$a \cong 0.95$$

and

$$r_c = \frac{5 \times 10^4}{0.05} = 10^6\ \Omega \qquad\qquad [15.69]$$

$$h_{11} = \frac{r_e r_b + r_c\{r_e + r_b(1 - a)\}}{r_e + r_c(1 - a)} \cong \frac{r_e + r_b(1 - a)}{1 - a}$$

$$\cong r_b + r_e/(1 - a) \cong r_b + 900 \cong 10^3 \qquad\qquad [15.70]$$

Therefore

$$r_b \cong 100\ \Omega \qquad\qquad [15.71]$$

The voltage amplification may be written as

$$A_v = \frac{-r_l(ar_c - r_e)}{r_b\{r_c(1 - a) + r_l + r_e\} + r_e(r_l + r_c)} \qquad\qquad [15.72]$$

(See eq. 4.27.)

Substituting the above values

$$A_v \cong \frac{-10^4(0.95) \times 10^6}{10^2\{5 \times 10^4 + 10^4 + 45\} + 45(10^4 + 10^6)} \qquad [15.72a]$$

$$\cong \frac{-(0.95)10^4}{10^6(6 + 45)} \qquad\qquad [15.73]$$

$$\cong \frac{-9500}{51} = -186 \qquad\qquad [15.74]$$

(b) Using the h matrix,

$$\Delta^h = h_{11}h_{22} - h_{12}h_{21} = \frac{10^3}{5 \times 10^4} - \frac{19 \times 9}{10^4}$$

$$\simeq 29 \times 10^{-4} \qquad\qquad [15.75]$$

Then voltage amplification is given by the following equation, from the tables at end of chapter.

$$A_v = \frac{-h_{21}r_l}{h_{11} + \Delta^h r_l} \tag{15.76}$$

$$= \frac{-19 \times 10^4}{1000 + 29} = -184.6 \tag{15.77}$$

The saving in labor is apparent. It should be mentioned here that the equivalent circuit concept for the transistor is a very valuable one, as it aids in giving a qualitative picture of the circuit behavior. When quantitative information is required, however, the use of the h matrix results in a considerable saving of time and labor.

15.4.5 Manipulation of Matrices in Network Analysis

Two four-terminal networks may be connected in any of the following ways: (a) series; (b) parallel; (c) series-parallel; (d) parallel-series;

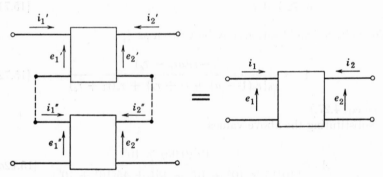

Fig. 15.6 Series connection.

and (e) cascade. The treatment of these connections will now be discussed.

(a) Series operation. See Fig. 15.6. Let the matrices for the two networks be, respectively,

$$\begin{bmatrix} e_1' \\ e_2' \end{bmatrix} = \begin{bmatrix} z_{11}' & z_{12}' \\ z_{21}' & z_{22}' \end{bmatrix} \begin{bmatrix} i_1' \\ i_2' \end{bmatrix} \quad \text{and} \quad \begin{bmatrix} e_1'' \\ e_2'' \end{bmatrix} = \begin{bmatrix} z_{11}'' & z_{12}'' \\ z_{21}'' & z_{22}'' \end{bmatrix} \begin{bmatrix} i_1'' \\ i_2'' \end{bmatrix} \quad \begin{matrix} [15.78] \\ \text{and} \\ [15.79] \end{matrix}$$

When the networks are connected in series, we have

$$e_1 = e_1' + e_1'' \tag{15.80}$$

$$e_2 = e_2' + e_2'' \tag{15.81}$$

$$i_1 = i_1' = i_1'' \qquad [15.82]$$

$$i_2 = i_2' = i_2'' \qquad [15.83]$$

Adding the matrices gives the combination matrix equation

$$\begin{bmatrix} e_1 \\ e_2 \end{bmatrix} = \begin{bmatrix} z_{11}' + z_{11}'', & z_{12}' + z_{12}'' \\ z_{21}' + z_{21}'', & z_{22}' + z_{22}'' \end{bmatrix} \begin{bmatrix} i_1 \\ i_2 \end{bmatrix} \qquad [15.84]$$

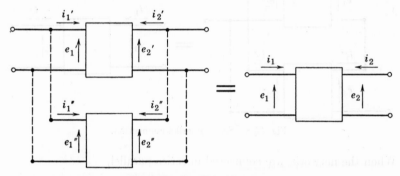

Fig. 15.7 Parallel connection.

(b) Parallel operation. See Fig. 15.7. Let the matrices for the two networks be

$$\begin{bmatrix} i_1' \\ i_2' \end{bmatrix} = \begin{bmatrix} y_{11}' & y_{12}' \\ y_{21}' & y_{22}' \end{bmatrix} \begin{bmatrix} e_1' \\ e_2' \end{bmatrix} \quad \text{and} \quad \begin{bmatrix} i_1'' \\ i_2'' \end{bmatrix} = \begin{bmatrix} y_{11}'' & y_{12}'' \\ y_{21}'' & y_{22}'' \end{bmatrix} \begin{bmatrix} e_1'' \\ e_2'' \end{bmatrix} \qquad \begin{matrix} [15.85] \\ \text{and} \\ [15.86] \end{matrix}$$

When the networks are connected in parallel,

$$e_1 = e_1' = e_1'' \qquad [15.87]$$

$$e_2 = e_2' = e_2'' \qquad [15.88]$$

$$i_1 = i_1' + i_1'' \qquad [15.89]$$

$$i_2 = i_2' + i_2'' \qquad [15.90]$$

Adding the matrices gives the combination matrix equation

$$\begin{bmatrix} i_1 \\ i_2 \end{bmatrix} = \begin{bmatrix} y_{11}' + y_{11}'', & y_{12}' + y_{12}'' \\ y_{21}' + y_{21}'', & y_{22}' + y_{22}'' \end{bmatrix} \begin{bmatrix} e_1 \\ e_2 \end{bmatrix} \qquad [15.91]$$

(c) Series-parallel operation. See Fig. 15.8. Let the matrices for the two networks be

$$\begin{bmatrix} e_1' \\ i_2' \end{bmatrix} = [h'] \begin{bmatrix} i_1' \\ e_2' \end{bmatrix} \quad \text{and} \quad \begin{bmatrix} e_1'' \\ i_2'' \end{bmatrix} = [h''] \begin{bmatrix} i_1'' \\ e_2'' \end{bmatrix} \qquad \begin{matrix} [15.92] \\ \text{and} \\ [15.93] \end{matrix}$$

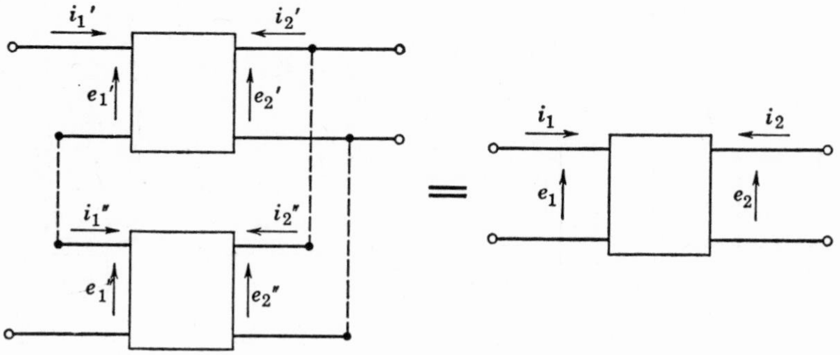

Fig. 15.8   Series-parallel connection.

When the networks are connected in series-parallel,

$$e_1 = e_1' + e_1'' \qquad [15.94]$$

$$i_2 = i_2' + i_2'' \qquad [15.95]$$

$$i_1 = i_1' = i_1'' \qquad [15.96]$$

$$e_2 = e_2' = e_2'' \qquad [15.97]$$

Adding the matrices gives the combination matrix equation

$$\begin{bmatrix} e_1 \\ i_2 \end{bmatrix} = [h' + h''] \begin{bmatrix} i_1 \\ e_2 \end{bmatrix} \qquad [15.98]$$

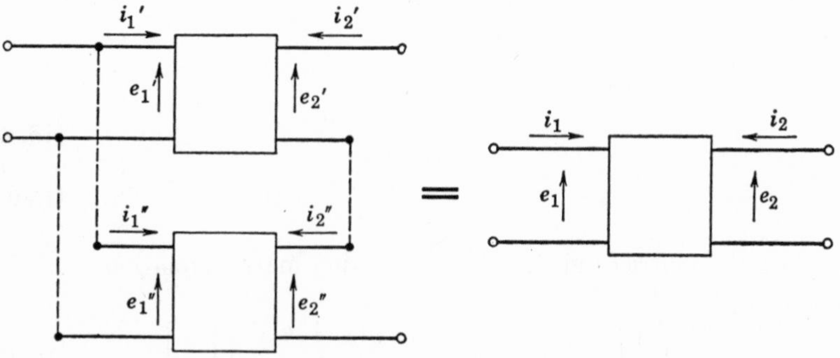

Fig. 15.9   Parallel-series connection.

(d) Parallel-series operation. See Fig. 15.9. Let the matrices for the networks be

$$\begin{bmatrix} i_1' \\ e_2' \end{bmatrix} = [g'] \begin{bmatrix} e_1' \\ i_2' \end{bmatrix} \quad \text{and} \quad \begin{bmatrix} i_1'' \\ e_2'' \end{bmatrix} = [g''] \begin{bmatrix} e_1'' \\ i_2'' \end{bmatrix} \qquad \begin{matrix} [15.99] \\ \text{and} \\ [15.100] \end{matrix}$$

When the networks are connected in parallel-series,

$$i_1 = i_1' + i_1'' \qquad [15.101]$$

$$e_2 = e_2' + e_2'' \qquad [15.102]$$

$$e_1 = e_1' = e_1'' \qquad [15.103]$$

$$i_2 = i_2' = i_2'' \qquad [15.104]$$

Adding the matrix equations gives the combination equation

$$\begin{bmatrix} i_1 \\ e_2 \end{bmatrix} = [g' + g''] \begin{bmatrix} e_1 \\ i_2 \end{bmatrix} \qquad [15.105]$$

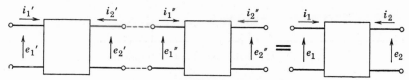

Fig. 15.10   Cascade connection.

(e) Cascade operation. See Fig. 15.10. Let the matrix equations for the networks be

$$\begin{bmatrix} e_1' \\ i_1' \end{bmatrix} = [a'] \begin{bmatrix} e_2' \\ -i_2' \end{bmatrix} \quad \text{and} \quad \begin{bmatrix} e_1'' \\ i_1'' \end{bmatrix} = [a''] \begin{bmatrix} e_2'' \\ -i_2'' \end{bmatrix} \qquad \begin{matrix} [15.106] \\ \text{and} \\ [15.107] \end{matrix}$$

When the networks are connected in cascade,

$$e_1 = e_1' \qquad [15.108]$$

$$i_1 = i_1' \qquad [15.109]$$

$$e_2 = e_2'' \qquad [15.110]$$

$$i_2 = i_2'' \qquad [15.111]$$

$$e_1'' = e_2' \qquad [15.112]$$

$$i_1'' = -i_2' \qquad [15.113]$$

Then the combination matrix equation is

$$\begin{bmatrix} e_1 \\ i_1 \end{bmatrix} = [a'] \times [a''] \begin{bmatrix} e_2 \\ -i_2 \end{bmatrix} \qquad [15.114]$$

15.4.6 Validity Tests

One important qualification should be made with regard to the various interconnections that are possible with four-terminal networks. For any such network, the matrix is set up on the basis that the current entering 1' is the same as that leaving 1, and the current

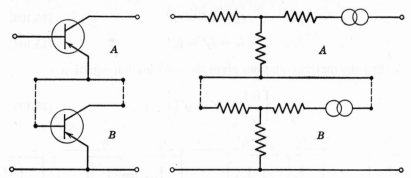

Fig. 15.11   Series connection of transistors.

entering 2' is the same as that leaving 2. This is obviously true for any one four-terminal network but may not be true when two networks are interconnected. The restriction, then, is that, after interconnecting, the current entering 1' and 2' is the same as that leaving 1 and 2 respectively, for, if this is not the case, the individual matrices cease to hold, and the methods of Sec. 15.4.5 are invalid.

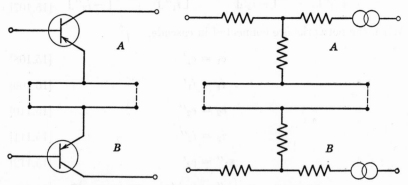

Fig. 15.12   Alternative series connection of transistors.

Ordinarily, the possibility of this occurrence is very slight and is recognized by inspection. However, it is well to show a few examples of where and how this situation will occur, as well as a few tests to check whether the matrix manipulations are valid.

Example. Series connection of transistors. See Fig. 15.11. It is obvious that matrix methods will fail in this case, since the horizontal

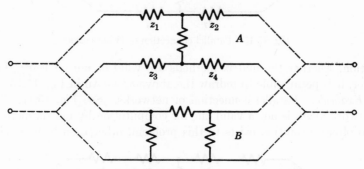

Fig. 15.13   Parallel connection of H and π networks.

limb of the transistor B is shorted by the common limb of transistor A. A simple rearrangement of the network so as not to invalidate the matrix is shown in Fig. 15.12.

Example. Parallel connection of networks. See Fig. 15.13. Here, too, it is obvious that the common leg of B is shorting the bottom leg

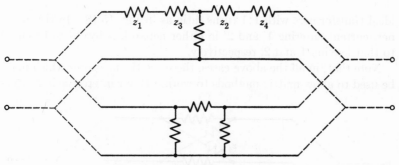

Fig. 15.14   Alternative connection.

of A, and the matrices will not hold. A simple rearrangement so as not to invalidate the matrix is shown in Fig. 15.14.

Example. Parallel connection of networks. See Fig. 15.15. With this connection, it is not possible to state, by looking at the configu-

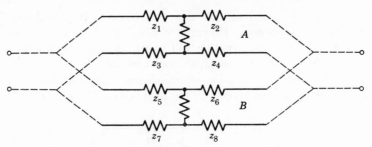

Fig. 15.15 Parallel connection of H networks.

ration, whether the matrix methods are valid or not. Clearly, however, it is permissible to redraw the above as shown in Fig. 15.16.

Example. Parallel connection of networks. See Fig. 15.17. This network again is not a valid one for computation by matrix methods. No obvious solution exists to this problem, other than by the use of

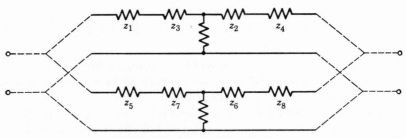

Fig. 15.16 Alternative connection.

ideal transformers with 1:1 turns ratio as in Fig. 15.18. In this manner, current entering 1′ and 2′ in either network is forced to be equal to that leaving 1 and 2, respectively.

Note that, in all the above cases, these are the measures which must be used to allow matrix methods to work. If our interest is in analyz-

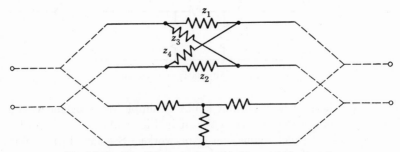

Fig. 15.17 Parallel connection of lattice and T networks.

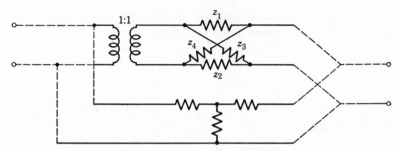

Fig. 15.18 Alternative connection.

ing a problem, regardless of whether matrix methods work or not, it becomes an even simpler matter.

Thus, the parallel connection of Fig. 15.17 is obviously the parallel connection of Fig. 15.19 since z_2 is shorted out. A simple validity

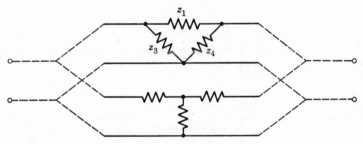

Fig. 15.19 Effect of direct parallel operation of lattice and T networks.

test may now be formulated. Suppose that we wish to make a parallel connection of networks. Connect one side of the networks together, as shown in Fig. 15.20, and terminate the other ends separately, such that $e_2' = e_2''$. Then, if points A and B are at the same poten-

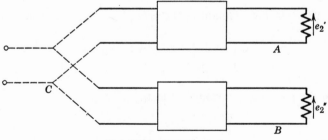

Fig. 15.20 Validity test.

tial, they may be connected without invalidating the matrices. Thus, since C is a common point, the networks may be connected if the voltage drop from C to A is the same as that from C to B. This requirement must hold for all load conditions, and all frequencies. In most transistor networks, the circuits encountered are those of the three-terminal type, i.e., the type where one terminal is common to both ends of the network. With such a network, one can tell at a glance whether the matrix method is valid or not.

15.5   The Terminated Four-Pole

A problem often encountered is that of the two-terminal pair, terminated at both ends in generators and impedances. The solution of this problem is always involved in the final evaluation of information from the matrix of the structure in question.

Consider a two-terminal pair, terminated as shown in Fig. 15.21. Generators and terminating impedances are used at both ends of the

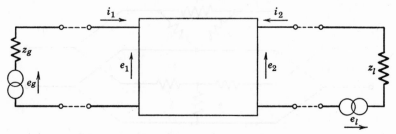

Fig. 15.21   Two-terminal pair with terminations.

network, to obtain a complete solution of the problem. Let the matrix equation for the two-terminal pair be

$$\begin{bmatrix} e_1 \\ e_2 \end{bmatrix} = \begin{bmatrix} z_{11} & z_{12} \\ z_{21} & z_{22} \end{bmatrix} \begin{bmatrix} i_1 \\ i_2 \end{bmatrix} \qquad [15.115]$$

and let Δ^z be the determinant of the array. Inversion of this equation gives

$$\begin{bmatrix} i_1 \\ i_2 \end{bmatrix} = \frac{1}{\Delta^z} \begin{bmatrix} z_{22} & -z_{12} \\ -z_{21} & z_{11} \end{bmatrix} \begin{bmatrix} e_1 \\ e_2 \end{bmatrix} \qquad [15.116]$$

When the network is terminated in z_l,

$$i_2 = -e_2/z_l \qquad [15.117]$$

$$-e_2/z_l = (1/\Delta^z)(-z_{21}e_1 + z_{11}e_2) \qquad [15.118]$$

whence forward voltage ratio

$$\mathbf{A}_v = e_2/e_1 = (z_{21}z_l)/(\Delta^z + z_{11}z_l) \qquad [15.119]$$

From eqs. 15.115 and 15.117,

$$-i_2z_l = z_{21}i_1 + z_{22}i_2 \qquad [15.120]$$

Forward current ratio,

$$\mathbf{A}_i = -i_2/i_1 = z_{21}/(z_{22} + z_l) \qquad [15.121]$$

When the input and output are terminated as shown in Fig. 15.21,

$$e_1 = e_g - i_1z_g \qquad [15.122]$$

$$e_2 = e_l - i_2z_l \qquad [15.123]$$

Then

$$\begin{bmatrix} e_g \\ e_l \end{bmatrix} = \begin{bmatrix} z_{11} + z_g, & z_{12} \\ z_{21} & , & z_{22} + z_l \end{bmatrix} \begin{bmatrix} i_1 \\ i_2 \end{bmatrix} \qquad [15.124]$$

Let Δ be the determinant of the array. Then

$$\Delta = \Delta^z + z_gz_l + z_{11}z_l + z_{22}z_g \qquad [15.125]$$

Inversion of eq. 15.124 gives

$$\begin{bmatrix} i_1 \\ i_2 \end{bmatrix} = \frac{1}{\Delta} \begin{bmatrix} z_{22} + z_l, & -z_{12} \\ -z_{21} & , & z_{11} + z_g \end{bmatrix} \begin{bmatrix} e_g \\ e_l \end{bmatrix} \qquad [15.126]$$

Setting $e_l = 0$, input impedance,

$$z_i = \left(\frac{e_g}{i_1} \right)_{z_g=0} = \left(\frac{\Delta}{z_{22} + z_l} \right)_{z_g=0} = \frac{\Delta^z + z_{11}z_l}{z_{22} + z_l} \qquad [15.127]$$

Setting $e_g = 0$, output impedance,

$$z_o = \left(\frac{e_l}{i_2} \right)_{z_l=0} = \left(\frac{\Delta}{z_{11} + z_g} \right)_{z_l=0} = \frac{\Delta^z + z_{22}z_g}{z_{11} + z_g} \qquad [15.128]$$

Using the table of matrix interrelations, these equations, which cover the various properties of the two-terminal pair, may be expressed in terms of the other matrix forms. For convenience, a table of these relations is given at the end of the chapter.

15.6 Application of Matrix Methods

15.6.1 Analysis of Feedback Amplifiers

Matrix methods are especially valuable in the analysis of feedback. In problems of this sort, transmission through the feedback loop is usually bidirectional, and an accurate solution is not obtainable by other methods. The advantage of the matrix method is that the problem is set up in a closed form and maintained in this form till the end when the eventual solution is required.

A single-stage junction-transistor amplifier with shunt feedback will be analyzed to show the simplicity of the method. In passing, it will

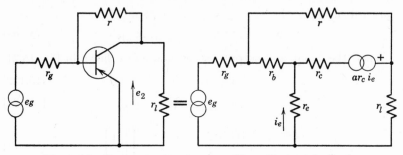

Fig. 15.22   Single-stage transistor amplifier with shunt feedback.

also be pointed out that the solution may be written almost by inspection when four matrix coefficients are used to define the transistor behavior.

Example. Analyze the circuit of Fig. 15.22. The equivalent circuit is redrawn in Fig. 15.23, as two four-terminal networks in parallel,

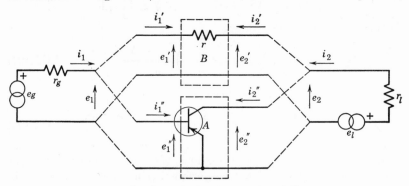

Fig. 15.23   Block diagram representation of Fig. 15.22.

with their terminations. For the network A (see table of matrix relations for the transistor)

$$
\begin{bmatrix} i_1'' \\ i_2'' \end{bmatrix} =
\begin{bmatrix} \dfrac{r_e + r_c(1-a)}{\Delta}, & \dfrac{-r_e}{\Delta} \\[2ex] \dfrac{-(r_e - ar_c)}{\Delta}, & \dfrac{r_e + r_b}{\Delta} \end{bmatrix}
\begin{bmatrix} e_1'' \\ e_2'' \end{bmatrix}
\qquad [15.129]
$$

where

$$\Delta = r_e r_b + r_c \{ r_e + r_b (1 - a) \} \qquad [15.130]$$

Let Δ_1 = determinant of the array.   Then

$$\Delta_1 = 1/\Delta \qquad [15.131]$$

For the network B

$$\begin{bmatrix} i_1' \\ i_2' \end{bmatrix} = \begin{bmatrix} 1/r & -1/r \\ -1/r & 1/r \end{bmatrix} \begin{bmatrix} e_1' \\ e_2' \end{bmatrix} \qquad [15.132]$$

Let Δ_2 = determinant of the array.   Then

$$\Delta_2 = 0 \qquad [15.133]$$

Adding eqs. 15.129 and 15.132 to obtain the parallel combination gives

$$\begin{bmatrix} i_1 \\ i_2 \end{bmatrix} = \begin{bmatrix} \dfrac{1}{r} + \dfrac{r_e + r_c(1 - a)}{\Delta}, & \dfrac{-r_e}{\Delta} - \dfrac{1}{r} \\[3mm] -\dfrac{1}{r} - \dfrac{(r_e - ar_c)}{\Delta}, & \dfrac{r_e + r_b}{\Delta} + \dfrac{1}{r} \end{bmatrix} \begin{bmatrix} e_1 \\ e_2 \end{bmatrix} \qquad [15.134]$$

Let Δ_3 = determinant of the array.   Then

$$\Delta_3 = (1/\Delta)\{1 + (r_b + r_c)/r\} \qquad [15.135]$$

Equation 15.134 defines a four-terminal network.   When such a network is terminated,

$$\mathbf{A}_v = e_2/e_1 = -y_{21}/(y_{22} + y_l) \qquad [15.136]$$

(see table of relations for the two-terminal pair with terminations)

$$\mathbf{A}_v = \dfrac{+\dfrac{1}{r} + \dfrac{(r_e - ar_c)}{\Delta}}{\dfrac{r_e + r_b}{\Delta} + \dfrac{1}{r} + \dfrac{1}{r_l}} \qquad [15.137]$$

$$= \dfrac{r_l \{ \Delta + r(r_e - ar_c) \}}{\Delta(r + r_l) + rr_l(r_e + r_b)} \qquad [15.138]$$

also,

$$z_i = \dfrac{y_{22} + y_l}{\Delta^y + y_{11} y_l} \quad \text{(see table)} \qquad [15.139]$$

$$= \dfrac{\dfrac{r_e + r_b}{\Delta} + \dfrac{1}{r} + \dfrac{1}{r_l}}{\Delta_3 + \left\{ \dfrac{1}{r} + \dfrac{r_e + r_c(1 - a)}{\Delta} \right\} \dfrac{1}{r_l}} \qquad [15.140]$$

whence

$$z_i = \frac{rr_l(r_e + r_b) + \Delta(r + r_l)}{\Delta + r\{r_e + r_c(1 - a)\} + rr_l + r_l(r_b + r_c)} \qquad [15.141]$$

(see table). Also,

$$z_o = \frac{y_{11} + y_g}{\Delta^y + y_{22}y_g} \qquad [15.142]$$

$$= \frac{\dfrac{r_e + r_c(1 - a)}{\Delta} + \dfrac{1}{r} + \dfrac{1}{r_g}}{\Delta_3 + \dfrac{1}{r_g}\left(\dfrac{r_e + r_b}{\Delta} + \dfrac{1}{r}\right)} \qquad [15.143]$$

$$= \frac{rr_g\{r_e + r_c(1 - a)\} + \Delta(r + r_g)}{\Delta + r(r_e + r_b) + rr_g + r_g(r_b + r_c)} \qquad [15.144]$$

If the transistor is defined in its behavior by the matrix

$$\begin{bmatrix} y_{11} & y_{12} \\ y_{21} & y_{22} \end{bmatrix} \qquad [15.145]$$

and $y = 1/r$, so that the matrix for the feedback loop is

$$\begin{bmatrix} y & -y \\ -y & y \end{bmatrix} \qquad [15.146]$$

Then $\mathbf{A}_v$ is written directly as

$$- \frac{y_{21} - y}{y_{22} + y + y_l} \qquad [15.147]$$

and z_i as

$$\frac{y_{22} + y + y_l}{\Delta^y + y(y_{11} + y_{12} + y_{21} + y_{22}) + y_l(y + y_{11})} \qquad [15.148]$$

and also z_o as

$$\frac{y_{11} + y + y_g}{\Delta^y + y(y_{11} + y_{12} + y_{21} + y_{22}) + y_g(y + y_{11})} \qquad [15.149]$$

We shall see later that this makes use of a π-network representation for the transistor, the feedback resistor acting as a shunt across the horizontal leg.

15.6.2 Equivalent Circuits

Equivalent circuits have been very widely used in the field of communication engineering. Since much of the training of the engineer is along active and passive circuit lines, the setting up of an equivalent circuit which will exhibit the characteristics of the actual problem is a step in the right direction and aids greatly in the interpretation of the physical phenomena.

Given the matrix equation for a two-terminal pair, it is possible to construct any number of equivalent circuits for the network. Of these equivalent circuits, the T and the π are the simplest configurations. The most useful matrices are the y and z, since, from these, the π and T configurations may be set up by inspection. Consider a passive circuit, defined in its behavior by

$$\begin{bmatrix} i_1 \\ i_2 \end{bmatrix} = \begin{bmatrix} y_{11} & y_{12} \\ y_{12} & y_{22} \end{bmatrix} \begin{bmatrix} e_1 \\ e_2 \end{bmatrix} \qquad [15.150]$$

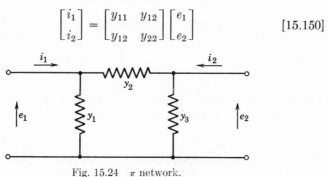

Fig. 15.24 π network.

Let the equivalent circuit configuration be as shown in Fig. 15.24. For this circuit,

$$\begin{bmatrix} i_1 \\ i_2 \end{bmatrix} = \begin{bmatrix} y_1 + y_2, & -y_2 \\ -y_2\,, & y_2 + y_3 \end{bmatrix} \begin{bmatrix} e_1 \\ e_2 \end{bmatrix} \qquad [15.151]$$

For the two matrices to be identical,

$$y_{11} = y_1 + y_2 \qquad [15.152]$$

$$y_{12} = -y_2 \qquad [15.153]$$

$$y_{22} = y_2 + y_3 \qquad [15.154]$$

and the equivalent circuit is obtained.

In like manner, the equivalent T may be obtained by equating the z matrix for the T network to the z matrix of the original passive circuit.

As has been mentioned earlier, for any linear passive bilateral network, $z_{12} = z_{21}$ and $y_{12} = y_{21}$. If a circuit is defined by a z or y

matrix whose diagonal terms are not equal, the equivalent circuit will have one or more active elements in it. The procedure will then be as follows:

(a) Make the diagonal terms equal by carrying over the excess to the left-hand side.

(b) Construct a passive T or π as before.

(c) Insert the active terms which were carried over.

An example will illustrate this. Suppose that

$$\begin{bmatrix} e_1 \\ e_2 \end{bmatrix} = \begin{bmatrix} z_{11} & z_{12} \\ z_{21} & z_{22} \end{bmatrix} \begin{bmatrix} i_1 \\ i_2 \end{bmatrix} \tag{15.155}$$

defines a device whose equivalent circuit is required. Let

$$z_{21} = z_{12} + z'_{12} \tag{15.156}$$

Then the term involving z'_{12} may be carried over to the left-hand side as follows.

$$\begin{bmatrix} e_1 \\ e_2 - z'_{12}i_1 \end{bmatrix} = \begin{bmatrix} z_{11} & z_{12} \\ z_{12} & z_{22} \end{bmatrix} \begin{bmatrix} i_1 \\ i_2 \end{bmatrix} \tag{15.157}$$

The z matrix is now a symmetrical one, and the equivalent circuit may be drawn as in Fig. 15.25. This is not complete, however, since

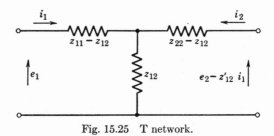

Fig. 15.25   T network.

the generator on the right-hand side involves a term other than e_2. The circuit is now redrawn as in Fig. 15.26. Clearly, no restriction is

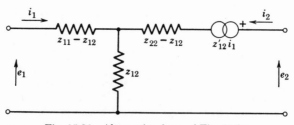

Fig. 15.26   Alternative form of Fig. 15.25.

placed on the transfer of part or all of one or more terms to the left-hand side of the equation as long as the impedance matrix is made symmetrical and is physically realizable. This will result in more complicated equivalent circuits.

Further variations may be made by replacing internal voltage sources by current sources, and vice versa. If other matrix forms are given for the device, they must first be converted to the z or y form.

It should be mentioned here that any passive four-terminal network made up of a finite number of linear elements is externally equivalent at a single frequency to a passive T or π network. This was proved in 1911 by Campbell; an obvious extension is to redefine this theorem for active networks and active T or π equivalents. For, if a multiloop four-terminal network is defined by

$$\begin{bmatrix} e_1 \\ e_2 \\ 0 \\ \cdot \\ \cdot \\ \cdot \\ 0 \end{bmatrix} = [z] \begin{bmatrix} i_1 \\ i_2 \\ i_3 \\ \cdot \\ \cdot \\ \cdot \\ i_n \end{bmatrix} \qquad [15.158]$$

where z is an n-order matrix, we have seen how this is equivalent to a four-terminal network defined by

$$\begin{bmatrix} e_1 \\ e_2 \end{bmatrix} = [Z] \begin{bmatrix} i_1 \\ i_2 \end{bmatrix} \qquad [15.159]$$

where Z is a matrix with two rows and two columns. And this matrix may be represented by an active T or π configuration.

Example. Construct equivalent circuits for a device whose behavior is defined by

$$\begin{bmatrix} e_1 \\ e_2 \end{bmatrix} = \begin{bmatrix} r_e + r_b, & r_e \\ r_e - ar_c, & r_e + r_c(1 - a) \end{bmatrix} \begin{bmatrix} i_1 \\ i_2 \end{bmatrix} \qquad [15.160]$$

Note that this is the low-frequency matrix equation for a grounded-emitter transistor. By moving a minimum number of terms to the left-hand side, we have

$$\begin{bmatrix} e_1 \\ e_2 + ar_c i_1 \end{bmatrix} = \begin{bmatrix} r_e + r_b, & r_e \\ r_e, & r_e + r_c(1 - a) \end{bmatrix} \begin{bmatrix} i_1 \\ i_2 \end{bmatrix} \qquad [15.161]$$

and the resultant equivalent circuit is shown in Fig. 15.27. A more complicated choice is to move yet another term to the left-hand side, say, for instance, the term $-ar_c i_2$.

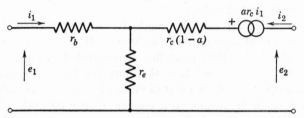

Fig. 15.27   Equivalent circuit for a grounded-emitter transistor.

The matrix equation is now in the form

$$\begin{bmatrix} e_1 \\ e_2 + ar_c(i_1 + i_2) \end{bmatrix} = \begin{bmatrix} r_e + r_b, & r_e \\ r_e, & r_e + r_c \end{bmatrix} \begin{bmatrix} i_1 \\ i_2 \end{bmatrix} \qquad [15.162]$$

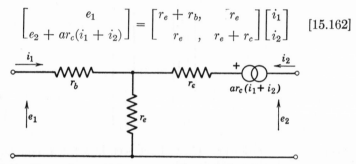

Fig. 15.28   Alternative equivalent circuit for a grounded-emitter transistor.

whence, the equivalent circuit is as shown in Fig. 15.28. If a π configuration is needed, the matrix must first be inverted thus

$$\begin{bmatrix} i_1 \\ i_2 \end{bmatrix} = \begin{bmatrix} \dfrac{r_e + r_c(1 - a)}{\Delta}, & \dfrac{-r_e}{\Delta} \\ \dfrac{-(r_e - ar_c)}{\Delta}, & \dfrac{r_e + r_b}{\Delta} \end{bmatrix} \begin{bmatrix} e_1 \\ e_2 \end{bmatrix} \qquad [15.163]$$

where

$$\Delta = r_e r_b + r_c\{r_e + r_b(1 - a)\} \qquad [15.164]$$

For the simplest circuit,

$$\begin{bmatrix} i_1 \\ i_2 - \dfrac{ar_c e_1}{\Delta} \end{bmatrix} = \begin{bmatrix} \dfrac{r_e + r_c(1 - a)}{\Delta}, & \dfrac{-r_e}{\Delta} \\ \dfrac{-r_e}{\Delta}, & \dfrac{r_e + r_b}{\Delta} \end{bmatrix} \begin{bmatrix} e_1 \\ e_2 \end{bmatrix} \qquad [15.165]$$

Figure 15.29 shows the equivalent circuit for this matrix equation.

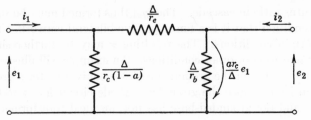

Fig. 15.29 Equivalent circuit using π network representation.

15.6.3 Vacuum-Tube Equivalent Circuits

A study of the equivalent circuit given in Fig. 15.29 shows that the circuit may be redrawn as in Fig. 15.30, where

$$g_m = ar_c/\Delta \qquad [15.166]$$

$$g_p = r_b/\Delta \qquad [15.167]$$

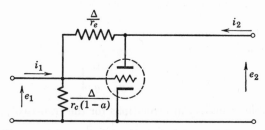

Fig. 15.30 Vacuum-tube equivalent circuit for a grounded-emitter transistor.

Physically realizable vacuum-tube equivalent circuits may be obtained for many of the tube and transistor configurations. The procedure is as follows: Referring to Fig. 15.31,

$$[y_V] + [y_\pi] = [y_T] \qquad [15.168]$$

Therefore,

$$[y_\pi] = [y_T] - [y_V] \qquad [15.169]$$

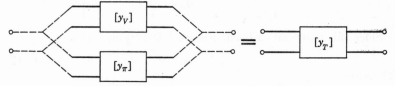

Fig. 15.31 Method of obtaining vacuum-tube equivalent circuits.

For those equivalent circuits where a 180° phase reversal is involved the $[y_V]$ matrix is written for a vacuum tube with an ideal transformer of 1:1 turns ratio in cascade. The $[y_\pi]$ thus formed must be subjected to the condition that it is a linear passive bilateral network. This imposes certain conditions. The resulting π may be further simplified by the imposition of other conditions. An example will illustrate this.

Example. Obtain the grounded-cathode equivalent for a grounded-base transistor. Since the grounded-cathode circuit has a 180° phase reversal, and the grounded-base has not, an ideal transformer will be

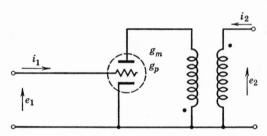

Fig. 15.32   Vacuum-tube configuration.

necessary. The vacuum-tube circuit is then as shown in Fig. 15.32 For this circuit,

$$[y_V] = \begin{bmatrix} 0 & 0 \\ -g_m & g_p \end{bmatrix} \qquad [15.170]$$

From the table of matrix interrelations for the transistor,

$$[y_T] = \frac{1}{\Delta} \begin{bmatrix} r_c + r_b & , & -r_b \\ -(r_b + ar_c), & r_e + r_b \end{bmatrix} \qquad [15.171]$$

where

$$\Delta = r_e r_b + r_c \{ r_e + r_b (1 - a) \} \qquad [15.172]$$

Then

$$[y_\pi] = \begin{bmatrix} \dfrac{r_c}{\Delta} + \dfrac{r_b}{\Delta} & , & \dfrac{-r_b}{\Delta} \\[3mm] \dfrac{-r_b}{\Delta} - \dfrac{ar_c}{\Delta} + g_m , & \dfrac{r_e}{\Delta} + \dfrac{r_b}{\Delta} - g_p \end{bmatrix} \qquad [15.173]$$

Since this represents a linear passive bilateral network,

$$y_{12} = y_{21} \qquad [15.174]$$

Therefore,

$$g_m = ar_c / \Delta \qquad [15.175]$$

Imposing the condition that

$$g_p = r_e / \Delta \qquad [15.176]$$

results in

$$[y_\pi] = \begin{bmatrix} \dfrac{r_c}{\Delta} + \dfrac{r_b}{\Delta}, & \dfrac{-r_b}{\Delta} \\[3mm] \dfrac{-r_b}{\Delta}, & \dfrac{r_b}{\Delta} \end{bmatrix}$$ [15.177]

And this gives the equivalent circuit shown in Fig. 15.33. This circuit is a π network with one leg missing. The equivalent circuit of

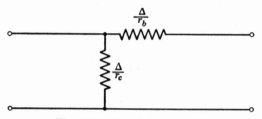

Fig. 15.33   Feedback network.

the combination is then as shown in Fig. 15.34. Circuits of this type are useful in that they afford a different way of thinking about the transistor.

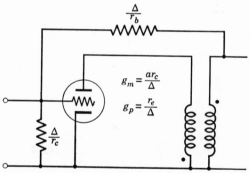

Fig. 15.34   Complete equivalent circuit for a grounded-base transistor.

15.6.4   Stability in Transistor Amplifiers

The Nyquist criterion for the stability of a single-loop feedback amplifier may be stated as follows: Cut a single-loop feedback network at any point of infinite impedance, and obtain its open-circuit forward transmission, $-T$. Then, if T is plotted in the T plane, the circuit is stable if the locus of this plot does not include the point $-1 \pm j0$. That this criterion is inapplicable to transistor circuits is evident from the fact that there exists no suitable "point of infinite impedance" at which to open the network. A more general stability theorem has been stated as follows: If a closed-loop system is open at any point, its h matrix may be written

$$\begin{bmatrix} e_1 \\ i_2 \end{bmatrix} = \begin{bmatrix} h_{11} & h_{12} \\ h_{21} & h_{22} \end{bmatrix} \begin{bmatrix} i_1 \\ e_2 \end{bmatrix} \qquad [15.178]$$

For oscillation on closing the loop, $e_1 = e_2$ and $i_1 = -i_2$, whence

$$h_{21} - h_{12} + \Delta^h = -1 \qquad [15.179]$$

The above criterion, though not too useful in attacking stability problems on account of its unwieldiness, is of interest in that it is a general criterion. If the point where the network is cut is one of infinite impedance, such as occurs at the grid of a vacuum tube (interelectrode capacities are considered as external to the tube), the criterion degenerates to that of Nyquist. If the loop is opened at a point of zero impedance, the criterion becomes

$$h_{21} = -1 \qquad [15.180]$$

This criterion may be stated as follows: Cut a single-loop feedback network at any point of infinite admittance, and obtain its short-circuit forward transmission current ratio, $-h_{21}$. Then, if h_{21} is plotted in the h_{21} plane, the circuit is stable if the locus of this plot does not encircle the point $-1 \pm j0$. This criterion is more nearly applicable to the transistor.

15.6.5   Dual Networks

Wallace and Raisbeck † have indicated that the concept of duality as a guide in transistor circuit design is a very interesting one. They have shown that a point-contact transistor in the grounded-base connection is very closely the dual of a high-vacuum triode in the grounded-cathode connection. On the basis of this relationship, it is claimed that a large number of transistor circuits may be designed by the mere substitution of a transistor for a triode, and a network dual for the triode circuit. Whereas the method is subject to a number of limitations, there is no denying that it has been used for various circuits.

The problem, then, is to obtain a network dual, given the original network. By means of matrices, this proves to be at once obvious.

† R. L. Wallace, Jr., and G. Raisbeck, "Duality as a Guide in Transistor Circuit Design," *Bell Sys. Tech. J.*, April, 1951.

Let

$$
\begin{bmatrix} e_1 \\ e_2 \\ \cdot \\ \cdot \\ \cdot \\ e_n \end{bmatrix} = [z] \begin{bmatrix} i_1 \\ i_2 \\ \cdot \\ \cdot \\ \cdot \\ i_n \end{bmatrix} \qquad\qquad [15.181]
$$

be the equation of a network whose dual is required.
  For the dual network, let

$$ i_D = e/r \qquad\qquad [15.182] $$

$$ e_D = ir \qquad\qquad [15.183] $$

where r is the transformation resistance.

$$
\begin{bmatrix} i_{1D}r \\ i_{2D}r \\ \cdot \\ \cdot \\ \cdot \\ i_{nD}r \end{bmatrix} = [z] \begin{bmatrix} e_{1D}/r \\ e_{2D}/r \\ \cdot \\ \cdot \\ \cdot \\ e_{nD}/r \end{bmatrix} \qquad\qquad [15.184]
$$

or

$$
\begin{bmatrix} i_{1D} \\ i_{2D} \\ \cdot \\ \cdot \\ \cdot \\ i_{nD} \end{bmatrix} = \left[\frac{z}{r^2}\right] \begin{bmatrix} e_{1D} \\ e_{2D} \\ \cdot \\ \cdot \\ \cdot \\ e_{nD} \end{bmatrix} \qquad\qquad [15.185]
$$

whence z/r^2 is the y matrix for the dual network. From this the dual circuit may be constructed. Note that, if z_{ij} is a series combination of r' ohms, L henries, and C farads,

$$ z_{ij} = r' + j\omega L + 1/j\omega C \qquad\qquad [15.186] $$

Then

$$ y_{ij} = \frac{z_{ij}}{r^2} = \frac{r'}{r^2} + \frac{j\omega L}{r^2} + \frac{1}{j\omega C r^2} \qquad\qquad [15.187] $$

and this is a parallel combination of r^2/r' ohms, r^2/L farads, and Cr^2 henries.
  An example will illustrate the power of this method.

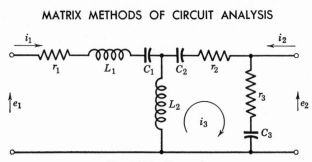

Fig. 15.35 Network.

Example. Find the network dual of the circuit shown in Fig. 15.35. The equation for this network (using p for $j\omega$) is

$$
\begin{bmatrix} e_1 \\ 0 \\ e_2 \end{bmatrix} =
\begin{bmatrix}
r_1 + pL_1 + pL_2 + \dfrac{1}{pC_1}, & -pL_2 & , & 0 \\[2ex]
-pL_2, & r_2 + r_3 + pL_2 + \dfrac{1}{pC_2 + pC_3}, & r_3 + \dfrac{1}{pC_3} \\[2ex]
0 \, , & r_3 + \dfrac{1}{pC_3} & , & r_3 + \dfrac{1}{pC_3}
\end{bmatrix}
\begin{bmatrix} i_1 \\ i_3 \\ i_2 \end{bmatrix}
$$

[15.188]

For the network dual, let

$$e_D = ir \qquad [15.189]$$

$$i_D = e/r \qquad [15.190]$$

Then

$$
\begin{bmatrix} i_{1D} \\ 0 \\ i_{2D} \end{bmatrix} =
\begin{bmatrix}
\dfrac{r_1}{r^2} + \dfrac{pL_1}{r^2} + \dfrac{pL_2}{r^2} + \dfrac{1}{pC_1 r^2}, & -\dfrac{pL_2}{r^2} & \\[2ex]
\dfrac{-pL_2}{r^2} & , & \dfrac{r_2}{r^2} + \dfrac{r_3}{r^2} + \dfrac{pL_2}{r^2} + \dfrac{1}{pC_2 r^2 + pC_3 r^2}, & \dfrac{r_3}{r^2} + \dfrac{1}{pC_3 r^2} \\[2ex]
0 & , & \dfrac{r_3}{r^2} + \dfrac{1}{pC_3 r^2} & , & \dfrac{r_3}{r^2} + \dfrac{1}{pC_3 r^2}
\end{bmatrix}
\begin{bmatrix} e_{1D} \\ e_{3D} \\ e_{2D} \end{bmatrix}
$$

This equation may be rewritten as

$$
\begin{bmatrix} i_{1D} \\ 0 \\ -i_{2D} \end{bmatrix} =
\begin{bmatrix}
\dfrac{r_1}{r^2} + \dfrac{pL_1}{r^2} + \dfrac{pL_2}{r^2} + \dfrac{1}{pC_1 r^2}, & -\dfrac{pL_2}{r^2} & , & 0 \\[2ex]
\dfrac{-pL_2}{r^2}, & \dfrac{r_2}{r^2} + \dfrac{r_3}{r^2} + \dfrac{pL_2}{r^2} + \dfrac{1}{pC_2 r^2 + pC_3 r^2}, & -\dfrac{r_3}{r^2} - \dfrac{1}{pC_3 r^2} \\[2ex]
0 \, , & -\dfrac{r_3}{r^2} - \dfrac{1}{pC_3 r^2} & , & \dfrac{r_3}{r^2} + \dfrac{1}{pC_3 r^2}
\end{bmatrix}
\begin{bmatrix} e_{1D} \\ e_{3D} \\ -e_{2D} \end{bmatrix}
$$

And the equivalent dual is shown in Fig. 15.36. Note that, whereas in the original network the input and output voltages are simultaneously positive, the input and output currents are simultaneously positive for the dual network.

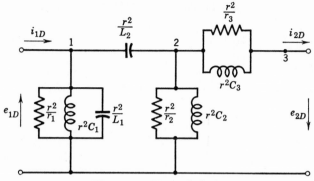

Fig. 15.36 Network dual.

15.7 Tables

Matrix Interrelations

From → To	$[z]$	$[y]$	$[h]$	$[g]$	$[a]$	$[b]$
$[z]$	$\begin{matrix} z_{11} & z_{12} \\ z_{21} & z_{22} \end{matrix}$	$\begin{matrix} \dfrac{y_{22}}{\Delta^y} & \dfrac{-y_{12}}{\Delta^y} \\[4pt] \dfrac{-y_{21}}{\Delta^y} & \dfrac{y_{11}}{\Delta^y} \end{matrix}$	$\begin{matrix} \dfrac{\Delta^h}{h_{22}} & \dfrac{h_{12}}{h_{22}} \\[4pt] \dfrac{-h_{21}}{h_{22}} & \dfrac{1}{h_{22}} \end{matrix}$	$\begin{matrix} \dfrac{1}{g_{11}} & \dfrac{-g_{12}}{g_{11}} \\[4pt] \dfrac{g_{21}}{g_{11}} & \dfrac{\Delta^g}{g_{11}} \end{matrix}$	$\begin{matrix} \dfrac{a_{11}}{a_{21}} & \dfrac{\Delta^a}{a_{21}} \\[4pt] \dfrac{1}{a_{21}} & \dfrac{a_{22}}{a_{21}} \end{matrix}$	$\begin{matrix} \dfrac{b_{22}}{b_{21}} & \dfrac{1}{b_{21}} \\[4pt] \dfrac{\Delta^b}{b_{21}} & \dfrac{b_{11}}{b_{21}} \end{matrix}$
$[y]$	$\begin{matrix} \dfrac{z_{22}}{\Delta^z} & \dfrac{-z_{12}}{\Delta^z} \\[4pt] \dfrac{-z_{21}}{\Delta^z} & \dfrac{z_{11}}{\Delta^z} \end{matrix}$	$\begin{matrix} y_{11} & y_{12} \\ y_{21} & y_{22} \end{matrix}$	$\begin{matrix} \dfrac{1}{h_{11}} & \dfrac{-h_{12}}{h_{11}} \\[4pt] \dfrac{h_{21}}{h_{11}} & \dfrac{\Delta^h}{h_{11}} \end{matrix}$	$\begin{matrix} \dfrac{\Delta^g}{g_{22}} & \dfrac{g_{12}}{g_{22}} \\[4pt] \dfrac{-g_{21}}{g_{22}} & \dfrac{1}{g_{22}} \end{matrix}$	$\begin{matrix} \dfrac{a_{22}}{a_{12}} & \dfrac{-\Delta^a}{a_{12}} \\[4pt] \dfrac{-1}{a_{12}} & \dfrac{a_{11}}{a_{12}} \end{matrix}$	$\begin{matrix} \dfrac{b_{11}}{b_{12}} & \dfrac{-1}{b_{12}} \\[4pt] \dfrac{-\Delta^b}{b_{12}} & \dfrac{b_{22}}{b_{12}} \end{matrix}$
$[h]$	$\begin{matrix} \dfrac{\Delta^z}{z_{22}} & \dfrac{z_{12}}{z_{22}} \\[4pt] \dfrac{-z_{21}}{z_{22}} & \dfrac{1}{z_{22}} \end{matrix}$	$\begin{matrix} \dfrac{1}{y_{11}} & \dfrac{-y_{12}}{y_{11}} \\[4pt] \dfrac{y_{21}}{y_{11}} & \dfrac{\Delta^y}{y_{11}} \end{matrix}$	$\begin{matrix} h_{11} & h_{12} \\ h_{21} & h_{22} \end{matrix}$	$\begin{matrix} \dfrac{g_{22}}{\Delta^g} & \dfrac{-g_{12}}{\Delta^g} \\[4pt] \dfrac{-g_{21}}{\Delta^g} & \dfrac{g_{11}}{\Delta^g} \end{matrix}$	$\begin{matrix} \dfrac{a_{12}}{a_{22}} & \dfrac{\Delta^a}{a_{22}} \\[4pt] \dfrac{-1}{a_{22}} & \dfrac{a_{21}}{a_{22}} \end{matrix}$	$\begin{matrix} \dfrac{b_{12}}{b_{11}} & \dfrac{1}{b_{11}} \\[4pt] \dfrac{-\Delta^b}{b_{11}} & \dfrac{b_{21}}{b_{11}} \end{matrix}$
$[g]$	$\begin{matrix} \dfrac{1}{z_{11}} & \dfrac{-z_{12}}{z_{11}} \\[4pt] \dfrac{z_{21}}{z_{11}} & \dfrac{\Delta^z}{z_{11}} \end{matrix}$	$\begin{matrix} \dfrac{\Delta^y}{y_{22}} & \dfrac{y_{12}}{y_{22}} \\[4pt] \dfrac{-y_{21}}{y_{22}} & \dfrac{1}{y_{22}} \end{matrix}$	$\begin{matrix} \dfrac{h_{22}}{\Delta^h} & \dfrac{-h_{12}}{\Delta^h} \\[4pt] \dfrac{-h_{21}}{\Delta^h} & \dfrac{h_{11}}{\Delta^h} \end{matrix}$	$\begin{matrix} g_{11} & g_{12} \\ g_{21} & g_{22} \end{matrix}$	$\begin{matrix} \dfrac{a_{21}}{a_{11}} & \dfrac{-\Delta^a}{a_{11}} \\[4pt] \dfrac{1}{a_{11}} & \dfrac{a_{12}}{a_{11}} \end{matrix}$	$\begin{matrix} \dfrac{b_{21}}{b_{22}} & \dfrac{-1}{b_{22}} \\[4pt] \dfrac{\Delta^b}{b_{22}} & \dfrac{b_{12}}{b_{22}} \end{matrix}$
$[a]$	$\begin{matrix} \dfrac{z_{11}}{z_{21}} & \dfrac{\Delta^z}{z_{21}} \\[4pt] \dfrac{1}{z_{21}} & \dfrac{z_{22}}{z_{21}} \end{matrix}$	$\begin{matrix} \dfrac{-y_{22}}{y_{21}} & \dfrac{-1}{y_{21}} \\[4pt] \dfrac{-\Delta^y}{y_{21}} & \dfrac{-y_{11}}{y_{21}} \end{matrix}$	$\begin{matrix} \dfrac{-\Delta^h}{h_{21}} & \dfrac{-h_{11}}{h_{21}} \\[4pt] \dfrac{-h_{22}}{h_{21}} & \dfrac{-1}{h_{21}} \end{matrix}$	$\begin{matrix} \dfrac{1}{g_{21}} & \dfrac{g_{22}}{g_{21}} \\[4pt] \dfrac{g_{11}}{g_{21}} & \dfrac{\Delta^g}{g_{21}} \end{matrix}$	$\begin{matrix} a_{11} & a_{12} \\ a_{21} & a_{22} \end{matrix}$	$\begin{matrix} \dfrac{b_{22}}{\Delta^b} & \dfrac{b_{12}}{\Delta^b} \\[4pt] \dfrac{b_{21}}{\Delta^b} & \dfrac{b_{11}}{\Delta^b} \end{matrix}$
$[b]$	$\begin{matrix} \dfrac{z_{22}}{z_{12}} & \dfrac{\Delta^z}{z_{12}} \\[4pt] \dfrac{1}{z_{12}} & \dfrac{z_{11}}{z_{12}} \end{matrix}$	$\begin{matrix} \dfrac{-y_{11}}{y_{12}} & \dfrac{-1}{y_{12}} \\[4pt] \dfrac{-\Delta^y}{y_{12}} & \dfrac{-y_{22}}{y_{12}} \end{matrix}$	$\begin{matrix} \dfrac{1}{h_{12}} & \dfrac{h_{11}}{h_{12}} \\[4pt] \dfrac{h_{22}}{h_{12}} & \dfrac{\Delta^h}{h_{12}} \end{matrix}$	$\begin{matrix} -\dfrac{\Delta^g}{g_{12}} & -\dfrac{g_{22}}{g_{12}} \\[4pt] -\dfrac{g_{11}}{g_{12}} & -\dfrac{1}{g_{12}} \end{matrix}$	$\begin{matrix} \dfrac{a_{22}}{\Delta^a} & \dfrac{a_{12}}{\Delta^a} \\[4pt] \dfrac{a_{21}}{\Delta^a} & \dfrac{a_{11}}{\Delta^a} \end{matrix}$	$\begin{matrix} b_{11} & b_{12} \\ b_{21} & b_{22} \end{matrix}$

335

Properties of the Terminated Four-Terminal Network

	z	y	h	g	a	b
z_i	$\dfrac{\Delta^z + z_{11}z_l}{z_{22} + z_l}$	$\dfrac{y_{22} + y_l}{\Delta^y + y_{11}y_l}$	$\dfrac{\Delta^h + h_{11}y_l}{h_{22} + y_l}$	$\dfrac{g_{22} + z_l}{\Delta^g + g_{11}z_l}$	$\dfrac{a_{11}z_l + a_{12}}{a_{21}z_l + a_{22}}$	$\dfrac{b_{22}z_l + b_{12}}{b_{21}z_l + b_{11}}$
z_o	$\dfrac{\Delta^z + z_{22}z_g}{z_{11} + z_g}$	$\dfrac{y_{11} + y_g}{\Delta^y + y_{22}y_g}$	$\dfrac{h_{11} + z_g}{\Delta^h + h_{22}z_g}$	$\dfrac{\Delta^g + g_{22}y_g}{g_{11} + y_g}$	$\dfrac{a_{22}z_g + a_{12}}{a_{21}z_g + a_{11}}$	$\dfrac{b_{11}z_g + b_{12}}{b_{21}z_g + b_{22}}$
A_v	$\dfrac{z_{21}z_l}{\Delta^z + z_{11}z_l}$	$\dfrac{-y_{21}}{y_{22} + y_l}$	$\dfrac{-h_{21}z_l}{h_{11} + \Delta^h z_l}$	$\dfrac{g_{21}z_l}{g_{22} + z_l}$	$\dfrac{z_l}{a_{12} + a_{11}z_l}$	$\dfrac{z_l\Delta^b}{b_{12} + b_{22}z_l}$
A_i	$\dfrac{z_{21}}{z_{22} + z_l}$	$\dfrac{-y_{21}y_l}{\Delta^y + y_{11}y_l}$	$\dfrac{-h_{21}y_l}{h_{22} + y_l}$	$\dfrac{g_{21}}{\Delta^g + g_{11}z_l}$	$\dfrac{1}{a_{22} + a_{21}z_l}$	$\dfrac{\Delta^b}{b_{11} + b_{12}z_l}$

Matrix Interrelations for the Transistor

$$\Delta = r_e r_b + r_c(r_e + r_b(1-a)).$$

	Grounded-Emitter	Grounded-Base	Grounded-Collector
[z]	$\begin{bmatrix} r_e + r_b, & r_e \\ r_e - ar_c, & r_e + r_c(1-a) \end{bmatrix}$	$\begin{bmatrix} r_e + r_b, & r_b \\ r_b + ar_c, & r_b + r_c \end{bmatrix}$	$\begin{bmatrix} r_b + r_c, & r_c(1-a) \\ r_c, & r_e + r_c(1-a) \end{bmatrix}$
[y]	$\dfrac{1}{\Delta}\begin{bmatrix} r_e + r_c(1-a), & -r_e \\ -(r_e - ar_c), & r_e + r_b \end{bmatrix}$	$\dfrac{1}{\Delta}\begin{bmatrix} r_b + r_c, & -r_b \\ -(r_b + ar_c), & r_e + r_b \end{bmatrix}$	$\dfrac{1}{\Delta}\begin{bmatrix} r_e + r_c(1-a), & -r_c(1-a) \\ -r_c, & r_b + r_c \end{bmatrix}$
[h]	$\dfrac{1}{r_e + r_c(1-a)}\begin{bmatrix} \Delta, & r_e \\ -(r_e - ar_c), & 1 \end{bmatrix}$	$\dfrac{1}{r_b + r_c}\begin{bmatrix} \Delta, & r_b \\ -(r_b + ar_c), & 1 \end{bmatrix}$	$\dfrac{1}{r_e + r_c(1-a)}\begin{bmatrix} \Delta, & r_c(1-a) \\ -r_c, & 1 \end{bmatrix}$
[g]	$\dfrac{1}{r_e + r_b}\begin{bmatrix} 1, & -r_e \\ r_e - ar_c, & \Delta \end{bmatrix}$	$\dfrac{1}{r_e + r_b}\begin{bmatrix} 1, & -r_b \\ r_b + ar_c, & \Delta \end{bmatrix}$	$\dfrac{1}{r_b + r_c}\begin{bmatrix} 1, & -r_c(1-a) \\ r_c, & \Delta \end{bmatrix}$
[a]	$\dfrac{1}{r_e - ar_c}\begin{bmatrix} r_e + r_b, & \Delta \\ 1, & r_e + r_c(1-a) \end{bmatrix}$	$\dfrac{1}{r_b + ar_c}\begin{bmatrix} r_e + r_b, & \Delta \\ 1, & r_b + r_c \end{bmatrix}$	$\dfrac{1}{r_c}\begin{bmatrix} r_b + r_c, & \Delta \\ 1, & r_e + r_c(1-a) \end{bmatrix}$
[b]	$\dfrac{1}{r_e}\begin{bmatrix} r_e + r_c(1-a), & \Delta \\ 1, & r_e + r_b \end{bmatrix}$	$\dfrac{1}{r_b}\begin{bmatrix} r_b + r_c, & \Delta \\ 1, & r_e + r_b \end{bmatrix}$	$\dfrac{1}{r_c(1-a)}\begin{bmatrix} r_e + r_c(1-a), & \Delta \\ 1, & r_b + r_c \end{bmatrix}$

Determinant Interrelations

To \ From	$\rightarrow \Delta^z$	Δ^y	Δ^h	Δ^g	Δ^a	Δ^b
$\downarrow \Delta^z$	Δ^z	$\dfrac{1}{\Delta^y}$	$\dfrac{h_{11}}{h_{22}}$	$\dfrac{g_{22}}{g_{11}}$	$\dfrac{a_{12}}{a_{21}}$	$\dfrac{b_{12}}{b_{21}}$
Δ^y	$\dfrac{1}{\Delta^z}$	Δ^y	$\dfrac{h_{22}}{h_{11}}$	$\dfrac{g_{11}}{g_{22}}$	$\dfrac{a_{21}}{a_{12}}$	$\dfrac{b_{21}}{b_{12}}$
Δ^h	$\dfrac{z_{11}}{z_{22}}$	$\dfrac{y_{22}}{y_{11}}$	Δ^h	$\dfrac{1}{\Delta^g}$	$\dfrac{a_{11}}{a_{22}}$	$\dfrac{b_{22}}{b_{11}}$
Δ^g	$\dfrac{z_{22}}{z_{11}}$	$\dfrac{y_{11}}{y_{22}}$	$\dfrac{1}{\Delta^h}$	Δ^g	$\dfrac{a_{22}}{a_{11}}$	$\dfrac{b_{11}}{b_{22}}$
Δ^a	$\dfrac{z_{12}}{z_{21}}$	$\dfrac{y_{12}}{y_{21}}$	$-\dfrac{h_{12}}{h_{21}}$	$-\dfrac{g_{12}}{g_{21}}$	Δ^a	$\dfrac{1}{\Delta_b}$
Δ^b	$\dfrac{z_{21}}{z_{12}}$	$\dfrac{y_{21}}{y_{12}}$	$-\dfrac{h_{21}}{h_{12}}$	$-\dfrac{g_{21}}{g_{12}}$	$\dfrac{1}{\Delta^a}$	Δ^b

15.8   Problems

1. (a) Set up the z matrix for the configuration of Fig. 15.37. From this matrix, set up the h matrix. (b) Set up the h matrix of the network without use of the z or y matrices.

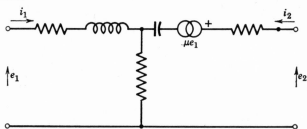

Fig. 15.37   Network configuration for problem 1.

2. Set up the a matrix for an ideal transformer, of turns ratio $1:k$.

3. Given a junction and a whisker-type transistor, with the following properties:

(a) Junction	(b) Whisker
$a = 0.95$	$a = 2.0$
$r_e = 45\ \Omega$	$r_e = 150\ \Omega$
$r_b = 100\ \Omega$	$r_b = 500\ \Omega$
$r_c = 10^6\ \Omega$	$r_c = 10^4\ \Omega$

The two are to be connected in parallel, both in a grounded-emitter configuration. What value of load resistance must be used so as to produce an infinite input im-

pedance for the parallel combination? What is the voltage amplification under
this condition?

4. (a) Given the multiloop amplifier in Fig. 15.38. How would you proceed to
attack this problem? (b) Given the h matrix for two transistors, it is required to

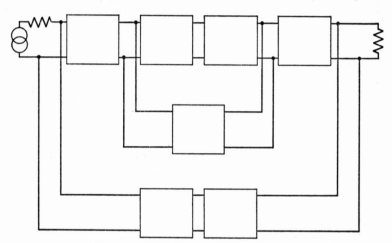

Fig. 15.38   Multiloop amplifier (problem 4).

connect them in series-parallel. Can the matrix of this circuit be obtained by the
addition of the h matrices? If not, how must they be connected so as not to invalidate the matrices?

5. (a) Obtain the equivalent π for the parallel combination of Fig. 15.39 (a) and
(b). (b) Obtain the equivalent T.

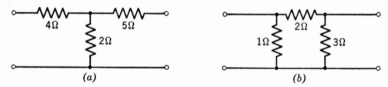

Fig. 15.39   T and π networks (problem 5).

6. Obtain the cathode-follower equivalent of a grounded-collector transistor
circuit. Under what conditions is this equivalent circuit physically realizable?

Fig. 15.40   Circuit for problem 7.

7. (a) Given Fig. 15.40. If $z_i = z_g$ and $z_o = z_l$, find z_i and z_o in terms of the
network. Express the result in terms of the g matrix. Note: Networks where the

above relations are satisfied are said to be terminated on an image parameter basis.

(b) Find the ratio $\dfrac{\text{(volt-amperes delivered to the load)}}{\text{(volt-amperes delivered to the network)}}$ for this condition.

8. Find the network dual for the circuit of Fig. 15.41 for a transformation resistance of 4.472 ohms. The figure is labeled in ohms, henries, and farads. If the

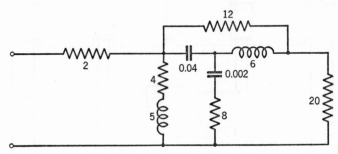

Fig. 15.41   Circuit for problem 8.

input impedance of the above network is z_i, what is the input impedance of the dual network?

15.9   Bibliography

1. F. Strecker and R. Feldtkeller, "Grundlagen der Theorie des allgemeinen Vierpols," *Elektrische Nachrichten Technik, 6,* 93 (1929).

2. L. A. Pipes, "The Matrix Theory of Four-Terminal Networks," *Phil. Mag., 30,* 370 (1940).

3. E. A. Guillemin, *Communication Networks,* Vol. 2, John Wiley & Sons, New York, 1935.

4. J. S. Brown and F. D. Bennet, "The Application of Matrices to Vacuum Tube Circuits," *Proc. IRE, 36,* 844 (1948).

5. LeCorbeiller, *Matrix Analysis of Electrical Networks,* Harvard University Press, Cambridge, Mass., 1950.

6. L. C. Peterson, "Equivalent Circuits of Linear Active Four-Terminal Networks," *Bell Sys. Tech. J., 27,* No. 4, pp. 593–622 (October, 1948).

7. E. A. Guillemin, *The Mathematics of Circuit Analysis,* pp. 37–75, John Wiley & Sons, New York, 1949.

8. R. L. Wallace and G. Raisbeck, "Duality as a Guide in Transistor Circuit Design," *Bell Sys. Tech. J.,* April, 1951.

Chapter 16

Feedback Amplifiers

16.1 Introduction

It is of considerable interest to note that the development of a transistor follows a close parallel with that of its predecessor, the vacuum tube. In the early stages of development of both these devices, most of the emphasis was laid on the amplifying properties of the device. With advances in transistor development, a stage has been reached where it is possible to secure any practical value of amplification. The emphasis next moves to the development of the other properties of the device. Properties such as stability under varying power supply conditions, stability to parameter variation, freedom from non-linearities and their attendant modulation effects—all these begin to assume increasing importance. It is at this stage that the application of feedback methods, specifically degenerative feedback methods where amplifier gain is traded for one or more of the other desirable qualities, may be entertained seriously.

16.2 Differences between Transistors and Vacuum Tubes

Before studying the circuits for attaining feedback, it is advisable to emphasize the difference between these two devices. Perhaps the most important difference is that whereas the maximum available power gain of a transistor stage is of the order of 40 db that of a vacuum tube operating over the same frequency range is considerably higher. This affects the entire approach to the problem of designing the amplifier, and of putting feedback around it. The design of a vacuum-tube amplifier may be taken up strictly as the design of a voltage amplifier, with all networks designed on a voltage transfer basis, and the entire burden of power amplification left to the output stage, which is designed to transfer power into the load efficiently. With a transistor amplifier, each stage must be designed for power transfer.

In a vacuum tube, a change of voltage on the control element produces a change in the output; in a transistor, a change of current to the control element serves to effect this purpose. We see then that, whereas a voltage must be fed back for vacuum-tube circuits, a current must be fed back in transistor circuits. This again shows up an essential difference between the corresponding circuits. In vacuum-tube amplifiers it is usually possible to design the feedback loop at such an impedance level that it neither loads the output circuit appreciably nor has an appreciable transmission in the forward direction. With transistor amplifiers, this is usually not the case.

16.3   Elementary Theory of Feedback

16.3.1   Current Ratio of a Feedback Amplifier

The elementary feedback configuration takes the form of an amplifier with a vector current ratio of $\mathbf{A}^0$ and between the input and output terminals of which is connected a four-terminal network. See Fig. 16.1.

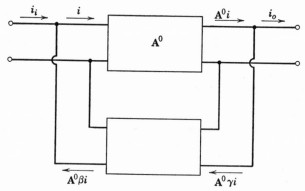

Fig. 16.1   Elementary feedback configuration.

Let γ be the percentage of the output current of the amplifier that is fed back to the network, and let β be the percentage of the output current of the amplifier that is fed back to the input of the amplifier. Then

$$i_o = \mathbf{A}^0 i (1 - \gamma) \qquad [16.1]$$

$$i = i_i + \mathbf{A}^0 \beta i \qquad [16.2]$$

whence

$$\frac{i_o}{i_i} = \mathbf{A}_i = \frac{\mathbf{A}^0 (1 - \gamma)}{1 - \mathbf{A}^0 \beta} \qquad [16.3]$$

This is the expression for the current ratio of a feedback amplifier. In commonly encountered feedback amplifiers, the quantity $|\gamma/\beta| \geq 1$, and, since all that the term γ does is to further reduce the gain, it is

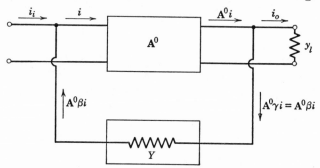

Fig. 16.2 Simplified version of feedback configuration.

usual to assume a two-terminal network for the feedback, as shown in Fig. 16.2.

With such a network, $\beta = \gamma$, and we have

$$\mathbf{A}_i = \mathbf{A}^0(1 - \beta)/(1 - \mathbf{A}^0\beta) \qquad [16.4]$$

16.3.2 Current Ratio for Large Values of $\mathbf{A}^0\beta$

$$\mathbf{A}_i = \mathbf{A}^0(1 - \beta)/(1 - \mathbf{A}^0\beta)$$

$$= [(1 - \beta)/\beta]\mathbf{A}^0\beta/(1 - \mathbf{A}^0\beta) \qquad [16.5]$$

For high-gain amplifiers with large amounts of feedback,

$$(\mathbf{A}^0\beta)_R \gg 1$$

whence

$$\mathbf{A}_i = (\beta - 1)/\beta \qquad [16.6]$$

Thus the current ratio of such an amplifier is determined by the transmission through the β loop.

16.3.3 Parameter Stability

Let us say that for some reason, such as aging of transistors or deterioration of the power supply, the current ratio $\mathbf{A}^0$ should change. What is the effect on the overall ratio? We have

$$\frac{i_o}{i_i} = \frac{\mathbf{A}^0(1 - \beta)}{1 - \mathbf{A}^0\beta} \qquad [16.7]$$

$$\frac{di_o}{d\mathbf{A}^0} = \frac{1 - \mathbf{A}^0\beta + \mathbf{A}^0\beta}{(1 - \mathbf{A}^0\beta)^2}(1 - \beta)i_i \qquad [16.8]$$

whence

$$\frac{di_o}{i_o} = \frac{1}{1 - \mathbf{A}^0\beta} \cdot \frac{d\mathbf{A}^0}{\mathbf{A}^0} \qquad [16.9]$$

Since $d\mathbf{A}^0/\mathbf{A}^0$ is the relative change in the current ratio without feedback, and di_o/i_o is the relative change with feedback, the application of degenerative feedback modifies the variation in this ratio by a factor $1/(1 - \mathbf{A}^0\beta)$. Note that the current ratio is, however, modified by the factor $(1 - \beta)/(1 - \mathbf{A}^0\beta)$.

In like manner we can show that there is a reduction in the noise and hum levels by the application of feedback.

16.3.4   Stability

Using matrix methods as outlined in Chapter 15, it is possible to obtain the general stability criterion for a closed loop system. The simplified form of this criterion may be stated as follows: If a plot of $-\mathbf{A}^0\beta$ is made in the complex $-\mathbf{A}^0\beta$ plane, oscillation will occur if this plot encloses the point $-1 \pm j0$. This criterion is similar in form to Nyquist's criterion for vacuum-tube amplifiers.

16.3.5   The Elementary Theory

It is interesting to investigate certain assumptions made in applying the above theory, together with their validity.

(a) Loading effect of γ on $\mathbf{A}^0$ is neglected. In vacuum-tube amplifiers, as mentioned earlier, the impedance level at which the feedback loop is designed is often such that the loading is negligible.

(b) The input impedance of the amplifier is neglected in computing the value of β. The value of β is a function both of the load impedance and of the impedance of the β network as seen from the load end. This latter impedance is in itself a function of β, and, as an accurate computation of β leads to considerable complication, its value is simply computed as

$$\beta = \frac{Y}{Y + y_l} \qquad [16.10]$$

with the approximation that the input impedance is negligible for this calculation. Using this approximation, $\mathbf{A}^0$ is redefined as the current ratio of the amplifier without feedback, for a load of $Y + y_l$.

(c) Direct transmission through the feedback loop is neglected. In transistor amplifiers this can be of considerable importance. It will be shown that direct transmission effects can be neglected when

$$\frac{z_i^0{}_{(sc)}}{\mathbf{A}^0{}_{sc}z_l} \ll 1 \qquad [16.11]$$

where $z_i{}^0{}_{(sc)}$ is the short-circuit input impedance of the amplifier alone, $\mathbf{A}^0{}_{sc}$ is the short-circuit current ratio of the amplifier alone, and $z_l = 1/y_l$.

The analysis for this may be easily made by the use of matrix algebra.

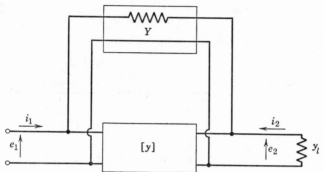

Fig. 16.3   Matrix representation of elementary feedback configuration.

For the amplifier (Fig. 16.3) we have

$$\begin{bmatrix} y_{11} & y_{12} \\ y_{21} & y_{22} \end{bmatrix} \qquad [16.12]$$

Let Δ^y = determinant of the array.   For the feedback loop,

$$\begin{bmatrix} Y & -Y \\ -Y & Y \end{bmatrix} \qquad [16.13]$$

For the combination,

$$\begin{bmatrix} y_{11} + Y, & y_{12} - Y \\ y_{21} - Y, & y_{22} + Y \end{bmatrix} \qquad [16.14]$$

Let Δ = determinant of this array.   Then

$$\Delta = \Delta^y + Y(y_{11} + y_{12} + y_{21} + y_{22}) \qquad [16.15]$$

Using the table of relations for the two-terminal pair with terminations, we have

$$\mathbf{A}_i = -\frac{i_2}{i_1} = -\frac{(y_{21} - Y)y_l}{\Delta + (y_{11} + Y)y_l} \qquad [16.16]$$

Making the approximation here that the input impedance is negligible compared to the impedance of the feedback loop, we have

$$\beta = \frac{Y}{Y + y_l} \qquad [16.17]$$

and

$$\mathbf{A}^0 = -\frac{y_{21}(Y + y_l)}{\Delta^y + y_{11}(Y + y_l)} \qquad [16.18]$$

since the load admittance is $Y + y_l$. Then

$$\mathbf{A}_i = -\frac{y_{21}(Y + y_l)}{\Delta^y + y_{11}(Y + y_l)} \frac{1 - Y\left[\dfrac{y_l + y_{21}}{y_{21}(Y + y_l)}\right]}{\left[1 + \dfrac{Y(y_{11} + y_{12} + y_{21} + y_{22} + y_l)}{\Delta^y + y_{11}(Y + y_l)}\right]}$$

$$= \mathbf{A}^0 \frac{1 - \beta\left(1 + \dfrac{y_l}{y_{21}}\right)}{1 + \dfrac{y_{21}(Y + y_l)}{\Delta^y + y_{11}(Y + y_l)}\left(\dfrac{Y}{Y + y_l}\right)\left(1 + \dfrac{y_l}{y_{21}} + \dfrac{y_{12} + y_{22}}{y_{21}}\right)}$$

$$= \mathbf{A}^0 \frac{1 - \beta\left(1 + \dfrac{y_l}{y_{21}}\right)}{1 - \mathbf{A}^0\beta\left(1 + \dfrac{y_l}{y_{21}} + \dfrac{y_{12} + y_{22}}{y_{21}}\right)} \qquad [16.19]$$

For the grounded-base or grounded-emitter connections,

$$\frac{y_{12} + y_{21}}{y_{22}} \ll 1 \qquad [16.20]$$

and may therefore be neglected if we confine the analysis to circuits where the last stage around which feedback is taken is one of the above types.

$$\frac{y_l}{y_{21}} = \frac{y_{11}}{y_{21}} \cdot \frac{y_l}{y_{11}}$$

$$= -\frac{z_i^0{}_{(sc)}}{\mathbf{A}^0{}_{sc} z_l} \qquad [16.21]$$

since the short-circuit current ratio of a four-terminal network is given by $-y_{21}/y_{11}$.

Since

$$\mathbf{A}_i = \mathbf{A}^0\left[\frac{1 - \beta(1 + y_l/y_{21})}{1 - \mathbf{A}^0\beta(1 + y_l/y_{21})}\right]$$

if forward transmission through the β loop is considered, and

$$\mathbf{A}_i = \mathbf{A}^0 \frac{1 - \beta}{1 - \mathbf{A}^0 \beta}$$

when this is neglected, we can say then that the term

$$\frac{y_l}{y_{21}} = -\frac{z_i^0{}_{(\mathrm{sc})}}{\mathbf{A}^0{}_{\mathrm{sc}} z_l} \qquad [16.21a]$$

contributes to the forward transmission through the β loop.

16.4   High-Frequency Behavior of Transistor Parameters

When a transistor is operated in the region where transit time effects become apparent, the parameters attain non-scalar values and become frequency-dependent. Their behavior is discussed in detail in Chapter 9, but the details that have a bearing on stability will be repeated here. Care must be taken in designing the transistor circuit so that it is stable at all frequencies even though it will be used only over its midband, and an analytical formulation for the stability at high frequencies, though exceedingly complex, is essential if an accurate analysis is to be made. It is generally more convenient to make the stability analysis using approximate formulations for the high-frequency effects, and then to make qualitative adjustments.

16.4.1   Behavior of α

Figure 16.4 shows a plot of α (full line) in the α plane. For comparison, a plot of $\alpha_0/(1 + \tau_\alpha p)$ is also shown (dotted line), where τ_α = time constant corresponding to α cut-off and $p = j\omega$.

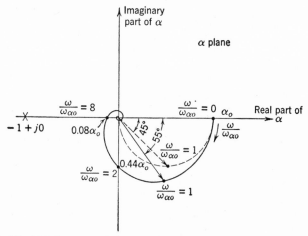

Fig. 16.4   The high-frequency behavior of α, together with an approximate representation.

16.4.2   Behavior of $\alpha/(1-\alpha)$

The behavior of $\alpha/(1-\alpha)$ is shown in Fig. 16.5. As α approaches unity, the initial phase lead forms a larger and more sharply defined peak, and the zero frequency value increases. At high frequencies, $\alpha/(1-\alpha)$ converges on the α locus.

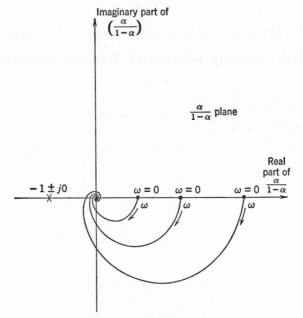

Fig. 16.5   High-frequency behavior of $\alpha/(1-\alpha)$.

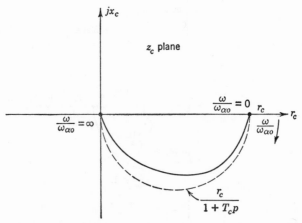

Fig. 16.6   High-frequency behavior of r_c, with an approximate representation.

16.4.3   Behavior of Collector Impedance

At high frequencies, the shunting effect of the collector capacitance assumes importance. Also, both r_c and C_c fall off with frequency, so that the behavior of the z_c locus in the z_c plane is of the form shown in Fig. 16.6. The dotted locus is that formed by a parallel RC network and is shown for comparison. T_c is its time constant.

16.5   Typical Circuits

We will now show a few of the methods of applying feedback to transistor amplifiers, and analyze them very briefly. The grounded-emitter circuit is considerably more useful for junction transistor applications, and emphasis will be placed on this type of configuration.

16.5.1   Shunt-Type Feedback   (See Fig. 16.7.)

Since the grounded-emitter circuit has a 180° phase shift in the region where high-frequency effects are negligible, such a circuit supplies negative feedback. The behavior of this circuit is very similar

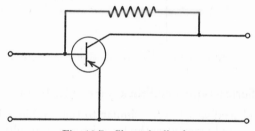

Fig. 16.7   Shunt feedback.

to that of a grounded-cathode vacuum tube with plate-to-grid feedback. For such a circuit we have, as a result of the feedback, a reduction in gain and in input impedance as well as in output impedance.

Since the current ratio of a grounded-emitter amplifier is approximately

$$\mathbf{A}_i \cong - \frac{a z_c}{z_c(1 - a) + r_l} \qquad [16.22]$$

its locus is of the same shape as that for $\alpha/(1 - \alpha)$. The effect of r_l is to lower the effective α for the circuit. If the feedback is resistive, the $-\mathbf{A}^0\beta$ diagram is, qualitatively, as shown in Fig. 16.8.

The effect of β is to shrink the diagram still further since $\beta < 1$. Clearly, even if the feedback were such as to produce a 90° phase lag or lead at high frequencies, the effect would be to rotate the high-frequency end of the diagram through 90°, and the network would still be stable. However, the network may be made unstable by reversing the phase of the feedback.

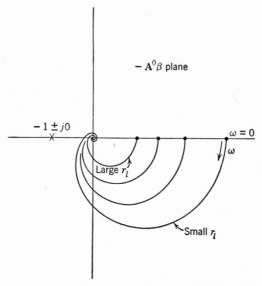

Fig. 16.8 $A^0\beta$ diagram for the circuit of Fig. 16.7.

16.5.2   Series-Type Feedback   (See Fig. 16.9.)

This type of feedback is very similar to that employed with a vacuum tube with unbypassed cathode resistor. It results in increased

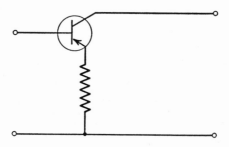

Fig. 16.9   Series feedback.

input and output impedances, and decreased gain. With such a circuit we cannot separate the A^0 and β terms, and so an elementary theory of feedback is insufficient in determining its stability.

16.5.3 Multistage Series or Shunt Feedback

The number of combinations of the above circuits is legion, and it serves no purpose to sketch more than one of each type.   Figure 16.10

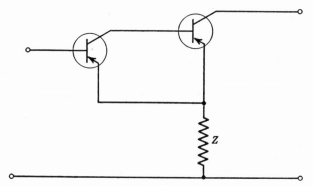

Fig. 16.10   Multistage series feedback.

shows a two-stage amplifier with series feedback, which resembles a cathode-coupled vacuum-tube amplifier in its behavior.

Figure 16.11 shows a multistage amplifier with shunt feedback. The behavior of such an amplifier resembles that of a multistage vacuum-tube amplifier with the added complication of the phase

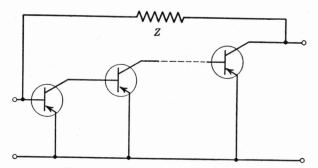

Fig. 16.11   Multistage shunt feedback.

shift of $\alpha/(1 - \alpha)$ outside the midband.   The behavior of z_c is of secondary importance in that this term usually appears in both numerator and denominator, and its effects tend to cancel.

16.6 Discussion of Elementary Theory

The foregoing has demonstrated a reasonably simple approach to the feedback problem, together with some of its weakness.   It is shown that the simple theory is adequate for the analysis of feedback loops when forward transmission through the β loop and input impedance of the amplifier are neglected. These conditions are completely violated in the very common type of feedback amplifier shown in Fig. 16.9.

It is easy to see that, with devices such as transistors, a general approach to the problem will be a very powerful tool. One means of obtaining a solution is matrix algebra; this is discussed in considerable detail in Chapter 15.

At the present time there is in existence a general feedback theory for vacuum-tube amplifier circuits.[1] It will now be shown that, after making certain redefinitions of some of the basic factors involved, this theory can also be applied to transistor circuits.

16.7 A General Feedback Theory for Transistor Amplifiers

Figure 16.12 shows any one transistor in a generalized circuit.

The equivalent circuit is shown in Fig. 16.13. The behavior of the device may now be expressed by thinking of the junction as something

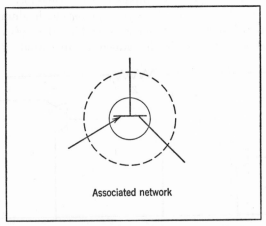

Associated network

Fig. 16.12   Generalized transistor network, showing one transistor in particular.

remote from the three resistances associated with it. Then, any current in the emitter leg, from $Y \rightarrow X$, shows up as a proportionate voltage in the collector side. The voltage of this generator is given by W times the current in $Y \rightarrow X$. W has the dimensions of impedance.

The loop equations for the entire network may now be set up. With currents i_5 and i_6 marked as shown, the terms involving W are restricted to, say, row 6, column 5, in the impedance matrix equation. Now, expanding the determinant about row 6, we have

$$\Delta = z_{61}\Delta_{61} + z_{62}\Delta_{62} + \cdots z_{65}\Delta_{65} + \cdots \qquad [16.23]$$

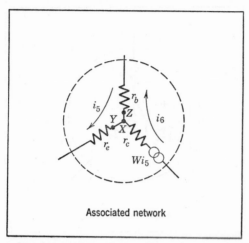

Associated network

Fig. 16.13   Equivalent circuit of Fig. 16.12.

where z_{61}, z_{62}, $\cdots$ are impedance elements of the sixth row, and Δ_{61}, Δ_{62}, $\cdots$ are the corresponding cofactors. Since terms involving W are restricted to row 6, column 5, let

$$z_{65} = z_{65}' + W \qquad [16.24]$$

Then

$$\Delta = z_{61}\Delta_{61} + z_{62}\Delta_{62} + \cdots z_{65}'\Delta_{65} + \cdots + W\Delta_{65} \qquad [16.25]$$

But

$$z_{61}\Delta_{61} + z_{62}\Delta_{62} + \cdots z_{65}'\Delta_{65} + \cdots$$

$$= \text{value of } \Delta \quad \text{when } W = 0 \quad [16.26]$$

$$= \Delta^0$$

Therefore

$$\Delta = \Delta^0 + W\Delta_{65} \qquad [16.27]$$

The transistor may be replaced by a T network of three resistances, with the generator replaced by e_6. If there are no external sources, and since $W = 0$,

$$i_5 = e_6\Delta_{65}/\Delta^0 \qquad [16.28]$$

Therefore current in the junction is Δ_{65}/Δ^0 times the voltage appearing in the collector circuit due to this current.

The above will also hold for an operative transistor whose junction is bypassed by a short circuit from $Y \to Z$, as in Fig. 16.14. If unit current is forced into $Y \to X$, we have a voltage W appearing in the

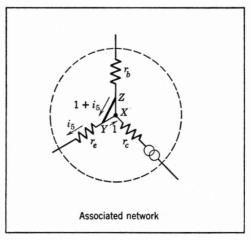

Associated network

Fig. 16.14 Equivalent circuit of Fig. 16.12, showing point of short circuit, and insertion of unit current.

collector circuit, and the current i_5 is obtained from eq. 16.28 as

$$i_5 = W \cdot 1 \cdot \Delta_{65}/\Delta^0 \qquad [16.29]$$

$$\text{Current in the short circuit} = 1 + i_5 = 1 + W\Delta_{65}/\Delta^0 \qquad [16.30]$$

$$= \Delta/\Delta^0 \qquad [16.31]$$

In order to maintain uniformity with Bode's terminology, the current i_5 is called the return ratio T, and $1 + i_5$ is called the return difference F.

Using the altered definitions for these two quantities it is now possible for us to apply all the theorems developed for vacuum-tube amplifiers.

16.8 Stability

16.8.1 Stability Considerations

Let us consider any network, and in this network one particular current i_n. If this network has only one impressed voltage, say e_m, then

$$i_n = e_m \Delta_{mn}/\Delta \qquad [16.32]$$

If e_m were made equal to zero, there would still exist various perturbation currents in the network. An investigation of the stability of the network is an investigation of these perturbations and their behavior in time. If they die out with time, the network is stable; if they increase with time, the network is unstable. The borderline case, where they neither increase nor decrease, is never encountered in practice but must be considered for mathematical reasons. Let us define this borderline behavior as stable.

Using the operator p, both Δ_{mn} and Δ are polynomials in p, and we have

$$i_n = e_m \frac{a_r p^r + a_{r-1} p^{r-1} + \cdots}{a_s p^s + a_{s-1} p^{s-1} + \cdots} \qquad [16.33]$$

Since e_m is to be set equal to zero, the differential equation of the network may be written

$$(a_s p^s + a_{s-1} p^{s-1} + \cdots) i_n = 0$$

Factorizing, we have

$$[(p - p_1)(p - p_2)(p - p_3) \cdots] i_n = 0 \qquad [16.34]$$

where p_1, p_2, $\cdots$ are solutions of the equation $\Delta = 0$ and are in general complex quantities. Then, the solution for [16.34] is

$$i_n = A e^{p_1 t} + B e^{p_2 t} + C e^{p_3 t} + \cdots \qquad [16.35]$$

if $p_1 \neq p_2 \neq p_3 \cdots$

Let us investigate this solution. For any term, let

$$p_i = \gamma_i + j\omega_i \qquad [16.36]$$

Then

$$A_i e^{p_i t} = A_i e^{\gamma_i t} e^{j\omega_i t} \qquad [16.37]$$

If γ_i is negative, the term decays in time. If γ_i is positive, the term increases in time. If γ_i is zero, the term is the borderline case and neither increases nor decreases. If ω_i is zero, the term is exponential in shape. If ω_i is non-zero, the term is oscillatory. Figure 16.15 shows the various types encountered.

The case where multiple roots occur is also to be considered. If the solutions of the equation $\Delta = 0$ are such that, say, $p_1 = p_2$, the equation for the perturbation currents is

$$i_n = A e^{p_1 t} + B t e^{p_2 t} + C e^{p_3 t} + \cdots \qquad [16.38]$$

In general, if we have a root of multiplicity n, the solution of the differential equation contains a term of the form $K t^{n-1} e^{pt}$.

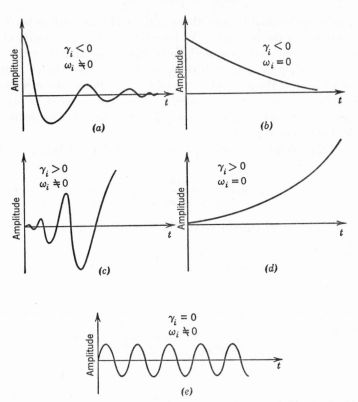

Fig. 16.15 Behavior of perturbation currents in (a) and (b) a stable circuit, (c) and (d) an unstable circuit, (e) a borderline circuit, defined as stable.

A sketch of the shape of these functions shows that their behavior with time is of approximately the same form as that for the non-repeated terms; the stability considerations are therefore the same in either case. Clearly, the condition for stability is satisfied in (a) and (b), and (e) of Fig. 16.15, and this is that the real parts of all the zeros of Δ are less than or equal to zero. Thus, if the zeros of Δ are plotted in the p plane, the network is stable if all points lie in the left half of this plane or on the boundary. Thus, if a search is made of the left half of the p plane, and all zeros are found there, the network is stable. Alternatively, if a search is made of the right half of the p plane, and *no* zeros are found, the network is stable. This latter method is the one that we shall use.

Writing Δ as a function of a complex variable $f(z)$, we have

$$f(z) = Ae^{jB} \qquad\qquad [16.39]$$

A and B are, respectively, the magnitude and phase angle of $f(z)$. Then

$$\ln f(z) = \ln A + \ln e^{jB} \qquad [16.40]$$

$$= \ln A + jB \qquad [16.41]$$

Since

$$\frac{d}{dz} \ln f(z) = \frac{f'(z)}{f(z)} \qquad [16.42]$$

we have

$$\frac{d}{dz} (\ln A + jB) = \frac{f'(z)}{f(z)} \qquad [16.43]$$

$$\oint \left[\frac{d}{dz} \ln A + j \frac{dB}{dz} \right] dz = \oint \frac{f'(z)}{f(z)} dz \qquad [16.44]$$

Then

$$\frac{1}{2\pi j} \oint \frac{f'(z)}{f(z)} dz = \frac{1}{2\pi j} \oint \left(\frac{d}{dz} \ln A + j \frac{dB}{dz} \right) dz \qquad [16.45]$$

But

$$\frac{1}{2\pi j} \oint \frac{f'(z)}{f(z)} dz = N - P \qquad [16.46]$$

where N is the number of zeros and P is the number of poles enclosed in the interior of the path of integration, each point counted as often as its order requires.[2]   Therefore,

$$\frac{1}{2\pi j} \oint \left(\frac{d}{dz} \ln A \right) dz + \frac{1}{2\pi j} \oint \left(j \frac{dB}{dz} \right) dz = N - P \qquad [16.47]$$

The integral on the left-hand side may be interpreted as follows: The first term is the difference in magnitude of $f(z)$ at the beginning and end of the path of integration.   Since this path of integration is a closed one, this term is zero.   The second term, then, is the total phase angle of $f(z)$ over the path.   Then

$$\frac{1}{2\pi} [\text{Phase shift}] = N - P \qquad [16.48]$$

Thus, if $f(z)$ is a single-valued regular function, and if the point z is moved over a closed path, in the positive direction, the number of zeros minus poles of $f(z)$ encountered in this region is given by the number of times the $f(z)$ plot in the $f(z)$ plane encloses the origin in a positive direction. Thus, if the entire right half p plane is enclosed by a path, the corresponding Δ plot in the plane must not enclose the origin for the network to be stable.

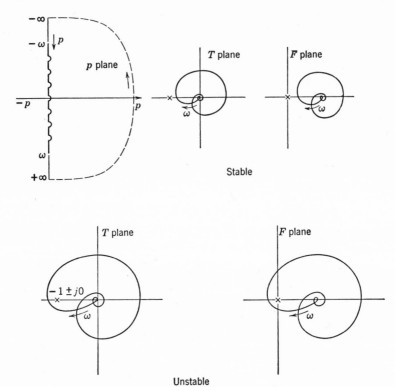

Fig. 16.16 (a) Plot of the right half p-plane. (b) and (c) Corresponding T and F plots for a stable circuit. (d) and (e) Corresponding T and F plots for an unstable circuit.

16.8.2 Single Loop Case

Consider a network which is known to be stable if a certain transistor is rendered inoperative (by making $\alpha = 0$). Then the network determinant Δ^0 can have no zeros in the right half of the p plane.

Since $F = \Delta/\Delta^0$, a plot of F in the F plane will therefore indicate stability if and only if it does not enclose the origin when p traverses the right half of the p plane. Since $F = 1 + T$, a similar plot for T gives the same information, with the critical point at $-1 \pm j0$. Figure 16.16 serves to show a few typical plots.

In traversing the right half of the p plane, we must be careful to avoid all poles known to be on the borderline. This may be done by going around them in semicircles of radius ϵ where ϵ is made vanish ingly small.

16.8.3 Multiloop Analysis

In a multiloop mesh, it is not enough to construct the F or T plot for one transistor, since these plots only give information on the zeros of Δ provided information is known on the behavior of Δ^0. In this case, we keep rendering transistors inoperative until we are sure the circuit is stable, and then start at this point. Let us say that we have an n-stage amplifier, and m transistors must be rendered inoperative for the circuit to be stable. Let

Δ_i = network determinant when there are i transistors rendered inoperative

F_i = return difference for the ith transistor with $i - 1$ transistors rendered inoperative

Then

$$F_i = \Delta_{i-1}/\Delta_i \qquad\qquad [16.49]$$

and

$$F_{m-1} = \Delta_{m-2}/\Delta_{m-1} \qquad\qquad [16.50]$$

$$F_{m-2} = \Delta_{m-3}/\Delta_{m-2} \qquad\qquad [16.51]$$

$$\vdots$$

$$F_2 = \Delta_1/\Delta_2 \qquad\qquad [16.52]$$

$$F_1 = \Delta/\Delta_1 \qquad\qquad [16.53]$$

Thus, a plot of F_m gives information on Δ_{m-1}, since Δ_m is for a stable network. With this information, F_{m-1} may be plotted to obtain information on Δ_{m-2}, and so on until finally the information on Δ is obtained. The criterion for determining stability may be written as follows:

Render the network stable by making as many transistors as necessary inoperative. Now, replacing the transistors one by one, plot the F or T locus in each case, until all are replaced. Then, the network is stable if the algebraic sum of *all* the clockwise and counterclockwise encirclements of the critical point is zero.

16.9   Impedance [3]

16.9.1   Impedance in Active Networks

Figure 16.17 shows a multimesh network. It is required to find the impedance looking into any branch. Making a cut in the branch, in-

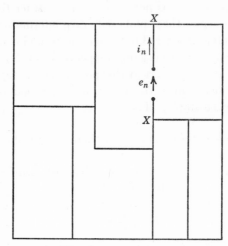

Fig. 16.17   Line diagram of a general network.

sert a generator e_n, and write the loop equations so that this branch is in only one loop. Then

$$i_n = e_n \Delta_{nn}/\Delta \qquad\qquad [16.54]$$

Therefore

$$z_n = e_n/i_n = \Delta/\Delta_{nn} \qquad\qquad [16.55]$$

Let us see how z_n is tied in with the behavior of a particular transistor in the circuit. For this transistor,

$$z_n = \Delta/\Delta_{nn} = (\Delta/\Delta^0)(\Delta^0/\Delta^0_{nn})(\Delta^0_{nn}/\Delta_{nn}) \qquad\qquad [16.56]$$

The above factors are interpreted as follows:

(a) Δ/Δ^0 is the return difference for this transistor in the original circuit, i.e., for the circuit obtained if the voltage e_n were shorted. We define this quantity as F_{sc}.

(b) Δ^0/Δ^0_{nn} has the value of Δ/Δ_{nn} when W for this transistor is zero. But

$$\Delta/\Delta_{nn} = z_n \qquad\qquad [16.57]$$

and so Δ^0/Δ^0_{nn} may be interpreted as the impedance z_n when the transistor in question is inoperative. We define this quantity as $z_n{}^0$.

(c) $\Delta_{nn}/\Delta^0{}_{nn}$ is the same as the return difference Δ/Δ^0 when row n, column n, is deleted. This is the same as if the generator e_n were replaced by an open circuit, and so we may define

$$\Delta_{nn}/\Delta^0{}_{nn} \qquad \text{as} \qquad F_{\text{oc}} \qquad\qquad [16.58]$$

whence

$$z_n = z_n{}^0 \frac{F_{\text{sc}}}{F_{\text{oc}}} \qquad\qquad [16.59]$$

In like manner, the admittance across XX may be set up as

$$y_n = y_n{}^0 \frac{F_{\text{oc}}}{F_{\text{sc}}} \qquad\qquad [16.60]$$

A few examples follow.

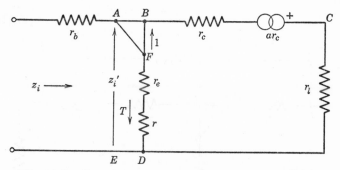

Fig. 16.18   Grounded-emitter transistor with series feedback.

16.9.2   Example of Input Impedance with Series Feedback

Obtain the low-frequency input impedance of a grounded-emitter transistor with series feedback.   Figure 16.18 shows the equivalent circuit.

$$z_i = r_b + z_i' \qquad\qquad [16.61]$$

$$z_i' = z_i'^0 \frac{F_{\text{sc}}}{F_{\text{oc}}} \qquad\qquad [16.62]$$

$$z_i'^0 = z_i'$$

when the transistor is rendered inoperative, i.e., when $a = 0$,

$$= \frac{(r + r_e)(r_c + r_l)}{r + r_e + r_c + r_l} \qquad\qquad [16.63]$$

$$F_{\text{sc}} = 1 + T_{\text{sc}} \qquad\qquad [16.64]$$

T_{sc} is the current flowing in $F \rightarrow D$ when unit current is forced in

$F \to B$ and a short circuit is placed across AE. Under this condition the current path is $C \to D \to E \to A \to F \to B \to C$, and clearly $T_{sc} = 0$. Therefore $F_{sc} = 1$. Now:

$$F_{oc} = 1 + T_{oc}$$

T_{oc} is the current flowing in $F \to D$ when unit current is forced in $F \to B$ and AE is open-circuited. Under this condition the current path is $C \to D \to F \to B \to C$, and

$$T_{oc} = \frac{-ar_c}{r + r_e + r_c + r_l} \qquad [16.65]$$

$$F_{oc} = \frac{r + r_e + r_l + r_c(1 - a)}{r + r_e + r_c + r_l} \qquad [16.66]$$

whence

$$z_i = r_b + \frac{(r + r_e)(r_c + r_l)}{r + r_e + r_l + r_c(1 - a)} \qquad [16.67]$$

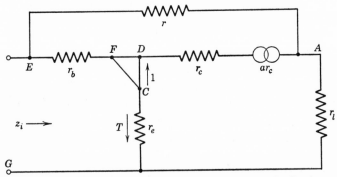

Fig. 16.19   Grounded-emitter transistor with shunt feedback.

16.9.3   Example of Input Impedance with Shunt Feedback

Find the low-frequency input impedance of a grounded-emitter transistor with shunt feedback. The equivalent circuit is shown in Fig.

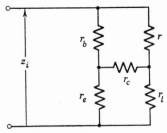

Fig. 16.20   Equivalent passive network for Fig. 16.19.

16.19. For the passive network, we have Fig. 16.20, whence

$$z_i{}^0 = \frac{rr_l(r_e + r_b) + r_e r_b(r + r_l) + r_c(r_e + r_b)(r + r_l)}{(r_e + r_l)(r_b + r) + r_c(r_e + r_b + r + r_l)} \qquad [16.68]$$

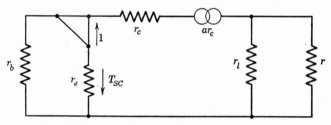

Fig. 16.21   Equivalent circuit for derivation of T_{sc}.

The equivalent circuit for T_{sc} is as shown in Fig. 16.21.   Then

$$T_{sc} = \frac{-ar_c r_b(r + r_l)}{rr_l(r_e + r_b) + r_e r_b(r + r_l) + r_c(r + r_l)(r_e + r_b)} \qquad [16.69]$$

$$F_{sc} = \frac{rr_l(r_e + r_b) + (r + r_l)\Delta}{rr_l(r_e + r_b) + r_e r_b(r + r_l) + r_c(r_e + r_b)(r + r_l)} \qquad [16.70]$$

where

$$\Delta = r_e r_b + r_c[r_e + r_b(1 - a)] \qquad [16.71]$$

also,

$$T_{oc} = \frac{-ar_c(r_b + r)}{(r_e + r_l)(r_b + r) + r_c(r_e + r_b + r + r_l)} \qquad [16.72]$$

whence

$$F_{oc} = \frac{\Delta + r[r_e + r_c(1 - a)] + r_l(r_b + r_c + r)}{(r_e + r_l)(r_b + r) + r_c(r_e + r_b + r + r_l)} \qquad [16.73]$$

In this case the current path is $A \rightarrow E \rightarrow F \rightarrow C \rightarrow D \rightarrow A$ as well as $A \rightarrow B \rightarrow D \rightarrow A$.   Then

$$z_i = z_i{}^0 F_{sc}/F_{oc}$$

$$= \frac{rr_l(r_e + r_b) + \Delta(r + r_l)}{\Delta + r[r_e + r_c(1 - a)] + r_l(r_b + r_c + r)} \qquad [16.74]$$

This agrees with eq. 15.141 previously derived for this circuit.

16.9.4 Approximate Solution of 16.9.3

Obtain an approximate expression for the low-frequency input impedance of a grounded-emitter transistor with shunt feedback.

With reference to Fig. 16.19, assume that

$$r_c \gg r, \quad \gg r_l, \quad \gg r_e, \quad \text{and} \quad \gg r_b \quad [16.75]$$

From inspection of Fig. 16.20, under the conditions of eq. 16.75 we obtain

$$z_i{}^0 \cong \frac{(r_e + r_b)(r + r_l)}{r_e + r_b + r + r_l} \quad [16.76]$$

Since r_c is very much greater than the other parameters, the collector current is dictated by it, and is equal to a, when unit current is forced into the junction. Then

$$T_{sc} \cong \frac{-ar_b}{r_e + r_b} \quad [16.77]$$

$$F_{sc} \cong \frac{r_e + r_b(1 - a)}{r_e + r_b} \quad [16.78]$$

$$T_{oc} \cong \frac{-a(r_b + r)}{r_e + r_b + r + r_l} \quad [16.79]$$

$$F_{oc} \cong \frac{r_e + r_b(1 - a) + r_l + r(1 - a)}{r_e + r_b + r + r_l} \quad [16.80]$$

whence

$$z_i \cong \frac{(r + r_l)[r_e + r_b(1 - a)]}{r_e + r_b(1 - a) + r_l + r(1 - a)} \quad [16.81]$$

This can be easily derived from eq. 16.74 under the conditions of [16.75].

16.10 Problems

1. A transistor amplifier has a low-frequency current amplification of 60 db. It is required to put feedback around the amplifier so as to improve its stability by a factor of 10. What value of β is required? If the load impedance is 1000 ohms, what is the value of the impedance in the β loop?

2. A three-stage grounded-emitter amplifier is shown in Fig. 16.22, with feedback from the output to the input. In the midband region, is this feedback regenerative or degenerative? Draw the $-A^0\beta$ locus for this amplifier, assuming that the parameters of the transistor are frequency-independent. Does this locus indicate stability or instability? If $a = 0.95$, $r_c = 2$ megohms, $r_e = 20$ ohms, $r_b = 1000$ ohms, $r_l = 1000$ ohms, sketch a curve of the behavior of the input impedance as a function of frequency.

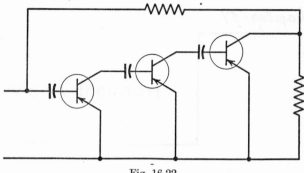

Fig. 16.22.

3. Repeat the above for a two-stage grounded-emitter amplifier.

4. Draw a family of curves showing the overall current amplification of a transistor amplifier with feedback, for a range of β from -1 to $+1$, and a range of A^0 from zero to 20. Compare the results obtained for A^0 less than unity (as is found in a single-stage grounded-base transistor amplifier) with the results obtained for A^0 greater than unity (single-stage grounded-emitter amplifier). (A^0,β scalar.)

5. Modify the $-A^0\beta$ locus of problem 2 so as to indicate the effect of frequency variation of the parameters.

6. Compute the value of F from the value of T for the circuit shown in Fig. 16.23. Check this value of F with that obtained by the expression Δ/Δ^0.

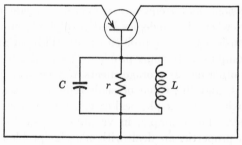

Fig. 16.23.

7. Neglecting all high-frequency effects, plot the T locus for problem 6 where the transistor is a junction type. Investigate the effect of increasing r.

8. Repeat problem 7 for a point-contact unit.

9. Show how to derive the expression for y_n given by eq. 16.60.

16.11   Bibliography

1. H. W. Bode, *Network Analysis and Feedback Amplifier Design*, pp. 44–82, New York, D. Van Nostrand Company, 1946.

2. K. Knopp, *Theory of Functions*, p. 132, Dover Publications.

3. See Bode, pp. 66–68.

Chapter 17

Transient Analysis

17.1 Introduction

The application of transistors to pulse amplifiers, computers, servo-mechanism amplifiers, etc., requires an understanding of transient behavior. All physically realizable mechanisms, whether electrical, mechanical, or acoustical, are subject to energy-storage effects. Thus, the response of a physical system to a suddenly applied force will never be instantaneous. Transient behavior of lumped-parameter R-L-C networks is well known.[1]

Whenever lumped-parameter electrical analogies are possible, the study of transient and frequency response is made comparatively simple. Even when the analogies lead to highly complex circuits, a solution of transient response problems may still be attained by use of an analogue computer. In many problems, the analogue representation of inertia and other energy-storage effects may be dealt with simply in design analysis, and the value of such representation, even if only roughly approximate to the physical case, is always appreciated by the design engineer. For example, in vacuum tubes, the interelectrode energy-storage properties are dealt with in design problems by assuming physical capacitors to exist between the electrodes. A vacuum-tube equivalent circuit, suitable in most examples for transient and frequency response analysis, will therefore contain grid-to-cathode, grid-to-plate, and plate-to-cathode capacitors. When more complex phenomena are involved, such as electron bunching due to space charge, the vacuum-tube lumped-parameter equivalent circuit becomes inadequate as a suitable representation of the physical case. This does not invalidate the use of the simple equivalent circuit, however, provided that its limitations are always kept in mind.

In this chapter, the transient behavior of transistors will be discussed from both a physical and circuit point of view. A simple equivalent circuit, suitable for the representation of a transistor in the study of

366

transient and frequency response, for small signals applied to the transistor input, will be developed. As with the vacuum tube, the limitations of the equivalent circuit must always be kept in mind.

17.2   The Physical Problem

To better understand the basis for the transient response of transistors, consideration of the physical phenomena involved in transistor action is helpful. Although the physics of transistor action was discussed in Chapter 1 the physical problem will be summarized from a slightly different viewpoint here. Figure 17.1 illustrates the electrostatic potential profile of a p-n-p junction transistor which is biased in the usual manner. As is pointed out in Chapter 18, a p-n junction may be thought of as a diode, the forward conduction of which is from the p region to the n region. Although not evident in Fig. 17.1, there is a slight potential rise across the emitter-base junction. However, current will flow freely from the emitter to the base. Practically no potential gradient exists across the base region. The base-collector junction is biased in the inverse diode direction, and thus almost all the potential drop between the external base and collector leads will occur across the base-collector barrier. Hence, the electrostatic potential distribution as a function of distance (x) through the transistor will have the form shown in Fig. 17.1.

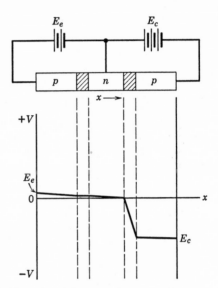

Fig. 17.1   Electrostatic potential profile of a p-n-p junction transistor.

A positive signal current, applied to the emitter of a p-n-p transistor, will cause holes to be injected from the emitter into the base. So that the emitter signal may cause a change in the collector current, these holes must traverse the base region and appear at the base-collector barrier. Since there is virtually no electric potential gradient through the base region, the process of hole travel through the base is essentially one of diffusion. The diffusion is motivated by a concentration gradient rather than an electric field gradient, the concentration of holes being much higher in the base region near the emitter than in the base region near the collector. If all the holes which enter the base from the emitter as the result of a signal current in the emitter were to do so with equal momentum vectors, and if, in the process of traveling through the base region from the emitter to the collector, the holes were to experience no collision or non-uniform field effects, the only result of hole diffusion through the base region would be a time delay between the collector and emitter signals. Such a hypothetical diffusion is illustrated in Fig. 17.2.

Fig. 17.2   Ideal hole diffusion through base region.

In practice, holes moving through the base region of a transistor are subject to many effects which cause individual hole paths to differ greatly. The initial hole momentum vectors are randomly distributed, and this alone would cause path variations. Furthermore, the holes are subject to collision with fixed charges, and are thus subject to non-uniform space charge forces. A more realistic picture of hole diffusion would therefore look like Fig. 17.3.

An apparent result of the random-type motion of holes traversing the base region is that the holes, which may have left the emitter at the

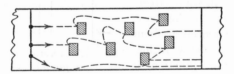

Fig. 17.3   Actual hole diffusion through base region.

same time, tend to arrive at the base-collector barrier at different times. A current pulse at the emitter would cause an instantaneous influx of holes into the base region, but the arrival of the holes at the collector would be spread out over a period of time. Thus, although the holes start out simultaneously from the emitter, they would be dispersed by the time they reached the collector. The dispersion effect in the transistor is analogous to the dispersion of a pulse as it is propagated in a transmission line. In the transmission line, the dispersion effect is treated by considering the line to have distributed capacitance, inductance, and resistance.

Diffusion of holes in the base region of a junction transistor has a striking physical analogy to the diffusion of heat in a thermal conductor or to the flow of a liquid in hydrodynamics. It is reasonable to expect, therefore, that the hole diffusion equation for a transistor will resemble, in form, the well-known equation of continuity of flow,

$$(\partial\rho/\partial t) + \text{div } \mathbf{i} = 0 \qquad\qquad [17.1]$$

where ρ is the fluid or thermal density and $\mathbf{i}$ is its current density. In the three-dimensional case, the divergence of the current vector, $\mathbf{i}$, is

$$\text{div } \mathbf{i} = \partial i_x/\partial x + \partial i_y/\partial y + \partial i_z/\partial z$$

for Cartesian coordinates. Equation 17.1 states that the time rate of change of material density in an elemental volume is due to some unbalanced flow of current, $\mathbf{i}$, across the boundaries of this volume.

Extension of the continuity of flow equation (17.1) to the process of hole diffusion through the base region of a junction transistor may be accomplished directly if the physical hole diffusion phenomena thus far mentioned are the only basis for the equation. To complete the picture, however, consideration must be given to the fact that not all holes which start their journey across the base from the emitter-base junction reach the collector-base barrier. This is because some of the holes are "captured" by electrons, i.e., they combine with electrons and disappear. They are thus ineffective in causing charge flow across the collector-base barrier. In the thermal analogy, hole capture by electrons would be represented by a heat loss. To account for the heat loss, eq. 17.1 may be modified as follows:

$$(\partial\rho/\partial t) + \text{div } \mathbf{i} - r\rho = 0 \qquad\qquad [17.2]$$

where r represents the loss in heat due to radiation.

The current vector, $\mathbf{i}$, in eq. 17.2 represents a diffusion current. Diffusion currents exist because of concentration gradients rather than gradients which are due to externally applied electrical forces. Consequently, $\mathbf{i}$ is given by

$$\mathbf{i} = K \text{ grad } \rho \qquad\qquad [17.2a]$$

where K is a proportionality factor. Equation 17.2 may now be written

$$(\partial\rho/\partial t) + K \text{ div grad } \rho - r\rho = 0 \qquad\qquad [17.2b]$$

Since

$$\text{div grad } \rho = \nabla^2\rho = \partial^2\rho/\partial x^2 + \partial^2\rho/\partial y^2 + \partial^2\rho/\partial z^2$$

eq. 17.2b is

$$(\partial\rho/\partial t) + K\nabla^2\rho - r\rho = 0 \qquad\qquad [17.2c]$$

Equations 17.1, 17.2, and 17.2a–c are three-dimensional in the space coordinate representation. In transistors, it is desirable to have the cross-sectional dimensions of the base much larger than its thickness. Such a design not only increases the mechanical strength of the transistor but also minimizes the very complex surface phenomena. Because of this geometry, the diffusion equation for the junction transistor may be written for hole "flow" in only one direction, this being the direction perpendicular to the cross section of the base.

Equation 17.2c, in the one-dimensional representation, is

$$\frac{\partial \rho}{\partial t} + K \frac{\partial^2 \rho}{\partial x^2} - r\rho = 0 \qquad [17.2d]$$

Shockley[2] has shown that the flow equation (17.2d), when applied to the transistor, may be written

$$\partial n / \partial t = (n_p - n)/\tau_n + D_n(\partial^2 n/\partial x^2) \qquad [17.3]$$

For an n-p-n junction transistor, the notation of eq. 17.3 is: n = electron concentration in the p region (cm^{-3}), t = time (sec), n_p = thermal equilibrium of n (cm^{-3}), τ_n = electron lifetime (sec), D_n = electron diffusion constant (cm^2/sec), x = space dimension of electron flow (cm). For the p-n-p junction transistor, the notation becomes: n = hole concentration in the n region, τ_n = hole lifetime, D_n = hole diffusion constant. It should be remembered that the one-dimensional equation 17.3 neglects both surface and electric field effects. The smaller the ratios of cross-sectional dimensions to base thickness, the greater will be the error in the one-dimensional equation.

The similarity of eq. 17.3 to eq. 17.2d is apparent. Thus carrier diffusion in a junction transistor may be treated mathematically as a special case of the more general thermodynamic, or hydrodynamic, equation of the continuity of flow. Equation 17.2 also has its counterpart in the probability interpretation of wave mechanics. Equation 17.3 may, therefore, be considered the one-dimensional classical limit of the more general quantum theory of carrier diffusion in transistors.

17.3 Solution of the Diffusion Equation

In eq. 17.3, $n - n_p$ represents the carrier concentration in excess of the thermal equilibrium value in the base region. For p-n-p junction transistors, the excess (minority) carriers are holes; for n-p-n transistors, the excess carriers are electrons. n represents the total carrier concentration in the base region and is a function of both space (x) and time (t).

The steady-state solution of eq. 17.3 is straightforward if the emitter current, or forcing function, is assumed to be of the form

$$i_e(t) = I_e + I_{e0}e^{j\omega t} \qquad [17.4]$$

where I_e is a direct current and $I_{e0}e^{j\omega t}$ is a sinusoidal current superimposed on the d-c component. Using such a forcing function, the steady-state solution of eq. 17.3 is assumed to be of the form

$$n = f(x) + g(x)e^{j\omega t} \qquad [17.5]$$

Equation 17.5 states that the steady-state solution of eq. 17.3, for the forcing function represented by eq. 17.4, is expected to result in a steady-state function which is the sum of some time-independent function, $f(x)$ (due to the d-c component of the forcing function) and the product of a periodic time function, $e^{j\omega t}$, with a space function, $g(x)$. When no time-varying component of the forcing function is present, i.e., when $I_{e0} = 0$ in eq. 17.4, the carrier concentration will be time-independent, i.e., $n = f(x)$. Hence, for the time-independent case, eq. 17.3 may be written

$$0 = \frac{n_p - f}{\tau_n} + D_n \frac{\partial^2 f}{\partial x^2} \qquad [17.6]$$

where f is understood to be the space function, $f(x)$. Substituting eq. 17.5 into eq. 17.3 gives

$$j\omega e^{j\omega t} g = \frac{n_p - f}{\tau_n} + D_n \frac{\partial^2 f}{\partial x^2} - \frac{ge^{j\omega t}}{\tau_n} + D_n e^{j\omega t}\left(\frac{\partial^2 g}{\partial x^2}\right)$$

which, using the relationship given by eq. 17.6, simplifies to

$$j\omega g = -(g/\tau_n) + D_n(d^2 g/dx^2) \qquad [17.7]$$

Equation 17.7 is a linear differential equation whose auxiliary equation has the roots

$$\pm (1/\sqrt{\tau_n D_n})\sqrt{1 + j\omega\tau_n}$$

The general solution of eq. 17.7 is, therefore,

$$g(x) = A_1 \exp\left(-\sqrt{\frac{1 + j\omega\tau_n}{\tau_n D_n}}\, x\right) + A_2 \exp\left(+\sqrt{\frac{1 + j\omega\tau_n}{\tau_n D_n}}\, x\right)$$

$$[17.8]$$

The steady-state solution of the time-dependent part of eq. 17.5 is

$$
m_s(x, t) = e^{j\omega t} \left[A_1 \exp\left(- \sqrt{\frac{1}{\tau_n D_n}} \sqrt{1 + j\omega\tau_n} \, x \right) \right.
$$

$$
\left. + A_2 \exp\left(+ \sqrt{\frac{1}{\tau_n D_n}} \sqrt{1 + j\omega\tau_n} \, x \right) \right] \quad [17.9]
$$

Constants A_1 and A_2 may be obtained from a knowledge of the boundary conditions. For steady-state conditions, the hole function, $m_s(x, t)$, at $x = 0$ must be identical to the forcing function, i.e.,

$$
m_s(0, t) = Be^{j\omega t} \qquad [17.10]
$$

where $B = g(0) = 1$. Thus, for the condition $x = 0$, $t = 0$, the initial boundary equation is

$$
m_s(0, 0) = A_1 + A_2 = 1 \qquad [17.11]
$$

As soon as holes reach the collector-base barrier in a p-n-p transistor (or electrons reach the collector-base barrier in an n-p-n transistor), they are drawn into the collector region by the high potential which exists across the barrier. Consequently, the carrier concentration at the collector-base boundary is assumed to be zero. If the width of the base is denoted by W, the steady-state boundary condition at the collector is

$$
m_s(W, t) = 0 \qquad [17.12]
$$

Substituting this condition into eq. 17.9 gives

$$
A_1 \exp\left(- \sqrt{\frac{1}{\tau_n D_n}} \sqrt{1 + j\omega\tau_n} \, W \right)
$$

$$
+ A_2 \exp\left(+ \sqrt{\frac{1}{\tau_n D_n}} \sqrt{1 + j\omega\tau_n} \, W \right) = 0 \quad [17.13]
$$

From eq. 17.11, $A_2 = 1 - A_1$. Thus, A_1 may be obtained from eq. 17.13 as

$$
A_1 = \frac{\exp\left(\sqrt{\dfrac{1}{D_n \tau_n}} \sqrt{1 + j\omega\tau_n} \, W \right)}{\exp\left(\sqrt{\dfrac{1}{D_n \tau_n}} \sqrt{1 + j\omega\tau_n} \, W \right) - \exp\left(- \sqrt{\dfrac{1}{D_n \tau_n}} \sqrt{1 + j\omega\tau_n} \, W \right)}
$$

$$= \frac{\exp\left(\sqrt{\dfrac{1}{D_n \tau_n}}\sqrt{1 + j\omega\tau_n}\, W\right)}{2\sinh\sqrt{\dfrac{1}{D_n \tau_n}}\sqrt{1 + j\omega\tau_n}\, W} \qquad [17.14]$$

The complete steady-state solution of eq. 17.5 is

$$m_s(x, t) = \frac{e^{j\omega t}}{\sinh\sqrt{\dfrac{1}{D_n \tau_n}}\sqrt{1 + j\omega\tau_n}\, W}\left[\exp\left(\sqrt{\dfrac{1}{D_n \tau_n}}\sqrt{1 + j\omega\tau_n}\, x\right)\right.$$

$$\times \sinh\left(\sqrt{\dfrac{1}{D_n \tau_n}}\sqrt{1 + j\omega\tau_n}\, W\right) - \exp\left(\sqrt{\dfrac{1}{D_n \tau_n}}\sqrt{1 + j\omega\tau_n}\, W\right)$$

$$\left. \times \sinh\left(\dfrac{1}{\sqrt{D_n \tau_n}}\sqrt{1 + j\omega\tau_n}\, x\right)\right] \qquad [17.15]$$

Now the hole current at the collector is given by [2]

$$i_c = -qD_n \frac{\partial m}{\partial x}\bigg|_{x=W} \qquad [17.16a]$$

and, similarly, the hole current at the emitter is

$$i_e = -qD_n \frac{\partial m}{\partial x}\bigg|_{x=0} \qquad [17.16b]$$

where q is the electron charge (the charge carried by a hole is the negative of the charge carried by an electron). The ratio of the collector current to the emitter current is α. From eqs. 17.16a and b, α is

$$\alpha = \frac{i_c}{i_e} = \left(\frac{\partial m}{\partial x}\bigg|_{x=W}\right)\bigg/\left(\frac{\partial m}{\partial x}\bigg|_{x=0}\right) \qquad [17.17]$$

The rate of change of hole concentration as a function of base distance may be found by partial differentiation (with respect to x) of eq. 17.15. As defined by eq. 17.17, α is then found to be given by

$$\alpha = \text{sech}\left(\sqrt{\dfrac{1}{D_n \tau_n}}\sqrt{1 + j\omega\tau_n}\, W\right) \qquad [17.18]$$

It is useful to write the radical in eq. 17.18 as follows:

$$\sqrt{\frac{1}{D_n \tau_n}} \sqrt{1 + j\omega\tau_n} = u_r + ju_j \qquad [17.19a]$$

from which it may readily be shown that

$$u_r = \frac{1}{\sqrt{2D_n\tau_n}} \sqrt{\sqrt{1 + \omega^2\tau_n^2} + 1} \qquad [17.19b]$$

$$u_j = \frac{1}{\sqrt{2D_n\tau_n}} \sqrt{\sqrt{1 + \omega^2\tau_n^2} - 1} \qquad [17.19c]$$

Applying eqs. 17.19a–c to eq. 17.18 gives

$$\alpha = \operatorname{sech}\ (u_r W + ju_j W) \qquad [17.20]$$

The hyperbolic secant is the inverse of the hyperbolic cosine, and the hyperbolic cosine of a complex number may be written

$$\cosh\ (y + jz) = \cosh y \cos z + j \sinh y \sin z$$

Equation 17.20 may therefore be written

$$\alpha = \frac{1}{\cosh u_r W \cos u_j W + j \sinh u_r W \sin u_j W} \qquad [17.21]$$

For convenience, eq. 17.15 may be expressed as

$$m_s(x, t) = e^{j\omega t}(Me^{j\phi}) \qquad [17.22a]$$

where M and ϕ are, respectively, the modulus and phase of the complex steady-state space function $g(x)$. It can be shown from eq. 17.15 that M and ϕ are given by

$$M = \sqrt{\frac{\cosh^2 u_r(W - x) - \cos^2 u_j(W - x)}{\cosh^2 u_r W - \cos^2 u_j W}} \qquad [17.22b]$$

$$\phi = \tan^{-1}\ [\tan u_j(W - x) \coth u_r(W - x)]$$
$$- \tan^{-1}\ (\tan u_j W \coth u_r W) \qquad [17.22c]$$

Equations 17.21–17.22c summarize the steady-state solution of the diffusion equation when the excess hole concentration m at the emitter-base barrier ($x = 0$) varies with time as a sinusoidal function. It should be emphasized that the assumption

$$m = f(t)\ |_{x=0}$$

does not imply that either the applied emitter voltage or the applied emitter current also varies as the function $f(t)$. If $m(x, t)$ is known, the emitter current may be found from eq. 17.16b. In the event $f(t) = e^{j\omega t}$, it is apparent that the emitter current will also be of the same form; i.e., a constant sinusoidal emitter current will give rise to a steady-state sinusoidal variation of carriers at the emitter-base boundary.

By application of Fermi statistics, it has been shown [3] that a valid relation between the carrier concentration m and the applied emitter voltage v_e is given by

$$m = n_p e^{qv_e/kT} \qquad [17.23]$$

where n_e is the concentration of carriers at thermal equilibrium, q is the electron charge, k is Boltzmann's constant, and T is the absolute temperature of the germanium. From eq. 17.23, it can be seen that a steady-state sinusoidal variation of m with respect to time does not lead to a similar variation in the emitter voltage v_e.

Although the steady-state solution of the diffusion equation, for a periodic forcing function, is comparatively straightforward, the transient solution is more difficult. In the transient problem, it will be assumed that the input function i_e is given by

$$i_e = I_0 \mu(t - t_0) \qquad [17.24]$$

where $\mu(t - t_0)$ represents a step function such as illustrated in Fig. 17.4. There are several methods by which eq. 17.5 may be solved for

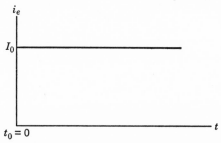

Fig. 17.4 Step-function input for transient solution of the diffusion equation.

the transient case. A popular technique is to assume a Fourier series for the solution, of the form

$$i_c = \sum_i A_i e^{\alpha_i x + \beta_i t} \qquad [17.25]$$

where α_i or β_i may be complex. This form leads to a series of exponential and sine term products, the constants of which are derived from consideration of the auxiliary equation of eq. 17.5 and the boundary conditions of the problem. (See, for example, reference 4.) However, a more direct approach is to apply Laplace transformation techniques directly to the partial differential diffusion equation. Discussion of this technique is not within the scope of this book, but reference may be made to advanced works on thermodynamics where the Laplace methods have been used to solve equations of the same form as eq. 17.5 in regard to heat flow problems.[5, 11]

Using the Laplace transformation techniques, the transient solution of eq. 17.5 to an input of the form illustrated in Fig. 17.4 is

$$i_c(t) = I_0 \sum_{r=1}^{\infty} \left\{ \exp\left[\frac{-(2r-1)W}{\sqrt{D_n\tau_n}}\right] \mathrm{erfc}\left[\frac{(2r-1)W}{2\sqrt{D_nt}} - \sqrt{\frac{t}{\tau_n}}\right]\right.$$

$$\left. + \exp\left[\frac{(2r-1)W}{\sqrt{D_n\tau_n}}\right] \mathrm{erfc}\left[\frac{(2r-1)W}{2\sqrt{D_nt}} + \sqrt{\frac{t}{\tau_n}}\right]\right\} [(-1)^{r+1}] \quad [17.26]$$

where $r = 1, 2, 3 \cdots$. The function erfc y is defined by

$$\mathrm{erfc}\, y = \frac{2}{\sqrt{\pi}} \int_y^{\infty} e^{-z^2}\, dz = 1 - \mathrm{erf}\, y \qquad \text{for positive } y \quad [17.27]$$

Erf y is the error function:

$$\mathrm{erf}\, y = \frac{2}{\sqrt{\pi}} \int_0^y e^{-z^2}\, dz$$

and is tabulated in several textbooks on mathematical functions (see reference 6). Equation 17.26 was derived using the following boundary conditions:

$$x = 0 \qquad m = 0$$

$$x = W \qquad \frac{dm}{dx}(s) = \frac{I_0}{s} \qquad (s = \text{Laplace operator}) \quad [17.28]$$

where W is the width of the base region. For convenience, the reference $x = 0$ is now taken to be at the base-collector barrier. The transient solution given by eq. 17.26 is a series of error functions, each succeeding term being reduced in amplitude. The transient solution given by eq. 17.26, though not convenient to work with in design problems, is nevertheless the simplest closed-form solution of eq. 17.5 that has been found. The first term of eq. 17.26 is plotted in Fig. 17.5 for the conditions

$$W = \tfrac{1}{6} \sqrt{D_n \tau_n}\dagger \qquad I_0 = 1 \qquad r = 1$$

and against the normalized variable γ, where

$$\gamma = \sqrt{t/\tau_n}$$

With these substitutions the first term of eq. 17.26 reduces to

$$i_c(t) = e^{-\frac{1}{6}} \operatorname{erfc}\left[\frac{1}{12\gamma} - \gamma\right] + e^{\frac{1}{6}} \operatorname{erfc}\left[\frac{1}{12\gamma} + \gamma\right] \qquad [17.29]$$

Figure 17.5 illustrates the time delay and the dispersion of the holes which result as they travel from the emitter-base barrier to the collector-base barrier, $W = \tfrac{1}{6}\sqrt{D_n\tau_n}$. For most of the available $p\text{-}n\text{-}p$

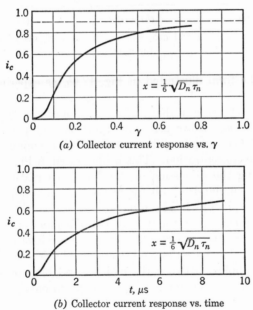

(a) Collector current response vs. γ

(b) Collector current response vs. time

Fig. 17.5 Normalized solution of the diffusion equation for a step-function input current.

junction transistors, the constants which appear in eq. 17.16 are of the following order of magnitude: $D_n = 40$ cm^2/sec and $\tau_n = 100 \times 10^{-6}$ sec. The width of the base region is approximately 0.01 cm, and the

† This value was chosen since it represents, approximately, the base width of present-day junction $p\text{-}n\text{-}p$ transistors.

thermal equilibrium value for holes (n_p in eq. 17.4) is approximately 10^{12} cm^{-3}.

As was emphasized in regard to the steady-state solution of the diffusion equation for a sinusoidal forcing function, the assumption of a step function in i_e does not imply a step function in the emitter voltage v_e, or in the hole concentration m. To find i_e when m is known requires the application of eq. 17.16b. When i_e is a step function, the emitter

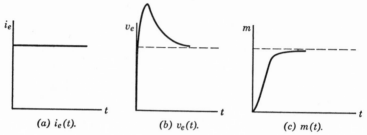

(a) $i_e(t)$.   (b) $v_e(t)$.   (c) $m(t)$.

Fig. 17.6   Emitter voltage and hole-concentration waveforms when i_e is a step function.

voltage has the form illustrated in Fig. 17.6b, as experimentally obtained.

From eq. 17.23 it is seen that a step function of v_e will give rise to a step function of m. However, a step function in emitter current will give rise to neither a step function in emitter voltage nor a step function in emitter hole concentration. This is illustrated in Fig. 17.6.

In concluding the discussion of the diffusion equation (17.5) it is appropriate to summarize both the explicit and implicit assumptions upon which the analysis has been based:

(a) Minority carriers in the base region of a junction transistor migrate from the emitter to the collector as the result of only a concentration gradient; i.e., essentially no electric field exists in the base. All the potential applied between the emitter and base or between the collector and base is, therefore, assumed to appear only across the junctions between these regions.

(b) Surface effects are negligible.

(c) The ratios of the cross-sectional dimensions to the length of the base are large enough to make the one-dimensional diffusion equation valid. This is almost always true in present-day junction transistors.

(d) The junctions are very abrupt; i.e., there is a step-function type boundary between the base and the collector or emitter.

(e) Conductivity of the base, emitter, or collector region is due only to the majority carriers present and is not influenced by the injected carriers. Thus, in a p-n-p junction transistor, the density of electrons in the base region is very large compared to the density of the holes there. Similarly, in the emitter and collector regions, the density of holes is very large compared to the density of electrons. Physically, this assumption implies that such parameters as lifetime and mobility are not changed by injection of the minority carriers into the base.

(f) The distribution of energy and density states of the carriers relative to the surrounding germanium are such as to make valid the Boltzmann approximation to Fermi statistics. This is a valid assumption for germanium at room temperatures.

(g) Current flow across the emitter and collector boundaries is due primarily to the motion of minority carriers. This assumes a current injection ratio (γ) of unity. (See Chapter 1.)

17.4   Junction Transistor Equivalent Circuit for Small-Signal Analysis

The solution of the diffusion equation represents an exact solution to the transient problem as far as the equation represents the physical case. For practical design purposes, however, the transient solution given by eq. 17.26 is too unwieldy. It is desirable to derive an equivalent circuit, which may be used in circuit work, for the solution of transient problems. The requirements of such a circuit are (1) that it lead to solutions which are good approximations to experimental results, (2) that it lead to a relatively simple method for calculating transient response, and (3) that it contain circuit elements that may be measured directly in the laboratory. Such a circuit, suitable for small-signal transient analysis and small-signal frequency response prediction, will be developed in this section.

There are essentially two diffusion effects which must be approximated in any transistor equivalent network if reasonable solutions to transient problems are to be achieved. As was pointed out in Sec. 17.2, these effects are delay and dispersion. Time delay may be achieved, theoretically, by an ideal delay line which has the following simple current transfer function:

$$\frac{i_o(s)}{i_i(s)} = e^{-Ks} \qquad [17.30]$$

In eq. 17.30, s is the Laplace operator,[1] and K is the time delay (sec) of the line. The attenuation and phase characteristics of this ideal delay line are plotted in Fig. 17.7. Dispersion may be achieved by any minimum phase-shift network which has a combination of both energy-dissipative and energy-storage elements. A very simple net-

work which exhibits dispersion is the low-pass RC filter illustrated in
Fig. 17.8a.

Figure 17.8b illustrates the response of this simple RC network to a
unit step-function input current. Thus, it may be anticipated that the

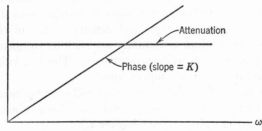

Fig. 17.7   Attenuation and phase characteristic of the ideal delay line.

ideal delay line, described by eq. 17.30, together with the low-pass filter
of Fig. 17.8a, may serve as a first physical approximation to the diffusion effects discussed in Sec. 17.2.

In Chapter 9, a high-frequency equivalent circuit was developed
which employed an RC transmission line in the collector. This circuit
is illustrated in Fig. 9.18. It is possible to use this equivalent circuit

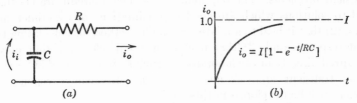

Fig. 17.8   Low-pass filter and its response to a step input.

for transient analysis. However, the inclusion of a transmission line in
the equivalent circuit will lead to hyperbolic functions in the Laplace
transform which relates the input current (or voltage) to the output
current (or voltage). The inverse transformation of such transfer
functions gives rise to transcendental expressions, in the time domain,
which are similar in form to eq. 17.26; hence, the requirement that the
equivalent circuit should lead to simple Laplace transformations would
not be met by any circuit of the distributed-parameter type such as the
one of Fig. 9.18.

If the circuit of Fig. 9.18 is simplified as illustrated in Fig. 17.9, it is
apparent that the dispersion and delay properties of the transmission
line are approximated separately by the low-pass filter network, con-

sisting of r and C, and by the ideal delay line, the transfer characteristics of which are illustrated in Fig. 17.7. The transfer function of the ideal delay line in Fig. 17.9 is given by eq. 17.30. Now if the current trans-

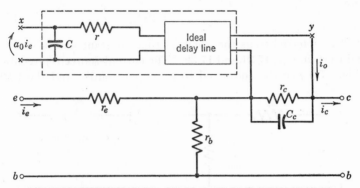

Fig. 17.9   Simplification of the equivalent circuit illustrated in Fig. 9.18.

form from x to y in Fig. 17.9 is considered, it is found to be

$$i_o(s)/i_e(s) = a_0 e^{-Ks}/(1 + rCs) \qquad [17.31]$$

The attenuation-frequency characteristic corresponding to eq. 17.31 is

$$\left| \frac{i_o(j\omega)}{i_e(j\omega)} \right| = \frac{a_0}{\sqrt{1 + \omega^2 r^2 C^2}} \simeq \frac{\alpha_0}{\sqrt{1 + \omega^2 r^2 C^2}} \qquad [17.32]$$

Equation 17.32 is plotted in Fig. 17.10 on a normalized basis. The 3-db attenuation point of Fig. 17.10 must correspond to the α cut-off

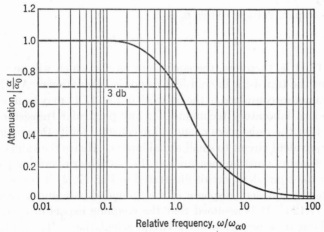

Fig. 17.10   Normalized attenuation characteristic, eq. 17.32.

frequency $f_{\alpha 0}$ of the transistor. Thus eq. 17.32 may be rewritten

$$\left|\, i_o(j\omega)/i_e(j\omega)\,\right| \;=\; \alpha_0/\sqrt{1 + \omega^2\tau_\alpha{}^2} \qquad [17.33a]$$

where

$$\tau_\alpha \;=\; 1/2\pi f_{\alpha 0} \qquad [17.33b]$$

τ_α will be referred to as the α cut-off time constant and is seen to be equal to rC in eqs. 17.31 and 17.32. The current-source representation of Fig. 17.9 may be converted to a voltage source, and the parallel

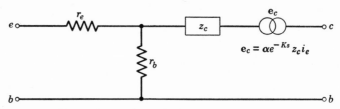

Fig. 17.11   Conversion of the equivalent circuit illustrated in Fig. 17.9.

combination of r_c and C_c may be combined as a single impedance, z_c. When this is done, the equivalent circuit of Fig. 17.11 is realized, where

$$\alpha \;=\; \frac{\alpha_0}{1 + \tau_\alpha s} \qquad [17.34a]$$

$$z_c \;=\; \frac{r_c}{1 + \tau_c s} \qquad [17.34b]$$

where $\tau_c = r_c C_c$.

The complex voltage source $\mathbf{e}_c$ is

$$\mathbf{e}_c \;=\; e_c(s) \;=\; \alpha e^{-Ks}\, z_c i_e(s) \qquad [17.34c]$$

Figure 17.11 is, therefore, the equivalent circuit which will be used to represent the transistor in transient response calculations. All the circuit parameters contained in the network of Fig. 17.11 may be measured by standard laboratory techniques for any particular transistor. Assuming that the resistances r_e and r_b are constant limits the application of the equivalent circuit to small-signal inputs. Hence the values of the circuit elements must be measured at the particular operating point.

Using the equivalent circuit illustrated in Fig. 17.11, it is possible to calculate the transient response of the grounded-base amplifier shown in Fig. 17.12a. It is assumed that the coupling capacitor C_s is sufficiently large to be negligible in the circuit calculations. The equivalent circuit, from which the transient calculations will be made, is illustrated in Fig. 17.12b. The signal generator e_s of Fig. 17.12a is represented as an ideal voltage source e_i in series with an internal generator

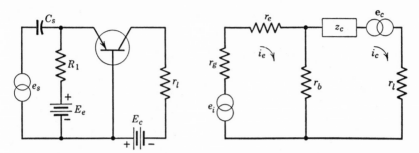

Fig. 17.12   Grounded-base p-n-p junction transistor amplifier.

resistance r_g. The Kirchhoff equations for the circuit of Fig. 17.12b are given in eqs. 17.35a and b

$$e_i = (r_g + r_e + r_b)i_e - r_b i_c \qquad [17.35a]$$

$$e_c = -r_b i_e + (z_c + r_l + r_b)i_c \qquad [17.35b]$$

The output voltage $e_o = i_c r_l$. In terms of the Laplace operator s the voltage transform $e_o(s)/e_i(s)$ may be calculated from eq. 17.35. When this is done, the solution will be of the form

$$\frac{e_o}{e_i}(s) = \frac{a_0 + a_1 s + a_2 s^2 + C_0 e^{-Ks}}{B_0 + B_1 s + B_2 s^2 + D e^{-Ks}} \qquad [17.36]$$

The term $D e^{-Ks}$ in the denominator of eq. 17.36 makes the transform difficult to solve in the time domain unless the following expansion is made:

$$D e^{-Ks} = D\left[1 - Ks + \frac{(Ks)^2}{2!} - \frac{(Ks)^3}{3!} + \cdots\right] \qquad [17.37]$$

In practice, K is very small. Hence, eq. 17.37 converges rapidly. If all but the first three terms of the expansion are neglected, eq. 17.36 may be written

$$\frac{e_o}{e_i}(s) = \frac{a_0 + a_1 s + a_2 s^2}{b_0 + b_1 s + b_2 s^2} + \frac{C_0 e^{-Ks}}{b_0 + b_1 s + b_2 s^2} \qquad [17.38]$$

Constants D, $-DK$, $D(K^2/2)$ of eq. 17.37 and B_0, B_1, and B_2 of eq. 17.36 are included in the coefficients b_0, b_1, and b_2, respectively, of eq.

17.38. The coefficients of s in eq. 17.38 are, in terms of the circuit constants,

$$a_0 = r_l r_b \qquad\qquad\qquad\qquad [17.38a$$

$$a_1 = r_l r_b (\tau_\alpha + \tau_c) \qquad\qquad\qquad [17.38b]$$

$$a_2 = r_l r_b \tau_\alpha \tau_c \qquad\qquad\qquad\qquad [17.38c]$$

$$C_0 = \alpha_0 r_l r_c \qquad\qquad\qquad\qquad [17.38d]$$

$$b_0 = (r_g + r_e)(r_l + r_b + r_c) + r_b[r_l + r_c(1 - \alpha_0)] \qquad [17.38e]$$

$$b_1 = [(r_g + r_e)(r_l + r_b) + r_b r_l](\tau_\alpha + \tau_c)$$
$$+ r_c[(r_b + r_g + r_e)\tau_\alpha + \alpha_0 r_b K] \qquad\qquad [17.38f]$$

$$b_2 = \tau_\alpha \tau_c[r_b(r_g + r_e + r_l) + r_l(r_g + r_e)] - \frac{\alpha_0 r_c r_b K^2}{2} \qquad [17.38g]$$

The time response of the transistor amplifier of Fig. 17.12b to a unit step input, which is given in operational form by

$$e_i(s) = 1/s$$

is

$$e_o(t) = \mathcal{L}^{-1}\left[\frac{a_0 + a_1 s + a_2 s^2}{s(b_0 + b_1 s + b_2 s^2)}\right] + \mathcal{L}^{-1}\left[\frac{C_0 e^{-Ks}}{s(b_0 + b_1 s + b_2 s^2)}\right]$$

$$[17.39]$$

The operational notation $\mathcal{L}^{-1}$ signifies an inverse Laplace transformation.[1]

A transform involving the multiplication of two complex terms can be evaluated in the time domain by means of the convolution integral.[1] Thus:

$$\mathcal{L}^{-1}[F(s)e^{-Ks}] = \int_0^t f(t - \tau)\delta(\tau - K)\, d\tau \qquad [17.40]$$

where $\delta(\tau - K)$ is a Dirac impulse at time K, the impulse being derived from the inverse transformation of e^{-Ks}. The convolution integral of eq. 17.40 is

$$\int_0^t f(t - \tau)\delta(\tau - K)\, d\tau = f(t - K)\mu(t - K) = g(t)$$

Therefore

$$g(t) = 0 \qquad \text{for} \qquad -\infty < t < K$$

$$g(t) = f(t - K) \qquad \text{for} \qquad K < t < +\infty$$

Hence, the inverse transformation of any function involving the product $F(s)e^{-Ks}$ is simply the inverse transformation of $F(s)$ for the time scale $t - K$, and is evaluated only for time from $t = K$ to $t = +\infty$. Making use of this fact, the transform of eq. 17.39 may be evaluated, in the time domain, by any of the common tables of transforms.[1]

For the junction transistors in use at the present time, the discriminant of the quadratic expression in the denominator of eq. 17.39 satisfies the relation

$$(b_1/2b_2)^2 - b_0/b_2 > 0$$

Hence, the time domain solution of eq. 17.39 is [1]

$$e_o(t) = \frac{a_2}{b_2} \left\{ \frac{a_0}{a_2 A B} + \left[\frac{A^2 - \dfrac{a_1}{a_2} A + \dfrac{a_0}{a_2}}{A(A - B)} \right] e^{-A} \right.$$

$$\left. - \left[\frac{B^2 - \dfrac{a_1}{a_2} B + \dfrac{a_0}{a_2}}{B(A - B)} \right] \cdot e^{-Bt} \right\}$$

$$+ \frac{C_0}{b_2} \left[\frac{1}{AB} + \frac{Be^{-A(t-K)} - Ae^{-B(t-K)}}{AB(A - B)} \right] [\mu(t - K)] \qquad [17.41]$$

A and B in eq. 17.41 are given by

$$A = \frac{b_1}{2b_2} - \sqrt{\left(\frac{b_1}{2b_2}\right)^2 - \frac{b_0}{b_2}} \qquad [17.41a]$$

$$B = \frac{b_1}{2b_2} + \sqrt{\left(\frac{b_1}{2b_2}\right)^2 - \frac{b_0}{b_2}} \qquad [17.41b]$$

The function $\mu(t - K)$ is defined by

$$\mu(t - K) = 0 \qquad \text{for} \qquad 0 < t < K$$

$$\mu(t - K) = 1 \qquad \text{for} \qquad K < t < \infty$$

Equation 17.41 is the complete transient response solution of the transistor circuit of Fig. 17.12b to a unit step input. The first term in eq. 17.41 is the response of the equivalent circuit to the step input when the transistor is acting primarily as a passive circuit, that is, before the carriers have reached the collector. For good amplifiers, this term will be negligible. Furthermore, it is generally found that $B \gg A$.

Where these conditions apply, eq. 17.41 may be written

$$e_o(t) \cong \frac{C_0}{b_2 A B} [1 - e^{-A(t-K)}][\mu(t - K)] \qquad [17.42]$$

Equation 17.42 is simply an exponential rise which is delayed by K seconds. This function is illustrated in Fig. 17.13. The rise time t_R

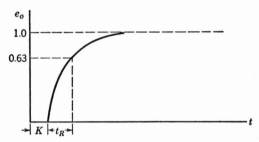

Fig. 17.13   Approximate theoretical transient response of transistor amplifier to unit step.

is defined in the usual manner; i.e., t_R is the time when the function $\{1 - \exp[-A(t - K)]\}$ is equal to $(1 - e^{-1})$ or 0.63.   Hence:

$$t_R = 1/A \qquad [17.43]$$

Example.   Consider a transistor pulse amplifier circuit of the type shown in Fig. 17.12a where the circuit parameters are as follows: $r_l = 10$ kilohms, $r_g = 50$ ohms, $r_e = 30$ ohms, $r_b = 200$ ohms, $r_c = 600$ kilohms, $\alpha_0 = 0.9$, $\tau_\alpha = 10^{-6}$ sec, $\tau_c = 10^{-5}$ sec, $K = 0.5$ microsecond. The constants defined by eqs. 17.38a–g are calculated as: $a_0 = 2 \times 10^6$ ohm^2, $a_1 = 22$ ohm^2 sec, $a_2 = 20 \times 10^{-6}$ ohm^2 sec^2, $C_0 = 54 \times 10^8$ ohm^2, $b_0 = 62 \times 10^6$ ohm^2, $b_1 = 253$ ohm^2 sec, $b_2 = 14.5 \times 10^{-6}$ ohm^2 sec^2. A and B of eqs. 17.41a–b are: $A = 0.27 \times 10^6$ sec^{-1} and $B = 17.2 \times 10^6$ sec^{-1}.   Hence, the output voltage, $e_o(t)$, as given by eq. 17.41, is

$$e_o(t) \cong 1.2e^{-17.2 \times 10^6 t}$$

$$+ \mu(t - 0.5 \times 10^{-6})(81.6)[1 - e^{-270,000(t-0.5 \times 10^{-6})}] \qquad [17.44]$$

Equation 17.44 is plotted in Fig. 17.14a and is compared to a photograph (Fig. 17.14b) of the transient response of the transistor amplifier as experimentally obtained.   The input to the experimental circuit consisted of a square wave of 10-microsecond duration and approximately 30-millivolt amplitude.

Both attenuation and phase characteristics may be determined for

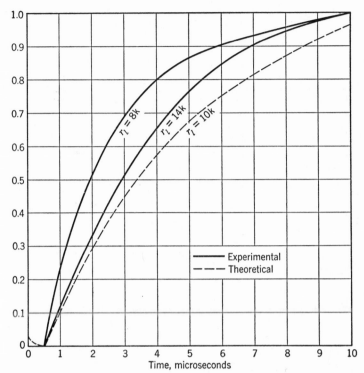

Fig. 17.14a   Theoretical and experimental transient response.

the amplifier circuit of Fig. 17.12a by substituting the complex variable $j\omega$ for s in eq. 17.38. The frequency response may then be written

$$\frac{e_o}{e_i}(j\omega) = \frac{(a_0 - a_2\omega^2) + j\omega a_1 + C_0 e^{-Kj\omega}}{(b_0 - b_2\omega^2) + j\omega b_1} \qquad [17.45]$$

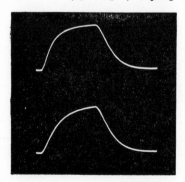

Fig. 17.14b   Transistor amplifier response to square wave of 10-μs duration.

The close agreement between experimental frequency response curves and the frequency response predicted by eq. 17.45 is an indication of close agreement between experimental and theoretical transient response. For the amplifier example cited above, the frequency response

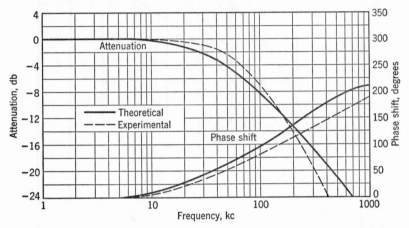

Fig. 17.15   Experimental and theoretical phase and attenuation characteristics.

of the circuit is compared to experimental results in Fig. 17.15. Because of the greater bandwidth of the experimental attenuation characteristic, it may be expected that the theoretical transient response calculation will predict a larger rise time than will be obtained experi-

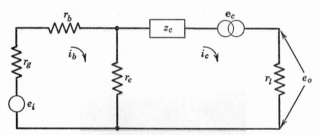

Fig. 17.16   A-c equivalent circuit for grounded-emitter amplifier.

mentally. Hence, the equivalent circuit of Fig. 17.12b will, in general, give a conservative estimate of the rise and decay times of transistor amplifier output to pulse inputs.

Grounded-emitter transistor networks may be treated on a transient basis in exactly the same manner as was described for grounded-base circuits. An a-c equivalent circuit for a grounded-emitter transistor amplifier is shown in Fig. 17.16. The transform $e_o(s)/e_i(s)$ for the grounded-emitter amplifier is the same as eq. 17.38, provided that the coefficients a_0, b_0, C_0, etc., of eq. 17.38 are replaced with new coefficients, a_0', b_0', C_0', etc. In terms of the circuit parameters, the coefficients for the grounded-emitter amplifier are found to be

$$a_0' = r_l r_e \qquad\qquad [17.46a]$$

$$a_1' = r_l r_e(\tau_\alpha + \tau_c) \qquad\qquad [17.46b]$$

$$a_2' = r_l r_e \tau_\alpha \tau_c \qquad\qquad [17.46c]$$

$$C_0' = -\alpha_0 r_l r_c \qquad\qquad [17.46d]$$

$$b_0' = (r_l + r_c)(r_e + r_g + r_b) + (r_e - \alpha r_c)(r_g + r_b) \qquad [17.46e]$$

$$b_1' = (r_g + r_e + r_b)[r_l(\tau_\alpha + \tau_c) + r_c \tau_\alpha]$$
$$+ (r_g + r_b)[r_e(\tau_\alpha + \tau_c) + \alpha r_c K] \qquad [17.46f]$$

$$b_2' = r_l(r_g + r_e + r_b)\tau_\alpha \tau_c$$
$$+ (r_g + r_b)(\tau_\alpha \tau_c r_e - \tfrac{1}{2}K^2 \alpha_0 r_c) \qquad [17.46g]$$

The transient response of the grounded-emitter amplifier to a unit step input is then given by eq. 17.41, where, again, the constants a_0, b_0, C_0, are replaced by the new constants a_0', b_0', C_0'.

17.5 General Circuit Considerations

17.5.1 Point-Contact Transistors

Both the one-dimensional diffusion equation of Sec. 17.2 and the small-signal equivalent circuit of Sec. 17.4 have been confined to the "ideal" junction transistor. However, both may be applied to point-contact transistors as far as the physical phenomena of the point-contact types approximate the conditions for junction transistors. Because of the geometry of point-contact transistors, surface effects probably play a considerable role in the transient behavior of the device. Surface effects were assumed negligible in the diffusion mechanism given by eq. 17.3, and so considerable error may be expected if this equation is used to describe the behavior of point-contact transistors. Little is known about surface phenomena at the present time.

It is reasonable to expect that the approximate equivalent circuit of Fig. 17.9 will describe transient behavior of point-contact transistor circuits, at least to a first approximation, if two conditions are met: (a) that the circuit will predict the frequency response of the network adequately, and (b) that non-linear effects are negligible (which implies small signal inputs). For some point-contact transistors, a channel path may have to be provided in the equivalent circuit. (See Sec. 18.6.)

17.5.2 Minimum-Phase-Shift Character of Junction Transistors

Under certain conditions, it is important to know whether a network is of minimum or non-minimum phase-shift type. For example, in a minimum-phase-shift network, the specification of the attenuation characteristic uniquely determines the phase characteristic.[7] Since, in linear networks, knowledge of the attenuation and phase properties is sufficient to calculate transient response, all that would be necessary for the calculation of the transient response of a minimum-phase-shift network would be the complete specification of the attenuation as a function of frequency.

The steady-state solution of the diffusion equation, for sine-wave inputs, is given by eq. 17.18. In terms of the complex variable s, the current transform, $i_c(s)/i_e(s)$, is

$$i_c(s)/i_e(s) = 1/(\cosh D\sqrt{1 + \tau_n s}) \qquad [17.47]$$

where $D = W/\sqrt{\tau_n D_n}$. In order to prove that eq. 17.47 represents a stable minimum-phase system, it is sufficient to show that both the poles and zeros of the transform are in the left-hand part of the complex plane. The equation

$$\cosh D\sqrt{1 + \tau_n s} = 0 \qquad [17.48]$$

must be solved for s. If eq. 17.48 is to be satisfied, the argument of the hyperbolic cosine must be

$$D\sqrt{1 + \tau_n s} = j\left(\frac{2n - 1}{2}\right)\pi \qquad n = 1, 2 \cdots$$

(See reference 8.) Solving for s yields

$$s = -\frac{1}{\tau_n}\left[1 + \frac{\pi^2}{D^2}\left(\frac{2n - 1}{2}\right)^2\right] \qquad [17.49]$$

Equation 17.49 indicates clearly that all the poles of eq. 17.47 will be in the left half of the complex plane. Since there are no zeros in the right-half plane, as is apparent from eq. 17.47, the diffusion of minority carriers through the base of a junction transistor may be represented by a minimum-phase-shift network. In a similar manner, the transmission-line equivalent circuit of Fig. 9.18 may be shown to be a minimum-phase-shift network.

17.5.3   Transient Analysis of Complex Transistor Networks

As often happens in practice, analysis based upon an equivalent circuit of the system under investigation leads to transforms which are too involved, algebraically, to solve. When this occurs, it is generally possible to obtain either the voltage transfer function or the system impulse response, or both, by experiment. For minimum-phase-shift networks, a knowledge of the transfer function is generally sufficient to approximate the system impulse response, or knowledge of the impulse response is sufficient to approximate the transfer function.[9]

For example, if the voltage transfer function of a minimum-phase-shift transistor network is known, then the impulse response $h(t)$ of the system is

$$h(t) = \frac{1}{2\pi j} \int_{-j\infty}^{+j\infty} \frac{e_o}{e_i}(s)e^{st} \; ds = \frac{2}{\pi} \int_0^\infty Re\left[\frac{e_o}{e_i}(j\omega)\cos\omega t\right] d\omega \quad [17.50]$$

Since

$$\frac{e_o}{e_i}(j\omega) = Re\left[\frac{e_o}{e_i}(j\omega)\right] + jIm\left[\frac{e_o}{e_i}(j\omega)\right]$$

$$= \left|\frac{e_o}{e_i}(j\omega)\right| e^{j\varphi(\omega)}$$

the real part of the voltage transfer function in eq. 17.50 is

$$Re\left[\frac{e_o}{e_i}(j\omega)\right] = \left|\frac{e_o}{e_i}(j\omega)\right| \cos\varphi(\omega) \quad\quad [17.51]$$

If the voltage transfer function, $(e_o/e_i)(j\omega)$, can be obtained experimentally, a normalized analytic expression may be approximated from it by use of the Bode logarithmic approximation technique.[7] The real

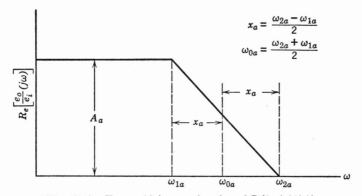

Fig. 17.17   Trapezoidal approximation of $R_e[(e_o/e_i)(j\omega)]$.

part of the transfer function may then be derived by eq. 17.51, and the impulse response of the system will be given by eq. 17.50. Various straight-line approximation techniques may be used to evaluate the integral of eq. 17.50 if it is too complicated to solve analytically. One such method [9] is to approximate the function of eq. 17.51 by a series of trapezoids such as the one illustrated in Fig. 17.17. For this trapezoidal function, the integral of eq. 17.50 is found to be

$$h_a(t) = \frac{2A_a\omega_{0a}}{\pi} \left(\frac{\sin \omega_{0a}t}{\omega_{0a}t}\right) \left(\frac{\sin x_a t}{x_a t}\right)$$

In general, several trapezoids will be required to approximate the real part of the voltage transfer function. Thus, the impulse response, $h(t)$, will be the sum of the individual responses of each trapezoidal section. The total system impulse response is, therefore,

$$h(t) = \sum_{n=1}^{K} \frac{2A_n\omega_{0n}}{\pi} \left(\frac{\sin \omega_{0n}t}{\omega_{0n}t}\right) \left(\frac{\sin x_n t}{x_n t}\right) \qquad [17.52]$$

Again it must be remembered that the technique here described applies only to linear systems. For multistage transistor networks, a system analysis based upon linear circuit theory requires that each transistor be operated in the linear range of its static characteristics. Such analysis also requires that the input to each individual transistor be small enough to justify the constant circuit elements in the equivalent circuit. More will be said about non-linear effects in Sec. 17.6.

17.5.4   Variations of the Equivalent Circuit

The equivalent circuit of Fig. 17.12b, which represents a junction transistor grounded-base amplifier, is one of the simplest that can be derived for approximate transient analysis. If other effects, such as input or output capacitance and feedback impedance between the collector and emitter, are taken into account, the degree of the resultant voltage transfer function is increased. Hence, if the load resistance r_l is shunted by an output capacitance C_l, the voltage transfer function of the circuit in Fig. 17.12b will be of the form

$$\frac{e_o}{e_i}(s) = \frac{f_1 + f_2 s + f_3 s^2 + f_4 e^{-Ks}}{d_0 + d_1 s + d_2 s^2 + d_3 s^3 + d_4 e^{-Ks}} \qquad [17.53]$$

where the constants f_1, d_0, etc., are calculated by the usual circuit techniques. The denominator of eq. 17.53 has three roots (if the e^{-Ks} term is expanded to the fourth term only).

It is possible to make the equivalent circuit of Fig. 17.9, which represents a junction transistor, more exact by taking into account such effects as space-charge layer widening,[10] but, again, this will result in an increase in the complexity of the transfer function. It is, as usual, a matter of judgment whether the increased accuracy is worth the increased algebraic involvement. Simplicity is always a virtue in engineering design but must be treated with discretion lest the end result be lost. Hence, it is desirable to summarize the assumptions upon which the equivalent transistor circuit of Fig. 17.9 is based. They are: (a) the resistances r_e and r_b are constant with frequency and input-signal amplitude; (b) the collector impedance z_c can be represented by lumped parameters which are constant with respect to emitter and collector currents and voltages; (c) the collector current or collector voltage does not affect the emitter circuit parameters except by coupling effects due to the base resistance r_b; and (d) the delay time K is constant despite variation of the collector voltage.

Although none of these assumptions is absolutely true, even for small input signals, they are nevertheless accurate enough to serve as a good first approximation in the transient analysis of junction transistors. An equivalent circuit which would discount these assumptions for greater accuracy in the final result would lead to such complex results as to be useless for most design purposes.

17.6 Large-Signal Transient Effects

When the magnitude of the input signal is large, two basic phenomena may be observed: variation of the input impedance, and saturation. Variation of the input impedance implies that α, r_e, r_b, r_c, and C_c may change with the magnitude of the signal. As is indicated in Chapter 18, some of these changes may be predetermined from an analysis of the static characteristics of the transistor. The method of transient analysis presented in Sec. 17.4 may still be used for large input signals provided that the transistor does not saturate. When this method is applied, the voltage transfer equation (17.38) must be

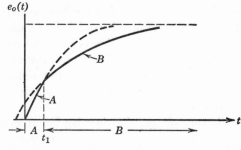

Fig. 17.18   Transistor amplifier response to large-signal step function.

written for each operating region where changes have occurred in the parameters (see Sec. 18.5). The inverse transformations of these equations must then be matched to one another for boundary conditions in order that the complete solution be obtained. Figure 17.18 illustrates the form a transient solution may take when the transform equations are solved for two linear operating regions of the transistor. In region A, the solution follows the form (A) which would apply for small signals. In region B, the circuit constants have changed, and hence a new response curve (B) results. The boundary conditions at $t = t_1$ are

$$e_{oA}(t_1) = e_{oB}(t_1) \qquad [17.54a]$$

$$\left.\frac{de_{oA}}{dt}\right|_{t=t_1} = \left.\frac{de_{oB}}{dt}\right|_{t=t_1} \qquad [17.54b]$$

Thus, by successive linear solutions, an approximation to the nonlinear transient response may be obtained.

When a transistor saturates, there results an excess concentration of minority carriers at the collector-base barrier. Owing to the large voltage drop across the load resistance r_l caused by the collector saturation current, the collector voltage is very small. If the large saturating input signal, such as a step, is maintained on the emitter, minority carriers will arrive at the collector barrier at a uniform rate and will be limited not by the emitter current but by the low collector voltage. Excess minority carriers are then stored in the base, and any further increase in the magnitude of the emitter signal will not affect the collector current.

If the transistor is saturated, and the emitter signal causing the saturation is suddenly removed, a minority carrier storage effect is observed. After the signal has been removed, the excess carriers in the base region will drift into the collector region very slowly, owing to the small collector voltage. Consequently, a collector current is maintained, even after the signal voltage drops to zero, until the excess minority carrier concentration at the base-collector barrier has been restored to its equilibrium value. (In Sec. 17.3, this equilibrium value was assumed to be $m = 0$, i.e., $n = n_p$.) When this occurs, the collector current drops to zero along the usual exponential, or error-function, curve. The continuation of collector current after the input signal has been reduced to zero is commonly known as the "back-porch" effect; it is also evidenced in junction diodes.

For a given collector voltage, the time lag before collector current decays is proportional to the magnitude of the saturating input current. The greater the excess minority carrier concentration at the collector barrier, the longer the time lag in the collector current "shut-off" operation. Figure 17.19 illustrates the response of a transistor amplifier to input pulses of different magnitudes and of 10-microsecond duration.

The range of input signal magnitudes which determines the class of operation of any transistor varies from transistor to transistor. At the present time, and for junction p-n-p transistors, the following may be

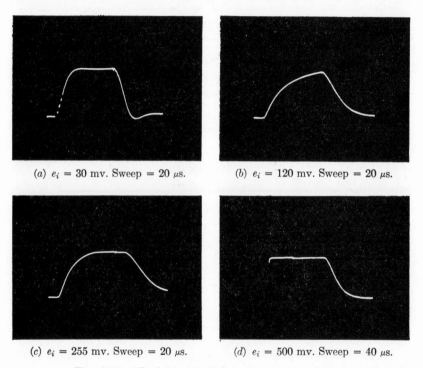

(a) $e_i = 30$ mv. Sweep $= 20$ μs.　　　(b) $e_i = 120$ mv. Sweep $= 20$ μs.

(c) $e_i = 255$ mv. Sweep $= 20$ μs.　　　(d) $e_i = 500$ mv. Sweep $= 40$ μs.

Fig. 17.19　"Back-porch" effect in transistor amplifiers.

said to be an estimate for commonly used grounded-base amplifiers (when the d-c operating biases are $V_c \cong 10$ volts, $I_e \cong 1$ ma, $I_c \cong 0.8$ ma): (a) linear operation, 0–50 mv input; (b) non-linear operation, 50–150 mv input; (c) saturation operation, 150 mv and up. Linear operation refers to that input voltage range where a single equivalent circuit of fixed linear parameters may be said to represent the transistor. Non-linear operation connotes an input signal of sufficient magnitude to require variable parameters in the equivalent circuit. Saturation implies that a signal of such magnitude is impressed on the emitter that low collector voltage at the collector barrier limits the minority carrier current.

17.7 Problems

1. Solve the diffusion equation (17.5) for the steady-state solution when the input emitter current is of the form $i_e = C' \sin \omega t$, and for the condition that all the holes which start from the emitter-base barrier reach the collector-base barrier, i.e., there is no recombination term in eq. 17.5. Compare this result with eq. 17.15.

2. Plot the attenuation and phase functions of m_s, as given by eq. 17.22a, with frequency, ω, as the independent variable. Assume the following values for the constants: $W = x = 10^{-2}$ cm; $\tau_n = 125 \times 10^{-6}$ sec; $D_n = 40$ cm^2/sec.

3. Calculate the transient response of the grounded-emitter amplifier of Fig. 17.14 when the circuit parameters are as follows:

$$r_l = 10 \text{ k}\Omega \qquad r_g = 100 \text{ }\Omega \qquad r_e = 20 \text{ }\Omega \qquad r_b = 100 \text{ }\Omega \qquad r_c = 10^6 \text{ }\Omega$$

$$\alpha_0 = 0.95 \qquad C_c = 10 \text{ }\mu\mu\text{f} \qquad f_{\alpha 0} = 5 \text{ mc} \qquad K = 0.1 \text{ }\mu\text{s}$$

4. Calculate and plot the attenuation and phase response of the amplifier in problem 3. Compare this to the response characteristic of a grounded-base amplifier having the same circuit constants.

5. Using the frequency response characteristic of the grounded-emitter amplifier of problem 4, calculate the impulse response $h(t)$ by means of the method outlined in Sec. 17.5.3.

6. Plot the dispersion of collector current, as given by eq. 17.29, when the series of eq. 17.26 is carried out to $r = 4$. Compare this to Fig. 17.5.

7. Show that the emitter voltage of a grounded-base amplifier is given by the approximation:

$$v_e(t) = i_e(t)(r_e + r_b) - r_b i_c(t)$$

Using $i_c(t)$ as determined in problem 6, plot $v_e(t)$ when $i_e(t)$ is a step function of unit amplitude. Compare this voltage response to that illustrated in Fig. 17.6b.

17.8 Bibliography

1. M. F. Gardner and J. L. Barnes, *Transients in Linear Systems*, Wiley, New York, 1942.

2. W. Shockley, "Theory of p-n Junctions in Semiconductors and p-n Junction Transistors," *Bell Sys. Tech. J.*, *28*, 435–489 (July, 1949).

3. H. K. Henisch, *Metal Rectifiers*, Oxford University Press, 1949.

4. A. Cohen, *An Elementary Treatise on Differential Equations*, 2nd ed., D. C. Heath and Co., 1933.

5. Carslaw and Jaeger, *Conduction of Heat in Solids*, Oxford University Press, 1947.

6. E. Jahnke and F. Emde, *Tables of Functions*, Dover Publications, New York, 1945.

7. H. W. Bode, *Network Analysis and Feedback Amplifier Design*, D. Van Nostrand Co., 1945.

8. B. O. Pierce, *A Short Table of Integrals*, 3rd ed., eq. 653, Ginn and Co., 1929.

9. G. S. Brown and D. P. Campbell, *Principles of Servomechanisms*, 2nd printing, John Wiley & Sons, 1948.

10. J. M. Early, "Effects of Space-Charge Layer Widening in Junction Transistors," *Proc. IRE*, November, 1952.

11. N. W. McLachlan, P. Humbert, and L. Poli, *Supplément au formulaire le calcul symbolique*, fascicule CXIII, *Mémorial des sciences mathématiques*, Gauthier-Villars, Paris, 1950.

Chapter 18

Large-Signal Operation

18.1 Introduction

Transistors, like vacuum tubes, are non-linear devices. Linearity in both transistors and vacuum tubes is restricted to a limited operating range. This range of linear operation is determined by the magnitude of the input signal and by the initial d-c operating point of the circuit for any given load. The equivalent circuit for a transistor, as derived in Chapter 3, is based upon the assumption that the parameters r_e, r_b, r_c and r_m are independent of the magnitude of the input current. For small signals, this assumption may be true for most calculations; but as the magnitude of the input signal is increased, the transistor exhibits two properties which are analogous to vacuum tubes: cut-off and saturation. In a p-n-p transistor which is operated as a grounded-base amplifier, cut-off occurs when the emitter becomes sufficiently negative to cause a reversal of current between the emitter and base. Similarly, in an n-p-n transistor, a sufficiently large positive signal applied on the emitter will drive the transistor to cut-off. Saturation occurs when increasing emitter current (in a positive direction for p-n-p transistors or in a negative direction for the n-p-n types) fails to increase the collector current. The fact that transistors and vacuum tubes exhibit saturation and cut-off effects with large-signal inputs limits their maximum theoretical power efficiencies to 50 per cent in class A amplifier operation. Nevertheless, these non-linear properties make possible the use of transistors and vacuum tubes in such applications as relaxation oscillators, switching circuits, frequency multipliers, square-wave generators, and counters.

Still another non-linear effect is observed with point-contact transistors. As the emitter current is varied, the input resistance of the point-contact types may be either positive or negative. With increasing emitter current, the input resistance of such transistors varies as an N-type characteristic; i.e., the input resistance is positive in one region, negative in the next, and positive again in the third region. This negative resistance effect observed in the input characteristics of point-contact transistors makes these units particularly suitable for such circuits as single-stage multivibrators and binary counters.

When large a-c signals are applied at the emitter of a transistor, with the collector circuit open and with zero emitter bias, rectification of the input is observed. For n-p-n transistors, current will flow from the base to the emitter, but, ideally, no current will flow from the emitter to the base. This situation is analogous to the rectification that occurs between the grid and cathode of a vacuum tube when the grid becomes positive with respect to the cathode. Thus, the emitter-base input circuit may be thought of as a diode which experiences a sharp increase in resistance when current in the forward direction is reversed. To prevent rectification with small applied input signals, the diode must be biased in the direction of forward conduction.

When the emitter is open-circuited, and a positive potential is applied to the collector of an n-p-n transistor, a small current will flow from the collector to the base. When the collector potential is reversed, the current will reverse and suddenly increase. The collector-base circuit of a transistor may therefore be thought of as a diode which is normally in the reverse, or low-conduction, direction. A large-signal equivalent circuit may be devised using these diode analogies, but such a circuit is best utilized rather from the point of view of understanding large-signal analysis than as a basis for accurate design calculations. Graphical techniques may be most readily utilized in the design of transistor circuits for large-signal operation.

18.2   Large-Signal Analysis by Graphical Techniques

The basis for graphical analysis of the behavior of transistor networks may be understood by considering the current and voltage relationships in a simple circuit. For example, consider the circuit of Fig. 18.1. The Kirchhoff equation for the collector loop is

$$E_c = V_c + R_l I_c \qquad [18.1]$$

$$I_c = \frac{E_c - V_c}{R_l}, \qquad [18.2]$$

Static characteristics for I_c as a function of V_c, keeping I_e constant, are given in Chapter 2 for the various transistor types. Hence

$$I_c = f(I_e, V_c) = (E_c - V_c)/R_l \qquad [18.3]$$

Equation 18.3 indicates a graphical solution for dynamic problems similar to the load-line technique employed in the graphical analysis of vacuum-tube circuits.

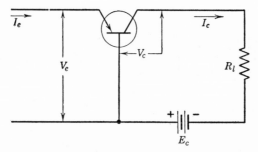

Fig. 18.1   Grounded-base p-n-p transistor amplifier.

Figure 18.2 illustrates the method used in constructing a load line on typical collector static-characteristic curves for the type of circuit illustrated in Fig. 18.1.   The abscissa and ordinate coordinates for the load line are E_c and E_c/R_l respectively, and the slope of the load line is

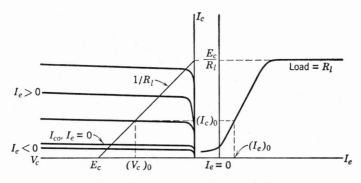

Static collector characteristics   Dynamic transfer characteristics

Fig. 18.2   Construction of dynamic transfer characteristic.

$1/R_l$. As with vacuum tubes, a dynamic transfer characteristic may be graphically constructed for a particular load, R_l, and for a particular collector supply, E_c. The quiescent d-c operating point is defined by $(I_e)_0$, $(I_c)_0$, and $(V_c)_0$, where $(I_e)_0$ is the emitter current supplied by the d-c bias. Distortion of the collector current due to a large emitter current input may be graphically derived directly from projection on the dynamic transfer characteristic. Two such projections are shown in Fig. 18.3 for a small- and large-signal input. It should be remembered that the use of static curves to determine dynamic transfer characteristics, and subsequently collector current waveforms, does not take into account frequency and transit time effects. Since the inherent parameters of a transistor, particularly the current amplification factor α, and the collector impedance z_c, are frequency-sensitive, graphical solution of large-signal input problems are limited to signals of comparatively low frequency. The frequency limit to which graphical analysis may be carried with reasonable accuracy will be deter-

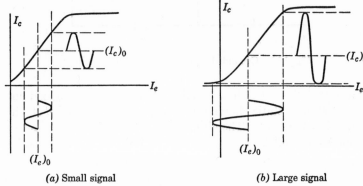

(a) Small signal   (b) Large signal

Fig. 18.3   Graphical determination of collector current for current-source emitter input.

mined by the α cut-off frequency of any particular transistor. Should the cut-off frequency be higher than that frequency at which the collector impedance begins to deviate substantially from a purely resistive parameter, the frequency corresponding to this deviation must be used as a limit to the accuracy of the graphical solution. In present-day transistors, this frequency limit may lie within the range of 50–500 kilocycles.

When an integrating element is present in the collector circuit, distortion in the collector current will give rise to an added d-c component due to the a-c input current. Any distorted periodic waveform may be expanded, by Fourier theory, as

$$i = I_0 + \sum_{n=1}^{\infty} a_n e^{j\omega_0 n t} \qquad [18.4]$$

If the distorted collector current is expanded by means of eq. 18.4, the d-c component, I_0, will cause a change in the operating point on the I_c-V_c static characteristics. If the integrating element has negligible effect upon the current-voltage relations in the collector circuit, such that eq. 18.1 remains unchanged for all practical purposes, straight-load-line analysis may still be resorted to, graphically, in order to determine the collector current waveform. To do this, the net d-c collector current $(I_c)_0 + I_0$, may be thought of as due to an increased collector supply voltage, $E_c + \Delta E_c$. Here,

$$\Delta E_c = I_0 R_l$$

A new load line is then drawn, corresponding to the increased collector supply voltage. Relating to the new load line is a new dynamic transfer characteristic from which a new collector current waveform is found. This revised collector current waveform leads to a new and reduced d-c distortion component I_0. Thus, by an iterative process the problem may be solved to a close approximation. The most tedious portion of such a graphical iteration is the solution for the d-c component of collector current, $I_{\text{d-c}}$. (Graphical integration may be used to solve for $I_{\text{d-c}}$.) When the impedance of the integrating element is not negligible, such that eq. 18.1 no longer holds, the operating path on the static V_c-I_c curves is no longer a straight line. For small input signals, such an operating path would be of an elliptical nature. But for large input signals, the operating path becomes extremely complicated; it is then best to solve the problem by experimental trials on the actual circuit.

18.3   Dynamic Current-Amplification Factor

In Chapter 1, the current amplification, α, was defined as

$$\alpha = \frac{\partial I_c}{\partial I_e}\bigg|_{V_c} \tag{18.5}$$

For small-signal operation, α is a constant of the transistor and varies from values of approximately 0.95 for junction types to approximately 2.5 for point-contact types. Consequently, for small input currents, the collector and emitter currents are related to each other by α as

$$I_c = \alpha I_e + I_{c0} \tag{18.6}$$

where I_{c0} is the collector current for $I_e = 0$. From the dynamic transfer characteristic illustrated in Fig. 18.2, it is apparent that for large-signal operation I_c varies as a non-linear function of I_e and that I_c is further dependent upon the load resistance R_l. The dynamic transfer characteristic may be used to define a dynamic current-amplification factor, α_D, which is given mathematically by

$$I_c = \alpha_D(R_l, I_e)I_e + I_{c0} \tag{18.7}$$

Equation 18.7 denotes α_D as a function of the emitter current and load resistance. When the I_c-V_c static characteristics of a transistor are very flat (i.e., almost perpendicular to the I_c axis), such as those shown in Fig. 18.2, α (as defined by eq. 18.5) will be nearly the same as α_D in the linear region of the I_c-I_e curve. But this is not the general case. Hence, where $\partial I_c/\partial I_e$ (for a given load resistance) is a constant in the dynamic transfer characteristic, the symbol α_0 will be used; α_0 defines

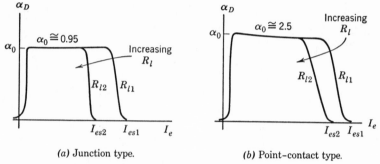

(a) Junction type.   (b) Point–contact type.

Fig. 18.4   Variation of α_D with emitter current.

the linear range of the dynamic current-amplification factor, α_D. For transistors having flat I_c-V_c curves, $\alpha_D \cong \alpha_0$.

The variation of α_D with I_e may be determined graphically from the dynamic transfer characteristic. In mathematical form, this is

$$da_D = \frac{\partial \alpha_D}{\partial R_l} dR_l + \frac{\partial \alpha_D}{\partial I_e} dI_e \qquad [18.8]$$

Figure 18.4 illustrates the variation of α_D with I_e for both junction and point-contact type transistors. I_e is positive when the transistors are of the p-n-p types, and negative when the transistors are of the n-p-n types. The emitter current at which α_D drops to near-zero value is denoted by I_{es}. We may assume, for simple straight-line approximation methods, that the variation of α_D with emitter current is as follows:

p-n-p Junction Transistor	I_e	p-n-p Point-Contact Transistor
$\alpha_D \cong 0$	$I_e < 0$	$\alpha_D \cong 0$
$\alpha_D \cong 0.95$	$0 < I_e < I_{es}$	$\alpha_D \cong 2.5$
$\alpha_D \cong 0$	$I_{es} < I_e < \infty$	$\alpha_D \cong 0$

It must be remembered that I_{es} is a function of the load resistance but may be considered constant for any given load.

The foregoing discussion assumes that the dynamic current-amplification factor α_D is a function only of the load resistance R_l and the emitter current I_e. In practice, α_D will also vary with frequency, but the same frequency limits are applied to considering α_D frequency invariant as are applied to considering the static I_c-V_c characteristics frequency invariant.

18.4 Large-Signal Equivalent Circuit, Passive Network

The small-signal equivalent circuit illustrated in Fig. 3.5 may be modified for large-signal applications as shown in Fig. 18.5. r_e and r_c

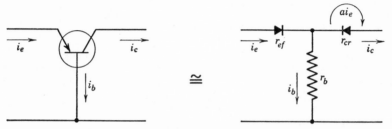

Fig. 18.5   Large-signal equivalent circuit.

of Fig. 3.5 have been replaced by r_{ef} and r_{cr}, respectively, where r_{ef} indicates the dynamic resistance of the emitter diode biased in the conductive direction, r_{cr} is the dynamic resistance of the collector diode biased in the reverse direction.

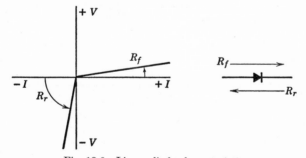

Fig. 18.6   Linear diode characteristic.

(Note: In the discussion that follows, a dynamic resistance will be indicated by small letters, e.g., r_{ef}. Where a d-c resistance is implied, capitals are used, e.g., R_{ef}, and if, as in idealized cases, the dynamic and d-c values are identical, capitals are used.)

With the diode directions as indicated, the equivalent circuit holds for a p-n-p transistor. To maintain the equivalence for an n-p-n type, the diode directions need only be reversed. The voltage-current characteristics of the diodes are assumed to be of the form illustrated in Fig. 18.6. For a typical p-n-p junction transistor, the emitter resistance in the forward direction, R_{ef}, is of the order of 30 ohms, while the emitter resistance in the back direction, R_{er}, is of the order of 500,000 ohms. Typical collector resistances for the p-n-p junction transistor are as follows:

$$R_{cr} = 500,000 \ \Omega \qquad R_{cf} = 50 \ \Omega$$

There are four possible combinations of operating conditions for the diodes of Fig. 18.5: (a) R_{ef} and R_{cr}, which is the normal operating condition for a p-n-p transistor; (b) R_{ef} and R_{cf}; (c) R_{er} and R_{cr}; and (d) R_{er} and R_{cf}. It should be pointed out that these operating conditions exist for a diode which is assumed to have the bivalued linear V-I characteristics depicted in Fig. 18.6. In general, the behavior of a real diode in both the positive and negative regions of current is dependent upon the current magnitude as well as the current sign; i.e., R_f and R_r are non-linear. The characteristics assumed in Fig. 18.6 suffice as a first approximation.

A passive large-signal equivalent circuit may be used to determine, at least qualitatively, the static characteristic curves of the transistor when the current amplification $\alpha = 0$. Referring to the circuit illus-

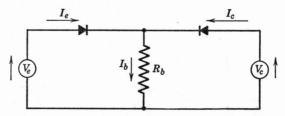

Fig. 18.7   Large-signal passive equivalent circuit.

trated in Fig. 18.7, which adopts the current and voltage directions most frequently used for the analysis of a four-terminal network, the following Kirchhoff circuit equations may be written

$$V_e = I_e R_{ef} + I_b R_b \qquad [18.9]$$

$$V_c = I_c R_{cr} + I_b R_b \qquad [18.10]$$

$$I_e = I_b - I_c \qquad [18.11]$$

Substituting eq. 18.11 into eq. 18.9 results in

$$V_e = I_e R_{ef} + R_b(I_e + I_c)$$
$$= I_e(R_{ef} + R_b) + I_c R_b \qquad [18.12]$$

From eq. 18.12, the passive V_e-I_e curves can be plotted for various values of I_c and for the condition that I_e is in the forward direction of

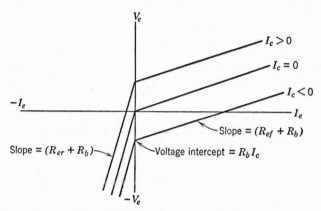

Fig. 18.8   Static V_e-I_e curves derived from passive equivalent circuit.

the emitter diode.   When I_e reverses sign, eq. 18.12 becomes

$$V_e = I_e(R_{er} + R_b) + I_c R_b \qquad [18.13]$$

The passive characteristics derived from eqs. 18.12 and 18.13 are illustrated in Fig. 18.8.   In a similar manner, the V_c-I_c curves may be approximated from the large-signal equivalent circuit.

18.5   Large-Signal Equivalent Circuit, Dynamic Network

The large-signal equivalent circuit for dynamic analysis follows directly from Fig. 18.7.   This dynamic equivalent is illustrated in Fig. 18.9.   From the circuit analysis the usual loop equations may be written for the current directions as shown:

$$v_e = i_e R_{ef} + i_b R_b \qquad [18.14]$$

$$v_c = i_c R_{cr} + i_b R_b + a i_e R_{cr} \qquad [18.15]$$

$$i_b = i_c + i_e \qquad [18.16]$$

where v_e, i_e, etc., are now increments.   In addition, the current amplification in the collector is given approximately (see Sec. 18.3) by

$$i_c = -\alpha_D i_e \qquad [18.17]$$

where α_D is a function of the emitter current (as shown in Fig. 18.4). Equation 18.16 may then be written

$$i_b = i_e(1 - \alpha_D)$$

which, when substituted into eq. 18.14, yields

$$v_e = i_e[R_{ef} + R_b(1 - \alpha_D)] \qquad [18.18]$$

Equation 18.18 indicates that the input resistance of the transistor is a function of α_D, which, in turn, varies with the emitter current. Furthermore, if α_D is greater than unity, as it is for point-contact tran-

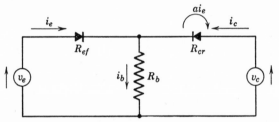

Fig. 18.9   Large-signal dynamic equivalent circuit.

sistors, the input resistance of the transistor may be negative. It is interesting to plot the change of input resistance as a function of I_e for both the junction and point-contact transistors, remembering that for reversal of the emitter current eq. 18.18 becomes

$$v_e = i_e[R_{er} + R_b(1 + \alpha_D)] \qquad [18.19]$$

Using the straight-line approximations for the variation of α_D with emitter current as described in Sec. 18.3, eqs. 18.18 and 18.19 are plotted for both the point-contact and junction transistors in Fig. 18.10. Figure 18.10 predicts the N-type characteristic of the point-contact transistor as well as the completely positive input resistance of the junction type.

A constant-current source of large sine-wave output feeding a transistor would develop a voltage, across the input, which is rich in harmonics. Based upon the V_e-I_e characteristics of Fig. 18.10, the input voltage waveforms, generated by a constant-current sine wave, for both the junction and point-contact transistors are illustrated in Fig. 18.11. The dotted lines in Fig. 18.11 illustrate the non-linear voltage waveforms at the transistor input when the emitter is biased with a positive direct current of magnitude $I_{es}/2$ and when the a-c source has a maximum peak amplitude in excess of $I_{es}/2$, so that it swings beyond the inflection points O and A of Fig. 18.10.

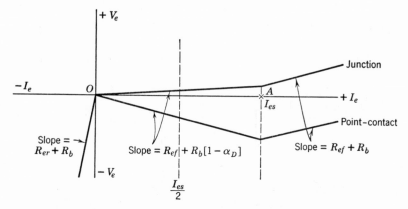

Fig. 18.10   Large-signal dynamic characteristics.

Once again, it should be pointed out that frequency limitations restrict the use of large-signal equivalent circuits. The same restrictions apply here as those mentioned in reference to the graphical analysis

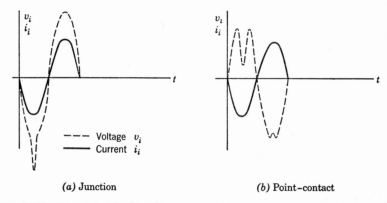

(a) Junction   (b) Point-contact

Fig. 18.11   Non-linear input voltages generated by a constant-current sine-wave source, p-n-p transistor.

(see Sec. 18.2). Furthermore, the diode characteristic that was assumed in Fig. 18.6 is approximately true only for a limited range in real diodes. *Thus, the equivalent circuit for large-signal analysis should be used primarily with a view to qualitative understanding.*

18.6 Channel Effect

In the construction of junction transistors, the p-n barriers formed by the emitter-base and collector-base junctions give rise to the diodes illustrated in the large-signal equivalent circuit. Electrons injected into the n region of a p-n junction cause a decrease in the potential across the barrier and thus effect a low-resistance path for current flow from the p region to the n region. However, electrons injected

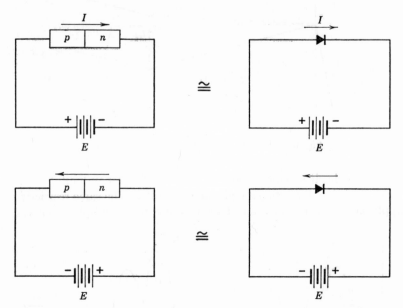

Fig. 18.12 Schematic representation of barrier resistance to current flow.

into the p region of a p-n junction cause an increase in the potential across the barrier and thus effect a high-resistance path for current flow from the p region to the n region. These effects are schematically illustrated in Fig. 18.12. When a p-n-p junction is formed, it is assumed that current flow from the emitter to the collector must occur in a path which includes direct transmission through the p-n and n-p barriers; i.e., there can be no barrier-circumventing feed-through from the emitter to the collector. This assumption was the basis for the equivalent circuits described in Secs. 18.4 and 18.5. However, under certain conditions it may be possible to have current flow, through a high impedance, between the emitter and collector. Such current flow is referred to as "channel effect."

Transistors of certain types are more susceptible to channel effect than others. For example, consider the construction illustrated in Fig. 18.13. If the base connection to the n region overlaps the p regions, it is quite apparent that the emitter current will be provided with a path to the collector which bypasses the p-n and n-p junctions. This path is illustrated by the dotted line in Fig. 18.13. Even if the base connection does not overlap the p regions, channel effect may still exist as the result of surface conductivity around the n region (through the base con-

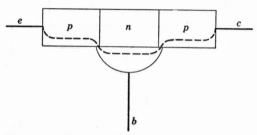

Fig. 18.13 Channel effect in rate-grown transistor.

nection). Although little is known about surface phenomena, much experimental evidence links channel effect to surface conductivity in junction transistors of the type illustrated in Fig. 18.13.

Channel effect due to surface conductivity is essentially non-existent for transistors of the type shown in Fig. 18.14. The only possible current path for such a surface effect would be the one indicated by the dotted line, and, since this current path is necessarily long, the surface resistance would be too high to be of any practical significance. However, there is a possibility that deep diffusion of the emitter and collector p regions into the n bar may cause the p-region boundaries to be too close to each other. For such a condition, space-charge effects may cause additional p diffusion

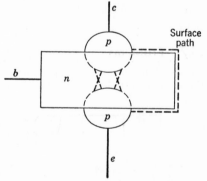

Fig. 18.14 Channel effect in diffused-type transistor.

through the n layer which would result in narrow and irregular, but direct, p-region contacts between the emitter and the collector. Channel effects due to space-charge-induced diffusion is not known to have been observed experimentally and is mentioned here only as a possibility.

When channel effect is present, the equivalent circuit of Fig. 18.9 may be modified as indicated in Fig. 18.15. The resistance R_h represents the channel between emitter and collector, and is estimated to be of the order of 5–10 megohms for a transistor of the type shown in Fig. 18.13.

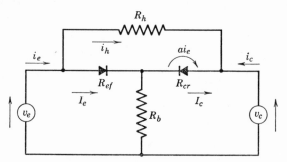

Fig. 18.15   Large-signal equivalent circuit modified to include channel effect.

Kirchhoff equations similar to those of eqs. 18.14–18.17 may be readily calculated for the bridge-T network of Fig. 18.15. It is apparent from the equivalent circuit that R_h will be of significance only if R_{cr} is high.

As construction details of transistors are brought under closer control, it may be expected that channel effect will be practically eliminated in all types. However, it may be well to keep in mind that deterioration of surface due to moisture absorption, impurity migrations, etc., may initiate channel currents. The transistor is much too recent a development for long-range information of this type to be available as yet.

18.7   Problems

1. Determine the instantaneous collector current for the circuit of Fig. 18.16 The static characteristics of the transistor are given in Fig. 2.8. Assume $R = 0$.

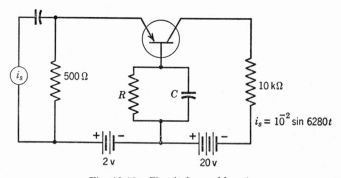

Fig. 18.16   Circuit for problem 1.

2. Repeat problem 1 when the resistance R is shunted by a large capacitor, C. Assume that the impedance of R and C is negligible in the circuit considerations but that they combine to form an ideal integrating circuit.

3. Determine the dynamic I_c-V_c characteristics for the large-signal equivalent circuit of Fig. 18.9 when the emitter diode characteristics are as shown in Fig. 18.17 and for the emitter currents $I_e = 0$ and $I_e = +1$ ma.

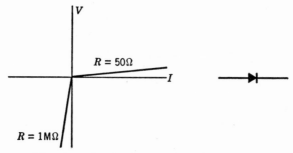

Fig. 18.17   Diode characteristic for problem 3.

18.8 Bibliography

1. R. B. Adler, "A Large Signal Equivalent Circuit for Transistor Static Characteristics," R.L.E., M.I.T., Transistor Group, Oct. 2, 1951.

2. B. G. Farley, "Dynamics of Transistor Negative-Resistance Circuits," *Proc. IRE*, November, 1952.

3. L. P. Hunter and H. Fleisher, "Graphical Analysis of Some Transistor Switching Circuits," *Proc. IRE*, November, 1952

Chapter 19

Computer Circuits

19.1 Introduction

Semiconductor devices, such as transistors, may never fully replace the vacuum tube in all electronic applications, but the field in which semiconductors seem likely to take over the functions of vacuum tubes most profitably is in the construction of electronic computers. Computer networks connote such applications as automatic industrial machinery, radar, flight-control instrumentation, digital computers, analogue computers, telephone switchboards, telemetering, and monitoring. Those areas of application in which the semiconductor holds immediate promise are those where such factors as temperature and humidity may be controlled.

Most computer-type controls are complex systems which involve the use of a great number of standardized circuits. Analogue computers may require a great number of high-gain d-c amplifiers for integrator, differentiator, and adding stages. Digital computers may require a great number of pulse amplifiers for logic stages. Electronic equipment of this type currently requires a great number of vacuum tubes and associated elements. For example, the general-purpose digital computer OARAC (Office of Air Research Automatic Calculator), completed in 1953 by the General Electric Company, contains approximately 1400 vacuum tubes and 7000 germanium diodes. Power consumption and heat dissipation are major problems in computer circuits, particularly if the computers are designed for mobile use.

The low heat dissipation, low power consumption, rugged mechanical construction, and small size of transistors make these devices well suited for computer-type circuitry. Currently available transistors present many problems in practical application. Variation of I_{c0} with temperature (see Chapter 3), surface effects due to moisture seepage through the transistor package, etc., indicate the necessity for air conditioning of complex transistorized equipment. As transistor development progresses, it is reasonable to expect that transistors will be "weatherproofed" to the same extent as vacuum tubes. However, regardless of the extent of future progress in the construction of semi-conductor devices, the vast savings in power consumption, heat dissipation, weight, and size which may be achieved by their use in computer equipment may well justify supplementary air conditioning if required.

This chapter will deal with specific examples of transistor circuits which may be used in either analogue or digital computers. The same circuits, or variations thereof, may be used in radar, pulse counters, correlators, etc. Naturally, all the problems that arise in computer design cannot be treated here. Hence, the object of the ensuing sections is to present an introductory summary of how computer circuits may be transistorized. Oscillators, which are part of synchronizing circuits in computers, are not discussed here, but are covered in detail in Chapter 13.

19.2   Analogue Computers

19.2.1   Analogue Principles

Analogue computers are designed to solve specific types of differential equations. The fact that many physical systems are describable by equations of the same form makes possible the analogy of electric-circuit behavior to mechanical, acoustical, hydrodynamic, or thermodynamic properties. A simple example of this is the analogy of a body of mass m, falling with velocity v through a viscous fluid, to a series R-L circuit. If the force exerted by the fluid on the falling body is assumed to be directly proportional to the velocity of the body, i.e., $f_r = kv$, then the Newtonian equation of motion is given by

$$m(dv/dt) = W - kv \qquad [19.1a]$$

For the series R-L circuit illustrated in Fig. 19.1, the loop equation is

$$L(di/dt) = E - Ri \qquad [19.1b]$$

The similarity of eq. 19.1a to eq. 19.1b is immediately apparent. Both these differential equations may be integrated to give

$$\int v \, dt + (m/k)v = (W/k)t \qquad [19.1c]$$

$$\int i \, dt + (L/R)i = (E/R)t \qquad [19.1d]$$

The electrical circuit of Fig. 19.1 can be used to solve dynamic problems relating to its hydromechanical analogy by consideration of the pa-

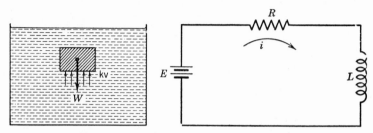

Fig. 19.1   Mechanical and electrical analogy.

rameter correspondence between eqs. 19.1c and 19.1d.   This correspondence is tabulated herewith.

Hydromechanical	Electrical
Velocity	Current
Mass	Inductance
Weight	Emf
Viscous damping	Resistance

Although the circuit of Fig. 19.1 is very simple to realize physically as a direct analogue of the damped-fall problem, the analogue solution of eq. 19.1c can be set up in a more general form by the block diagram of Fig. 19.2.   A block diagram of this form simply pictorializes the

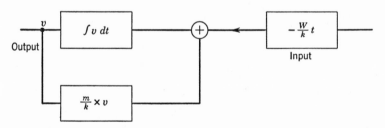

Fig. 19.2   General block diagram solution of eq. 19.1c.

operations required to solve the desired differential equation.   Any differential equation, or set of simultaneous differential equations, with physically realizable coefficients, may be solved by analogue techniques. The principal components of an analogue computer are the integrator and adding mechanisms, and any number of these may be combined, at least theoretically, to solve the dynamic equations of a physical system.

Many types of function generators may be required in the solution of non-linear equations, but these devices will not be discussed here. In essence, only the integrator and differentiator will be considered. Relative to this it should be remembered that any differential equation of the form given by eq. 19.1a may be converted to an integral equation, e.g., eq. 19.1c, by successive integration.

19.2.2   Integrating Circuits

A simple integrating circuit is illustrated in Fig. 19.3. Its network transform, in terms of the Laplace operator s ($s = j\omega$ in the frequency domain), is

$$\frac{e_o(s)}{e_i(s)} = \frac{1}{1 + RCs} \tag{19.2}$$

If the RC time constant is made considerably greater than unity, such that $\omega RC \gg 1$, the corresponding inverse transform of eq. 19.2 is

$$e_o(t) \cong \frac{1}{RC}\int e_i(t)\ dt \tag{19.3}$$

Equation 19.3 indicates that the circuit of Fig. 19.3 may be used to integrate a time-varying function, $e_i(t)$, provided that the major components of the frequency spectrum of $e_i(t)$ are such that $\omega RC \gg 1$. Passive networks of this type are not suitable as integrating elements in

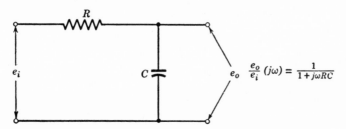

Fig. 19.3   Simple integrating circuit.

computer networks because isolating resistances are required between the networks to prevent loading effects, thus giving rise to excessive signal attenuation. To overcome such an objection, amplifiers must be used in conjunction with the integrating circuits.

A popular type of vacuum-tube analogue integrator is illustrated in Fig. 19.4.[2] It consists of a d-c amplifier with capacity feedback from

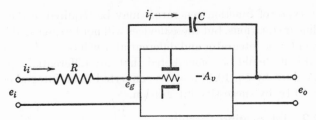

Fig. 19.4 Block diagram for feedback-type vacuum-tube integrator.

plate to grid. Assuming very high input and load impedances, the following equations may be written for the feedback integrator:

$$i_i = i_f \qquad [19.4a]$$

hence

$$\frac{e_g - e_i}{R} = \frac{e_o - e_g}{1/Cs} \qquad [19.4b]$$

The output voltage of the amplifier, e_o, is equal to the product of the grid signal, e_g, and the amplification A_v, i.e.:

$$e_o = -A_v e_g \qquad [19.4c]$$

Substituting eq. 19.4c into 19.4b gives

$$\frac{e_o}{e_i} = -\frac{1}{RCs}\left[\frac{1}{1 + (1/A_v)[1 + (1/RCs)]}\right] \qquad [19.4d]$$

It is apparent from eq. 19.4d that, if the amplification A_v is made very large (5000 is considered a practical value), eq. 19.4d becomes

$$e_o/e_i \cong -1/RCs$$

which is the operational equation of a perfect integrator.

The d-c vacuum-tube amplifier employing feedback of various types has been widely used in analogue computers for such functions as integrators, differentiators, and adders, etc.[2] When amplifiers are used in computational circuits, they must be stabilized against drift and circuit instability. Drift stability connotes an amplifier stable against temperature, humidity, and power-supply changes. Various circuits have been designed that meet these requirements (see, for example, reference 2).

To insure against circuit instability, an odd number of phase-shift stages (or the equivalent phase-shift due to passive circuitry) must be employed in the amplifier such that the operational feedback circuit is degenerative. The accuracy of an analogue computer is, in general, directly contingent upon the quality of the amplifiers employed in its basic circuits.

Equation 19.4d may be written

$$e_o/e_i = -A_v/[1 + (1 + A_v)RCs] \qquad [19.4e]$$

From eq. 19.4e, it may be seen that the integrating time constant, RC, is effectively multiplied by $(1 + A_v)$. This so-called "Miller effect" is one of the advantages of the capacitive feedback integrator.

Since the vacuum tube is basically a voltage-amplifying device, whereas the transistor is primarily a current amplifier, it may be ex-

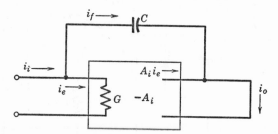

Fig. 19.5   Block diagram for "voltage-feedback" transistor integrator.

pected that material circuit differences will exist between the vacuum-tube computer and the transistorized computer if full advantage is to be made of either device. A transistorized d-c integrator, similar to the vacuum-tube type illustrated in Fig. 19.4, may be built; the basic d-c amplifier circuit for such an integrator was discussed in Chapter 8. The block diagram of the transistor "voltage-feedback" integrator is shown in Fig. 19.5. The terminology "voltage feedback" is used to describe this circuit because of its similarity to the voltage-feedback connection in vacuum-tube circuits. Figure 19.5 assumes that the input admittance of the amplifier, G, is effectively isolated from the output circuit, and that the output current $A_i i_e$ feeds into a high-admittance (low-resistance) stage, the latter being sufficiently represented by a short circuit, compared to the reactance of C. The following equations may then be written for the circuit of Fig. 19.5:

$$i_f/Cs \cong i_e/G \qquad [19.5a]$$

$$i_i = i_e + i_f \qquad [19.5b]$$

$$i_o = A_i i_e + i_f \qquad [19.5c]$$

Eliminating i_f and i_e in eq. 19.5a by use of eqs. 19.5b and c results in

$$\frac{i_o}{i_i} = -A_i \frac{1 - (RCs/A_i)}{1 + RCs} \qquad [19.5d]$$

where $R = 1/G$. If A_i is very large, eq. 19.5d may be written

$$i_o/i_i \cong -A_i/(1 + RCs) \qquad [19.5e]$$

Equation 19.5e is of the same form as eq. 19.2, indicating that the transistor circuit of Fig. 19.5 gives integrating action equivalent to a passive

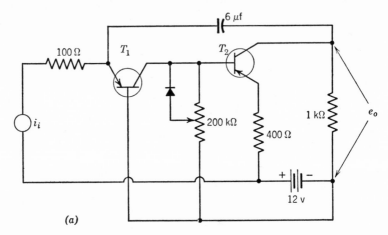

(a)

Fig. 19.6a   Temperature-stabilized d-c integrator.

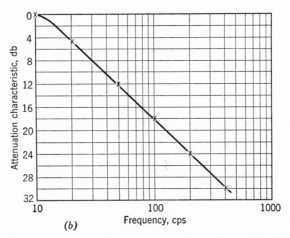

(b)

Fig. 19.6b   Attenuation vs. frequency, experimental transistor integrator.

R-C circuit, such as the one shown in Fig. 19.3. However, the transistor voltage-feedback integrator has a current amplification, A_i, and thus may be cascaded in computer applica-
tions without signal attenuation. An experimental d-c integrator of the voltage-feedback type is illustrated in Fig. 19.6a. (For details concerning the d-c amplifier, see Chapter 8.) Its frequency and time responses are illustrated in Figs. 19.6b and 19.6c respectively.

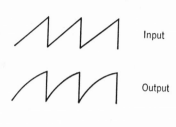

Input

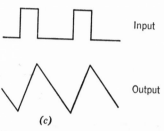

Output

19.2.3   General Transistor Analogue Operational Circuit

Although the transistor analogue integrator of Fig. 19.5 can be used in computer circuitry, it is desirable to have a general operational device which may serve as integrator, differentiator, adder, or scale changer, much as the general vacuum-tube feedback circuit does. (See references 1 and 2.)

Fig. 19.6c Response of transistor integrator to sawtooth and square wave.

A current analogue of the vacuum-tube circuit is illustrated in Fig. 19.7. The block A_i represents a high gain d-c transistor amplifier. The amplifier is connected through an admittance, Y, to ground, and the combination is shunted by an input conductance, G. It is assumed that the input to the amplifier is a very low-resistance path, so that it

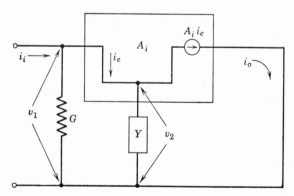

Fig. 19.7   Ideal transistor analogue operational circuit.

essentially can be represented by a short circuit, and that the amplifier is loaded by a very low-impedance output, which is also essentially a short circuit. If it is further assumed that the output current is supplied by an ideal current source, $A_i i_e$, the following equations may be written:

$$v_1 = v_2 \qquad [19.6a]$$

Therefore,

$$(i_i/G) - (i_e/G) = (i_e/Y) - (i_o/Y) \qquad [19.6b]$$

Since

$$i_o = A_i i_e \qquad [19.6c]$$

eq. 19.6b becomes

$$i_o/i_i = A_i Y/[Y + G(1 - A_i)] \qquad [19.6d]$$

If there is a reversal of phase between the input and output currents of the amplifier, such that

$$i_o/i_e = A_i = -u_i$$

eq. 19.6d becomes

$$\frac{i_o}{i_i} = -\frac{Y}{G}\left[\frac{1}{1 + (1/u_i)[1 + (Y/G)]}\right] \qquad [19.6e]$$

Equation 19.6e is the current equivalent of the voltage transfer function which was derived for the feedback-type operational amplifier employing vacuum tubes.

Consider the circuit of Fig. 19.7 when Y is an inductive admittance, $1/Ls$. Equation 19.6e is then written

$$\frac{i_o}{i_i} = -\frac{1}{GLs}\left[\frac{1}{1 + (1/u_i)[1 + (1/GLs)]}\right] \qquad [19.7]$$

If $u_i \gg 1$, eq. 19.7 is the condition for an analogue integrator. The similarity between eq. 19.4d and eq. 19.7 is apparent. When Y, in Fig. 19.7, is a capacitor having an admittance Cs, eq. 19.6e becomes

$$i_o/i_i \cong -RCs \qquad (u_i \gg 1)$$

which is the condition for differentiation. When Y is a resistor having conductance G_f, eq. 19.6e is

$$i_o/i_i \cong G_f/G \qquad (u_i \gg 1)$$

which is the condition for a scale changer.

The transistor network of Fig. 19.7 is the generalized operational circuit for use in analogue design problems. As was seen above, it is capable of serving as an integrator, differentiator, or scaler, depending upon the nature of element Y. It should be noted that, when Y and G

are interchanged, the operational function of the circuit is inverted. Thus, if $Y = Cs$, the circuit of Fig. 19.7 is a differentiator; if Cs and G are then interchanged, the circuit becomes an integrator. Because of this, it is possible to use both differentiator and integrator with only

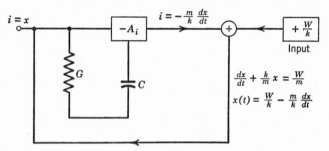

Fig. 19.8   Block diagram of transistorized computer.

resistive and capacitive elements in the transistorized analogue computer.

A transistorized analogue computer, in block diagram form, is illustrated in Fig. 19.8. This computer is the circuit mechanization of the diagram in Fig. 19.2, and solves the differential equation 19.1c.

19.3   Digital Computers

19.3.1   Nature of Digital Computers

Although analogue computers have found wide application in the physical sciences as means for solving equations, very often their accuracy has proved insufficient. Furthermore, it is very often desirable to have numerical solutions as the end products of design calculations, and for such purposes the analogue computer is not always suitable. Still another shortcoming of analogue devices is that the non-linear functions which may be required in the solution of certain important types of non-linear equations may not be conveniently generated.

To meet the objections of analogue devices, digital computers were developed. The basis for digital computation is that many equations can be solved by successive approximation methods, the accuracy of which depends upon the interval of iteration. Numerical integration is an illustration of this. A fundamental theorem in the calculus is given by

$$\int_a^b f(x)\, dx = \lim_{\substack{n \to \infty \\ \Delta x_i \to 0}} \sum_{i=1}^n f(x_i)\, \Delta x_i \qquad \text{for } a \le x_i \le b \qquad [19.8]$$

which states that the definite integral $\int_a^b f(x) \, dx$ is the limiting value
of the sum of $f(x_i) \, \Delta x_i$ evaluated between the limits a and b as the
number of terms approaches infinity (or the interval between successive
terms approaches zero). Thus, any definite integral may be evaluated
numerically to any required degree of accuracy by performing the
summation of discrete quantities as indicated by eq. 19.8. For example, the integral:

$$\int_0^1 x \, dx$$

may be evaluated by use of eq. 19.8. The result of this method is
tabulated in Table 19.1 for intervals (Δx_i) of 0.5, 0.2, 0.1 and 0.05.

Table 19.1

Δx_i	$\Sigma x_i \, \Delta x_i$	Error, %
0.5	0.75	50
0.2	0.60	20
0.1	0.55	10
0.05	0.525	5
lim $\to$ 0	0.500	0

Differential equations, and systems of differential equations, may be
solved in a manner similar to numerical integration by a method of
finite differences and similar techniques. There is a great deal of literature in this field (see references 3–7), and no attempt will be made here
to summarize this work.

From the simple example summarized in Table 19.1, it is apparent
that a digital computer must be capable of arithmetic processes like
addition and multiplication, and must furthermore be capable of some
method of storage so that the results of the arithmetic operations may
be utilized, at the proper time, in giving the desired result. Implied
in the operations of computation and storage are such other functions
as programming (input devices such as tapes), timing or synchronizing
and reading (output devices such as automatic typewriting and coded
tapes). Many systems of digital computer networks have been designed to solve problems ranging from weather and economic predictions to machine shop and guided-missile direction. (See references
8-14.) All these computers operate on essentially the same principles,
but even the simplest are too detailed for a comprehensive description
here. Consequently, the ensuing material will be devoted to the application of transistors in only a few basic circuits which find wide appli-

cation not only in digital computers but also in those electronic systems, in general, which use quantized signals, i.e., pulses, as information carriers.

19.3.2 Basic Types of Digital Computer Circuits

The operation of digital computers has been divided into two principal categories: "logic" and "memory." By the very nature of the digital mechanism, both these major operations require the handling or processing of numbers. The basic number system used throughout the world is the decimal type, which is, as the name implies, a numbering based on a 10-digit vocabulary. All numbers, or logic translations based upon numerical representation (see reference 15, for example), can be derived from the basic 10 digits of the decimal system. Thus, the number 29 may be written

$$10^1 \times 2 + 10^0 \times 9 = 29$$

In order to utilize mechanically the numbers based upon a decimal system, ten different elements or circuit combinations must be available and recognizable in a digital computer. Rather than adapt computers to the decimal system, however, it eventually became apparent that it might be more practical and more convenient to adapt a number system to computers.

The simplest type of such a number system is the binary plan, which is based upon the digits 0 and 1. Not only is the binary system based upon the simplest of numerical combinations, but it also corresponds directly to simple electrical operations, such as the "on" or "off" operation of a relay or flipflop. Shannon [16] based his measure of information, the bit, on the binary choice. In the binary system, the number 29 may be written

$$29 = 2^4 \times 1 + 2^3 \times 1 + 2^2 \times 1 + 2^1 \times 0 + 2^0 \times 1 = 11101$$

All the arithmetic operations applicable to the decimal system are also applicable to the binary system. Thus, $16 + 13 = 29$ in the decimal system is, in the binary system,

$$
\begin{array}{ll}
1101 & (2^3 \times 1 + 2^2 \times 1 + 2^1 \times 0 + 2^0 \times 1 = 13) \\
10000 & (2^4 \times 1 + 2^3 \times 0 + 2^2 \times 0 + 2^1 \times 0 + 2^0 \times 0 = 16) \\
\hline
11101 & (2^4 \times 1 + 2^3 \times 1 + 2^2 \times 1 + 2^1 \times 0 + 2^0 \times 1 = 29)
\end{array}
$$

Since the flipflop, or Eccles-Jordan, circuit is ideally suited to the binary system in high-speed digital operation, many of the circuits in the storage or "memory" stages of digital computers may be combinations of flipflop circuits. The point-contact transistor, as a single active element in a flipflop circuit, offers considerable possibilities in the transistorization of computer networks. Specific circuits for the design of monostable and bistable flipflops, using point-contact transistors, will be presented in Sec. 19.4.

The logic functions of digital computers can be divided into the "or," "and," and "negation" operations. An n-terminal "or" circuit will have an output if any one of its input terminals is energized. The

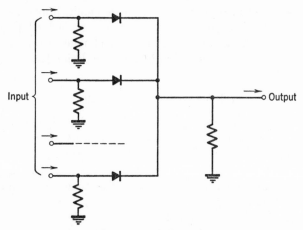

Fig. 19.9   "Or" circuit.

"and" circuit, however, will have an output only if all its n-input terminals are energized. "Inhibition" or "negation" circuits prevent a signal from appearing on its output as long as there is a signal on any one of its input leads. All these fundamental logic circuits may be constructed from purely passive elements such as diodes and resistors. Figure 19.9 illustrates an "or" circuit, and it is evident from the circuit that a positive signal applied to any of the input terminals will appear at the output. Figure 19.10 illustrates an "and" circuit. In the "and" circuit, the output diode, D_o, is conducting through any one of the input-terminal paths as long as there is at least one input terminal which has no applied (positive) signal. Thus, the output is slightly below ground owing to the voltage drop in the forward direction across D_o. When all the input terminals are energized, so that all the input voltages rise above ground, the other diodes are cut off, and only then will the diode D_o be cut off. With D_o cut off, a voltage appears at the output, thus fulfilling the condition that an output appear only when all the input terminals are energized.

A simple inhibitor circuit is illustrated in Fig. 19.11.   The symbol nD represents a delay of n digits, the digit time, D, being the interval between successive pulses.   As in the "and" circuit, the diode D_o clamps

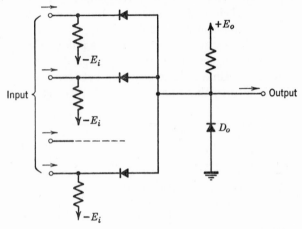

Fig. 19.10   "And" circuit.

the output terminal to ground as long as no signal is applied to the input terminal.   When the inhibiting pulse is present, the diodes D_{iN} are conducting and thus keep the output at ground potential.   The

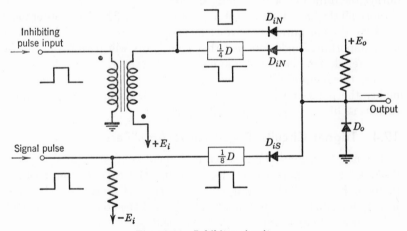

Fig. 19.11   Inhibitor circuit.

particular delay scheme indicated [17] in Fig. 19.11 insures that the inhibiting pulse will arrive $\frac{1}{8}D$ seconds ahead of the signal pulse and will persist for $\frac{1}{8}D$ seconds after the termination of the signal pulse.

Many combinations of the circuits illustrated in Figs. 19.9–11 are possible, from which may be derived storage cells, switches, retiming circuits, adders, multipliers, accumulators, etc. (see reference 17). None of these circuits depend upon active elements, i.e., vacuum tubes or transistors, for their design functions, but in a digital computer which uses these fundamental "building blocks of logic," energy losses must still be supplied by active elements. The pulse retiming circuit of Fig. 19.12, for example, contains a pulse amplifier A. Thus, the circuit amplifies as well as retimes. (The feedback between the amplifier and the "or" circuit insures that the output pulse will not fall until the

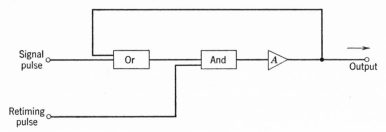

Fig. 19.12   Pulse retiming circuit.

timing pulse does, even though the original signal may have terminated during the duration of the timing signal.)

Since all the basic logic and storage circuits of a digital computer may be derived from purely passive elements, it may be assumed that the most important single function that transistors will perform in future computer designs is as pulse amplifiers. However, as was intimated earlier, the adaptability of the flipflop circuit to binary operations makes the point-contact transistor a valuable element in such applications as binary counters and bit registers.[18, 19, 20]

19.4   Trigger Circuits, Regenerative Amplifiers

The negative input characteristics of point-contact transistors were discussed in Chapters 13 and 18. Because the current amplification factor α is greater than unity for point-contact transistors, but not usually for junction transistors, it is likely that the point-contact device will find its greatest application in the field of switching and regenerative circuits. Hence, the discussion regarding trigger circuits and regenerative amplifiers will be confined to point-contact transistors. This does not mean that the junction transistor cannot be used for similar purposes, but, rather, that it is more likely that point-contact types will predominate in the field of switching because of their inherent negative-resistance properties.

The three principal regions of transistor operation are generally referred to as the cut-off, transition, and saturation regions. Nomenclature here refers to the positive-, negative-, and positive-resistance regions of the N-curve input characteristic of the point-contact transistor circuit. Figures 19.13a–c illustrate the approximate equivalent

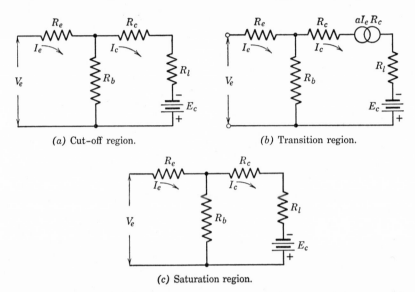

(a) Cut-off region.   (b) Transition region.

(c) Saturation region.

Fig. 19.13 Equivalent circuits for the three regions of operation of a grounded-base transistor amplifier.

circuits for each of these three regions. Only in the transition region is the transistor considered an active element. In the cut-off region, I_e is in the reverse direction from that of easy current flow for the emitter diode, and so the assumption that $R_e = R_{er} \gg R_b$ may be made. (R_e, R_b, and R_c are the resistances of idealized diodes representing the emitter, base and collector, respectively.) In the saturation region, there is effectively little resistance between the emitter and collector terminals, which implies that R_e and R_c may be considered short circuits.

The Kirchhoff equations for the equivalent circuits of Figs. 19.13a and c are

$$V_e = I_e(R_e + R_b) - I_c R_b \qquad [19.9a]$$

$$E_c = I_e R_b + (R_b + R_c + R_l)I_c \qquad [19.9b]$$

Solving for I_c in eq. 19.9b gives

$$I_c = \frac{E_c}{R_b + R_c + R_l} + \frac{I_e R_b}{R_b + R_c + R_l} \qquad [19.9c]$$

For the cut-off region, $R_e = R_{er} \gg R_b$; hence

$$V_e \cong I_e R_{er} - \frac{R_b E_c}{R_b + R_c + R_l} \qquad [19.10]$$

For the saturation region, R_e, $R_c \cong 0$; hence

$$V_e \cong I_e \frac{R_b R_l}{R_b + R_l} - \frac{R_b E_c}{R_b + R_l} \qquad [19.11]$$

For the transition region, for which the equivalent circuit of Fig. 19.13b applies, the Kirchhoff equations are

$$V_e = I_e(R_e + R_b) - R_b I_c \qquad [19.12a]$$

$$E_c = -I_e(R_b + aR_c) + [R_b + R_c + R_l]I_c \qquad [19.12b]$$

If it is assumed that $R_b \gg R_e$ in the transition region, solving for V_e from eqs. 19.12a and b gives

$$V_e \cong I_e R_b \left[\frac{R_c(1 - a) + R_l}{R_b + R_c + R_l} \right] - \frac{R_b E_c}{R_b + R_c + R_l} \qquad [19.13]$$

Equations 19.10, 19.11, and 19.13 give the input voltage-current characteristics, for a grounded-base transistor amplifier, in the cut-off, saturation, and transition regions respectively. For point-contact tran-

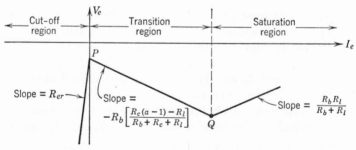

Fig. 19.14   Input characteristic of amplifier.

sistors, when $a > 1.0$, the input characteristics take the form illustrated in Fig. 19.14. Point P, which marks the change from the cut-off to the transition regions in the transistor characteristic, is referred to as the peak point. Point Q, which marks the change from the transition region to saturation, is referred to as the valley point. The coordinate values at point P are

$$(I_e, V_e) = \left(0, -\frac{R_b E_c}{R_b + R_c + R_l}\right) \qquad [19.14]$$

At the valley point, Q, the coordinate values are

$$(I_e, V_e) = \left(\frac{E_c}{a(R_l + R_b) - R_b}, \frac{R_b E_c(1 - a)}{a(R_l + R_b) - R_b}\right) \qquad [19.15]$$

It should be emphasized that the above equations are calculated on the basis of non-varying parameters. Thus, it is assumed that R_b, R_c, R_e, and a remain constant in the three regions of operation. This, of

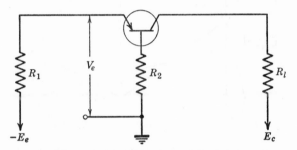

Fig. 19.15   Basic transistor switching circuit.

course, is not strictly true, but the characteristic determined by eqs. 19.10, 19.11, and 19.13 are good approximations to the exact case. The peak and valley point coordinates given by eqs. 19.14 and 19.15 deviate the most from experimental results, but this is to be expected since the change from the transition region to saturation does not occur in the well-defined manner of our theory. More will be said on this subject in Sec. 19.4.1.

The basic transistor switching circuit is illustrated in Fig. 19.15. When an external base resistance is used, such as R_2, R_b in eqs. 19.9–15 should be replaced by R_b', where

$$R_b' = R_b + R_2 \qquad [19.16]$$

The emitter circuit current-voltage equation, for Fig. 19.15, is

$$-E_e = R_1 I_e + V_e \qquad [19.17]$$

When $I_e = 0$, $V_e = -E_e$; the emitter load-line slope is $+R_1$. For the bistable trigger circuit, the emitter load line must intersect the V_e-I_e

characteristic in all three regions of operation. This is illustrated by load line R_{1b} in Fig. 19.16. The intersection of R_{1b} with the $V_e\text{-}I_e$ characteristic in the cut-off region determines the triggering sensitivity of the bistable circuit from its "off" state. As is evident from Fig. 19.16, the signal voltage required to trigger the circuit to its "on" state is $+V_{S1}$. Similarly, the signal voltage required to trigger the circuit to its "off" state is $-V_{S2}$. Choosing R_1 and E_e determines the sensitivity and reliability of the triggering circuit. In practice, whether a circuit is designed for high sensitivity or high reliability will depend upon the operating conditions. If the trigger circuit must operate under con-

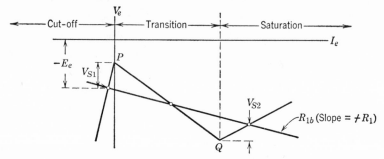

Fig. 19.16   Load-line intersection of N-curve.

ditions where wide temperature variations are expected, drift of R_c and I_{c0} must be anticipated. The effect of such drift will be to cause changes in the positions of the peak and valley points on the $V_e\text{-}I_e$ characteristic (see Fig. 19.14). Hence, sensitivity must be sacrificed to make certain that enough signal voltage magnitude, V_{S1} and V_{S2}, is applied to insure triggering despite the drift of the peak and valley points. The limiting values of the magnitudes of R_1 and E_e, for the bistable trigger circuit, are

$$\left| R_1 \right| < \left| R_b \left[\frac{R_c(1 - a) + R_l}{R_b + R_c + R_l} \right] \right| \qquad [19.18a]$$

$$\left| \frac{R_b E_c}{R_b + R_c + R_l} \right| < \left| E_e \right| < \left| \frac{R_b E_c(1 - a)}{a(R_l + R_b) - R_b} \right| \qquad [19.18b]$$

A bistable trigger circuit, if preceded by a differentiator circuit, may be used as a regenerative pulse amplifier. Another arrangement for the bistable trigger circuit, in regenerative amplifier operation, is illustrated in Fig. 19.17. Here, the signal to be regenerated is used to trigger the circuit from the "off" to the "on" position. A timing signal, synchronized with the pulse input signal, switches the trigger circuit from the "on" to the "off" position.[21] Thus, the pulse termination is controlled by the timing signal.

If the emitter load line in Fig. 19.16 intersects the V_e-I_e characteristic in only the transition region, an astable circuit is realized. In

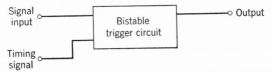

Fig. 19.17   Regenerative amplifier circuit.

order that a complete cycle of oscillation is obtained, however, an energy-storage element must be included in the circuit. Figure 19.18a illustrates the basic circuit for a monostable or astable point-contact transistor device. If the input load line R_{1a} intersects the V_e-I_e characteristic in the transition region, the circuit of Fig. 19.18 will be un-

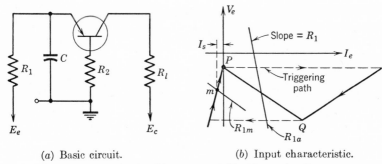

(a) Basic circuit.   (b) Input characteristic.

Fig. 19.18   Astable or monostable trigger circuit.

stable and will oscillate. On the other hand, if the load line R_{1m} intersects the V_e-I_e characteristic in the cut-off region only, the circuit will be stable. However, such a circuit will be capable of instability if, by means of an a-c input signal, the stable point m is moved to the peak point P. The result is a monostable device. Referring to Fig. 19.18b, a positive signal current of magnitude I_s will trigger the monostable circuit. From the point P on the V_e-I_e characteristic, the triggered circuit will snap over to the saturation region along a line parallel to the I_e axis and intersecting the V_e-I_e characteristic. When the condenser C begins to charge again, current decreases in the emitter until it reaches the point Q on the input characteristic. The transistor then snaps back into the cut-off region along the triggering path indicated in Fig. 19.18b, and the current finally returns to point m until the next trigger signal. Monostable transistor action is very similar to that in vacuum tubes.[23]

The dynamics of the monostable transistor trigger circuit may be determined by graphical and analytical means.[22] An approximate technique is to use the equivalent circuits of Fig. 19.13a and c. In the quiescent state, the basic monostable trigger circuit is given by the equivalent network illustrated in Fig. 19.19a. When the triggering pulse is

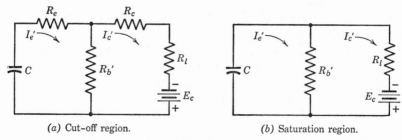

(a) Cut-off region. (b) Saturation region.

Fig. 19.19   Monostable trigger equivalent circuits.

applied, at time $= 0$, the circuit switches to the saturated state, and hence at $t = 0$ the circuit of Fig. 19.19b will govern the response. By the usual Laplace techniques, it can be shown that the emitter current is given by

$$I_e' = \frac{R_c E_c}{(R_b' + R_c + R_l)R_l} \exp\left[- \frac{R_b' + R_l}{(R_b')(R_l)(C)} t \right] \quad [19.19]$$

between $0 < t < T$. T is the period of the pulse. Equating eq. 19.19 to the emitter current at the valley point, Q (see eq. 19.15), T is found to be

$$T = \left[\frac{R_b' + R_l}{R_b R_l C} \right]^{-1} \ln \left\{ \frac{R_c[a(R_l + R_b') - R_b']}{(R_b' + R_c + R_l)R_l} \right\} \quad [19.20]$$

The approximate theoretical pulse waveform describing the emitter current of the monostable circuit is illustrated in Fig. 19.20. It should be remembered that the dynamic analysis described here is based upon the assumption that the rate at which the transistor switches from the cut-off region to the saturation region is infinite. This is never true, and introduces a serious error in the analysis when the repetition rate of the trigger signal approaches the α cut-off frequency of the transistor.

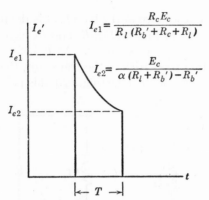

$$I_{e1} = \frac{R_c E_c}{R_l (R_b' + R_c + R_l)}$$

$$I_{e2} = \frac{E_c}{\alpha (R_l + R_b') - R_b'}$$

Fig. 19.20   Emitter current wave form.

19.4.1   Diode Stabilization of Trigger Circuits

Transistor parameters tend to vary over a considerable range for a given type of transistor. Besides this, the parameters for a given transistor may vary widely because of ambient temperature changes, etc. (see Chapter 3). In trigger circuits, change of the operating points due to any reason may completely change the character of the network. To minimize these effects, certain measures may be taken to increase the stability of the circuit. In particular, two techniques will be discussed here: valley-point and peak-point stabilization.

Equation 19.14 gives the I_e-V_e coordinates, of a point-contact transistor, at the peak point. In order to stabilize V_e around this point, R_c should be as constant as possible. The effect of changes in R_c may be minimized, however, by making R_b' small. On the other hand, to insure a pronounced negative resistance characteristic in the transistor region, R_b' should be large. To obtain both effects, a circuit of the type illustrated in Fig. 19.21a may be used.[18, 25] When I_e is positive and very

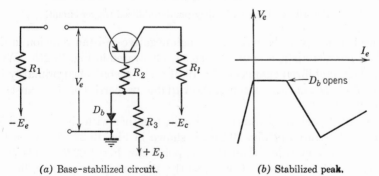

(a) Base-stabilized circuit.   (b) Stabilized peak.

Fig. 19.21   Base-stabilized trigger circuit.

small, the effective resistance in the base lead is the forward resistance of diode D_b, plus R_2. In Fig. 19.21a, R_2 and R_3 have typical values of 1 kilohm and 10 kilohms respectively. As I_e increases, owing to the current amplification properties of the transistor, the base current reverses and D_b becomes non-conducting. At this point the base resist-

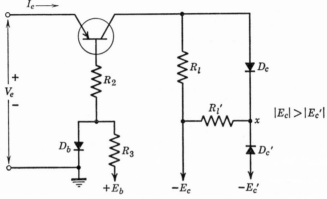

(a) Peak and valley stabilized circuit.

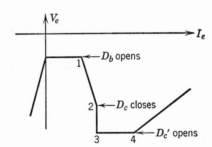

(b) V_e-I_e characteristic for stabilized circuit.

Fig. 19.22   Peak-and-valley-point-stabilized trigger circuit.

ance becomes very large, and the high negative-resistance region in the V_e-I_e characteristic is entered. This is illustrated in Fig. 19.21b. With the base-stabilized circuit of Fig. 19.21a, R_b' is controlled primarily by the diode D_b, notwithstanding the variable properties of the transistor itself.

A valley-stabilized transistor circuit, together with the base stabilization illustrated in Fig. 19.21a, is shown in Fig. 19.22a.[24] When the emitter current is less than that at point 2 of Fig. 19.22b, diode D_c is open and D_c' is closed. Consequently, the voltage at point x, in Fig. 19.22a, is clamped to the potential of E_c'. At point 2, the collector voltage has risen enough so that it is equal to $-E_c'$, and the diode D_c closes. For this condition, the a-c load resistance is, effectively, the sum of the two closed diodes, D_c and D_c'. At point 3, the equivalent diode in the collector circuit of the transistor (see Chapter 18) closes, i.e., the transistor saturates, and hence the emitter voltage is virtually clamped to the potential $-E_c'$. As the collector current increases, point x of Fig. 19.22a becomes increasingly positive so that, eventually, the diode D_c' opens. This occurs at point 4 in Fig. 19.22b. For I_e greater than that at point 4, the effective load resistance is the parallel combination of R_l and R_l'. Certain limitations of the valley-point stabilization circuit of Fig. 19.22a must be kept in mind. For example, α must be small enough to insure that the equivalent collector diode of the transistor does not close before D_c closes [$(I_e)_2 < (I_e)_3$], and yet must be large enough to insure that the equivalent collector diode closes before D_c' opens [$(I_e)_3 < (I_e)_4$].

19.5 Problems

1. Using only R-C elements, besides the transistors, draw the analogue circuit which solves the following differential equation:

$$E \sin \omega t = \frac{d^2e}{dt^2} + K_1 \frac{de}{dt} + K_2$$

Use the operational circuit of Fig. 19.7 as the basic "building block."

2. Prove the duality between the circuits shown in Fig. 19.23. Assume the amplification to be of the order of 5000.

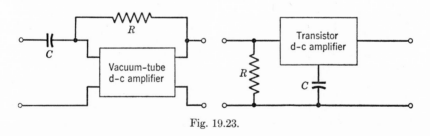

Fig. 19.23.

3. Derive the peak- and valley-point coordinates (for the trigger circuit of Fig. 19.15) as given by eqs. 19.14 and 19.15.

4. Derive the V_c-I_c characteristics for the three regions of operation of the trigger circuit illustrated in Fig. 19.15. Use the equivalent circuits shown in Fig. 19.13. Calculate the I_c-V_c coordinates for the peak and valley points.

5. Prove the limiting conditions for R_1 and E_e, in the bistable trigger circuit, given by eqs. 19.18a and b.

6. Derive the V_e-I_e characteristic for the base-stabilized circuit of Fig. 19.21.

19.6 Bibliography

1. Greenwood, Holdan, and Macrae, *Electronic Instruments*, R.L.S. 21, McGraw-Hill, New York, 1948.

2. J. R. Ragazzini, R. H. Randall, and F. A. Russell, "Analysis of Problems in Dynamics by Electronic Circuits," *Proc. IRE*, May, 1947.

3. R. Courant, "Method of Finite Differences for the Solution of Partial Differential Equations," *Annals*, Computation Laboratory of Harvard University, Cambridge, Mass., *16*, 153 (1948).

4. D. Moskovitz, "The Numerical Solution of Laplace's and Poisson's Equations," *Quarterly of Applied Mathematics*, Brown University, Providence, R. I., *2*, 148 (1944).

5. G. O'Brien, M. Hyman, and S. Kaplan, "A Study of the Numerical Solution of Partial Differential Equations," *J. Math. and Phys.*, M.I.T., Cambridge, Mass., *29*, 223 (1950).

6. L. F. Richardson, "The Approximate Arithmetical Solution by Finite Differences of Physical Problems Involving Differential Equations," *Phil. Trans. Roy. Soc. London*, London, England, *A210*, 307 (1910).

7. H. Huskey, "On the Precision of a Certain Procedure of Numerical Integration," *J. Research, Nat. Bur. Standards*, Washington, D. C., *42*, 57 (1949).

8. R. D. Hartree and J. R. Womersley, "A Method for the Numerical or Mechanical Solution of Certain Types of Partial Differential Equations," *Proc. Roy. Soc. London*, London, England, *161*, 353 (1937).

9. W. J. Eckert, *Punched Card Methods in Scientific Computation*, Columbia University Press, New York, 1940.

10. R. D. Hartree, *Calculating Instruments and Machines*, University of Illinois Press, Urbana, Ill., 1949.

11. Engineering Research Associates, *High Speed Computing Devices*, McGraw-Hill, New York, 1950.

12. M. Tormes, "Numerical Solution of the Boundary Value Problem for the Potential Equation by Means of Punched Cards," *Rev. Sci. Instruments*, American Institute of Physics, New York, *14*, 248 (1943).

13. "SEAC, the National Bureau of Standards Eastern Automatic Computer," *Tech. News Bull.* National Bureau of Standards, Washington, D. C., *34*, No. 9, pp. 1–8 (September, 1950).

14. "DINA, a Digital Analyzer for Laplace, Poisson, Diffusion, and Wave Equations," *Communications and Electronics*, A.I.E.E., No. 3, p. 303 (November, 1952).

15. M. Cohen and E. Nagel, *An Introduction to Logic and Scientific Method*, Harcourt, Brace and Co., New York, 1934.

16. Shannon and Weaver, *The Mathematical Theory of Communication*, University of Illinois Press, Urbana, Ill., 1949.

17. J. H. Felker, "Typical Block Diagrams for a Transistor Digital Computer," *Communications and Electronics*, A.I.E.E., No. 1 (July, 1952).

18. R. L. Trent, "A Transistor Reversible Binary Counter," *Proc. IRE*, November, 1952, pp. 1562–1572.

19. A. G. Follingstad, J. N. Shive, and R. E. Yaeger, "An Optical Position Encoder and Digit Register," *Proc. IRE*, November, 1952, pp. 1573–1583.

20. J. R. Harris, "A Transistor Shift Register and Serial Adder," *Proc. IRE*, November, 1952, pp. 1597–1602.

21. J. H. Felker, "Regenerative Amplifier for Digital Computer Applications," *Proc. IRE*, November, 1952, pp. 1584–1596.

22. B. G. Farley, "Dynamics of Transistor Negative-Resistance Circuits," *Proc. IRE*, November, 1952, pp. 1497–1508.

23. L. B. Arguimbau, *Vacuum Tube Circuits*, Chapter XI, Sec. 7, John Wiley & Sons, New York, 1948.

24. R. V. Baker, I. Lebow, R. Rediker, "A Transistor Switching Circuit with Stabilized Valley Point," Unclassified, *Tech. Memo 11*, Lincoln Laboratory, M.I.T., Cambridge, Mass., July 22, 1952.

25. A. E. Anderson, "Transistors in Switching Circuits," *Proc. IRE*, November, 1952, pp. 1541–1558.

26. A. W. Lo, "Transistor Trigger Circuits," *Proc. IRE*, November, 1952, pp. 1531–1541.

Chapter 20

Noise in Transistors

20.1 Characteristics of Transistor Noise

Transistor noise differs from other common types like thermal and shot noise in that transistor noise power per unit bandwidth varies approximately inversely with frequency.[1] From Fig. 20.1, which shows

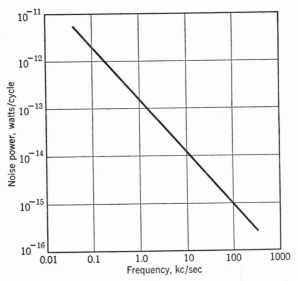

Fig. 20.1 Typical frequency characteristic of transistor noise.

this variation, it will be noted that each octave of the frequency range contains the same noise power.

In the equivalent circuit representation of the transistor it is convenient to represent noise by adding two noise-voltage generators with rms voltages e_{ne} and e_{nc} as shown in Fig. 20.2. It is then assumed that the other elements of the equivalent circuit are noiseless.

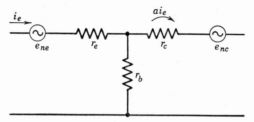

Fig. 20.2   Equivalent diagram of the transistor amplifier with noise generators.

20.2   Open-Circuit Noise of Transistors

Figure 20.3 shows the variation of these open-circuit noise voltages with frequency for a typical point-contact transistor.[2,3] Representative values for e_{nc} and e_{ne} for point-contact transistors are 100 microvolts

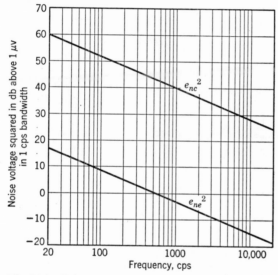

Fig. 20.3   Point-contact transistor noise vs. frequency.

and 1 microvolt respectively, measured at a frequency of 1000 cps for a bandwidth of 1 cycle.[2,3]

Figure 20.4 shows the variation of the collector open-circuit noise voltage, e_{nc}, squared, with frequency for three junction-type transistors. This variation, as can be noted, is also roughly inversely proportional to frequency. Representative value of the collector open-circuit noise voltage is about 5 microvolts. The emitter open-circuit voltage e_{ne} for the junction transistor is also very small (of the order of 0.05 microvolt).

From these typical values of noise voltage it can be seen that the junction transistor is superior to the point-contact transistor.

The noise voltages e_{nc} and e_{ne} are not quite independent. As indicated by measurements made at Bell Telephone Laboratories [3,4] some

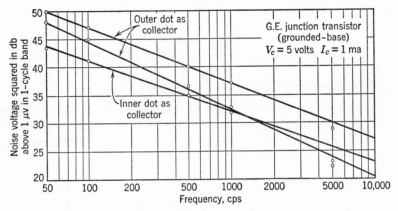

Fig. 20.4   Transistor noise vs. frequency (junction transistors).

correlation apparently exists between them, with correlation coefficients ranging from −0.8 to 0.4 (point-contact transistors).

20.3   Transistor Noise Figures

For practical applications, it is more convenient to express the noise characteristics of the transistor by giving its noise figure. The noise figure is defined as the ratio of the total noise power in the output (disregarding the noise originating in the load impedance) to that portion of the output noise resulting from thermal agitation in the source resistance r_g. The noise figure provides a convenient way of comparing the noise properties of transistors. Representative values for noise figures, measured at a frequency of 1000 cps, are 40–60 db for point-contact transistors and 10–25 db for junction transistors.

Mathematically, the noise figures for the **three basic types** of amplifier circuits may be expressed as follows:

For grounded-emitter

$$F = 1 + \frac{1}{4kTBr_g}\left[e_{ne}^2 \left(\frac{r_g + ar_c + r_b}{ar_c - r_e}\right)^2 \oplus e_{nc}^2 \left(\frac{r_g + r_b + r_e}{ar_c - r_e}\right)^2\right]$$

$$[20.1]$$

For grounded-base

$$F = 1 + \frac{1}{4kTBr_g}\left[e_{ne}^2 \oplus e_{nc}^2 \left(\frac{r_g + r_e + r_b}{ar_c - r_b}\right)^2\right] \qquad [20.2]$$

For grounded-collector

$$F = 1 + \frac{1}{4kTBr_g}\left[e_{ne}^2 \left(\frac{r_g + r_c + r_b}{r_c}\right)^2 \oplus e_{nc}^2 \left(\frac{r_g + r_b}{r_c}\right)^2\right] \qquad [20.3]$$

In these equations a, r_e, r_c, r_b, r_m are equivalent circuit parameters of the transistor; e_{ne} and e_{nc}, open-circuit voltages; r_g, source resistance; B, frequency band; k, Boltzmann's constant ($k = 1.347 \times 10^{-23}$);

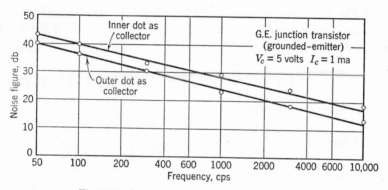

Fig. 20.5   Transistor noise figure vs. frequency.

T, temperature in degrees Kelvin. The addition sign $\oplus$ in these equations expresses addition with attention to any correlation between e_{ne} and e_{nc}. If no correlation exists, then this operation may be replaced by simple addition.

Figure 20.5 shows a plot of noise figure versus frequency for a typical junction-type transistor.

The noise figure of a transistor depends on the operating point.[5] For example, although the emitter noise is almost independent of the collector voltage V_c, the collector noise depends strongly on it. Figure 20.6 shows separately the contributions to the noise figure due to the emitter and the collector, together with total noise figure.

Figure 20.7 shows in detail the variation of the noise figure of three typical junction transistors with collector current and collector voltage.

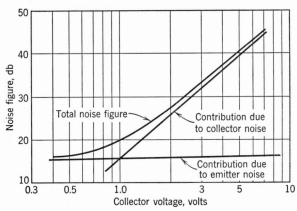

Fig. 20.6   Contribution to the noise figure due to emitter and collector noise

From Fig. 20.7 it can be seen that it is desirable to operate the junction transistor at a low collector voltage, of the order of 1 volt, if low noise operation is required.

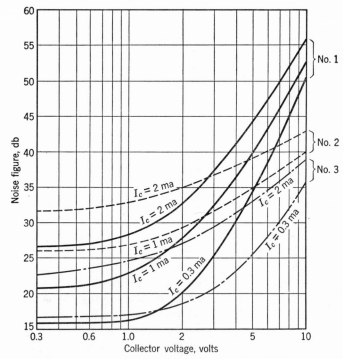

Fig. 20.7   Transistor noise vs. operating point.

20.4   Signal-to-Noise Ratio of the Transistor Amplifier

Since, as was shown in Sec. 20.1, transistor noise power varies in approximately inverse linear relation to frequency, the total noise power in a frequency band $f_2 - f_1$ may be expressed as

$$P_n = \int_{f_1}^{f_2} \frac{K}{f} \, df = K \ln \frac{f_2}{f_1} \qquad [20.4]$$

On the other hand, the thermal noise power due to source resistance r_g is proportional to the bandwidth $(f_2 - f_1)$. Therefore, the noise figure for the bandwidth limited by the frequencies f_2 and f_1 is

$$F = 1000F_0 \frac{\ln f_2/f_1}{f_2 - f_1} \qquad [20.5]$$

where F_0 is the noise figure at a frequency of 1000 cps for a bandwidth of 1 cycle. If the bandwidth is small, such that $f_2/f_1 \cong 1$, then $\ln (f_2/f_1) = (f_2 - f_1)/f_1$, and

$$F \cong F_0 1000/f_1 \qquad [20.6]$$

The noise figure may, therefore, be considered fairly independent of bandwidth if this bandwidth remains relatively small, but inversely proportional to midband frequency, for the same bandwidth. The signal-to-noise ratio of a transistor amplifier can be now derived by using the following procedure:

The available noise power due to thermal agitation in the source resistor r_g is

$$(P_n)_{r_g} = kT(f_2 - f_1) \qquad [20.7]$$

An equivalent transistor noise power referred to the input of an amplifier may then be expressed as

$$P_{ni} = F(P_n)_{rg} = FkT(f_2 - f_1) \qquad [20.8]$$

Substituting the value of F derived in eq. 20.5,

$$P_{ni} = kT[1000 \, F_0 \ln(f_2/f_1)] \qquad [20.9]$$

Changing to common logarithms and substituting values for k and T, we obtain the following equation for the transistor "equivalent noise power" at input:

$$P_{ni} = 0.9 \times 10^{-17} F_0 \log(f_2/f_1) \qquad \text{(watts, at room temperature)} \quad [20.10]$$

which shows that noise power depends on the ratio of the frequencies

f_2 and f_1 rather than on their magnitudes. Equation 20.10 may also be written

$$P_{ni} = 0.9 \times 10^{-17} F_0 \log [1 + (\Delta f/f)] \qquad [20.11]$$

where Δf is the bandwidth and f the center frequency. This equation shows that for a constant bandwidth the noise power will decrease as the center frequency increases.

The signal-to-noise ratio can now be expressed as

$$\frac{S}{N} = \frac{e_g^2}{4r_g P_{ni}} = \frac{e_g^2}{3.6 \times 10^{-17} r_g F_0 \log (f_2/f_1)} \qquad [20.12]$$

where e_g is the rms value of the signal voltage. Using this equation it is possible to determine the maximum permissible noise figure F_0 of a transistor for the first stage of an amplifier. This is illustrated in Fig. 20.8, which is a plot of eq. 20.10 for different values of F_0.

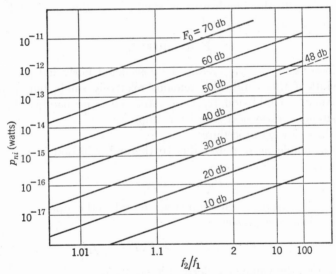

Fig. 20.8 The available "equivalent noise power."

20.5 Noise Figure as Affected by Source Resistance

In Sec. 20.3, eqs. 20.1, 20.2, and 20.3 give the noise figure for the three basic types of amplifier circuits. For a given operating point and given transistor, e_{ne} and e_{nc} are constant. We can, therefore, introduce a factor

$$\rho = e_{ne}/e_{nc} \qquad [20.13]$$

typical values for which are between 10^{-2} and 10^{-3}.

The equations for the noise figures are then (neglecting minor terms):

For grounded-emitter

$$F \cong 1 + \frac{r_n[\rho^2(r_g + ar_c)^2 + (r_g + r_e + r_b)^2]}{r_g a^2 r_c^2} \qquad [20.14]$$

For grounded-base

$$F \cong 1 + \frac{r_n[\rho^2 a^2 r_c^2 + (r_g + r_e + r_b)^2]}{r_g a^2 r_c^2} \qquad [20.15]$$

For grounded-collector

$$F \cong 1 + \frac{r_n[\rho^2(r_g + r_c)^2 + (r_g + r_b)^2]}{r_g r_c^2} \qquad [20.16]$$

where

$$r_n = \frac{e_{nc}^2}{4kT(f_2 - f_1)} \qquad [20.17]$$

As can be see, the only parameter of these equations that may be varied externally is the source resistance r_g. Figure 20.9 shows the variation of F with r_g for different values of the factor ρ.

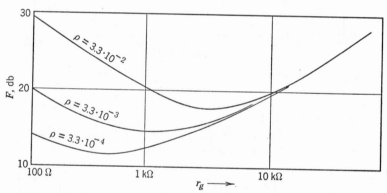

Fig. 20.9   Variation of F with r_g for different values of the factor ρ.

The noise figure F has a minimum for the following values of r_g:

For grounded-emitter

$$r_g' \cong \left[\frac{\rho^2 a^2 r_c^2 + (r_e + r_b)^2}{1 + \rho^2} \right]^{\frac{1}{2}} \qquad [20.18]$$

For grounded-base

$$r_g' \cong [\rho^2 a^2 r_c^2 + (r_e + r_b)^2]^{\frac{1}{2}} \qquad [20.19]$$

For grounded-collector

$$r_g' \cong \left[\frac{\rho^2 r_c^2 + r_b^2}{1 + \rho^2} \right]^{\frac{1}{2}}$$

[20.20]

This minimum, however, is not very critical, as may be seen from the experimental curves of Fig. 20.10. Therefore, somewhat larger or

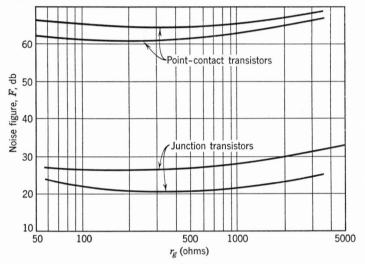

Fig. 20.10   The noise figure as a function of r_g.

smaller values of r_g can be used, if necessary, without an appreciable increase in amplifier noise.

For example, using eqs. 20.15 and 20.19 for the grounded-base connection, the minimum noise figure will be

$$F_{\min} = r_n \left[\frac{2(r_e + r_b)}{a^2 r_c^2} + \frac{2\rho^2}{\sqrt{\rho^2 a^2 r_c^2 + (r_e + r_b)^2}} \right]$$

[20.21]

Now if we increase (or decrease) the value of r_g four times, the noise figure will be

$$F = r_n \left[\frac{2(r_e + r_b)}{a^2 r^2} + \frac{17\rho^2}{4\sqrt{\rho^2 a^2 r_c^2 + (r_e + r_b)^2}} \right]$$

[20.22]

which indicates that the noise figure changes at most 2.12 times, or 3.2 db, the change being actually much less for most practical cases.

20.6   Consideration of the Noise Figure of the Second Stage of an Amplifier

Generally, in multistage transistor amplifiers, the first stage will contribute most significantly to the noise figure.   However, if the equivalent source impedance of the second stage differs very much from the value of r_g given by eqs. 20.18 to 20.20, the noise of the second stage must also be taken into account.

The noise figure of a two-stage amplifier is

$$F = F_1 + \frac{F_2 - 1}{G_1} \qquad [20.23]$$

where F_1 and F_2 are the noise figures of the first and second stages respectively and G_1 is the available power gain of the first stage.   This available power gain has the following values: [6]

For grounded-base

$$G_1 = \frac{a^2 r_c r_g}{(r_e + r_b + r_g)[r_e + r_b(1 - a) + r_g]} \qquad [20.24]$$

For grounded-emitter

$$G_1 = \frac{a^2 r_c r_g}{(r_e + r_b + r_g)[r_e + r_b(1 - a) + r_g(1 - a)]} \qquad [20.25]$$

For grounded-collector

$$G_1 = \frac{r_c r_g}{(r_c + r_b + r_g)[r_e + r_b(1 - a) + r_g(1 - a)]} \qquad [20.26]$$

The noise figure of the second stage will depend on the operating point of the second transistor and the output resistance of the first stage.   This output resistance can be changed if desired by coupling the two stages by transformer.   This coupling will leave G_1 unchanged. Adjusting the turns ratio of the transformer so that the apparent source impedance of the second stage is that given in eqs. 20.18 to 20.20 will reduce the influence of the second stage.

If the two stages are coupled without a transformer, we have the following approximate expressions (for the grounded-emitter stage): Assuming that, in eq. 20.1, $e_{nc}^2 \gg e_{ne}^2$, $r_{g2} = r_{o1}$, and $r_{o1} \gg r_e + r_b$, where r_{o1} is the output resistance of the first stage of the amplifier,

$$(F_2 - 1) \cong \frac{e_{nc2}{}^2}{4kTB} \cdot \frac{r_{o1}}{a_2{}^2 r_{c2}{}^2}$$

$$G_1 = \frac{a_1{}^2 r_{c1} r_g}{(r_{e1} + r_{b1} + r_g)[r_{e1} + r_{b1}(1 - a_1) + r_g(1 - a_1)]} \qquad [20.27]$$

$$r_{o1} = r_{c1} \left[\frac{r_{e1} + r_{b1}(1 - a_1) + r_g(1 - a_1)}{r_{e1} + r_{b1} + r_g} \right]$$

[see Chapter 4] and, therefore,

$$F = F_1 + \frac{e_{nc2}{}^2}{4kTB} \frac{[r_{e1} + r_{b1}(1 - a_1) + r_g(1 - a_1)]^2}{a_2{}^2 r_{c2}{}^2 a_1{}^2 r_g} \qquad [20.28]$$

20.7   Transistor Noise Measurements

20.7.1   The Measurement of Open-Circuit Noise Voltages

Figure 20.11 shows one possible arrangement for the measurement of emitter and collector open-circuit noise voltages e_{ne} and e_{nc}. The transistor under test is biased to the desired d-c operating point through the

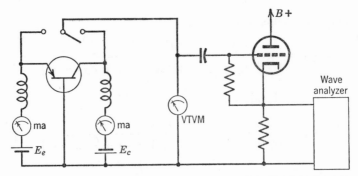

Fig. 20.11   Circuit for the measurement of open-circuit noise voltages.

chokes, which should have practically infinite impedance at all frequencies of interest. The emitter and collector noise voltages are measured by means of a wave analyzer, having a narrow bandwidth, connected through a cathode follower to the terminals of the transistor.

The meter of the wave analyzer may show slow random fluctuations that can make reading the noise voltages difficult. In order to facilitate the measurements, it is convenient to increase the time constant of the d-c amplifier of the wave analyzer and to place a large capacitance across the meter. Instead of the wave analyzer, a high-gain amplifier together with a high-Q filter may be used. It is important, particularly for the measurements of the emitter open-circuit noise voltage, that the noise level of the amplifier used be very low. To be rigorous the indicating meter should accurately record the rms value of the signal.

20.7.2   The Measurement of Noise Figure

For the measurement of noise figures, techniques similar to those used for vacuum-tube amplifiers may be employed. One of the most common of these methods is the following: A noise generator is connected in series with r_g to the input of the transistor (Fig. 20.12). With

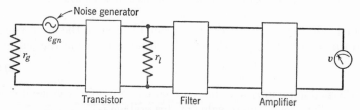

Fig. 20.12   Circuit for the measurement of noise figures.

the generator turned off, the noise power at the output is measured. Then, with the noise generator turned on, its voltage level is adjusted so that the power at the output of the transistor is doubled.

If the corresponding rms voltage of the noise generator is e_{gn}, then the noise figure is

$$F = e_{gn}{}^2/[4kTr_g(f_2 - f_1)] \qquad [20.29]$$

If we designate the mean-square value of the thermal agitation noise in r_g ("Johnson noise") as M, where $M = 4kTr_g(f_2 - f_1)$, then

$$F = e_{gn}{}^2/M \qquad [20.30]$$

For a given set-up the quantity M can usually be calculated in advance.

The noise figure may also be measured by means of a signal generator (Fig. 20.13). First the voltage amplification $A_v = v_2/e_g$ of the transistor amplifier is measured by conventional methods, where e_g is the output voltage of the signal generator. Then, with the generator turned off, the rms value of the noise voltage v_{nc} across r_l at a given frequency is measured through a wave analyzer with very narrow bandwidth or by means of a filter and amplifier as is shown in Fig. 20.13. From these measurements, the noise figure may be determined directly as follows.

By definition, the noise figure F is defined as the total noise power in the output divided by that portion of the output noise that results from

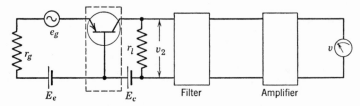

Fig. 20.13   Circuit for the measurement of noise figures.

thermal agitation in r_g. If the mean-square value of the noise voltage appearing across r_l is v_{nc}^2, then the total noise power in the output is

$$P_{no} = v_{nc}^2/r_l \qquad [20.31]$$

The thermal noise in r_g may be represented by a noise voltage in series with r_g. The mean-square value of this voltage is

$$e_n^2 = 4kTr_g(f_2 - f_1) \qquad [20.32]$$

The noise power in the output due to thermal agitation in r_g is

$$P_{no}' = \frac{4kTr_g(f_2 - f_1)}{r_l} \times A_v^2 \qquad [20.33]$$

The noise figure is, therefore,

$$F = \frac{P_{no}}{P_{no}'} = \frac{v_{nc}^2}{4kTr_g(f_2 - f_1)A_v^2} \qquad [20.34]$$

If the bandwidth $f_2 - f_1$ is known, then, for a given set-up, the quantity $4kTr_g(f_2 - f_1) = M$ may again be calculated in advance as before and the noise figure will then be

$$F = v_{nc}^2/MA_v^2 \qquad [20.35]$$

this method is not quite as simple as the first, particularly if these measurements are to be carried out at different frequencies, since the quantity A_v must be measured at each frequency. However, the use of a calibrated noise generator is hereby made unnecessary.

The noise figures for grounded-base and grounded-emitter amplifiers are approximately equal. The average difference for a large number of transistors was found to be 1 db. Therefore, it is unimportant which type of amplifier is used for the measurement of noise figure.[5]

Figure 20.14 shows the distribution of noise figures measured on 60 experimental transistors. Curve A is for junction transistors measured at $V_c = 1$ volt, $I_c = 0.5$ ma; curve B for the same units at $V_c = 5$ volts, $I_c = 1.0$ ma; and curve C is for point-contact transistors at $V_c = 10$ volts, $I_c = 0.5$ ma. It should be emphasized that these curves

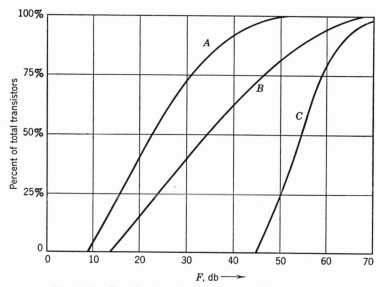

Fig. 20.14   Distribution of noise figures of 60 transistors.

do not represent the ultimate performance of either point-contact or junction units.

20.8   Problems

1. Determine the maximum permissible noise figure of the transistor to be used in an i-f amplifier if the available input signal power is 10^{-11} watt and the minimum signal-to-noise ratio is 50 db. The bandwidth of the amplifier may be taken as 10 kc, and center frequency as 455 kc.

2. Assuming that the bandwidth of a d-c transistor amplifier is limited by the frequencies $f_1 = 1/\text{day}$ and $f_2 = 10$ kc, compute the maximum permissible noise figure of the transistor if the available signal power is 10^{-10} watt and $S/N = 40$ db.

3. Prove that the addition of a resistance in series with the source impedance will not improve the signal-to-noise ratio of the transistor amplifier.

4. Prove that any resistance in parallel with the input terminals of the transistor amplifier will decrease the signal-to-noise ratio.

5. Prove that the noise figures for grounded-base and grounded-emitter connections of the transistor amplifier are approximately equal.

20.9 Bibliography

1. H. C. Montgomery, "Background Noise in Transistors," *Bell Lab. Rec.*, September, 1949, pp. 400–402.

2. R. M. Ryder and R. J. Kircher, "Some Circuit Aspects of the Transistor," Bell Telephone System Technical Publications, Monograph 1726, p. 62, 1949.

3. J. A. Becker and J. N. Shive, "The Transistor—A New Semiconductor Amplifier," *Elec. Engg.*, March, 1949, pp. 215–220.

4. H. C. Montgomery, "Transistor Noise in Circuit Applications," *Proc. IRE*, *40*, No. 11, pp. 1461–1471 (November, 1952).

5. E. Keonjian and J. S. Schaffner, "An Experimental Investigation of Transistor Noise," *Proc. IRE*, *40*, No. 11, pp. 1456–1460 (November, 1952).

6. E. Keonjian and J. S. Schaffner, "Noise in Transistor Amplifiers," *Electronics*, 25, No. 2, pp. 104–107 (February, 1953).

7. E. Keonjian and J. S. Schaffner, "Noise in Transistor Amplifiers," *Proc. NEC*, October, 1952, pp. 343–345.

8. R. L. Petritz, "On the Theory of Noise in p-n Junctions and Related Devices," *Proc. IRE*, *40*, No. 11, pp. 1440–1456 (November, 1952).

9. H. C. Montgomery, "Electrical Noise in Semiconductors," *Bell Sys. Tech. J.*, *31*, 950–975 (September, 1952).

Chapter 21

Associated
Semiconductor Devices

Although this book is concerned chiefly with various important aspects of the triode transistor, the basic component of most transistor circuits, many other devices have come into being which utilize the same physical principles. The special-purpose devices described in this chapter are the first members of a rapidly growing family of semiconductor components both active and passive which will ultimately provide the systems design engineer with a wealth of versatile circuit elements. The potentialities have been only partially explored. As new devices become available, their usefulness to the engineer will be determined chiefly by his familiarity with their operation and by his ingenuity in applying this knowledge.

21.1 Diodes

Semiconductor diodes possess, in general, the same advantages over vacuum-tube diodes as transistors have over triode vacuum tubes. This type of diode does not require filament power, is extremely rugged, and small in size. These definite advantages of the semiconductor diode open a wide field for its application. The first germanium diodes were of the point-contact or whisker type. The junction type of diode which was developed subsequently exhibited capabilities (except for frequency response) far beyond those of point-contact diodes. In Chapter 1 the reader will find a general description of the principles of semiconductors. The behavior of both types of germanium diodes, as well as of any other type of diode, is characterized by a high resistance in one direction and a low resistance in the opposite direction, permitting rectification. A typical voltage-current characteristic of a germanium diode is shown in Fig. 21.1. This characteristic is similar to that for tube diodes, except that the inverse voltage causes some back current

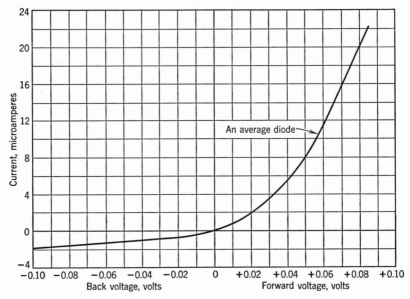

Fig. 21.1 Typical low-voltage-current characteristic of an average diode at 25° C.

to flow and, further, if the inverse voltage becomes too large, the germanium diode becomes highly conductive again.

21.1.1 Ratings of Diodes

The characteristics of semiconductor diodes are usually specified by the following terms:

21.1.1.1 Maximum Inverse Current

The maximum current through the diode when a given d-c potential is applied across it with the negative polarity connected to the whisker lead of a point-contact diode or to the p region of a junction diode.

21.1.1.2 Back Resistance

The ratio of the applied inverse voltage across the diode to the back current flow. For General Electric diodes this resistance is usually specified at -50 volts.

21.1.1.3 Minimum Forward Current

The smallest amount of current through the diode when a specified d-c potential is applied across it with the positive polarity connected to the whisker or p region of the diode.

21.1.1.4 Forward Resistance

The ratio of the applied positive voltage across the diode to the forward current flow. For General Electric diodes this resistance is usually specified at $+1$ volt.

21.1.1.5 Peak Inverse Voltage

The maximum transient inverse voltage that can be applied to the diode without danger of voltage breakdown of the diode. Voltage breakdown is the point at which the dynamic back resistance of the diode suddenly becomes very small.

21.1.1.6 Average Rectified Current

The maximum average current that can be carried safely by the diode without appreciable change in its characteristics.

21.1.1.7 Peak Rectified Current

The peak to which the rectified current may be allowed to rise provided that the duty cycle and wave shape are such that the rms current does not exceed the average rating and the frequency of application is at least 25 cps.

21.1.1.8 Maximum Surge Current

The maximum forward current that can flow for 1 second without damage to the diode.

21.1.1.9 Ambient Temperature Range

The range of temperature over which the diode exhibits reversible changes, in that the characteristics return to their original room-temperature values after being subjected to other temperatures in the rated range. (See Figs. 21.7 and 21.8.)

21.1.1.10 Shunt Capacitance

The capacitance measured across the diode at a frequency of 75 mc.

21.1.2 Point-Contact Diodes

Figure 21.2 shows the actual size and Fig. 21.3 is a cut-away view of the construction of the General Electric point-contact (whisker) ger-

Fig. 21.2 Actual size of the General Electric point-contact diode.

manium diode. These diodes are rated at 10,000 hours of life under normal operating conditions. Actually, there is no known reason why they should not last longer without serious changes in character- istics when operated within ratings. Laboratory tests have shown that during the rated life the back resistance may decrease on the average

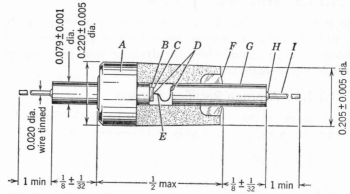

Fig. 21.3 Cut-away view of the General Electric point-contact diode.

by 25 per cent and the forward resistance may increase by 5 per cent. The shunt capacitance of this type of diode is of the order of 0.5 $\mu\mu$f, with 0.8 $\mu\mu$f representing the maximum value. The usual schematic symbol for this type of diode is shown in Fig. 21.4. The arrow points in the direction of easy conventional current flow, the electron flow, of course, being in the opposite direction.

Figure 21.5 shows typical static forward current-voltage character- istics, and Fig. 21.6 the inverse current-voltage characteristics, at 25° C for four General Electric general-purpose diodes. Table 21.1 gives specifications for three of these diodes at a temperature of 25° C.

Fig. 21.4 Schematic symbol for the diode.

Table 21.1 Specifications (Characteristics) for Three Point-Contact Diodes

RTMA Designation	1N48	1N52	1N63
Maximum inverse current, ma, at −50 volts	0.833	0.15	0.05
Corresponding back resistance at −50 volts	60 kilohms	333 kilohms	1 megohm
Minimum forward current, ma, at +1 volt	4.0	4.0	4.0
Corresponding forward resistance, ohms, at +1 volt	250	250	250
Peak inverse voltage	85	85	125
Average rectified current, ma	50	50	50
Peak rectified current, ma	150	150	150
Surge current, amperes	0.4	0.4	0.4
Average shunt capacitance, $\mu\mu$f	0.8	0.8	0.8

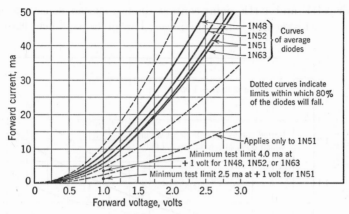

Fig. 21.5 Typical forward current-voltage characteristics of four diodes at 25° C.

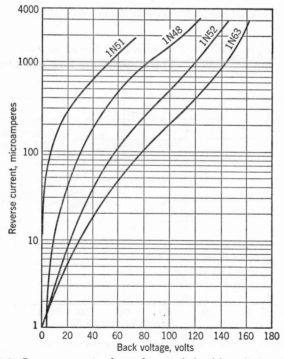

Fig. 21.6 Inverse current-voltage characteristic of four diodes at 25° C.

For VHF and UHF point-contact diodes, special consideration is given to whisker and pin inductances, barrier capacitance, case con-

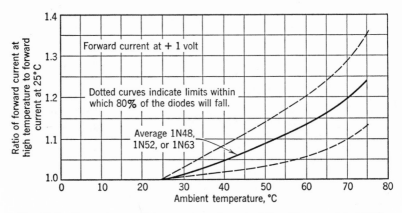

Fig. 21.7   Forward current-temperature characteristic with respect to 25° C.

ductance, etc., to minimize their effects on the operation of the diode in the high-frequency region. These diodes are now available for such

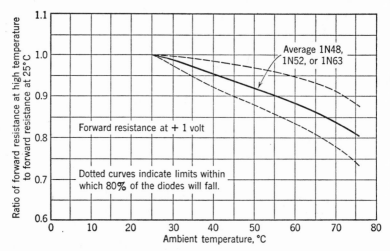

Fig. 21.8   Forward resistance-temperature characteristic with respect to 25° C.

applications as VHF detectors, UHF mixers, frequency multipliers, meter rectifiers, and many others (see circuit applications, Sec. 21.1.4).

A typical example of the VHF and UHF diode is the General Electric diode 1N72 used as a UHF mixer. Some features and specifications of that diode are given in Table 21.2.

Table 21.2   Characteristics of UHF Diode 1N72

Peak inverse voltage	15 volts
Average d-c rectified current	25 ma
Peak d-c rectified current	75 ma
Temperature range	-50 to $+75°$ C
Operating frequency (maximum)	1000 megacycles

Figures 21.7 and 21.8 show typical forward-current vs. temperature and forward-resistance vs. temperature characteristics of point-contact

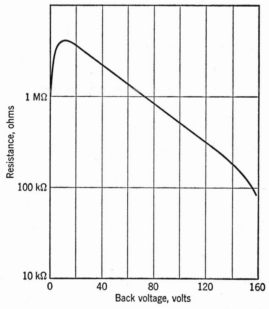

Fig. 21.9   Back resistance-voltage characteristic at 25° C (Type 1N63).

diodes with respect to the values of 25° C and at $+1$ volt. The back resistance-voltage characteristic of the 1N63 diode is illustrated in Fig. 21.9. The reverse current vs. temperature variation and the back resistance vs. temperature variation in general have the same character as forward-current and forward-resistance temperature ratio characteristics; i.e., reverse current increases with temperature whereas the back resistance drops with temperature. Figure 21.10 shows how the rectification efficiency is affected by frequency.

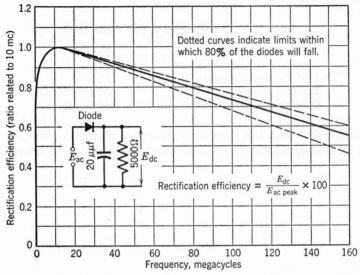

Fig. 21.10   Typical rectification efficiency-frequency ratio characteristic at 25° C

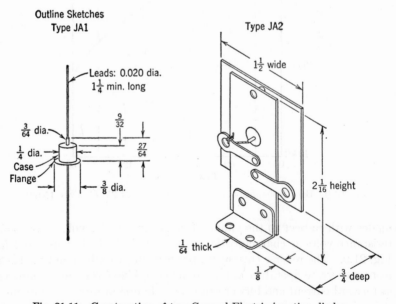

Fig. 21.11   Construction of two General Electric junction diodes.

21.1.3   Junction Diodes

Junction diodes have certain advantages over point-contact diodes. Among these advantages are the very low forward resistance, very low reverse current, large rectification ratio (ratio of back to forward re-

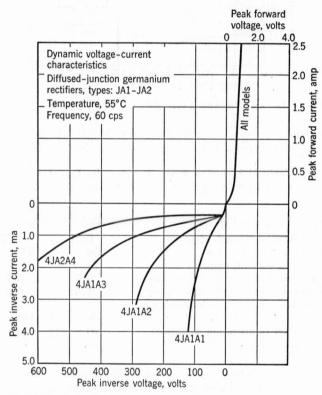

Fig. 21.12   Typical voltage vs. current characteristics of type 4JA diodes.

sistance at a given voltage), the ability to pass large currents, and the ability to withstand high peak inverse voltages.

Figure 21.11 shows the construction and actual size of two General Electric type JA junction diode rectifiers. Figure 21.12 shows the current vs. voltage characteristic of these diodes; Fig. 21.13 illustrates the power-handling capability of the diodes at a temperature of 55° C and with a resistive load. The last curve permits a direct choice of values of forward current and peak back voltage for operation into a

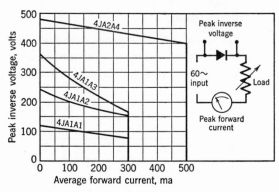

Fig. 21.13   Power-handling capability curves for type 4JA diodes.

resistive load at 55° C.   Table 21.3 gives maximum ratings of the General Electric type 4JA junction diodes (rectifiers) at 55° C.

Table 21.3   Typical Maximum Ratings for Type 4JA
Junction Diodes (Rectifiers) for Resistive Load at 55° C

	4JA1A2	4JA1A4
Peak inverse voltage, volts	200	400
Peak forward current, amperes	0.31	1.57
D-c output current, ma	100	500
D-c surge current, amperes	25	25
Full-load voltage drop, volts peak	0.5	0.7
Forward resistance at full load, ohms	1.5	0.5
Continuous reverse working voltage, volts d.c.	30	185
Frequency of operation, kilocycles	50	50
Storage temperature, °C	85	85

In 1953 another type of diode was developed that uses silicon instead of germanium.[1]   The silicon p-n junction diodes have some additional advantages.   In particular they have much lower reverse currents and a higher rectification ratio and can operate at much higher ambient temperatures.   The reverse currents of silicon junction diodes may be of the order of 10^{-4} microampere at room temperature, the rectification ratio as high as 10^8 at 1 volt, and they can operate at frequencies up to 20 mc.   Figure 21.14 shows a voltage vs. current characteristic for a silicon p-n junction diode prepared by alloying.   This characteristic shows the low reverse current and high rectification ratio of this type of diode.   The maximum power dissipation in silicon diodes,[1] as in germanium diodes, is determined by the geometry and cooling techniques used.   One disadvantage of silicon diodes should be mentioned.   Although the rectification ratio can be much larger than for germanium, the magnitude of the forward voltage drop is greater for the silicon diode.

Power diodes of germanium are now being developed. In one type of germanium fused-junction diode, forward currents in excess of 500 amperes in a centimeter square of germanium have been obtained. According to measurements, a 1 cm^2 germanium diode (0.025 in. thick)

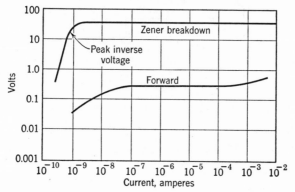

Fig. 21.14   Voltage-current characteristics of the silicon p-n junction diode.

had a forward voltage drop of less than 1 volt at 1000 amperes forward current. The back current of the same germanium diode was less than 10 ma at 100 volts and less than 30 ma at 250 volts. The power dissipation at 1000 amperes for a centimeter square diode of germanium is approximately 300 watts for 2 cm^2 of surface area (both sides of the germanium wafer) or 150 watts for 1 cm^2 of area. These data give a picture of the power capabilities of germanium diodes and suggest a promising future for power transistors.

21.1.4   Circuit Applications

Semiconductor diodes are widely used in many circuit applications as detectors, mixers, rectifiers, etc. The following examples of circuit applications are only a few of many possible arrangements which can be achieved with these diodes. Figure 21.15 shows two circuits of a probe

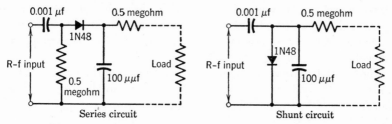

Fig. 21.15   Two possible arrangements for a detector probe.

in which germanium diodes are employed. The load is an oscilloscope or a vacuum-tube voltmeter. These probes are suitable for frequencies of the order of several hundreds of megacycles. Figure 21.16 shows a

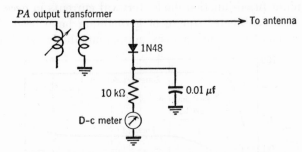

Fig. 21.16   Antenna coupling meter for transmitter.

circuit for checking the degree of antenna coupling of a radio transmitter. Figure 21.17 shows an application with two diodes as a second detector and automatic volume control in an a-m broadcast receiver.

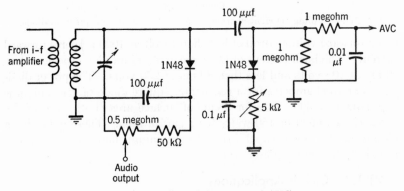

Fig. 21.17   Second detector and AVC.

Circuit values in such arrangements are similar to those employed with vacuum-tube detectors. In f-m receivers diodes can be used in frequency discriminator circuits as shown in Fig. 21.18. In order to avoid costly matching of diodes for the above discriminator, resistors are connected in parallel with the diodes, the circuit being left in balance regardless of the back resistance of the diodes. Other circuit values are typical for a discriminator circuit.

Figure 21.19 shows a circuit of a voltage quadrupler which uses power junction diodes. This circuit produces approximately 500 volts d.c. from a 110-volt line without a transformer and requires considerably less space than a transformer voltage supply. Two diodes in

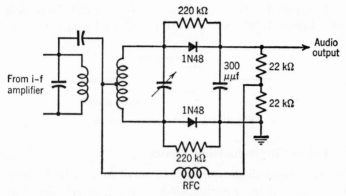

Fig. 21.18   Frequency discriminator for f-m receiver.

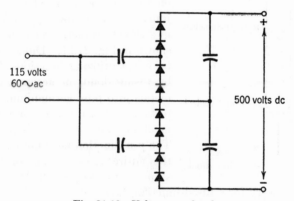

Fig. 21.19   Voltage quadrupler.

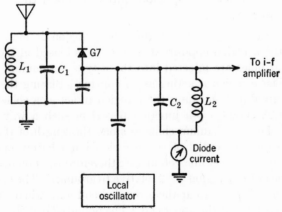

Fig. 21.20   UHF mixer.

series are required for each leg in order to withstand the peak inverse voltage. Figure 21.20 shows a UHF mixer employing a point-contact diode.

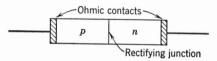

Fig. 21.21   Grown-junction diode.

21.2   Other Single-Junction Devices

The germanium diode can be fabricated in two basic forms, the point-contact and the junction diodes. p-n junction diodes may be

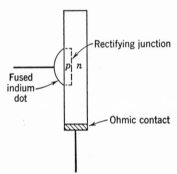

Fig. 21.22   Fused-junction diode.

subdivided into two classes depending on the method of producing the p-n junction. The grown junction results in a diode geometry such as the one shown in Fig. 21.21. Diodes may also be made utilizing junctions produced by fusing donor or acceptor impurity metals into pure germanium. By this technique, p-n junctions may be made in almost any desired shape or size. The p-n junction need not extend over the entire cross section of the final structure. Figure 21.22 shows a possible geometry for a fused-junction diode.

21.2.1   Simultaneous Injection and Collection at a p-n Junction [2]

If a p-n junction is biased so that the p region is made positive relative to the n region opposite it, the diode is biased in the forward direction and holes are injected into the n-type germanium from the p region. The p region is acting as an emitter. Biasing the junction in the opposite direction causes the p region to act as a collector.

Figure 21.23 shows a p-n junction biased in such a way that the potential of the n germanium changes along the length of the bar relative to the fixed potential of the p region immediately opposite it. The indium dot is a metallic conductor; therefore the potential is uniform over the entire p region ($E/2$ relative to ground). The germanium bar has a potential of zero at the grounded end and, when switch S is closed, a potential E at the upper end. The potential distribution along the bar will be initially essentially linear as shown in Fig. 21.24a. Thus the bias is such that the p region is positive relative to the germanium from $x = 0$ to $x = L/2$ and negative from $x = L/2$ to $x = L$. The p region will now act as an emitter over the lower half of the junction and as a collector over the upper half of the junction.

The situation described above and illustrated in Fig. 21.24a is not a stable condition, however. As the holes diffuse into the n germanium bar from the p emitter region, they drift toward the negative end of the bar under the influence of the transverse electric field in the bar. The presence of the holes lowers the resistivity of the bar in that region so that the potential along the bar redistributes itself in a way represented

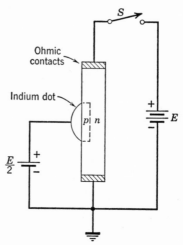

Fig. 21.23   Double-base diode.

by Fig. 21.24b. The shape of the curve from $x = 0$ to $x = L/2$ is largely determined by the hole density variation with x, due to recombination of holes with electrons in the n germanium, and is unimportant in the present discussion. Notice that $E/2$ now occurs at $x > L/2$ so that more than half of the p region is biased as an emitter.

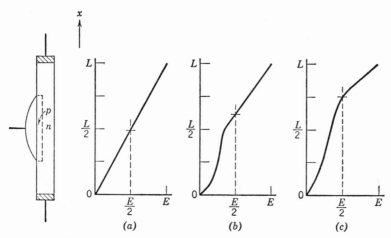

Fig. 21.24   Potential distribution in double-base diode.

In a very short time after the closing of switch S, the stable condition shown in Fig. 21.24c has been established.   All the p region is now acting as an emitter.   If desired, it is possible by choice of different bias batteries to operate such a double-base diode in a stable condition with a portion of the p region acting continuously as an emitter and the remainder of the p region acting continuously as a collector.

21.2.2   Circuit Application of the Double-Base Diode

If the double-base diode circuit of Fig. 21.25 is constructed, the input characteristic of the device may be examined.   Figure 21.26 shows the

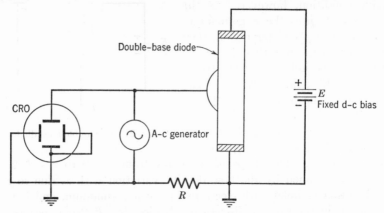

Fig. 21.25   Circuit for obtaining input characteristic of double-base diode.

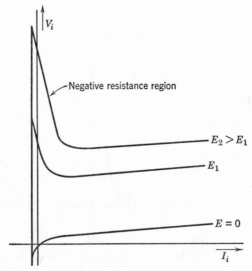

Fig. 21.26   Input characteristic of double-base diode.

curves obtained for three values of d-c bias E. The curve for $E = 0$ is a normal diode rectifier characteristic. Notice that the curves for $E > 0$ exhibit a large negative resistance region. This type of char-

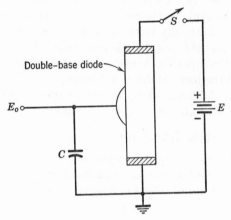

Fig. 21.27   Sawtooth oscillator.

acteristic suggests its use in many devices such as pulse generators, flipflops, multivibrators, and other oscillators.

Figure 21.27 shows a simple sawtooth oscillator circuit utilizing a double-base diode. When switch S is closed, the capacitor C begins to

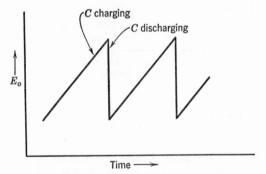

Fig. 21.28   Waveform of sawtooth oscillator.

charge through the back resistance of the junction diode, since the p region is negative relative to the n germanium. The voltage across the capacitor rises linearly with time, since the capacitor is charging from an essentially constant-current source. The time required to charge the capacitor is the RC product of the capacitance and the back diode resistance. E_o vs. time is shown in Fig. 21.28.

Eventually, the voltage across the capacitor becomes large enough so that the p region becomes positive relative to the germanium over a small part of the junction area. Holes are now injected into the base region. This causes a quick shift in potential distribution along the bar by the mechanism explained in Sec. 21.2.1. When the potential shifts, the diode is biased strongly in the forward direction and capacitor C discharges through the forward diode resistance. The time required for the discharge of the capacitor depends on the RC product of the external capacitance and the forward diode resistance.

The ratio of useful linear sweep to retrace time may be of the order of the ratio of back to forward diode resistances.

21.3 Multielectrode Transistors

In Sec. 21.2, the discussion concerned some consequences of adding a second ohmic base contact to a fused-junction germanium diode. Here, we will first investigate the effect of a second ohmic contact on a fused-junction transistor.

21.3.1 The Double-Base Transistor [3]

A double-base tetrode is shown in Figs. 21.29a and 21.29b. Note that the structure of Fig. 21.29a is exactly the same as that of the con-

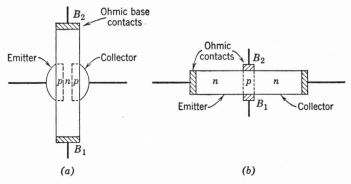

Fig. 21.29   Double-base tetrodes.

ventional fused-junction transistor except for the addition of the second ohmic base contact. If no bias voltage is applied between the bases B_1 and B_2, the device behaves like a conventional transistor. Figure 21.30 shows the bias circuits for this tetrode. The potentiometer P allows adjustment of the interbase bias to positive or negative values. Two effects are of interest in the operation of the device, as described below.

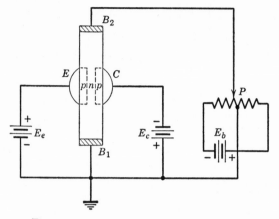

Fig. 21.30   Bias potentials for p-n-p tetrode.

21.3.1.1   Effect of Double-Base Diode

Double-base diode action (Sec. 21.2.1) results in non-uniform hole injection from the p region into the germanium bar. If base B_2 is biased so that it is positive relative to B_1, the p region emits as shown

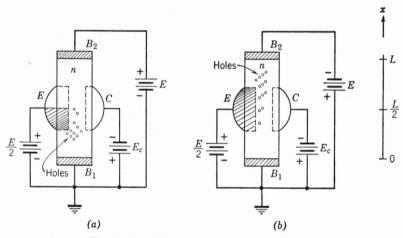

Fig. 21.31   Effect of interbase bias on emitter.

in Fig. 21.31a. The lower section of the p region emits more strongly, and the junction may not emit over its entire area. If B_2 is negative relative to B_1 (Fig. 21.31b), the entire p region emits, but the number of holes injected is greater for the upper section of the junction.

21.3.1.2   Effect of Transverse Field

The tranverse electric field in the bar causes the holes to drift in a preferred direction. In Fig. 21.31a the holes drift in the direction of B_1; in Fig. 21.31b, in the direction of B_2.

These two mechanisms complement each other; i.e., if B_2 is positive, both mechanisms cause the number of holes to increase below $x = L/2$ relative to the number of holes above $x = L/2$. Conversely, if B_2 is negative, the region above $x = L/2$ becomes richer in holes.

For the purposes of this discussion it is assumed that the total number of holes is independent of the interbase bias. (Experimentally this would mean readjusting the emitter bias to give constant emitter current.)

In a practical embodiment of the device, the variation of I_e might be made small by proper choice of geometry in the design and of biases in the circuit.

21.3.2   Control of Gain

With a conventional transistor, it is possible to control the gain of an amplifier circuit (a) by varying the operating point of the transistor;

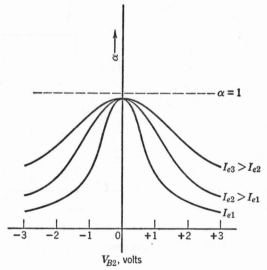

Fig. 21.32   Variation of α with interbase bias.

(b) by varying the values of the external circuit impedances. The double-base tetrode provides an additional method for controlling gain—a very convenient method in that the operating point of the tetrode may be kept constant and no change of circuit parameters is required for the control.

Assuming a constant hole injection rate, the net effect of the application of interbase bias is to cause the holes to drift through the bar toward B_1 or B_2 away from the collector junction, which is directly opposite the emitter (Fig. 21.31). Holes drifting away from the region of the collector will recombine with electrons in the n germanium bar and will not contribute to α. Recalling the fact that, for α = unity, all the holes must arrive at the collector, the application of interbase bias voltage of either polarity will result in a decrease in α and, hence, a decrease in the gain of the amplifier. Figure 21.32 shows the variation of α with interbase bias.

21.3.3 Control of Cut-off Frequency

Figure 21.33 shows a plot of α vs. frequency for a transistor tetrode such as that of Fig. 21.29b with and without an interbase bias. Note that the α cut-off is improved but the value of α_0 is substantially reduced. Two factors contribute to the improved high-frequency re-

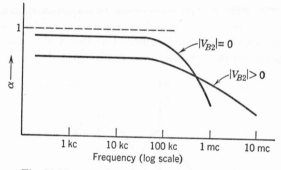

Fig. 21.33 α vs. frequency for transistor tetrode.

sponse: (a) The reduced effective area of the emitter and collector caused by the application of the transverse interbase field results in a decrease of effective output capacity so that the output impedance of the amplifier is higher for a given frequency. (b) Current flow is limited to a shorter length of the base region, resulting in a marked reduction in base resistance. For high gain, the ratio of output impedance to base resistance should be as large as possible, as has been shown in preceding chapters (see Chapter 10).

21.3.4 Variations of the Double-Base Transistor

The improvements in performance described in Secs. 21.3.2 and 21.3.3 can be obtained with a fused-junction transistor of the geometry shown in Fig. 21.29a or with a grown-junction device such as the one illustrated in Fig. 21.29b. With a fused-junction transistor, it is possible to vary the sizes and locations of the emitter and collector junctions to obtain improved overall performance. In addition, it is possible to

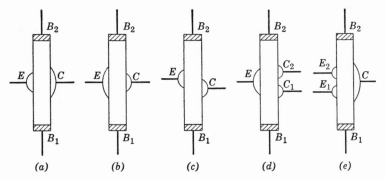

Fig. 21.34   Variations of the double-base transistor.

employ more than one emitter or collector junction to obtain certain desired effects. Figure 21.34 shows some of the possible arrangements.

Consideration of the principles of operation of the double-base tetrode leads to certain conclusions. For the device shown in Fig. 21.34a, application of interbase bias results in a decrease in r_b with

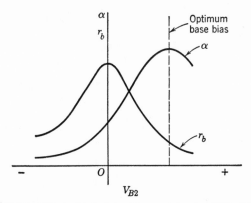

Fig. 21.35   Effect of interbase bias on tetrode of Fig. 21.34c.

little change in α. The tetrode of Fig. 21.34b will have an α which is highly sensitive to interbase bias of either polarity. The unit shown in Fig. 21.34c will have an α which rises with application of a positive potential to B_2, but α will fall to a very low value for a negative bias on B_2. The base resistance, r_b, will be reduced by applying interbase bias in all cases. Thus for Fig. 21.34c in particular the result of bias application is shown in the curves of Fig. 21.35. Here the improved frequency response is obtained with an *increase* in α_0 over the zero bias value of α_0.

Figure 21.34d shows a double-base pentode in which the signal applied to the emitter activates either of two collectors, depending on the applied interbase bias. Figure 21.34e shows another pentode in which one of two emitter signals is chosen to activate the collector, again depending on the interbase bias. Figure 21.36 shows an experimental push-pull amplifier circuit employing the device of Fig. 21.34d.

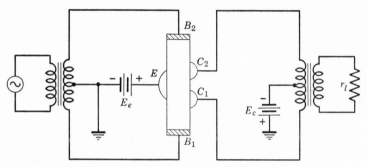

Fig. 21.36   Push-pull amplifier using transistor pentode.

The operation of this device makes use of a linear variation of α for each of the transistor combinations EB_1C_1 and EB_2C_2, as interbase bias is applied.

The possibilities inherent in such germanium devices may be exploited still further by adding more ohmic contacts and p-n junctions.

21.3.5   Transistors with p-n Hook Collector [4]

The presence of an additional junction in the collector region of a transistor can result in multiplication of collected carriers so that changes in emitter current may produce much larger changes in collector current.

For example, consider an n-p-n transistor as shown in Fig. 21.37 with an additional p-type region M in the collector. Electrons injected at the emitter junction diffuse through the base region and are collected at the collector junction just as in the bipolar junction transistor discussed in Sec. 1.4. The electrons collected will be neutralized by holes, either in the collector region C, or in the p-type multiplier region M. In the former case, the holes required diffuse in from the p region. Some of these holes may cross the collector junction instead of neutralizing collected electrons. In fact, if the thickness of region C is small compared to a diffusion length, many holes will cross the collector junction for each electron neutralized, resulting in collector-current multiplication. Some electrons cross the multiplier junction. These, too, result in multiplication, since a portion of the current across the junction according to eq. 1.5 must be carried by holes, many of which will diffuse over to the collector junction as above. The multiplier junction

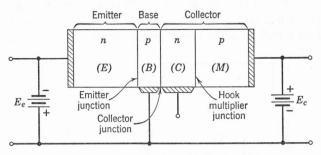

Fig. 21.37 n-p-n-p hook multiplier transistor.

should therefore have the properties of a good emitter so that nearly all the current across it is carried by holes. Region C should have the properties of a good base region. In fact, the multiplication theoretically available by this arrangement is the same as the current gain of a hypothetical grounded-emitter p-n-p transistor circuit using M for the emitter, C for the base, and B for the collector (region E not used).

The total result of the hook multiplication mechanism is that each electron collected causes the ejection of x holes from collector to base. The effective carrier multiplication α^* is then $(1 + x)$. The n-p-n-p transistor has been described above; a p-n-p-n transistor would operate in a corresponding manner with reversed polarities. It is also possible to provide region C with an external connection which can be used to control the effective current amplification of the device.

Hook multiplier junction transistors have been made with α^* of 10^2 to 10^3. However, the frequency response of this complicated mechanism is poor, limiting application of the device in this form principally to audio-frequency use. A p-n hook mechanism acting over a much more restricted region is believed to play an important role in the multiplication at the collector of point-contact transistors.

21.4   Field-Controlled Devices

The transistors described elsewhere in this book are devices characterized by relatively low input impedance. The control of current by mechanisms involving pure field action is attractive wherever high-input impedances are desirable. Magnetic field effects such as magneto-resistance or Hall effect could conceivably be applied to control devices but have thus far contributed only to instrumentation (e.g., Hall effect fluxmeter). Electric field mechanisms have been exploited a described below.

21.4.1   Fieldistor

The concept of utilizing an electric field to modify the conductivity of a semiconductor is actually older than the transistor.[12] An electric field normal to the surface of a semiconductor will cause a rearrange-ment of charge distribution near the surface. The number of mobile carriers in the underlying region may be altered in the process, and a limited control can be achieved. The field may be applied through a small air gap or a thin layer of insulating material. Fieldistors have been made using thin films or junction bars. With the junction bars the inverse leakage current is modulated by surface field effects at and near the junction.[5] Fieldistors at present have been made with reason-ably high gain only under conditions that severely limit their frequency response and stability.

21.4.2   Unipolar Field-Controlled Transistors

Shockley has described a unipolar transistor in which the extension of the non-conducting junction barrier region with increasing inverse voltage, as discussed in Chapter 1, can be used to control the effective cross section of a conducting region.[6] This does not involve modu-lating the resistivity of the region by injecting carriers as in a junction transistor, and avoids the surface effects that plague the fieldistor.

The operating principle can be inferred from Fig. 21.38, which shows another type of unipolar transistor in which a p-type band surrounds an n-type bar and is maintained at an inverse bias with respect to the

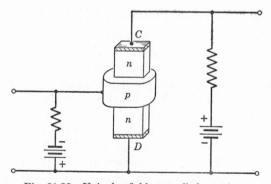

Fig. 21.38   Unipolar field controlled transistor.

bar. The resistance of the device between points C and D depends upon the effective cross section of the encircled n-type region. This cross section decreases with increased barrier penetration at higher voltages. A variable voltage applied to the high impedance of the inversely biased annular junction results in a corresponding variation of the output resistance.

The high-frequency effects include charging current for the barrier capacitance, and transit time of carriers where the finite mobilities must be taken into account. Operation above 1 megacycle has been achieved, and frequency response is expected to be superior to that of junction transistors of comparable dimensions.

Input impedances can be made much higher in this type of unipolar transistor than with conventional p-n junction transistors, but not as high as fieldistors, since the impedance here is that of an inversely biased p-n junction. More information concerning characteristics of these devices will become available as their development continues.

21.5   Photosensitive Semiconductor Devices

Several advantages of semiconductor electron devices over vacuum-tube devices have already been pointed out. Specifically, the semiconductor diode compares favorably with the vacuum-tube diode, and the transistor is superior to the vacuum-tube amplifier in many respects. Similarly, semiconductor photodevices have many advantages over vacuum photoemission cells. The number of announced p-n junction devices employing light as a control element is increasing rapidly. Units are now in existence which are mechanically strong, small, light, noise-free, and extremely sensitive. Furthermore, they are sensitive in the long-wavelength region of the spectrum (suitable for use with incandescent bulbs), have good high-frequency response (at least up to 200 kc) and have high spatial resolving power.

21.5.1   Construction of Germanium Photocells

The cells may be grouped into two categories: point-contact devices and junction devices. A point-contact coaxial phototransistor is shown in Fig. 21.39. The response is a maximum for light falling on the germanium directly opposite the phosphor-bronze wire and decreases rapidly elsewhere. The lens is included to increase the effective area of the cell by focusing the incoming radiation precisely on the sensitive spot. Electrical connections are made to the pin and to the metal shell. A p-n junction photocell is shown in Fig. 21.40. Here the photosensitive region is the junction between the p-type and n-type germanium. Light enters through the transparent plastic case in which

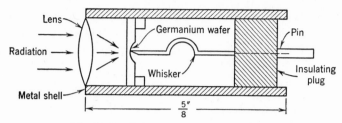

Fig. 21.39   Point-contact phototransistor.

the cell is potted.   Incident light from a large source may be focused on the junction by an optical system to provide maximum sensitivity. Many variations of structure are possible, but all must provide means for (a) housing the germanium in a moisture-free environment, (b) directing the light onto the sensitive area, (c) applying a bias voltage.

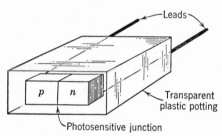

Fig. 21.40   p-n junction photocell.

21.5.2   Properties of Germanium Photocells

The behavior of the photocell will be described with reference to Fig. 21.41. A bias battery E is connected to the cell through a load resistance R_l such that the p region is biased negative with respect to the n region.   (For the point-contact device the whisker is biased negatively.) With no radiation falling on the junction, the dark current

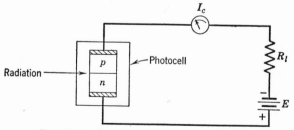

Fig. 21.41   Semiconductor photocell circuit.

I_{c0} is the back current of a germanium diode and has all the normal properties of I_{c0} for conventional transistors. For example, the temperature dependence of I_{c0} discussed in previous chapters applies equally well for this device.

Spectral response curves for constant radiation flux for the types of cells shown in Figs. 21.39 and 21.40 are shown in Fig. 21.42. The decrease in response on the short-wavelength side of the maximum is due to absorption of light in the germanium before reaching the sensitive region of the cell. For the point-contact cell, all the incident radiation

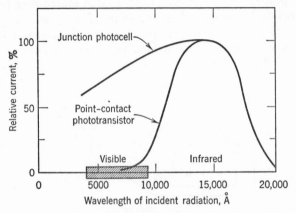

Fig. 21.42   Spectral response of germanium photocells.

must first penetrate a several mil thickness of germanium in order to reach the sensitive area near the point. Since radiation shorter than 10,000 Å will not penetrate germanium for more than a few angstroms, the cell is not sensitive in the visible-light range. In the junction photocell the edge of the photosensitive p-n junction is exposed, so that the overall range of sensitivity of the device is much greater. The sensitivity increases in the infrared region, where the radiation can penetrate more deeply, making use of a greater depth of the sensitive area. In fact, germanium is practically transparent to radiation whose wavelength is greater than 15,000 Å. On the long-wavelength side, the output falls off owing to the decreasing energy of the incident quanta, this energy being proportional to $1/\lambda$. A quantum energy of at least 0.61 electron volt ($\backsim$ 19,000 Å) is required to produce any photocurrent at all in germanium.

21.5.3   Operation of the Photocell

Figures 21.43 and 21.44 show the characteristics of point-contact and junction photocells, respectively. The curves show a strong resemblance to the V_c-I_c curves for point-contact and junction transistors, as would be expected. The several values of light flux are analogous to the several values of emitter current for transistor characteristics.

For the junction device, the collector is essentially a constant-current source whereas the point-contact cell has an r_c of about 20

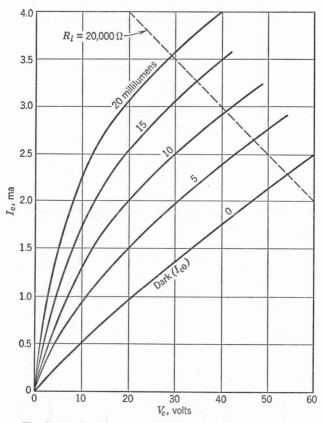

Fig. 21.43   Performance of point-contact phototransistor.

kilohms and must be properly matched for maximum output. Performance of these cells can be computed from the curves, for specific loads and operating points. Shive [7] has suggested the a-c equivalent circuit of Fig. 21.45, where C_c may be neglected at low frequencies as for the transistor. Here

$$i_c = kl\, r_c/(r_c + r_b + r_l) = Kl \qquad [21.1]$$

where l is the effective light flux on the photocell.

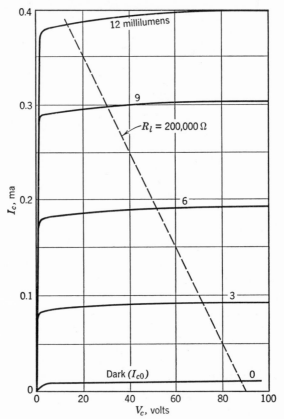

Fig. 21.44   Performance of junction photocell.

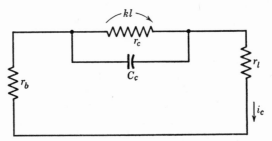

Fig. 21.45   Equivalent a-c circuit of photocell.

21.5.4 Physical Mechanisms of the Germanium Photocell

Basically, the increase in collector current when radiation is incident on the sensitive area of the cell is due to the production of hole-electron pairs in the germanium by the radiant energy. For the junction photocell, the quantum efficiency is approximately unity; i.e., one quantum produces a maximum of one hole-electron pair. For multijunction devices (such as the point-contact phototransistor for which a p-n hook mechanism is suspected), the quantum efficiency may be even greater than unity, owing to a current multiplication process. If a hole-electron pair is produced in the immediate vicinity of the p-n junction, the resultant free charges may be collected before recombination occurs and hence will contribute to the photocurrent.

Ideally, in a photoelectric device, it might be desirable that even very low-energy quanta (far infrared) would produce a photocurrent. However, in practice, a compromise is necessary. If a semiconducting material were selected whose energy levels were such that a very small amount of energy would produce a photocurrent, thermal energy would also raise electrons into the conduction band. This would result in a large dark current. For germanium, an energy of about 0.75 electron volt is required to raise electrons into the conduction band. This means that quanta of wavelength greater than 15,000 Å should have energies below the photoelectric threshold. Experimentally the threshold occurs at about 19,000 Å.

Detailed discussions of the mechanisms involved in the photo processes in germanium may be found in the references cited in the bibliography.

21.6 Bibliography

1. L. G. Pearson and B. Sawyer, "Silicon p-n Junction Alloy Diodes," *Proc. IRE*, *40*, 1348–1351 (November, 1952).

2. I. A. Lesk and V. P. Mathis, "The Negative Resistance Diode—A New Semiconducting Device," Convention record of the IRE, paper presented March 24, 1953.

3. I. A. Lesk, "A Tetrode Transistor," paper presented at AIEE winter convention, New York, Jan. 20, 1953.

4. J. J. Ebers, "Four-Terminal p-n-p-n Transistors," *Proc. IRE*, *40*, 1361–1363 (November, 1952).

5. O. M. Stuetzer, "Junction Fieldistors," *Proc. IRE*, *40*, 1377 (November, 1952).

6. W. Shockley, "A Unipolar Field Effect Transistor," *Proc. IRE*, *40*, 1365–1377 (November, 1952).

7. J. N. Shive, "Properties of M1740 p-n Junction Photocell," *Proc IRE*, *40*, 1410–1413 (November, 1952).

8. "A New Type of Electric Eye Developed by Bell Laboratories," *Elec. Engg.*, May, 1950, pp. 476–477.

9. J. N. Shive, "The Phototransistor," *Bell Lab. Rec.*, *28*, No. 8, pp. 337–342 (August, 1950).

10. F. S. Goucher, "Photon Yield of Electron Hole Pairs in Germanium," *Phys. Rev.*, *78*, 816 (June, 1950).

11. W. J. Pietenpol, *"p-n* Junction Rectifier and Photocell," *Phys. Rev.*, *82*, No. 1, pp. 121–122 (April, 1951).

12. W. C. Dunlap, Jr., "Germanium Photocells," *Gen. Elec. Rev.*, *55*, 26–31 (March, 1952).

13. Kurt Lehovec, "New Photoelectric Devices Utilizing Carrier Injection," *Proc. IRE*, *40*, 1407–1409 (November, 1952).

14. W. Shockley, *Electrons and Holes in Semiconductors*, Van Nostrand, New York, 1950.

15. R. L. Wallace, Jr., L. G. Schimpf, and E. Dickten, "A Junction Transistor Tetrode for High-Frequency Use," *Proc. IRE*, *40*, 1395–1400 (November, 1952).

16. J. H. Scaff and R. S. Ohl, "Development of Silicon Crystal Rectifiers for Microwave Radar Receivers," *Bell Sys. Tech. J.*, *26* (January, 1947).

17. W. Shockley and G. L. Pearson, "Modulation of Conductance of Thin Film of Semiconductors by Surface Charges," *Phys. Rev.*, *74*, 232 (1948).

18. R. N. Hall, "Power Rectifiers and Transistors," *Proc. IRE*, *40*, 1512–1518 (November, 1952).

19. C. L. Roualt and G. N. Hall, "A High-Voltage, Medium-Power Rectifier," *Proc. IRE*, *40*, 1519–1521 (November, 1952).

Chapter 22

Small-Signal
Parameter Measurement

22.1 Introduction

In Chapter 3 the transistor was examined as a four-terminal active network. Several useful equivalent circuits have been set up and related to the four-pole impedances. In order to make use of these equivalent circuits in practical circuit design problems it is necessary to know the numerical values of the impedances that appear in the equivalent circuits. It has been pointed out that: (1) the values of the impedances depend on such factors as operating point, frequency, magnitude of signal, and temperature; (2) the impedances may be approximated by pure resistances at low frequencies.

It has been found experimentally that the equivalent circuit parameters measured at a low audio frequency will apply over the range of frequencies where: (1) the phase shift of the collector current with respect to the emitter current is negligible; (2) the effect of collector capacity may be neglected. This range of frequencies extends to at least 3000 cps for most transistors.

It may be necessary, however, to measure the parameters at the operating point that will be used in the circuit to be constructed. This restriction is due to the strong dependence of the parameters on the operating point. Hence for a given set of parameter values, V_c and I_c, or V_c and I_e are usually specified.†

The magnitude of the measuring signal should be kept as small as possible, but is not critical as long as the transistor is kept at all times well within the region of linear operation.

Measurements are ordinarily made at room temperature ($\backsim 20°C$) for the sake of simplicity.

---

† It may be shown that any two of the four d-c quantities, V_c, I_c, V_e, or I_e, are sufficient to fix the d-c operating point. One of the two combinations mentioned is usually chosen as being easiest to set up from a practical viewpoint.

The relations between the four-pole resistances and the low-frequency resistive parameters of the grounded-base and grounded-emitter equivalent circuits developed in Chapter 3 are summarized in Table 22.1 for convenience.

Table 22.1   Transistor Equivalent Resistances at Low Frequencies

Open-Circuit Resistance	Grounded-Base	Grounded-Emitter
r_{11}	$r_e + r_b$	$r_e + r_b$
r_{12}	r_b	r_e
r_{21}	$r_b + r_m$	$r_e - r_m$
r_{22}	$r_b + r_c$	$r_e + r_c - r_m$

In the measurement procedures frequent use will be made of approximations such as that of eq. 22.1.

$$r_{11} = \left(\frac{\partial V_e}{\partial I_e}\right)_{I_c} \cong \left(\frac{\Delta V_e}{\Delta I_e}\right)_{I_c} \cong \left(\frac{v_e}{i_e}\right)_{I_c} \qquad [22.1]$$

Thus the partial derivatives are approximated by ratios of small a-c voltages and currents. The magnitudes of the a-c swings are kept small relative to the d-c condition.

22.2   Measurements of α, a, and b at Low Frequencies

Figures 22.1 and 22.2 show the equivalent circuits for the grounded-base and the grounded-emitter transistor.

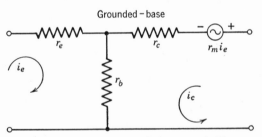

Fig. 22.1   Equivalent circuit for grounded-base.

In Figure 22.1 consider the ratio of collector to emitter currents when a signal is applied to the input, and the output terminals are shorted to alternating current. Equating voltage drops,

$$i_c(r_c + r_b) + i_e r_b = -r_m i_e \qquad [22.2]$$

$$\left| \frac{i_c}{i_e} \right| = \frac{r_m + r_b}{r_c + r_b} = \alpha \qquad [22.3]$$

as defined in Chapter 3. This agrees with the definition of α which is the short-circuit current amplification in the grounded-base configuration.

It is convenient to define $r_m/r_c = a$. Then, if $r_b \ll r_m$ and $\ll r_c$,

$$\alpha \cong a$$

α can be assumed equal to a for most junction transistors and is so assumed throughout the present chapter.

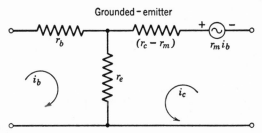

Fig. 22.2   Equivalent circuit for grounded-emitter.

Similarly, in Fig. 22.2 the ratio of collector to base currents is obtained.

$$i_c(r_c - r_m + r_e) + i_b r_e = r_m i_b$$

$$\left| \frac{i_c}{i_b} \right| = \frac{r_m - r_e}{r_c - r_m + r_e} \qquad [22.4]$$

If r_m and $(r_c - r_m) \gg r_e$, which is the usual junction transistor condition,

$$\left| \frac{i_c}{i_b} \right| \cong \frac{r_m}{r_c - r_m} = \frac{a}{1 - a} = b \qquad [22.5]$$

as defined in Chapter 3. The parameter b is approximately the short-circuit current amplification of the grounded-emitter transistor amplifier.

Values of a and b as high as possible are desirable in transistor amplifiers. For most junction transistors a has a maximum value of unity. Thus for most purposes b is a more desirable quantity to measure than *a* owing to the fact that the magnitude of *b* does not approach a limiting value.   Table 22.2 illustrates this point.

Table 22.2   Comparison of *a* and *b*

a	b
0.800	4.00
.850	5.67
.900	9.00
.950	19.00
.970	32.3
.990	99
.999	999

For point-contact transistors where *a* is greater than unity, the *a* measurement must usually be used rather than the *b* measurement or oscillation may occur in the measurement circuit.

So far the discussion has been limited to the a-c circuits involved in the measurement process.   Since it is necessary to maintain a specific

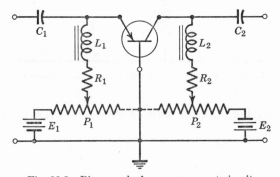

Fig. 22.3   Bias supply for measurement circuit.

d-c operating point, bias must be supplied to the transistor during the measurement procedures.   Figure 22.3 shows a method of supplying the d-c biases.   Note that either input or output terminals may be connected to a generator, may be effectively short-circuited to alternating current by making C_1 or C_2 very large and grounding the appropriate terminal, or may be effectively open-circuited to alternating current by making L_1 and L_2 very large with the appropriate terminal open.   A large value of R_1 insures a constant current supply to the emitter.

A practical α measurement circuit is shown in Fig. 22.4.   In use, the a-c voltage v_0 measured across R_{ie} is set at unity.   The voltage v_1 across R_{ic} then indicates α directly.

$$v_1/v_0 = i_c R_{ic}/i_e R_{ie} = i_c/i_e = \alpha \qquad [22.6]$$

and therefore

$$\alpha = v_1$$

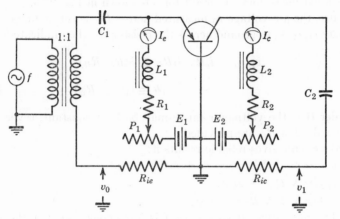

Fig. 22.4   α measurement circuit.

The error is small if the following conditions are met:

1. $x_{L1} \gg r_i$ [where $r_i = r_e + r_b(1 - a)$].
2. $x_{L2} \gg \sqrt{R_{ic}^2 + x_{C2}^2}$.
3. $r_c \gg \sqrt{R_{ic}^2 + x_{C2}^2}$. x_{L1}, x_{L2}, x_{C2} are the magnitudes of the re-actances of L_1, L_2, and C_2, respectively.

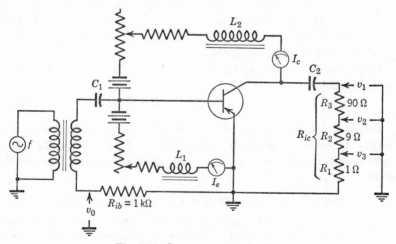

Fig. 22.5   b measurement circuit.

4. The measurement frequency f is low enough so that the phase angle of α is very small. This circuit is suitable for either point-contact or junction transistors.

A similar measurement circuit for b is shown in Fig. 22.5.

In use, the a-c voltage v_0 measured across R_{ib} is set at unity. The voltages v_1, v_2, v_3 to ground across the resistor R_{ic} then indicate b thus:

$$v_1/v_0 = i_c R_{ic}/i_b R_{ib} \cong b(R_{ic}/R_{ib})$$

$$b \cong v_1(R_{ib}/R_{ic}) \qquad [22.7]$$

In order that the voltmeter range may be kept constant, several different values of R_{ic} are provided.

The b circuit gives reliable results if:

1. $x_{L1} \gg r_i$ [where $r_i = r_b + r_e/(1 - a)$].
2. $x_{L2} \gg \sqrt{R_{ic}^2 + x_{C2}^2}$.
3. $(r_c - r_m) \gg \sqrt{R_{ic}^2 + x_{C2}^2}$.
4. The measurement frequency f is low enough so that the phase angle of b is very nearly zero.†

It is recommended that a sensitive a-c vacuum-tube voltmeter (such as the Hewlett Packard 400C or equivalent) be used for all measurements. It is desirable to observe the waveforms of all measured currents and voltages on an oscilloscope to insure that the transistor is operating in its linear region.

22.3 Measurement of r_c and $(r_c - r_m)$ at Low Frequencies

Figure 22.1 shows the equivalent circuit for the grounded-base configuration. The open-circuit output resistance may be measured by applying a generator to the output terminals with the input terminals open-circuited to alternating current.

In this case the resistance is the four-pole resistance r_{22}. Referring to Table 22.1,

$$r_{22} = r_b + r_c \cong r_c \qquad \text{if } r_c \gg r_b \qquad [22.8]$$

Hence the measurement of r_c is simply the measurement of the output resistance. Similarly, from Fig. 22.2 and Table 22.1, the open-circuit output resistance of the grounded-emitter connection gives

$$r_{22} = r_e + r_c - r_m \cong r_c - r_m \qquad \text{if } (r_c - r_m) \gg r_e \qquad [22.9]$$

† It can be shown that the maximum allowable frequency for low-frequency b measurement is of the order of $(1 - a)$ times the maximum allowable frequency for low-frequency α measurement.

A practical circuit for measuring the r_c is shown in Fig. 22.6. In use, the output of the signal generator is adjusted until v_1, the voltage from base to ground across R_{ic}, is equal to unity. Then v_0 is read at

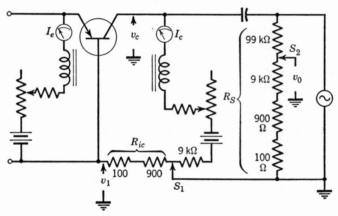

Fig. 22.6 r_c measurement circuit.

one of the taps on resistor R_S. The output resistance is obtained from v_0 directly.

$$\frac{v_0}{v_1} = \frac{v_c F}{i_c R_{ic}} = (r_c + r_b) \frac{F}{R_{ic}} \cong r_c \frac{F}{R_{ic}}$$

and therefore

$$r_c = v_0 R_{ic}/F \qquad\qquad [22.10]$$

where F is the fraction of the generator voltage being measured by the

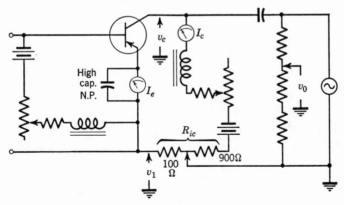

Fig. 22.7 $(r_c - r_m)$ measurement circuit.

voltmeter (switch S_2); R_{ic} is the value of resistance between base and ground (switch S_1).

For $(r_c - r_m)$ measurement the circuit is similar, as shown in Fig. 22.7, and the operation is analogous.

$$\frac{v_0}{v_1} = \frac{v_c F}{i_c R_{ic}} = (r_c - r_m + r_e)\frac{F}{R_{ic}} \cong (r_c - r_m)\frac{F}{R_{ic}}$$

and therefore

$$(r_c - r_m) = v_0 R_{ic}/F \qquad [22.11]$$

For r_c and $(r_c - r_m)$ measurement (as for the α and b measurement) it is desirable to observe continuously the waveform of the measured voltages to be certain that the measurement signals being used are not large enough to be distorted at the chosen d-c operating point.

22.4   Measurement of r_b and r_e at Low Frequencies

Referring to Table 22.1 it is seen that some combination of measurements of r_{11} and r_{12} should give the required values of r_b and r_e.   For point-contact transistors (operated in the grounded-base connection), measurements of $r_{11} = r_e + r_b$ and $r_{12} = r_b$ are sometimes used to give the required values.   However, the r_{11} measurement, somewhat difficult for point-contact transistors, becomes more difficult for junction transistors.

r_{11} is the input resistance with the output open-circuited to alternating current.   Practically speaking, we mean that the impedance of the collector d-c bias supply must be very large relative to the output resistance of the circuit.   Table 22.3 gives some idea of the problem. Tuned circuits, chokes, and resistances may be used as bias supply impedances, but the problems are still formidable.

Table 22.3   Impedance of Collector Bias Supply Required for Measurement of r_{11}

Transistor Circuit	Typical Output Resistance, r_{22}	Approximate Bias Impedance Required, z_{bias}
Point-contact (grounded-base)	$r_c = 25$ kilohms	>250 kilohms
Junction (grounded-emitter)	$r_c - r_m = 50$ kilohms	>500 kilohms
Junction (grounded-base)	$r_c = 1$ megohm	>10 megohms

The measurement of r_{12} is another matter.   It is relatively easy to open-circuit the input circuit to alternating current and measure the transfer resistance r_{12}.   For the grounded-base stage this gives r_b, and for the grounded-emitter case we obtain r_e.   The limitations on the measurement of r_b and r_e are the sensitivity and noise level of the measuring equipment. For the grounded-base connection the measurement circuit is essentially as shown in Fig. 22.8.

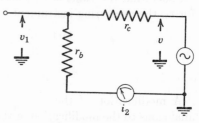

$$v_1/i_2 = r_{12} = r_b \quad [22.12]$$

and

$$v_1 = vr_b/(r_b + r_c) \quad [22.13]$$

Fig. 22.8 Technique for r_b measurement. Simplified diagram.

The value of $r_b/(r_b + r_c)$ may be as low as 10^{-4}.

Assuming the lowest value of v_1 easily measurable to be 1 mv rms, the signal applied to the collector must be 10 volts rms. This sets a minimum allowable d-c collector voltage of 14.14 volts even if the collector is allowed to swing over the entire class A operating range. Even with such restrictions this technique is useful for r_b and r_e measurements. A practical circuit for measuring r_b in this manner is shown in

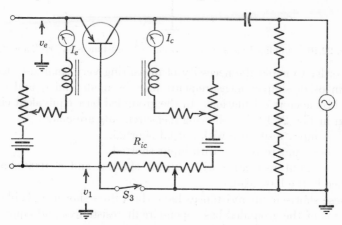

Fig. 22.9 r_b measurement circuit.

Fig. 22.9. Note that this is the same circuit as that of Fig. 22.6, the r_c measurement circuit, modified only by including the switch S_3.

In use, the current i_c, determined by reading the voltage v_1 across R_{ic}, is set to unity. Then switch S_3 is closed, and v_e, the voltage between emitter and base, is read to ground. r_b may be obtained directly from v_e.

$$v_e/v_1 = v_e/i_c R_{ic} = r_b/R_{ic}$$

whence

$$r_b = v_e R_{ic} \quad [22.14]$$

R_{ic} is chosen such that $R_{ic} \ll r_c$. If the relative values of R_{ic} and r_b are such that the value of R_{ic} chosen is an inconvenient full-scale value for r_b, the measuring instrument is switched to another range.

Meter Range	r_b (full scale)
0.1	$0.1R_{ic}$
1	R_{ic}
10	$10R_{ic}$

A modification of the $(r_c - r_m)$ measurement circuit of Fig. 22.7 analogous to the modification of the r_c circuit shown in Fig. 22.9 allows the measurement of r_e by the technique described above.

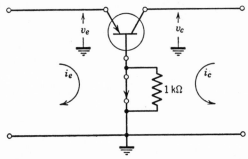

Fig. 22.10   Simplified measurement circuit for resistances $r_{11}{}'$, $r_{11}{}''$, and $r_{22}{}'$.

In order to avoid the necessity of measuring very small a-c signals, certain other simpler measurements may be made and r_e and r_b obtained by a short calculation. In the grounded-base equivalent circuit shown in Fig. 22.10 the following measurements are made:

$r_{11}{}'$ = input resistance with output shorted.

$r_{22}{}'$ = output resistance with input shorted.

$r_{11}{}''$ = input resistance with output shorted and a 1000-ohm resistance in the base lead.

These short-circuit resistances have the values shown in Table 22.4 in terms of the grounded-base open-circuit resistances and equivalent circuit parameters.

Table 22.4   Short-Circuit Resistances

Short-Circuit Resistance	Open-Circuit Resistances	Grounded-Base Parameters
$r_{11}{}'$ =	$r_{11} - \dfrac{r_{12}r_{21}}{r_{22}}$ =	$r_e + r_b(1 - a)$
$r_{22}{}'$ =	$r_{22} - \dfrac{r_{12}r_{21}}{r_{11}}$ =	$r_c\left(1 - \dfrac{ar_b}{r_b + r_e}\right)$
$r_{11}{}''$ =	$r_{11} - \dfrac{r_{12}r_{21}}{r_{22}}$ =	$r_e + (r_b + 1000)(1 - a)$

The relations shown below may be derived from Table 22.4.

$$(1 - a) = \frac{r_{11}'' - r_{11}'}{1000} \qquad [22.15]$$

$$r_b = \frac{r_{11}'}{a}\left(\frac{r_c}{r_{22}'} - 1\right) \qquad [22.16]$$

$$r_e = r_{11}' - r_b(1 - a) \qquad [22.17]$$

Equation 22.15 is used to obtain a value of $(1 - a)$ accurate within a few per cent for substitution in eq. 22.17 to give reasonably accurate results. It is not satisfactory for values of a near unity to obtain $(1 - a)$ by simply subtracting a from unity.

22.5   A Multipurpose Low-Frequency Parameter Measurement Device

An instrument has been designed and built for making parameter measurements with the grounded-base circuit. This equipment will measure r_{11}', r_{11}'', α, r_b, r_c, and r_{22}' directly. From these quantities $(1 - a)$, r_e, and r_b may be calculated.

Provisions are made for setting up and measuring the required d-c operating point. Both n-p-n and p-n-p junction transistors may be measured as well as point-contact transistors.

The following auxiliary equipment is required for the measurements: (1) audio oscillator with 10 volts rms output at 1000 cps; (2) multirange a-c vacuum-tube voltmeter with 1 mv full-scale maximum sensitivity; (3) monitoring oscilloscope.

For these a-c measurements the parameter measurement device is essentially a six-circuit nine-position switch which sets up the necessary input and output conditions for the resistance measurements required. A circuit diagram of the equipment is given in Fig. 22.11.

The magnitudes of the a-c signals to be used are best determined by the operator for they depend on: (1) characteristics of transistor; (2) d-c operating point chosen; (3) magnitude of signal swing to be encountered in operation. The value of the current measuring resistance chosen depends on the output resistance of the transistor being measured.

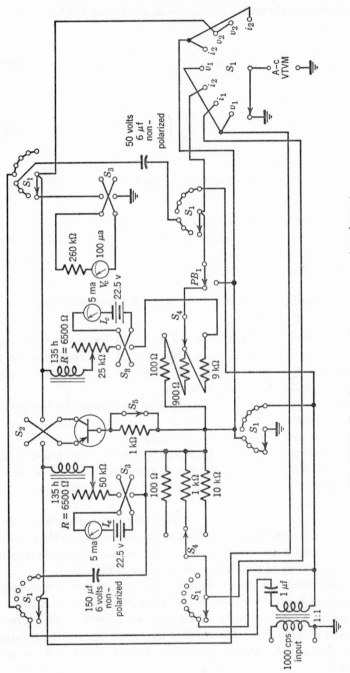

Fig. 22.11 Transistor parameter measurement equipment.

22.6   Measurement Problems at Higher Frequencies

If the restrictions mentioned in Sec. 22.1 are removed, the measurement problem becomes increasingly complex. First, even the simplest modification must include a collector capacitance C_c as shown in Fig. 22.12. In addition, the parameters become impedances rather than pure resistances and the phase of a becomes important. Finally, the magnitude of a decreases with frequency and the values of r_c and C_c are functions of frequency. Though the frequency dependence of r_e may

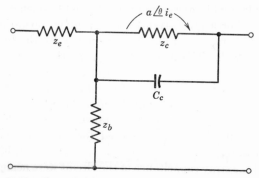

Fig. 22.12   Grounded-base transistor at higher frequencies.

often be neglected, the variations of a, r_b, r_c, and C_c must always be considered for high-frequency work. Even so, for any one particular set of operating conditions (including frequency), values of impedances exist which, when inserted into the equivalent circuit, will represent the transistor.

R. L. Pritchard of the General Electric Research Laboratory has suggested an equivalent circuit using physically realizable elements that will accurately represent the behavior of α, r_c, and C_c over a wide range of frequency. This has been discussed in Chapter 9.

For completeness any measurements of parameters made at higher frequencies should include both magnitude and phase. The problems that will be encountered depend on the operating point chosen and the measurement frequency. In general, however, some type of bridge technique is recommended.

22.7   Measurement of the α Cut-off Frequency

The high-frequency effects in transistors were discussed in Chapter 1. In Chapter 9 the variation of the magnitude and the phase angle of the short-circuit current amplification α with frequency was discussed, and analytical expressions were derived to predict this variation. In those expressions a term called α cut-off frequency is frequently used. This α cut-off frequency is defined as the frequency at which the magnitude of α drops 3 db from its low-frequency value.

Since the α cut-off frequency is used very often in high-frequency applications of transistors, it becomes an important parameter which will indicate, to a certain degree, the performance of a given transistor at high frequencies. Consequently, the α cut-off frequency of a transistor is usually given along with the other a-c parameters of a transistor.

The principle used in measuring the α cut-off frequency follows from its definition. For a given transistor at a given operating point the value of α is first measured at a low-frequency by the techniques described in Sec. 22.2. The magnitude of α at the α cut-off frequency will be, by definition, $0.707 \times \alpha_0$, where α_0 represents the magnitude of α at low frequencies. The signal frequency at which the magnitude of α is $0.707 \times \alpha_0$ is then found as described below.

Theoretically the circuit and equipment used in low-frequency parameter measurement could be used for the α cut-off frequency measurement provided that the isolating transformer in Fig. 22.4 were adequate and the stray capacitance of the circuit were negligible. However, in practice it is very difficult to provide an isolating transformer that can be operated over a frequency range from several hundred cycles per second to several megacycles per second and which has negligible capacitance from secondary to ground which would shunt resistor R_{ie} (see Fig. 22.4). This problem can be solved either by using a signal generator isolated from ground or by having a sensitive a-c millivoltmeter isolated from ground. When neither the perfect isolating transformer nor the isolated a-c meter is available, the above difficulty can be overcome by simply omitting the isolating transformer and the series resistance in the emitter circuit in Fig. 22.4. This will connect the base of the transistor directly to the grounded side of the signal generator as shown in Fig. 22.13.

The input current i_e is now calculated by using the fact that the input impedance of a grounded-base transistor amplifier is small. If the resistance r_1 is much larger than the input impedance of the transistor amplifier, the input current is practically controlled by the resistance r_1. Thus

$$i_e \cong e_g/r_1 \qquad (r_g \ll r_1) \qquad [22.18]$$

The output current i_c can be found by measuring the voltage drop across resistance r_2. This resistance r_2 should be very small so that the current flowing in it is practically the same as if r_2 were zero. The ratio of the output current i_c and the input current i_e will give the magnitude of α at the signal frequency.

In the actual instrument, the d-c bias circuits must be added to the circuit of Fig. 22.13. The complete circuit is shown in Fig. 22.14.

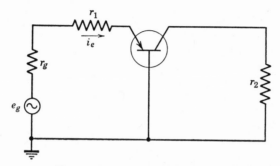

Fig. 22.13 α measurement circuit.

Here, the signal strength is varied by R_5 and the d-c bias currents are controlled by R_6 and R_7. The switches $S_1, S_2, S_3,$ and S_4 are ganged so that, when S_1 and S_2 are in the upper position, S_3 and S_4 open the battery connections. The procedure for measuring the magnitude of α

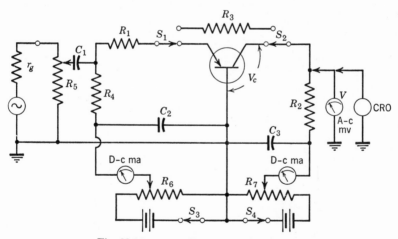

Fig. 22.14 α cut-off measurement circuit.

at a given frequency is as follows. First set the signal frequency to the desired value, and switches S_1 and S_2 in the lower position. Adjust the d-c bias currents to the desired operating point. The collector voltage V_c can be measured with a vacuum-tube voltmeter. Second, put S_1 and S_2 in the upper position, adjusting R_5 so that the voltage across R_2 is a convenient value, say 100 mv. Third, with the switches S_1 and S_2 in the lower position, the voltage drop across R_2 will be proportional to the magnitude of α. The waveform of this output voltage should be monitored with an oscilloscope to be certain that the input signal is not large enough to cause distortion.

If the signal generator output voltage is reasonably constant, the α cut-off frequency can be found by simply increasing the signal frequency to a value such that the output voltage across R_2 is 0.707 times the low-frequency output voltage. Then, by definition, this signal frequency is the α cut-off frequency.

22.8 Measurement of Collector Capacitance

In the measurement of the collector capacitance of a transistor the following problems are encountered: (1) The output impedance is that of a capacitance and a resistance in parallel. The equivalent Q of the circuit is low. (2) The capacitance is a non-linear function of collector voltage. The application of a test signal on the collector makes the capacitance a time-variant quantity. (3) Capacitive and resistive components are both frequency-variant; thus measurement at a high frequency is not the answer to the low-Q problem.

(Note: For a parallel RC circuit, $Q = \omega\, CR$. If CR is constant with frequency, the Q rises with ω.)

These problems may be solved as follows:

1. Measurement of output impedance z_o should be made using the grounded-base configuration, since

$$z_o = \frac{z_e z_b + z_c[z_e + z_b(1-a)] + r_g(z_b + z_c)}{z_e + z_b + r_g} \qquad [22.19]$$

Since $z_c \gg z_e$ and $z_c \gg z_b$,

$$z_o \cong z_c \left[\frac{z_e + z_b(1-a) + r_g}{z_e + z_b + r_g} \right] \qquad [22.20]$$

If $r_g \gg z_e + z_b$, then

$$z_o \cong z_c$$

Since the Q is very low, an ordinary Q-meter is not suitable for the measurement. For the frequency range of 50 kc to 5 mc, apparatus of a type similar to the Wayne Kerr B601 bridge or its equivalent is suitable for the purpose. This bridge is capable of measuring the parallel RC equivalent of active or passive networks. The measure-

ment circuit is given in Fig. 22.15.   The input transformer A has a
balanced secondary.   Both A and B are tapped to produce a large
number of range factors.

For measurements at lower frequencies (2.5 to 50 kc), a special bridge
may be designed to read the impedance as a parallel RC combination.

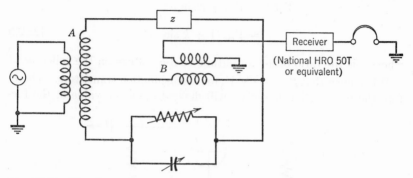

Fig. 22.15   Experimental setup for measurement of collector capacitance (frequencies above 50 kc).

The circuit appears in Fig. 22.16.   A suitable input transformer is a
General Radio 578C, designed to cover the range of 2 to 500 kc.   Any
other equivalent transformer covering this range could be used.   The

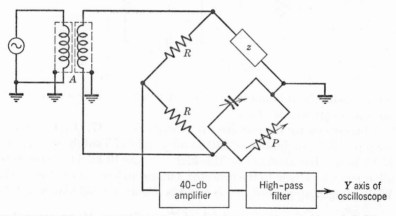

Fig. 22.16   Experimental setup for measurement of collector capacitance (frequencies from 2.5 kc to 50 kc).

standard potentiometer (P) is a precision unit, chosen so as to have a
very small rate of change of capacitance with respect to the angular
rotation of the sliding contact of the potentiometer.

2. Let the signal used for measurement be

$$v \sin \omega t \qquad [22.21]$$

Then the voltage on the collector

$$V_c(t) = V_{c0} + v \sin \omega t$$

$$= V_{c0} (1 + k \sin \omega t) \qquad [22.22]$$

where k is the ratio of a-c amplitude to d-c voltage on the collector.

It is known that $C_c \backsim 1/\sqrt{V_c}$ for fused-junction transistors. Therefore the measured value of C_c will depend upon the value of the fac-

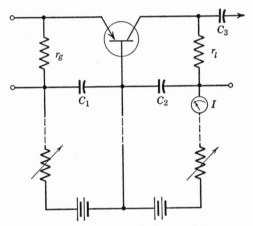

Fig. 22.17   Bias circuit for transistors.

tor k. It has been found in practice that values of k less than 0.1 do not cause appreciable error.

A bias circuit for the transistor is given in Fig. 22.17. C_1, C_2, and C_3 are a parallel combination of 0.01 μf mica and 6 μf Tantalytic.† r_g was 150 kilohms, but need not be this high. r_l was 10 kilohms, chosen to allow enough voltage to the collector, but not to lower the Q too much. With a larger supply voltage, r_l could be higher, e.g. 50 kilohms.

22.8.1   Alternative Method of Capacitance Measurement
(See Fig. 22.18.)

1. Connect to a constant current source consisting of an RF generator and a 100-kilohm resistance.

2. Plug in transistor; adjust trimmer for peak on VTVM.

† Trademark of General Electric Company for tantalum electrolytic capacitors.

3. Plug in capacitor in place of transistor, and adjust it to give the same reading on VTVM. The value of this capacitor is the collector capacitance.

Sources of Error. (*a*) The input circuit may not be a good enough constant current source, especially near resonance. (*b*) To be rigorous the transistor should be replaced by a *CR* combination to reproduce

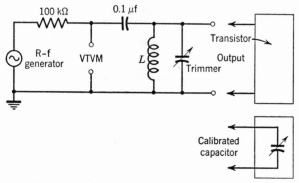

Fig. 22.18   Substitution method of capacitance measurement.

the effect of the Q of the transistor. (*c*) There is difficulty in getting a sharp resonance for frequencies below 100 kc.

Results obtained by this method were in fair agreement with the bridge method up to 250 kc.

22.9   Oscilloscopic Presentation of Characteristics

So far the discussion has dealt with measurement techniques for determining accurate numerical values of the transistor parameters. Another piece of equipment has been found useful for rapid qualitative examination of transistors. This device, called a "curve tracer," plots certain characteristics of the transistor on a conventional oscilloscope.

A circuit which may be used to portray a voltage vs. current curve is shown in Fig. 22.19. The current measuring resistance R_i has a value

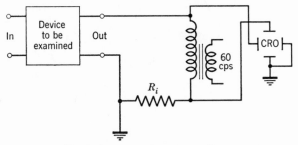

Fig. 22.19   Circuit for portraying output *V-I* characteristic.

such that $R_i \ll r_o$ of the circuit under test. The pattern on the scope is shown in Fig. 22.20. In general, the curve will appear in diagonally opposite quadrants and need not be symmetrical about the origin.

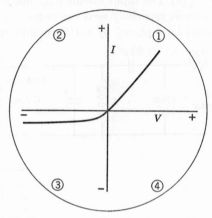

Fig. 22.20 Scope pattern given by circuit of Fig. 22.19.

This type of circuit is adequate for the transistor V_c-I_c curves or for other transistor curve families. For the V_c-I_c curves, the circuit is shown in Fig. 22.21. The diode D is used to limit the collector current

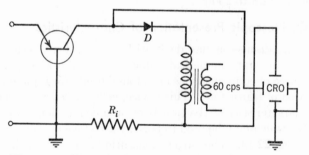

Fig. 22.21   Circuit for V_c-I_c characteristic, grounded-base.

when the 60-cycle sweep biases the collector of the transistor in the forward direction. Any desired value of emitter current may be fed in at the input, or the emitter may be left open to give the I_{c0} curve for the grounded-base transistor. Similarly, the grounded-emitter circuit is shown in Fig. 22.22. This arrangement portrays the V_c-I_c curve for the grounded-emitter transistor. If the base is left open,

$$I_c = I_{c0} + \alpha I_e \qquad\qquad [22.23]$$

$$I_b = I_e - I_c = 0 \qquad\qquad [22.24]$$

and therefore

$$I_c = I_e = I_{c0}/(1 - \alpha) \qquad\qquad [22.25]$$

where I_{c0} is the collector current for the grounded-base open-emitter condition.

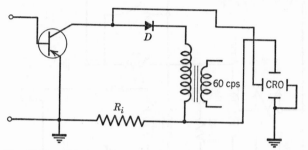

Fig. 22.22   Circuit for V_c-I_c characteristic, grounded-emitter.

Combining the scope patterns given by these two circuits gives at a glance much useful information about the transistor under test.   The pattern appears as shown in Fig. 22.23.   The ratio of the ordinate of curve E at any voltage to the ordinate of curve B is

$$\frac{I_{c0}/(1 - \alpha)}{I_{c0}} = \frac{1}{1 - \alpha} \cong \frac{1}{1 - a}$$

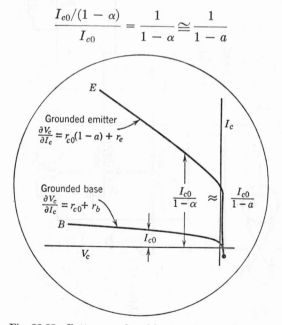

Fig. 22.23   Pattern produced by transistor under test.

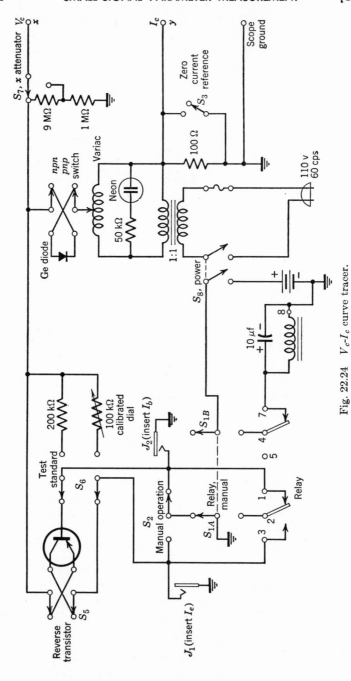

Fig. 22.24 V_c-I_c curve tracer.

The inverse slopes of curves B and E are approximately r_{c0} and $r_{c0}(1 - a)$ respectively. The variation of $1/(1 - a)$ or r_{c0} with operating voltage is shown, and the position of the knee is indicated. r_{c0} represents a maximum value of r_c, approached for very small emitter currents.

This information (1) permits the choice of a reasonable operating point for the transistor; (2) gives limitations, such as peak inverse voltage for the collector diode; (3) allows the user to decide whether the parameter variations may be tolerated in his circuit. (For example, α may vary such that $\alpha >$ unity for some operating voltages or temperatures.) A complete circuit for a curve tracer designed to portray the curves described above is given in Fig. 22.24. The 100-kilohm calibrated potentiometer is used to provide a comparison slope to give an idea of the value of $r_{c0}(1 - a)$ for the transistor under test. The 200-kilohm resistance allows a rough comparison for r_{c0} of the transistor under test.

The preceding discussion of the details of a particular curve tracer serves only as an example of the possibilities. Many modifications of curve tracers are possible, and several authors have published circuits designed to combine several functions in one piece of equipment. For example, several curves may be portrayed simultaneously on the scope, or calibration marks of some sort may be added. In general, it seems advisable for the user to design his curve tracer to fit the requirements of his particular application.

22.10   Problems

1. In Table 22.3 typical output resistances are quoted. These resistance values assume $r_g \gg r_i$, where r_g is the resistance of the driving generator and r_i is the input resistance of the transistor. If $r_g \ll r_i$, the output resistance is reduced. For a grounded-base stage, determine the ratio of the output resistance for $r_g = 0$ to the output resistance for $r_g = \infty$.

2. In Fig. 22.6, why is the current-measuring resistance R_{ic} included in the d-c circuit rather than in the a-c circuit only as in Fig. 22.4?

3. The current-measuring resistance on the collector side R_{ic} must be small compared to r_c for both α and r_c measurements in the grounded-base circuit. If $R_{ic} = r_c/10$, what is the error in α? What is the error for $R_{ic} = r_c/100$?

4. The measurement of $(1 - a)$ is usually to be recommended over the direct α measurement. For $\alpha = 0.985$, what error is allowable in a measurement of $(1 - a)$ to give α accurate to 1 per cent? (Assume that $\alpha = a$.)

5. By referring to the basic equations for a four-pole active network given in Chapter 3, prove the relations given in Table 22.4.

22.11   Bibliography

1. Geyer, "Oscillographic Presentation of Transistor Characteristics," M.I.T. E.E. thesis, 1949.

2. Mataré, "Transistor Measurement Technique," *Elecktron Wiss. Tech.*, October–November, 1950, pp. 368–379.

3. G. B. B. Chaplin, "Display of Transistor Characteristics on Cathode Ray Oscilloscope," *J. Sci. Instruments*, *29*, 142–145 (May, 1952).

4. N. Golden and R. Nielsen, "Oscilloscopic Display of Transistor Static Electrical Characteristics," *Proc. IRE*, *40*, 1437–1439 (November, 1952).

Appendix I

Matrix Algebra

The system of linear transformations

$$y_1 = a_{11}x_1 + a_{12}x_2 + \cdots + a_{1n}x_n$$
$$y_2 = a_{21}x_1 + a_{22}x_2 + \cdots + a_{2n}x_n$$
.
.
. [1]
.

$$y_m = a_{m1}x_1 + a_{m2}x_2 + \cdots + a_{mn}x_n$$

may be written in the form

$$\begin{bmatrix} y_1 \\ y_2 \\ \cdot \\ \cdot \\ \cdot \\ y_m \end{bmatrix} = \begin{bmatrix} a_{11} & a_{12} & \cdots & a_{1n} \\ a_{21} & a_{22} & \cdots & a_{2n} \\ \cdot \\ \cdot \\ \cdot \\ a_{m1} & a_{m2} & \cdots & a_{mn} \end{bmatrix} \begin{bmatrix} x_1 \\ x_2 \\ \cdot \\ \cdot \\ \cdot \\ x_n \end{bmatrix}$$ [2]

This is known as a matrix equation, and may be written in abbreviated form as

$$[y] = [a][x]$$ [3]

Then the rectangular array of coefficients, [a], is known as the matrix of the transformation.

A matrix is more flexible than a determinant in that the number of rows and columns may be dissimilar. Thus, a matrix may have m rows and n columns, and is referred to as an (m, n) matrix. When $m = n = p$, the matrix is called a pth-order matrix.

The subscripts of a matrix element are used to set its location in the matrix; thus a_{ij} represents the element of the ith row, jth column of an a matrix. The set of terms is called an array; the determinant of an array is denoted by a Δ with the alphabet letter of the array. Thus,

$$\Delta^a = \begin{vmatrix} a_{11} & a_{12} & \cdots & a_{1n} \\ a_{21} & a_{22} & \cdots & a_{2n} \\ \cdot & & & \\ \cdot & & & \\ \cdot & & & \\ a_{m1} & a_{m2} & \cdots & a_{mn} \end{vmatrix} \qquad [4]$$

Clearly, Δ^a exists only if m and n are equal.

Matrix algebra comprises a set of rules describing the behavior of these arrays. The rules are easily verified by reverting to the original algebraic form.

Rule 1. Two matrices are equal only when there is a one-to-one correspondence of their terms. Thus,

$$[a] = [b] \qquad \text{if} \qquad a_{ij} = b_{ij} \qquad [5]$$

Rule 2. The sum or difference of two matrices is a matrix which is term for term equivalent to the sum or difference of the terms of the two matrices. Thus,

$$[a] \pm [b] = [c] \qquad \text{if} \qquad c_{ij} = a_{ij} \pm b_{ij} \qquad [6]$$

Rule 3. When a matrix is multiplied by a factor, each element of the matrix is multiplied by the factor. Thus,

$$k[a] = [b] \qquad \text{if} \qquad b_{ij} = ka_{ij} \qquad [7]$$

It is important to note that the array in this case is $[ka]$. Thus, if $k[a]$ is a matrix with n rows and n columns, its determinant is $k^n \Delta^a$.

Rule 4. Multiplication of matrices.

$$[c] = [a][b] \qquad \text{when} \qquad c_{ij} = \sum_{k=1}^{k=n} a_{ik}b_{kj} \qquad [8]$$

This restricts the multiplication of matrices to only those where the number of columns of $[a]$ is equal to the number of rows of $[b]$. In the above equation, this number is n, and the final result is a matrix of order (a, b). By way of example,

$$\begin{bmatrix} a_{11} & a_{12} & a_{13} \\ a_{21} & a_{22} & a_{23} \end{bmatrix} \begin{bmatrix} b_{11} & b_{12} \\ b_{21} & b_{22} \\ b_{31} & b_{32} \end{bmatrix}$$

$$= \begin{bmatrix} a_{11}b_{11} + a_{12}b_{21} + a_{13}b_{31}, & a_{11}b_{12} + a_{12}b_{22} + a_{13}b_{32} \\ a_{21}b_{11} + a_{22}b_{21} + a_{23}b_{31}, & a_{21}b_{12} + a_{22}b_{22} + a_{23}b_{32} \end{bmatrix} \qquad [9]$$

Here a (2, 3) matrix is multiplied by a (3, 2) matrix to result in a second-order matrix.

If we wish to multiply

$$\begin{bmatrix} a_{11} & a_{12} & a_{13} \\ a_{21} & a_{22} & a_{23} \end{bmatrix} \begin{bmatrix} b_1 \\ b_2 \\ b_3 \end{bmatrix}$$

we understand that this is equivalent to

$$\begin{bmatrix} a_{11} & a_{12} & a_{13} \\ a_{21} & a_{22} & a_{23} \end{bmatrix} \begin{bmatrix} b_1 & 0 \\ b_2 & 0 \\ b_3 & 0 \end{bmatrix} = \begin{bmatrix} a_{11}b_1 + a_{12}b_2 + a_{13}b_3 \\ a_{21}b_1 + a_{22}b_2 + a_{23}b_3 \end{bmatrix} \qquad [10]$$

Here a (2, 3) matrix is multiplied by a (3, 1) matrix to obtain a (2, 1) matrix.

In network analysis, the problem most often encountered is

$$\begin{bmatrix} a_{11} & a_{12} \\ a_{21} & a_{22} \end{bmatrix} \times \begin{bmatrix} b_{11} & b_{12} \\ b_{21} & b_{22} \end{bmatrix} = \begin{bmatrix} a_{11}b_{11} + a_{12}b_{21}, & a_{11}b_{12} + a_{12}b_{22} \\ a_{21}b_{11} + a_{22}b_{21}, & a_{21}b_{12} + a_{22}b_{22} \end{bmatrix} \qquad [11]$$

Here, a second-order matrix multiplied by a second-order matrix results in a second-order matrix.

Rule 5. In multiplying matrices, the distributive law holds; i.e.,

$$([a] + [b]) \times [c] = [a] \times [c] + [b] \times [c] \qquad [12]$$

Rule 6. In multiplying matrices, the associative law holds; i.e.,

$$[a] \times [b] \times [c] = ([a] \times [b]) \times [c] = [a] \times ([b] \times [c]) \qquad [13]$$

Rule 7. In multiplying two matrices, the commutative law does not generally hold; i.e.,

$$[a] \times [b] \neq [b] \times [a] \qquad [14]$$

Thus

$$\begin{bmatrix} b_{11} & b_{12} \\ b_{21} & b_{22} \end{bmatrix} \begin{bmatrix} a_{11} & a_{12} \\ a_{21} & a_{22} \end{bmatrix} = \begin{bmatrix} b_{11}a_{11} + b_{12}a_{21}, & b_{11}a_{12} + b_{12}a_{22} \\ b_{21}a_{11} + b_{22}a_{21}, & b_{21}a_{12} + b_{22}a_{22} \end{bmatrix} \qquad [15]$$

which is different from the product

$$\begin{bmatrix} a_{11} & a_{12} \\ a_{21} & a_{22} \end{bmatrix} \begin{bmatrix} b_{11} & b_{12} \\ b_{21} & b_{22} \end{bmatrix}$$

which is obtained in eq. 11.

The terms "premultiplication" and "postmultiplication" are commonly used to differentiate between the two ways that one matrix may be multiplied by another.

Rule 8. Inversion of matrices.

$$[a]^{-1} = [b] \quad \text{if} \quad b_{ij} = \frac{\Delta_{ji}{}^a}{\Delta^a} \tag{16}$$

where $\Delta_{ji}{}^a$ is the cofactor for the jth row, ith column. Since inversion of an array requires obtaining its determinant, inversion can exist only if the number of rows and columns are equal.

A common inversion is that for the second-order matrix.

$$\begin{bmatrix} a_{11} & a_{12} \\ a_{21} & a_{22} \end{bmatrix}^{-1} = \frac{1}{\Delta^a} \begin{bmatrix} a_{22} & -a_{12} \\ -a_{21} & a_{11} \end{bmatrix} \tag{17}$$

Rule 9.

$$[a] \times [a]^{-1} = [a]^{-1} \times [a] = [1] \tag{18}$$

[1] is defined as the unit matrix. Thus,

$$\begin{bmatrix} a_{11} & a_{12} \\ a_{21} & a_{22} \end{bmatrix} \begin{bmatrix} \dfrac{a_{22}}{\Delta^a} & \dfrac{-a_{12}}{\Delta^a} \\ \dfrac{-a_{21}}{\Delta^a} & \dfrac{a_{11}}{\Delta^a} \end{bmatrix} = \begin{bmatrix} \dfrac{a_{11}a_{22}}{\Delta^a} - \dfrac{a_{12}a_{21}}{\Delta^a}, & \dfrac{-a_{11}a_{12}}{\Delta^a} + \dfrac{a_{11}a_{12}}{\Delta^a} \\ \dfrac{a_{21}a_{22}}{\Delta^a} - \dfrac{a_{22}a_{21}}{\Delta^a}, & -\dfrac{a_{21}a_{12}}{\Delta^a} + \dfrac{a_{11}a_{22}}{\Delta^a} \end{bmatrix} \tag{19}$$

$$= \begin{bmatrix} 1 & 0 \\ 0 & 1 \end{bmatrix} \tag{20}$$

The unit matrix consists of a matrix whose main diagonal terms, a_{ii}, are all unity, and whose other terms are zero. In like manner,

$$\begin{bmatrix} \dfrac{a_{22}}{\Delta^a} & \dfrac{-a_{12}}{\Delta^a} \\ \dfrac{-a_{21}}{\Delta^a} & \dfrac{a_{11}}{\Delta^a} \end{bmatrix} \begin{bmatrix} a_{11} & a_{12} \\ a_{21} & a_{22} \end{bmatrix} = \begin{bmatrix} 1 & 0 \\ 0 & 1 \end{bmatrix} \tag{21}$$

Any matrix may be premultiplied or postmultiplied by the unit matrix, and remain unchanged. Thus

$$\begin{bmatrix} c_{11} & c_{12} \\ c_{21} & c_{22} \end{bmatrix} \begin{bmatrix} 1 & 0 \\ 0 & 1 \end{bmatrix} = \begin{bmatrix} 1 & 0 \\ 0 & 1 \end{bmatrix} \begin{bmatrix} c_{11} & c_{12} \\ c_{21} & c_{22} \end{bmatrix} \tag{22}$$

$$= \begin{bmatrix} c_{11} & c_{12} \\ c_{21} & c_{22} \end{bmatrix} \tag{23}$$

Rule 10. Division by a matrix is not permissible. However, multiplication by the inverse matrix may be used to this end. For example, if

$$[e] = [z][i] \tag{24}$$

Then

$$[z]^{-1}[e] = [z]^{-1}[z][i] \tag{25}$$

$$= [1][i] \tag{26}$$

$$= [i] \tag{27}$$

Therefore

$$[i] = [z]^{-1}[e] \tag{28}$$

Note that

$$[i] \neq [e][z]^{-1} \tag{29}$$

The above is a brief summary of that part of matrix algebra that is of particular value in the solution of the four-terminal network. For further information on the subject, the reader is referred to the references at the end of Chapter 15.

Problems

1. (a) Multiply

$$\begin{bmatrix} 3 & -4 \\ -5 & 6 \end{bmatrix} \text{ by } \begin{bmatrix} 7 & -8 \\ -9 & 10 \end{bmatrix}$$

(b) Multiply

$$\begin{bmatrix} a_{11} & a_{12} & a_{13} & a_{14} \\ a_{21} & a_{22} & a_{23} & a_{24} \end{bmatrix} \text{ by } \begin{bmatrix} b_{11} & b_{12} \\ b_{21} & b_{22} \\ b_{31} & b_{32} \\ b_{41} & b_{42} \end{bmatrix}$$

(c) Multiply

$$\begin{bmatrix} z_{11} & z_{12} \\ z_{21} & z_{22} \\ z_{31} & z_{32} \end{bmatrix} \text{ by } \begin{bmatrix} y_{11} & y_{12} & y_{13} \\ y_{21} & y_{22} & y_{23} \end{bmatrix}$$

(d) Multiply

$$\begin{bmatrix} h_{11} + h_{11}', & h_{12} \\ h_{21} - h_{21}', & h_{22} \end{bmatrix} \begin{bmatrix} g_{11} & g_{12} \\ g_{21} & g_{22} \end{bmatrix}$$

both directly and by application of the distributive law.

2. Multiply

$$[a_{11} \quad a_{12} \quad a_{13} \quad a_{14} \quad a_{15} \quad a_{16}] \begin{bmatrix} b_{11} \\ b_{21} \\ b_{31} \\ b_{41} \\ b_{51} \\ b_{61} \end{bmatrix} [y_{11} \quad y_{12} \quad y_{13} \quad y_{14}]$$

both in the form $([a] \times [b]) \times [y]$ and in the form $[a] \times ([b] \times [y])$. Which method involves less operations? Why?

3. (a) Invert

$$\begin{bmatrix} y_{11} & y_{12} & y_{13} & y_{14} & y_{15} \\ y_{21} & y_{22} & y_{23} & y_{24} & y_{25} \\ y_{31} & y_{32} & y_{33} & y_{34} & y_{35} \\ y_{41} & y_{42} & y_{43} & y_{44} & y_{45} \\ y_{51} & y_{52} & y_{53} & y_{54} & y_{55} \end{bmatrix}$$

and give the answer in terms of the determinant and cofactors.

(b) Give answer in determinants and minors.

4. (a) Given

$$\begin{bmatrix} h_{11} & h_{12} \\ h_{21} & h_{22} \end{bmatrix} \begin{bmatrix} g_{11} & g_{12} \\ g_{21} & g_{22} \end{bmatrix} = \begin{bmatrix} 1 & 0 \\ 0 & 1 \end{bmatrix}$$

compute the relationship between the terms of the g and h matrices.

(b) Given $[a][b] = [c][d][e][f]$. Find $[e]$ in terms of the other matrices.

Appendix II

Definitions of Terms

Acceptor impurity. An impurity that induces hole conduction in a semiconductor.

Active transducer. A transducer whose output waves are dependent upon sources of power, apart from that supplied by any of the actuating waves, which power is controlled by one or more of these waves.

Amplification. The magnitude of the complex ratio of the value of a quantity at the output point of a system to its value at the input point. Amplification is the magnitude of the transfer ratio.

Attenuation. The magnitude of the complex ratio of the value of a quantity at the input point of a system to its value at the output point. Attenuation is the reciprocal of amplification and is the term generally employed when the output value of the quantity is less than the input value.

Available conversion power gain (of a conversion transducer). The ratio of the available output-frequency power from the output terminals of the transducer to the available input-frequency power from the driving generator with termination conditions specified for all frequencies which may affect the result.

Note 1. This applies to outputs of such magnitude that the conversion transducer is operating in a substantially linear condition.

Note 2. The maximum available conversion power gain of a conversion transducer is obtained when the input termination admittance, at input frequency, is the conjugate of the input-frequency driving-point admittance of the conversion transducer.

Available power. Of a linear source of electric energy, the quotient of the mean square of the open-circuit terminal voltage of the source divided by 4 times the resistive component of the impedance of the source.

Note. The available power would be delivered to a load impedance that is the conjugate of the internal impedance of the source and is the maximum power that can be delivered by that source.

Available power gain (of a linear transducer). The ratio of the available power from the ouput terminals of the transducer, under specified input termination conditions, to the available power from the driving generator.

Note. The maximum available power gain of an electric transducer is obtained when the input termination admittance is the conjugate of the driving-point admittance at the input terminals of the transducer. It is sometimes called "completely matched power gain."

Boundary, *p-n*. The hypothetical surface between *p*- and *n*-type semiconductors at which the donor and acceptor concentrations are equal.

515

Conversion transconductance (of a heterodyne conversion transducer). The quotient of the magnitude of the desired output-frequency component of current by the magnitude of the input-frequency (signal) component of voltage when the impedance of the output external termination is negligible for all the frequencies that may affect the result.

Note. Unless otherwise stated, the term refers to the cases in which the input-frequency voltage is of infinitesimal magnitude. All direct electrode voltages and the magnitude of the local-oscillator voltage must be specified, fixed values.

Current amplification. The ratio of the magnitude of the current in a specified load impedance connected to a transducer to the magnitude of the current in the input circuit of the transducer.

Note 1. If the input and/or output current consist of more than one component, such as a multifrequency signal, or noise, then the particular components used and their weighting must be specified.

Note 2. By an extension of the term decibel this amplification is often expressed in decibels by multiplying its common logarithm by 20.

Current attenuation. The ratio of the magnitude of the current in the input circuit of a transducer to the magnitude of the current in a specified load impedance connected to the transducer.

Note 1. If the input and/or output current consist of more than one component, such as a multifrequency signal, or noise, then the particular components used and their weighting must be specified.

Note 2. By an extension of the term decibel this attenuation is often expressed in decibels by multiplying its common logarithm by 20.

Depletion layer. The region about a *p-n* boundary in which fixed charges are in excess of mobile charges.

Donor impurity. An impurity that induces electronic conduction in a semiconductor.

Gain. (See Power gain.) The increase in transmitted power between the input and output points of a system, or at the output point of a system, resulting from a change in the system. Gain is usually expressed in decibels.

Note 1. Gain was formerly used to denote transducer gain, but this practice is now deprecated in view of the general acceptance of the latter term for the restricted meaning.

Note 2. The use of "gain" as a synonym for "amplification" is deprecated.

Hole. A mobile defect in the electronic valence structure of a semiconductor which acts like a positive electronic charge with a positive mass.

I-type semiconductor. A semiconductor in which the difference between the conduction electron density and the hole density is much less than the total carrier density.

Note. May be *n* or *p* type.

Impurity. A chemical or physical defect in the otherwise-perfect crystal. (Opinion at the moment is about evenly divided for and against broadening the concept to include physical imperfections. There is also commercial objection to the use of the word "impurity.")

Impurity, acceptor. An impurity that induces hole conduction in a semiconductor.

Impurity, donor. An impurity that induces electronic conduction in a semiconductor.

Insertion gain. Resulting from the insertion of a transducer in a transmission system, the ratio of the power delivered to that part of the system following the transducer to the power delivered to that same part before insertion.

Note 1. If the input and/or output power consist of more than one component, such as multifrequency signal, or noise, then the particular components used and their weighting must be specified.

Note 2. This gain is usually expressed in decibels.

Insertion loss. Resulting from the insertion of a transducer in a transmission system, the ratio of the power delivered to that part of the system following the transducer, before insertion of the transducer, to the power delivered to that same part of the system after insertion of the transducer.

Note 1. If the input and /or output power consist of more than one component, such as multifrequency signal, or noise, then the particular components used and their weighting must be specified.

Note 2. This loss is usually expressed in decibels.

Intrinsic properties. The electrical properties of an intrinsic semiconductor.

Intrinsic temperature range. The temperature range in which the electrical properties of an impurity semiconductor are superseded by properties of the material without impurities. The temperature at the lower bound of the range is sometimes called the "intrinsic temperature." The concept is not sharply defined and depends upon the impurity concentration.

Junction, collector. A junction biased in the reverse direction, the conductance of which can be controlled by the introduction of minority carriers.

Junction, emitter. A junction biased in the forward direction for the purpose of injection of minority carriers into a semiconducting region.

Loss. (1) The decrease in transmitted power between the input and output points of a system, or at the output point of a system resulting from a change in the system. Loss in this sense is usually expressed in decibels and when so expressed is the negative of gain.

(2) The power lost in a component or transmission system. Loss in this sense is usually expressed in watts.

Maximum peak inverse voltage (of a semiconductor device). The maximum rated peak inverse voltage.

Noise factor (noise figure). Of a linear system at a selected frequency, the ratio of (1) the noise power per unit bandwidth (at a corresponding output frequency), available at the output terminals, to (2) the portion thereof engendered at the input frequency by the input termination, whose noise temperature is standard ($290°$ K) at all frequencies.

p-type semiconductor. An impurity semiconductor in which the hole density exceeds the electron density.

Peak inverse voltage. The maximum voltage excursion in the low-conductivity direction.

Power gain. Of an amplifying device, the ratio of the signal power delivered to a specified load impedance to the signal power absorbed by its input. This ratio is usually expressed in decibels.

Semiconductor. A solid electronic conductor with a range of resistivities between those of insulators and metals. The resistivity in general increases with decreasing temperature over the major range.

Semiconductor, impurity. A semiconductor with electrical properties dependent upon active impurity concentration.

Semiconductor, I-type. A semiconductor in which the difference between the conduction electron density and the hole density is much less than the total carrier density.

Note. May be n or p type.

Semiconductor, intrinsic. An ideal I-type semiconductor in which the concentrations of acceptors and donors is zero.

Semiconductor, n-type. An impurity semiconductor in which the conduction electron density exceeds the hole density.

Semiconductor, p-type. An impurity semiconductor in which the hole density exceeds the conduction electron density.

Semiconductor device. A device which makes use of the electrical properties of a semiconductor.

Transducer. A device capable of being actuated by waves from one or more transmission systems or media and of supplying related waves to one or more other transmission systems or media.

Transducer gain. The ratio of the power that the transducer delivers to the specified load under specified operating conditions to the available power of the specified source.

Note 1. If the input and/or output power consist of more than one component, such as multifrequency signal, or noise, then the particular components used and their weighting must be specified.

Note 2. This gain is usually expressed in decibels.

Transducer loss. The ratio of the available power of the specified source to the power that the transducer delivers to the specified load under specified operating conditions.

Note 1. If the input and/or output power consist of more than one component, such as multifrequency signal, or noise, then the particular components used and their weighting must be specified.

Note 2. This loss is usually expressed in decibels.

Transistor. A semiconductor device having three or more terminals in which the resistance between two electrodes is controlled by the carrier density from a third electrode. .

Voltage Amplification. The ratio of the magnitude of the voltage across a specified load impedance connected to a transducer to the magnitude of the voltage across the input of the transducer.

Note 1. If the input and/or output power consist of more than one component, such as multifrequency signal, or noise, then the particular components used and their weighting must be specified.

Note 2. By an extension of the term "decibel" this amplification is often expressed in decibels by multiplying its common logarithm by 20.

Voltage attenuation. The ratio of the magnitude of the voltage across the input of the transducer to the magnitude of the voltage delivered to a specified load impedance connected to the transducer.

Note 1. If the input and/or output power consist of more than one component, such as multifrequency signal, or noise, then the particular components used and their weighting must be specified.

Note 2. By an extension of the term "decibel" this attenuation is often expressed in decibels by multiplying its common logarithm by 20.

Appendix III

Bibliography

1945

"Temperature Dependence of High Voltage Germanium Rectifier D-C Characteristics," Purdue University NDRC Report 14-579 (October 31, 1945).

1947

Bardeen, "Surface States and Rectification at a Metal-to-Semiconductor Contact," *Phys. Rev.*, *71*, 717 (1947).

1948

Arnand, "Transistor: The Crystal Amplifier and Oscillator," *Rev. Telegr.* (*Buenos Aires*), October, 1948, pp. 715–720.

J. Bardeen and W. H. Brattain, "The Transistor, a Semi-Conductor Triode," *Phys. Rev.*, *74*, 230 (July, 1948).

Brattain and Bardeen, "Nature of the Forward Current in Germanium Point Contacts," *Phys. Rev.*, *74*, 231 (July, 1948).

Chritien, "The Transistor, or the Return of the Crystal," *TSF Pour Tous*, October, 1948, pp. 260–262.

F. H. Rockett, "The Transistor," *Sci. American, 179*, 52-s (September, 1948).

Shockley and Pearson, "Modulation of the Conductance of Thin Films of Semi-Conductors by Surface Charges," *Phys. Rev. 74*, 232 (July, 1948).

Wells and White, "Experimental Germanium Crystal Amplifier (The Transistor)," *Audio Eng., 32*, 6 and 8 (July, 1948); 28, 29, and 39 (August, 1948).

White, "Design of Amplifying Crystal Units," *Audio Eng. 32*, 26, 27, and 45 (September, 1948); 32–33 and 51–52 (October, 1948); 18–19 (November, 1948); 40–44 (December, 1948).

White, "Clarification of Germanium Triode Characteristics," *Audio Eng., 32*, 19–21 (December, 1948).

"The Transistor," *Bell Labs. Rec., 26*, 321 (August, 1948).

"The Transistor — a Crystal Triode," *Electronics, 21*, 68–71 (September, 1948).

"Transistor Amplifier," *Engineering*, December 31, 1948, pp. 630–631.

Product Eng., September, 1948, pp. 158–159.

Sci. American, September, 1948.

Telephone and Telegraph Age, August, 1948, pp. 7 and 30.

Wireless World, October, 1948, pp. 358–359.

1949

Aisberg, "Transistron = Transistor + ?" *Toute la Radio*, July–August, 1949, pp. 218–220.

Bardeen, "On the Theory of the A-C Impedance of a Contact Rectifier," *Bell Sys. Tech. J.*, *28*, 428–434 (July, 1949).

Bardeen and Brattain, "Physical Properties Involved in Transistor Action," *Bell Sys. Tech., J.*, *28*, 239–245 (April, 1949); *Phys. Rev.*, *75*, 1208–1225 (April, 1949).

Becker, "Recent Developments in Semi-Conductors and the Transistor," *Elec. Eng.*, *67*, 1201 (December, 1949).

Becker and Shive, "The Transistor—a New Semi-Conductor Amplifier," *Elec. Eng.*, *68*, 215–221 (March, 1949).

Brown, "Magnetically Biased Transistors," *Phys. Rev.*, *76* (December, 1949) (letter).

Dunlap, Jr., "Germanium, Important New Semi-conductor," *G.E. Rev.*, *52*, 15–17 (February, 1949).

Eberhard, Endres, and Moore, "Counter Circuits Using Transistors," *RCA Rev.*, *10*, 459–476 (December, 1949).

Fink, D. G., and F. H. Rockett, "The Transistor, A Crystal Triode," *Electronics*, *21*, no. 9, pp. 68–71 (September, 1949).

Geyer, "Oscillographic Presentation of Transistor Characteristics," M.I.T. E.E. thesis, 1949.

Haegele, "Crystal Tetrode Mixer," *Electronics*, *22*, 80–81 (October, 1949); *Sylvania Technologist*, July, 1949, pp. 2–4.

Haynes and Shockley, "Investigation of Hole Injection in Transistor Action," *Phys. Rev. 75*, 691 (February, 1949).

Herring, "Theory of Transient Phenomena in the Transport of Holes in an Excess Semi-Conductor," *Bell Sys. Tech. J.*, *28*, 401–427 (July, 1949).

Horton and Kalb, *A Preliminary Investigation of Transistors for Computer Circuits*, ERA Inc., St. Paul, Minn., October 7, 1949.

Hutcheson, "Possible Significance of Transistors in the Power Field," *Elec. Eng.*, *68*, 689 (August, 1949).

Knczynski, G. C., "Elementary Principles of Solid State Physics, Part I, Metals," *Sylvania Technologist*, July, 1949, pp. 6–9.

Kock and Wallace, "The Co-axial Transistor," *Elec. Eng.*, *68*, 222–223 (March, 1949).

Lehan, "Transistor Oscillator for Telemetering," *Electronics*, *22*, 90 (August, 1949).

Lehovec, "On Hole Current in Germanium Transistors," *Phys. Rev.*, *75*, 1100–1101 (April, 1949).

Lehovec, "Testing Transistors," *Electronics*, *22*, 88–89 (June, 1949).

Martin, "Patents on Solid State Amplifying Devices," *Sylvania Technologist*, July, 1949.

Mooers, "Low Frequency Noise in Transistors," *Proc. NEC*, *5*, 17–22 (1949).

Mott, "Notes on the Transistor and Surface States in Semi-Conductors," *Rep. Brit. Elect. Res. Ass.* (Ref L/T216) (1949), 6 pp.

Pfann and Scaff, "The *p*-Germanium Transistor," *Phys. Rev.*, *76* (August, 1949).

Posthumas, H. G., "The Transistor," *Elec. Eng.*, *68*, (July, 1949) (letter to the Editor).

Reich and Ungvary, "A Transistor Trigger Circuit," *Rev. Sci. Instruments*, August, 1949, pp.586–588.

Ryder, "Characteristics of Three Transistor Circuits," *Electronics*, August, 1949.

Ryder, "The Type A Transistor," *Bell Labs. Rec.*, *27*, 68–71 (March, 1949).

Ryder and Kircher, "Some Circuit Aspects of the Transistor," *Bell Sys. Tech. J.*, *28*, 367–400 (July, 1949).

Ryder and Shockley, "Interpretation of the Dependence of Resistivity of Germanium on Electric Fields," *Phys. Rev.*, *75*, 310 (January, 1949).

Shive, "The Double Surface Transistor," *Phys. Rev.*, *75*, 690 (February 15, 1949).

Shockley, "The Theory of *p-n* Junctions in Semi-Conductors and *p-n* Junction Transistors," *Bell Sys. Tech. J.*, *28*, 435–489 (July, 1949).

Shockley and Becker, "Transistor Characteristics," *Electronics*, *22*, 132 (January, 1949).

Shockley, Pearson, and Haynes, "Hole Injection in Germanium—Quantitative Studies and Filamentary Transistors," *Bell Sys. Tech. J.*, *28*, 344–366 (July, 1949).

Smith, "Characteristics and Applications of Transistors," M.I.T. E.E. thesis, 1949.

Sueur, "The Transistor Triode Type P.T.T. 601," *Onde Élect.*, November, 1949, pp. 389–397 (French).

Webster, W. M., E. Eberhard, and L. E. Barton, "Some Novel Circuits for the Three Terminal Semi-Conductor Amplifier," *RCA Rev.*, *10*, no. 1, pp. 5–16 (March, 1949).

"Coaxial Transistor," *Bell Labs. Rec.*, *27*, 2–4 (April, 1949).

Some Contributions to Transistor Electronics, Monograph 1726, Bell System Technical Publication.

"Transistor," *Elec. News and Eng.*, September, 1949, pp. 89, 92, and 94.

"Transistor," *Railway Signaling and Communications*, August, 1949.

1950

Adam, "Transistor and Transistron," *Tech. Mod. (Paris)*, July 1–15, 1950, pp. 220–224.

Aigrain and Dugas, "Characteristics of Transistors," *Compt. Rend. Asad. Sci. (Paris)*, January 23, 1950, pp. 377–378.

Banbury and Henish, "On the High Frequency Response of PbS Transistors," *Proc. Phys. Soc. London*, July, 1950, pp. 540–541.

Bardeen, "Theory of Relation between Hole Concentration and Characteristics of Germanium Point Contacts," *Bell Sys. Tech. J.*, *29*, 469–495 (October, 1950).

Bardeen and Pfann, "Effects of Electrical Forming on the Rectifying Barriers of *n*- and *p*-Germanium Transistors," *Phys. Rev.*, *77*, 401–402 (February, 1950).

Becker, "Transistors," *Elec. Eng.*, *69* (January, 1950).

Bell Telephone Labs. Progress Reports to the Signal Corps on Transistor Development, Six Quarterly Reports through December 1, 1950.

Brown, "High Frequency Operation of Transistors," *Electronics*, *23*, 81–83 (July, 1950).

Brown, C. B., "Magnetically Biased Transistors," *Phys. Rev.*, *76*, 1736–1737 (December, 1950).

Eberhard, E., and others, "Counter Circuits Using Transistors," *RCA Rev.*, *10*, 459–476 (December, 1950).

Gaule, "The Transistor—Bibliographical Survey," *Fernmeldetech. Z.*, October, 1950, pp. 390–400.

Gebbie, Banbury, and Hogarth, "Crystal Diode and Triode Action in Lead Sulphide," *Proc. Phys. Soc. London*, May, 1950, p. 371.

Haegele, "The Crystal Tetrode, Its Use as a Frequency Converter," *Onde Élect.*, May, 1950, pp. 239–241.

Heins, "The Germanium Crystal Triode," *Sylvania Technologist*, January, 1950, pp. 13–18.

Hungarman, "Physics and Technology of Transistors," *Elecktron Wiss. Tech.*, October–November, 1950, pp. 357–367.

Hunter, "Graphical Analysis of Transistor Characteristics," *Proc. IRE*, *38*, 1387–1391 (December, 1950).

Hunter, "Physical Interpretation of Type A Transistor Characteristics," *Phys. Rev.*, *77*, 558–559 (February, 1950).

Hunter, L. P., and R. E. Brown, "Production Tester for Transistors," *Electronics*, *23*, no. 10, pp. 96–99 (October, 1950).

Mataré, "Transistor Measurement Technique," *Elecktron Wiss. Tech.*, October–November, 1950, pp. 368–379.

Mataré, "The Amplification Observed in Semi-Conductors," *Onde Élect.*, November, 1950, pp. 469–475.

Meacham and Michaels, "Observations of the Rapid Withdrawal of Stored Holes from Germanium Transistors and Varistors," *Phys. Rev.*, *77*, 175–176 (April, 1950).

Montgomery, "Background Noise in Transistors," *Bell Labs. Rec.*, *28*, 400–403 (September, 1950).

Pearson, G. L., and others, "Mobility Anomalies in Germanium," *Phys. Rev.*, *78*, 295–296 (May, 1950).

Pfann, "The Transistor as a Reversible Amplifier," *Proc. IRE*, *38*, 1222 (October, 1950).

Pfann and Scaff, "The *p*-Germanium Transistor," *Proc. IRE*, *38*, 1151–1154 (October, 1950).

Reich, Barker, Schultheiss, and Susskind, "Development of High Speed Trigger Circuits," Yale University Report U-14052 (July 1, 1950), Navy Research Project N7 onr-28808.

Scott, "Crystal Triodes," Institution of Electrical Engineers' Paper 990 (1950).

Shive, J. N., "The Phototransistor," *Bell Labs. Rec.*, *28*, no. 8, pp. 337–342 (August, 1950).

Shockley, "Holes and Electrons," *Physics Today*, III, pp. 16–24 (October, 1950).

Shockley, "Theories of High Values of Alpha for Collector Contacts on Germanium," *Phys. Rev.*, *78*, 294–295 (May, 1950).

Slade, "A High Performance Transistor with Wide Spacing between Contacts," *RCA Rev.*, *11*, 517–526 (December, 1950).

Stuetzer, "A Crystal Amplifier with High Input Impedance," *Proc. IRE*, *38*, 449–466 (August, 1950).

Stuetzer, O. M., "The Transistor and Fieldistor," *Electronics*, *23*, 167–168 (July, 1950).

Tillman and Yemm, "A Note on the Decay of Current in Germanium Diodes," *Phil. Mag.*, December, 1950, pp. 1281–1283.

Toth, *The Potentialities of Transistors in Digital Computing Circuits*, ERA Inc., St. Paul, Minn., July 12, 1950.

Turner, R. P., "A Crystal Receiver with Transistor Amplifier," *Radio and TV News*, January, 1950, pp. 38–39.

Van Roosbroeck, "Theory of the Flow of Electrons and Holes in Germanium and Other Semi-Conductors," *Bell Sys. Tech. J.*, *29*, (October, 1950).

"A New Type of Electric Eye Developed by Bell Labs.," *Elec. Eng.*, May, 1950, pp. 476–477.

"Transistor Circuits," *The C-D Capacitor*, February, 1950, pp. 3–7.

1951

Bardeen, J., "Theory of Relation between Hole Concentration and Characteristics of Germanium Point Contacts," *Bell Sys. Tech. J.*, *29*, pp. 469–495 (October, 1951).

Bowers, W. B., "Transistor Frequency Multiplying Circuit," *Electronics*, *24*, 140 (March, 1951).

Fink and Jurgen (Editors), "The Junction Transistor," *Electronics*, *24*, no. 11, pp. 82–85 (November, 1951).

Hunter, "The Inverse Voltage Characteristic of a Point Contact on n-Type Germanium," *Phys. Rev.*, *79*, 151–152 (January, 1951).

Hunter, L. P., "Graphical Analysis of Transistor Characteristics," *I.R.E. Proc.*, *38*, 1387–1391 (December, 1951).

Koros and Schwartz, "Transistor Frequency Modulator Circuit," *Electronics*, *24*, 130–132 (July, 1951).

Longini, R. L., "Electric Forming of n-Germanium Transistors Using Donor-Alloy Contacts," *Phys. Rev.*, *84*, 1254 (December, 1951).

Muller, R. H., "The Junction Transistor," *Anal. Chem.*, *23*, Sup. 19A (December, 1951).

Pfann, W. G., "Significance of Composition of Contact Point in Rectifying Junctions on Germanium," *Phys. Rev.*, *81*, 882 (March, 1951).

Pietenpol, W. J., "p-n Junction Rectifier and Photocell," *Phys. Rev.*, *82*, no. 1, pp. 121–122 (April, 1951).

Prim, R. C., "Some Results Concerning the Partial Differential Equations Describing the Flow of Holes and Electrons in Semi-Conductors," *Bell Sys. Tech. J.*, *30*, no. 4, pt. II, p. 1174 (October, 1951).

Raisbeck, G., "Transistor Circuit Design," *Electronics*, *24*, no. 12, pp. 128–132 (December, 1951).

Reich, H. J., and others, Effect of Auxiliary Current on Transistor Operation," *J. Appl. Phys.*, *22*, 682–683 (May, 1951).

Ridenour, L. N., "Revolution in Electronics," *Sci. American*, *185*, 13–17 (August, 1951).

Saby, J. S., "Recent Developments in Transistors and Related Devices," *Tele-Tech.*, *10*, 32–34 (December, 1951).

Scott, "Crystal Triodes," *Electrical Communication*, *28*, no. 3, pp. 195–208 (September, 1951).

Scott, T. R., "Crystal Triodes," *I.R.E. Proc.*, *98*, pt. 3, pp. 169–177 (May, 1951).

Schultheiss and Reich, "Transistor Trigger Circuits," *Proc. IRE*, *39*, 627 (June, 1951).

Shockley, W., "Hot Electrons in Germanium and Ohm's Law," *Bell Sys. Tech. J.*, *30*, no. 4, pt. I, p. 990 (October, 1951).

Shockley, W. G., "Transistor Electronics," *Science*, *114*, 487 (November, 1951).

Shockley, Sparks, and Teal, "p-n Transistors," *Phys. Rev.*, *83*, 151–162 (July, 1951).

Slade, B. N., "High-Performance Transistor with Wide Spacing between Contacts," *RCA Rev.*, *11*, 517–526 (December, 1951).

Slade, B. N., "Method of Improving the Electrical and Mechanical Stability of Point-Contact Transistors." *RCA Rev.*, *12*, 651–659 (December, 1951).

Stelmark, J. P., "Electric Forming in n-Germanium Transistors Using Phosphorus Alloy Contacts," *Phys. Rev.*, *83*, 165 (July, 1951).

Wallace, R. L., Jr., "Duality, a New Approach to Transistor Circuit Design," *I.R.E. Proc.*, *39*, 702 (June, 1951).

Wallace and Pietenpol, "*n-p-n* Transistors," *Bell Sys. Tech. J.*, *30*, (August, 1951).

Wallace and Pietenpol, "Properties and Applications of *n-p-n* Transistors," *Proc. IRE*, *39*, 753–767 (July, 1951); *Bell Sys. Tech. J.*, *30*, 530–563 (July, 1951).

Wallace and Raisbeck, "Duality as a Guide in Transistor Circuit Design," *Bell Sys. Tech. J.*, *30*, 381–417 (April, 1951).

"Auxiliary Current Alters Transistor Characteristics," *Electronics*, *24*, no. 9, p. 192 (September, 1951).

"The Transistor," *Sci. American*, August, 1951.

1952

Aronson, M. H., "Instrument Electronics, Solid State Amplifiers," *Instruments*, *25*, 608–609 (July, 1952).

Billig, E., "Effect of Minority Carriers on the Breakdown of Point Contact Rectifiers," *Phys. Rev.*, *87*, 1060 (September 15, 1952).

Carswell, H. J., "Transistor Electronic Aids to Communications," *Pub. Util.*, *50*, 135–142 (July 31, 1952).

Chaplin, G. B. B., "Display of Transistor Characteristics on Cathode Ray Oscilloscope," *J. Sci. Instruments*, *29*, 142–145 (May, 1952).

Debye, P. P., and E. M. Cromwell, "Mobility of Electrons in Germanium," *Phys. Rev.*, *87*, 1131 (September 15, 1952).

Epstein, G. S., and others, "Transistorizing Communication Equipment," *Electronics*, *25*, 98–102 (May, 1952).

Fuller, C. S., and J. O. Struthers, "Copper as Acceptor Element in Germanium," *Phys. Rev.*, *87*, 526 (August, 1952).

Golay, M. J. E., "Equivalent Circuit of the Transistor," *I.R.E. Proc.*, *40*, 360 (March, 1952).

Hall, R. N., "Electron-Hole Recombination in Germanium," *Phys. Rev.*, *87*, 387 (July 15, 1952).

Howe, G. W. O., "Duality between Triode and Transistor," *Wireless Eng.*, *29*, 57–58 (March, 1952).

Kingsbury, E. F., and R. S. Ohl, "Photoelectric Properties of Ionically Bombarded Silicon," *Bell Sys. Tech. J.*, *31*, 104–121 (January, 1952).

Montgomery, H. C., "Electrical Noise in Semi-Conductors," *Bell Sys. Tech. J.*, *31*, 950–975 (September, 1952).

Morton, J. A., "New Transistor Gives Improved Performance," *Electronics*, *25*, 100–103 (August, 1952).

Morton, J. A., "Present Status of Transistor Development," *Bell Sys. Tech. J. 31*, 411–442 (May, 1952).

O'Connor, J. A., "Germanium's Electronic Upsurge," *Chem. Eng.*, *59*, pp. 158–160 (April, 1952).

O'Connor, J. A., "What Can Transistors Do?" *Chem. Eng.*, *59*, 154–156 (May, 1952),

Oser, E. A., R. O. Endres, and R. P. Moore, Jr., "Transistor Oscillators," *RCA Rev.*, September, 1952, p. 369.

Renne, H. S., "The Junction Transistor," *Radio and TV News*, *47*, 38–39 (April, 1952).

Scott, T. R., "Crystal Triodes," *I.E.E. Proc.*, pt. 3, pp. 168–177 (May, 1952).

Shea, R. F., "Transistor Power Amplifiers," *Electronics*, *25*, 106–108 (September, 1952).

Sittner, W. R., "Current Multiplication in the Type A Transistor," *I.R.E. Proc.*, *40*, 448–454 (April, 1952).

Sparks, M., "The Junction Transistor," *Sci. American*, *187*, 28–32 (July, 1952).

Teal, G. K., M. Sparks, and E. Buehler, "Single Crystal Germanium," *Proc. IRE*, *40*, 906–908 (August 1, 1952).

Trent, R. L., "Binary Counter Uses Two Transistors," *Electronics*, *25*, 100–101 (July, 1952).

Valdes, L. B., "Transistor Forming Effects in *n*-Type Germanium," *I.R.E. Proc.*, *40*, 445–448 (April, 1952).

The following articles appeared in *Proc. IRE*, vol. 40, November, 1952:

Coblenz, Abraham, and Harry L. Owens, "Variation of Transistor Parameters with Temperature," pp. 1472–1476.

Alexanderson, E. F. W., "Control Applications of the Transistor," pp.1508–1512.

Anderson, A. Eugene, "Transistor Reversible Binary Counter," pp. 1541–1559.

Armstrong, L. D., "*p-n*-Junctions by Impurity Introduction through an Intermediate Metal Layer," pp. 1341–1342.

Bryan, G. W., "Application of Transistors to High-Voltage Low-Current Supplies," pp. 1521–1524.

Conwell, E. M., "Properties of Silicon and Germanium," pp. 1314–1327.

Danko, S. F., and R. A. Gerhold, "Printed Circuitry for Transistors," pp. 1524–1529.

Early, J. M., "Effects of Space-Charge Layer Widening in Junction Transistors," pp. 1401–1407.

Ebers, J. J., "Four-Terminal *p-n-p-n* Transistors," pp. 1361–1365.

Farley, B. G., "Dynamics of Transistor Negative-Resistance Circuits," pp. 1497–1508.

Felker, J. H., "Regenerative Amplifier for Digital Computer Applications," pp. 1584–1597.

Follingstad, H. G., J. N. Shive, and R. E. Yaeger, "An Optical Position Encoder and Digit Register," pp. 1573–1584.

Giacoletto, L. J., "Junction Transistor Equivalent Circuits and Vacuum Tube Analogy," pp. 1490–1493.

Golden, N., and R. Nielsen, "Oscilloscopic Display of Transistor Static Electrical Characteristics," pp. 1437–1440.

Hall, R. N., "Power Rectifiers and Transistors," pp. 1512–1519.

Harris, James R., "A Transistor Shift Register and Serial Adder," pp. 1597–1603.

Hunter, L. P., and H. Fleisher, "Graphical Analysis of Some Transistor Switching Circuits," pp. 1559–1562.

Keonjian, E., and J. S. Schaffner, "An Experimental Investigation of Transistor Noise," pp. 1456–1461.

Lehovec, Kurt, "New Photoelectric Devices Utilizing Carrier Injection," pp. 1407–1410.

Lindberg, Olof, "Hall Effect," pp. 1414–1420.

Lo, A. W., "Transistor Trigger Circuits," pp. 1531–1541.

McDuffie, G. E., Jr., "Pulse Duration and Repetition Rate of a Transistor Multivibrator," pp. 1487–1490.

Montgomery, H. C., "Transistor Noise in Circuit Applications," pp. 1461–1472.

Morton, J. A., "Present Status of Transistor Development," pp. 1314–1327.

Navon, D., R. Bray, and H. Y. Fan, "Lifetime of Injected Carriers in Germanium," pp. 1342–1348.

Pearson, G. L., and B. Sawyer, "Silicon p-n Junction Alloy Diodes," pp. 1348–1352.

Petritz, Richard L., "On the Theory of Noise in p-n Junctions and Related Devices," pp. 1440–1456.

Pritchard, R. L., "Frequency Variations of Current-Amplication Factor for Junction Transistors," pp. 1476–1481.

Roth, Louise, and W. E. Taylor, "Preparation of Germanium Single Crystals," pp. 1338–1341.

Rouault, C. L., and G. N. Hall, "A High-Voltage, Medium-Power Rectifier," pp. 1519–1521.

Saby, John S., "Fused Impurity p-n-p Junction Transistors," pp. 1358–1361.

Shea, Richard F., "Transistor Operation: Stabilization of Operating Points," pp. 1435–1437.

Shekel, Jacob, "Matrix Representation of Transistor Circuits," pp. 1493–1497.

Shive, J. N., "Properties of M-1740 p-n Junction Photocell," pp. 1410–1414.

Shockley, W., "A Unipolar 'Field Effect' Transistor," pp. 1365–1377.

Shockley, W., "Transistor Electronics: Imperfections, Unipolar and Analog Transistors," pp. 1289–1314.

Slade, B. N., "The Control of Frequency Response and Stability of Point-Contact Transistors," pp. 1382–1385.

Steele, Earl L., "Theory of Alpha for p-n-p Diffused Junction Transistors," pp. 1424–1429.

Stuetzer, O. M., "Junction Fieldistors," pp. 1377–1382.

Stuetzer, O. M., "Transistors in Airborne Equipment," pp. 1529–1531.

Thomas, D. E., "Low-Drain Transistor Audio Oscillator," pp. 1385–1395.

Thomas, D. E., "Transistor Amplifier-Cutoff Frequency," pp. 1481–1483.

Trent, Robert L., "A Transistor Reversible Binary Counter," pp. 1562–1573.

Valdes, L. B., "Effect of Electrode Spacing on the Equivalent Base Resistance of Point-Contact Transistors," pp. 1429–1435.

Valdes, L. B., "Measurement of Minority Carrier Lifetime in Germanium," pp. 1420–1424.

Wallace, R. L., Jr., L. G. Schimpf, and E. Dickten, "A Junction Transistor Tetrode for High-Frequency Use," pp. 1395–1401.

Waltz, M. C., "On Some Transients in the Pulse Response of Point-Contact Germanium Diodes," pp. 1483–1487.

Books

F. Seitz, *Modern Theory of Solids*, McGraw-Hill, New York, 1940.

W. Shockley, *Imperfections in Nearly Perfect Crystals*, Wiley, 1952.

W. Shockley, *Electrons and Holes in Semi-Conductors*, Van Nostrand, New York, 1950.

Torrey and Whitmer, *Crystal Rectifiers*, McGraw-Hill, M.I.T. Radiation Lab. Series, New York.

D. A. Wright, *Semi-Conductors*, Wiley, New York, 1950.

Index